PHYSICS
an experimental science

PHYSICS
an experimental science

HARVEY E. WHITE

DONALD H. WHITE

MAURI GOULD

d. van nostrand company, inc.

PRINCETON, NEW JERSEY

LONDON   TORONTO   MELBOURNE

Harvey E. White, Professor of Physics and Director of the Lawrence Hall of Science, University of California, Berkeley, California

Donald H. White, Nuclear Physicist, Lawrence Radiation Laboratory, University of California, Livermore, California

Mauri Gould, Formerly High School Physics and Chemistry Teacher, Albany High School, Albany, California; now Staff Chemist and Physicist, Lawrence Hall of Science, University of California, Berkeley, California

VAN NOSTRAND REGIONAL OFFICES: *New York, Chicago, San Francisco*

D. VAN NOSTRAND COMPANY, LTD., *London*

D. VAN NOSTRAND COMPANY (Canada), LTD., *Toronto*

D. VAN NOSTRAND AUSTRALIA PTY, LTD., *Melbourne*

Library of Congress Catalog Card No. 68-13154

Preface

On the premise that the historical advances in science provide a logical and easily followed line of development, *Physics, an Experimental Science* brings together in one volume the elementary principles of classical physics, atomic structure, and nuclear energy. In this introduction to the basic principles of physics, we have assumed only that the student has a working knowledge of the simplest elements of algebra and plane geometry.

Based on Harvey E. White's *Physics, an Exact Science,* the present book takes advantage of the improved elementary and secondary science instruction that has become fact since the earlier book was published. Thus, the number of traditional topics has been reduced and far more space and attention than previously has been allotted to selected topics in atomic structure and nuclear phenomena. Because of the increasing importance of space science and electronics, lasers, and semiconductors, these and other topics have been incorporated at the appropriate places.

Each lesson has purposely been kept short and self-contained so that it may be used as one day's assignment. The lesson is followed by questions, problems, and project experiments that can be performed with inexpensive materials. The numbers of questions and problems are more than the average student should be expected to solve in one year of study, making for flexibility in assignments.

In many class situations, the number of lessons in this book will be far too large to cover in a one-year course and the teacher will want to plan which topics are to be studied. To assist in this task, we have suggested, in the *Teachers Guide and Manual,* three different course plans. The manual also includes suggestions for lesson presentations, as well as additional questions and problems, special projects, and answers to questions and problems in the text.

The laboratory manual that accompanies *Physics, an Experimental Science* departs from the traditional oversized formats, with their fill-in blanks. The approach to the experiments in the manual emphasizes discovery, rather than the confirmation of previously learned information, part of that discovery being gained through construction of the necessary apparatus as far as possible.

It is hoped that you, the student, will realize that the mastery of the material in this textbook will bring you close to the forefront of present-day knowledge in the field of physics.

It is equally important to understand that while a great deal is known about the physical world around us, there is far more that is not known or understood and there are many problems yet to be solved. Many of you, the students, will be the scientists of tomorrow, and it is you, with your imagination and creative minds, who will, through research and experimentation, find some of the answers.

HARVEY E. WHITE
DONALD H. WHITE
MAURI GOULD

Contents

Introduction

Nor should it be considered rash not to be satisfied with those opinions which have become common. No one should be scorned in physical disputes for not holding to the opinions which happen to please other people best.

Galileo

◀ The United States' first astronaut, John H. Glenn, Jr., looks to the future in the training model of earth and its so-called celestial sphere.

NASA

Lesson 1 INTRODUCTION

Physics is a natural science concerned primarily with the principles and laws governing the behavior of the inanimate world around us. As a science, it is a continuous time-ordered process by which civilized man, through experimentation, reasoning, and mathematical analysis, learns more and more of the seemingly endless detail of natural phenomena.

In attempting to establish the origin of science, many historians go back in time, more than two thousand years, to the era of the great philosophers Thales, Pythagoras, Democritus, Hippocrates, Aristotle, Archimedes, Ptolemy, and their contemporaries. Others prefer to begin with Roger Bacon, Copernicus, Tycho Brahe, Kepler, William Harvey, and men of science who lived less than a thousand years ago. All of these men are considered great, because in their respective lives they exhibited a keen sense of observation, and they applied their powers of reasoning to the explanation of many natural phenomena. Many of the concepts they formulated showed remarkable insight. However, progress was relatively slow, because they overlooked one all-important factor—they failed to recognize the importance of experimentation. Herein lies the secret to the rapid advancement of science in this, the twentieth, century.

The two most powerful tools of modern science are (1) *the empirical method,* often called *experimental physics* and (2) *the method of mathematical analysis,* often called *theoretical physics.* Because these two methods supplement each other, we can well expect both to find their way into this book. In the following pages, then, we will see not only the development of the experimental method through the explanation of many experiments, but also the application of the simplest mathematical relations to the recorded measurements made during the experiments.

It should be realized from the beginning that there are many sciences and that physics is but one of them. It is common practice to divide all of the recognized sciences into three classes: the physical sciences, the life sciences, and the social sciences. Under these headings we find:

Physical Sciences
    Physics
    Chemistry
    Astronomy
    Geology, etc.

Life Sciences
    Biology
    Botany
    Physiology
    Paleontology, etc.

Social Sciences
    Psychology
    Anthropology, etc.

What Is Physics? Physics is a science that involves many different subjects. These subjects may be divided and grouped under one of two headings, *classical physics* and *modern physics.* Classical physics is concerned largely with macroscopic bodies, that is, with those phenomena in which the objects involved are large and can be seen with the eye. Modern physics, on the other hand, is concerned primarily with the submicroscopic world, that is, with those phenomena in which the structure and the behavior of individual atoms and molecules are of prime importance.

The present frontier of physics research faces these submicroscopic phenomena. However, the methods and principles of classical physics provide the framework for these studies. Both aspects, therefore, are essential to the present-day study of physics.

Many of the more popular aspects of physics, such as space travel, nuclear reactors, and the like, are actually engineering, that is, applied physics. In these fields, much of the information learned from submicroscopic studies may be applied to the macroscopic world.

It will be worthwhile, at this point, to consider briefly the various subdivisions of physics and to note the order in which they will be studied.

Classical Physics
> *Mechanics*
> *Properties of Matter*
> *Heat*
> *Sound*
> *Light*
> *Electricity*
> *Magnetism*

Modern Physics
> *Electronics*
> *Atomic Physics*
> *Nuclear Physics*

Mechanics. Mechanics is a branch of physics dealing largely with the state or motion of bodies resulting from the action of applied forces. As we study mechanics, such fundamental concepts as *speed, velocity,* and *acceleration*—as well as *force, mass, work, energy,* and *momentum*—will become familiar terms.

Properties of Matter. This is a general classification applied to many and varied

subjects involving the *solid, liquid,* and *gaseous,* or *vapor,* states of matter. As we delve into the subject, we will see how such practical things as the *stretching, twisting,* and *bending* of solid objects, and the *pressure, density,* and *buoyancy* of liquids and gases, can all be described in terms of simple rules and laws.

Heat. Under this heading, we will study not only the nature of heat, but also the physical changes brought about by raising or lowering the temperature of a body. We will also study, for example, the principles upon which a refrigerator or a natural geyser operates, and the basis upon which an automobile, turbojet, or rocket engine performs.

Sound. Here is a practical branch of physics that should be of interest to everyone. In addition to the general subject of waves and vibrations, we will study the science of sounds, along with the transmission and speed of sound through solids, liquids, and gases, and the detection of sound which we call hearing.

Light. Visible and invisible light will be studied under many and varied conditions. The reflection, refraction, and polarization of light, as well as the optical properties of mirrors, prisms, and lenses, will be taken up in detail. The nature of light itself will also be studied.

Electricity. No one can deny the importance of this area of physics in our lives today. We will study the principles of static and moving electricity. Their generation and use both in science and industry will be explained.

Magnetism. In our investigation of magnetism, we will study the earth's magnetic field, as well as the fields of electromagnets. The origin of magnetic forces and the production of electromagnetic waves will also be covered.

Electronics. Any mention of the word "electronics" brings many devices to mind. Here, we will study such things as electrons, vacuum tubes, transistors, oscillators, amplifiers, radar, television, and the oscilloscope.

Atomic Physics. This is a field in which we study atoms and their external structure, electrons, isotopes, X-rays, and lasers. Much of our present-day knowledge of atomic structure has been determined by studies of light sources and the spectra, or wavelengths, of the light they emit.

Nuclear Physics. As we study the atomic nucleus, nuclear energy, and atomic accelerators, we step onto the threshold of scientific research as it is being carried on today. Among other things we will study nuclear disintegration, transmutation, cosmic rays, fission, and elementary particles.

Such are the diverse branches of that science we call physics.

QUESTIONS

1. Explain what is meant by the "empirical method."
2. Propose a particular question, and describe how the empirical method would apply to it.
3. (a) What is the major contribution of the Greek philosophers? (b) What was their major failing?
4. Classify as physical, life, or social science the following: (a) anatomy, (b) ecology, (c) cosmology, (d) archaeology, and (e) geophysics.
5. Classify as classical or modern physics the following: (a) vacuum tubes, (b) cosmic rays, (c) the reason for the blue sky, (d) the science of musical sounds, and (e) the operation of a geyser.
6. Why does physics qualify as an exact science, whereas medicine does not?
7. Would it have been possible for scientists to develop the transistor without the work of scientists of the nineteenth century to guide them? Explain.
8. An experiment is conducted with a certain result. (a) How could you prove that you would always get the same result? (b) Is this an important phase of the scientific method?
9. Can you think of some way the scientific method could be used in your own daily life?
10. What branches of physics are used in the construction of a modern automobile?
11. Why is magic inconsistent with the principles of physics?

PROJECTS

1. Report on the life of a famous physicist, emphasizing, if possible, why he became a scientist.

2. Make a study of the opportunities for bright, dedicated young people today in the fields of scientific research and teaching.
3. Report on the early years of science when its major battle was with superstition and magic.

INTRODUCTION

Lesson 2 OPTICAL ILLUSIONS

Physics as an Objective Method. It has long been known that when experiments are to be performed one cannot rely too much upon the human senses of touch, sight, hearing, etc., to make accurate observations. Methods of measurement that rely upon the senses entirely are called *subjective methods*. Methods that make use of scientific instruments are generally called *objective methods*.

In the early history of science, laws were frequently discovered using subjective methods. Progress was slow, however, until such methods were replaced by objective methods using measuring instruments devised to give greater and greater precision.

It is true that many scientific discoveries have been made in the past with what we now would call the crudest of equipment. It is the development of precision instruments and apparatus, however, that has led to the recent discoveries that are far-reaching in their theoretical implications and are of extreme practical importance to the advancement of civilization.

As an introduction to the subject of physics we will first consider a number of experiments illustrating the false impressions so easily arrived at from the use of subjective methods of observation. Although these experiments are of the nature of an entertainment, they do have more seri-ous aspects, for they demonstrate the necessity of using objective methods in advancing science.

Subjective Methods. If someone is asked to determine the temperature of a pan of water, the first impulse, if the water is not too hot, is to use a hand or finger tips and not to bother looking for a thermometer. To illustrate the gross inaccuracy of the touch in determining temperature, consider the three pans of water as shown in Fig. A. If

cold   warm   hot

Fig. A. Experiment illustrating the uncertainty of subjective methods of measurement.

the hand is first held for some little time in the pan containing *cold* water and then plunged into the *warm* water, the senses say that the latter is hot. If, however, the hand is first held in the *hot* water and then plunged into the *warm* water, the senses say that the latter is cold. The conclusion in either case is thus influenced by the experiences immediately preceding the determination of the temperature of the middle pan. When a thermometer is used in this experiment, the same temperature will be found in either case. Although this latter would be called an objective method of measurement, one still relies upon the senses to obtain a reading of the thermometer scale.

Optical Illusions. In making many scientific measurements, the eye is considered the most useful of all recording instruments. In some instances, however, the eye is not, and should not be, used directly in making observations, because it cannot be relied upon to observe what is really there. To illustrate how unreliable the sense of vision can be in some cases, we will consider a number of examples commonly referred to as "optical illusions."

Of the hundreds of well-known optical illusions only a few of the most interesting ones will be presented here. In Fig. B is a

means of slanting lines these figures are made to appear to have different heights. Experiences from early childhood have trained us to interpret the slanting lines as depth.

The next set of illusions, shown in Fig. D, are classified as *equivocal figures*. These illustrate the phenomenon of the *fluctuation* of the process of vision. In (*a*) six cubes appear to be stacked three, two, one, or seven cubes appear to be stacked two, three, two. In (*b*) a folded sheet of paper is seen to be opening either toward or away from the reader. In (*c*) a flight of steps appears to be seen from above looking down, or from below looking up.

Fig. D(*d*) is one of the most interesting of all illusions. To fully appreciate the effect, one must himself perform the experiment with a small wire cube about one inch

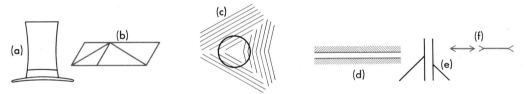

Fig. B. Optical illusions with lines and angles.

group of six figures classified as illusions due to *lines* and *angles*. In (*a*), the first figure, the brim of the hat is as long as the hat is high; in (*b*) the diagonal lines of each parallelogram are of the same length; and in (*c*) the perfect circle appears to be distorted. In figure (*d*) the two horizontal lines are parallel and straight, and in (*e*) the lower right-hand line, if extended, will intersect the left-hand line where it joins the vertical. In (*f*) the horizontal lines are of equal length.

Fig. C is an example of *perspective,* an illusion suggesting depth to the picture, when in reality, it is flat. Actually, this shows three figures of equal height. By

in size. The cube is held by a small handle at one corner and viewed with one eye at a distance of from 1 to 2 ft. By the principle of fluctuation the observer next tries to make the farthest corner of the cube appear as the nearest corner. When this condition is attained, the cube, when turned about a horizontal or vertical axis, will appear to turn in the opposite direction. A little practice in the fluctuation of the visual senses is required in this experiment, and it is well worth performing.

In Fig. E are two pairs of similar figures of equal area. The slanting lines at the ends make the lower figure in each case appear to be larger than the one immediately

Fig. C. Which figure is tallest? Measure them.

above. Such figures should be cut from white cardboard and held one above the other. When the upper figure is interchanged with the corresponding lower figure, one figure seems to grow and the other to shrink before the eyes.

In Fig. F(a) are two small squares of equal size, a white square on a black background and a black square on a white background. When an image of this is formed on the retina of the eye, the cones and rods

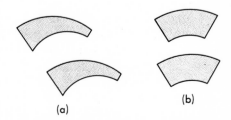

(a)   (b)

Fig. D. Optical illusions illustrating fluctuations of the attention.

Fig. E. Optical illusions of area.

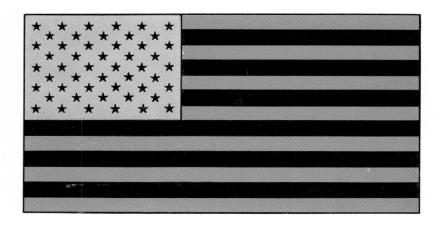

Fig. 2G. Fatigue images enable the above objects to appear in their natural colors.

just beyond the white are stimulated by those nearby. This causes the white image to be larger than the black one. This phenomenon is called *irradiation,* or *brightness contrast.* A similar phenomenon is illustrated in Fig. F(b) where gray spots are seen at the intersections of the white lines.

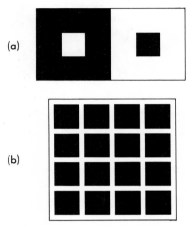

(a)

(b)

Fig. F. Illustrations of irradiation.

trated in Fig. F(b) where gray spots are seen at the intersections of the white lines.

Complementary Images. When the eyes are subjected to bright light for some little time, the retina seems to show tiring, or *fatigue.* Furthermore, continued subjection of any part of the retina to one particular color causes only those cones sensitive to that color to tire. When the same retinal area is subsequently subjected to white light, the previously inactive cones respond more strongly than those originally stimulated, and a complementary color is seen.

To observe these colored images a bright light should be used. Fix the attention on the black star in the lower right-hand corner of the field of the flag in Fig. G, and keep it there for about 15 to 20 sec. Then turn the eyes toward a white wall of the room, or toward the open sky, and in one or two

seconds the American flag will appear in all of its true colors. Similar effects can be observed with other colored pictures.

Delayed images of this kind are always complementary in color to the original pictures, black becomes white, yellow becomes blue, green becomes magenta, magenta becomes green, etc. (For an explanation of complementary colors see Lesson 66.)

The Stroboscopic Effect. When a wagon with spoked wheels is coming to a stop in motion pictures, the wheels often appear to stand still, then turn backward, stop, turn forward, and then stop again. This phenomenon, the stroboscopic effect, is due to interrupted illumination of the motion-picture screen and can be illustrated in many ways. An interesting experiment illustrating the phenomenon is shown in Fig. H.

Two disks are mounted on the shafts of two separate motors. The smaller disk, *A,* with a narrow slot is used to interrupt the light beam illuminating the larger disk. The disk *B* is white with black circles and dots arranged exactly as shown. Suppose now that disk *A* makes sixteen revolutions per second, thus illuminating disk *B* with sixteen short flashes of light per second. Suppose also that *B* makes only one revolution per second and that one flash of light comes when the disk has the position shown in the figure. Confining the attention to the circle at position *1,* the two enclosed dots are one above the other. When the second flash of light appears, the circle *2* will be in position *1,* and the two dots will appear to have shifted slightly clockwise. When the next flash of light comes, the circle *3* will be in position *1* and the two dots will have shifted still farther. This process continued shows that the circles will appear to stand still and the dots will appear to rotate within them.

The three rings in the center, with

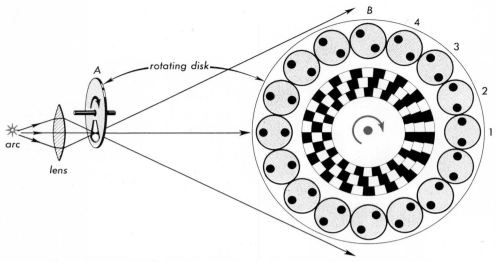

Fig. H. Experimental arrangement for demonstrating the stroboscopic effect.

checkerboard patches, are made so that, at the proper speed described above, the middle ring appears to stand still, the outer ring rotates slowly clockwise, and the inner ring counterclockwise.

If the light flashes in any experiment, such as the one described above, are slower than 16 per second, the illuminated object will appear to flicker badly. If, however, the flashes come at an increasingly higher rate, the flicker will soon disappear entirely, and the illumination will seem to be steady. The reason for this is that each retinal image is somehow retained by the vision mechanism for about one-sixteenth of a second. This is called the *persistence of vision.*

QUESTIONS

1. How would you measure the length of a car using (a) a subjective method? (b) an objective method?
2. How would you measure a person's pulse rate using (a) a subjective method? (b) an objective method?
3. How do you explain the fact that, in winter, when you enter a room with normal temperature after having been outside, the room feels very warm?
4. Briefly explain how the subjective method enters into the measurement of
   (a) temperature with a thermometer.
   (b) time with a stopwatch.
   (c) length with a tape measure.
5. If a zebra's stripes are of equal width, the white stripes would appear to be slightly larger than the black stripes. What is the cause of this effect, and what is it called?

6. How could a dress designer use a knowledge of how the eye is fooled to advantage in his vocation?

7. Give an example of your own that would demonstrate
   (a) color fatigue.
   (b) fluctuation of vision.
   (c) irradiation.
   (d) the stroboscopic effect.

8. (a) How could you use a stroboscope to measure the speed of a phonograph turntable? (b) What is a simple single-speed stroboscope that is available in most homes today at little or no cost?

9. Explain why the wheels of a wagon may appear to turn backward on a motion-picture screen when the wagon is moving forward.

10. Briefly explain why motion pictures flicker when the projector runs too slowly, but do not flicker when it runs fast.

11. Why does a Fourth-of-July sparkler that is spun rapidly appear to the eye as a circle of light?

12. Do motion pictures really move? Explain.

13. In what ways are any of the principles developed in this lesson involved in things happening in the world around us?

PROJECTS

1. Make a simple stroboscope using a wheel with thin slits evenly spaced on radii of the wheel. Arrange the wheel so it can be spun uniformly by hand or with a variable-speed motor.

2. Make an electronic strobe that can be used to study all kinds of repetitious motions too rapid for the eye to see unaided.

INTRODUCTION

Lesson 3 *UNITS OF MEASUREMENT*

Because physics is a science based upon exact measurement, it is essential that the student first become familiar with several of the more commonly used measuring devices and the units into which each is usually divided. Every measurement, whether it be a distance, a weight, an interval of time, or anything else, requires *two* things: first, a *number;* and second, a *unit.*

Although there are numerous different units, such as ergs, joules, watts, minutes, candle power, and decibels, each one can be expressed in terms of not more than three special units. These three, called *funda-*

mental units, are the units of *length, mass,* and *time.* All other units are called *derived units,* because as we shall see later, they can always be written as some combination of the three fundamental units.

The choice of a unit of length, mass, and time is quite arbitrary. Once having made a decision on these fundamental units, all other units can be derived from them. To be useful, a great many people would have to agree to use them.

There are, in general, two widely used sets of unit systems: the *metric* and the *English.* Throughout the civilized world scientific observations are nearly always expressed in terms of metric units. This set employs the *standard meter* as the unit of length, the *standard kilogram* as the unit of mass, and the *second* as the unit of time.

The Standard Meter and Yard. The standard meter is a platinum-iridium bar about forty inches long that is kept in the vaults of the International Bureau of Weights and Measures near Paris, France. Three facsimiles of this bar are to be found at the United States Bureau of Standards in Washington, D.C. Each of these duplicate copies may be called an *International Prototype Meter* and is now the standard of length in the United States. From these prototypes all other measuring rods and tapes are standardized.

When the standard meter was first devised, it was intended that it have a length equal to one ten-millionth part of the distance from one of the earth's poles to the equator. Although more recent measurements of the earth's dimensions have shown that the distance from pole to equator is about 10,000,880 *standard meters,* the two groove marks—one on either end of the original platinum-iridium bar—are still taken to be exactly one meter apart.

The standard meter is usually divided into one hundred equal parts. Each of these parts is the *centimeter.*

1 meter = 100 centimeters

or, abbreviated,

1 m = 100 cm

The centimeter is further divided into ten equal parts. Each of these parts is the *millimeter.*

1 cm = 10 mm
1000 mm = 1 m

For nonscientific purposes, the *yard* is used as the standard unit of length in the United States. By an act of Congress in 1866, the standard yard to be used legally in the United States was defined as 3600/3937 part of a standard meter. Because the yard is divided into thirty-six inches,

1 m = 39.37 in.

With twelve inches to one foot,

3 ft = 1 yd
1 ft = 30.48 cm
1 in. = 2.54 cm

The sizes of the inch, fractions of an inch relative to the centimeter, and millimeter, are illustrated in Fig. A.

When large distances are to be measured, it is convenient as well as customary to use large units of length. Such units are the *kilometer* in the metric system and the *mile* in the English system. One kilometer is equivalent to one thousand meters, and one mile is equivalent to five thousand, two hundred and eighty feet.

1 Km = 1000 m
1 mi = 5280 ft

The Standard Kilogram and Pound. The standard unit of mass is the *kilogram,* a cylinder of platinum-iridium also preserved at the International Bureau of Weights and Measures near Paris. Two copies of this kilogram, which may be called *International Prototype Kilograms,* are kept in the vaults of the United States Bureau of Standards.

that 1 Kg is equivalent to the mass of 2.205 lb.

Historical Time Pieces. Instruments for the measurement of time go back histori-

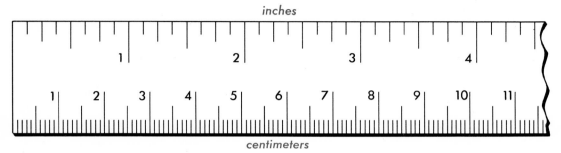

inches

centimeters

Fig. A. Diagram comparing the centimeter scale with the inch scale.

The kilogram is divided into one thousand equal parts each called the *gram.*

1000 gm = 1 Kg

The original intent was to base the standard kilogram upon the gram, the gram being the mass of one cubic centimeter of pure water taken at a temperature of four degrees Celsius. See Fig. B.

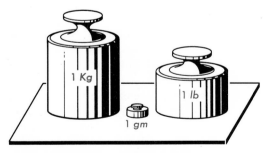

Fig. B. Mass of a standard kilogram is 2.205 times the mass of a standard pound weight.

The standard *pound* is defined in terms of the standard kilogram by the relation that the mass of a pound shall equal 0.4536 kilogram. From this we obtain the relation

cally to the Babylonians, at least, and probably to the time of the Greeks, 500 B.C. The earliest time pieces on record were chiefly water clocks, some of very simple design and others of more elaborate design. These clocks were based upon the elementary principle that it takes the same time for equal amounts of water to flow through a small opening. The *hour glass,* employing the same principle, but using sand instead of water, is an outgrowth of the water clock and dates back to medieval times.

A water clock of moderately simple design is shown in Fig. C. Small holes at the edge of the vanes (shown in the detail diagram) allow the water to flow from one compartment to the other. This permits the cylinder to turn slowly, thus unwinding the suspending cords.

The *sundial* dates back to the Chaldean astronomer Berossus, who lived about the time of Alexander the Great, 300 B.C. Today, similar instruments serve as ornaments in many public parks. A sundial of common design, as shown in Fig. D, consists essentially of a pin, called a *gnomon,* mounted

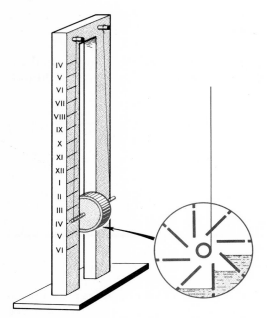

Fig. C. Diagram of an early water clock.

at an angle on a circular plate, called the *dial*. The gnomon is mounted in the vertical North-South plane. The edge of the gnomon is parallel to the earth's rotational axis, and

Fig. D. Diagram of a sundial.

its purpose is to cast a shadow on the dial, which is marked with the hours of the day. Because of slight variations in the earth's motion, small corrections must be made to the time shown by the shadow. A list of these corrections, amounting to several minutes, are usually engraved upon every sundial. The sundial on the University of California campus, for example, has marked on it the following corrections:

Jan. 10, + 17 min	May 20, + 5 min
Feb. 9, + 23 min	June 19, + 10 min
Mar. 11, + 19 min	July 19, + 15 min
Apr 10, + 11 min	Aug. 18, + 13 min

Sept. 17, + 4 min
Oct. 17, − 5 min
Nov. 16, − 6 min
Dec. 16, + 5 min

Other clocks depend for their regulation upon the swinging of a pendulum or the oscillation of a balance wheel. Examples of these are the grandfather clock and the modern wrist watch. Such devices will be discussed in Lesson 51. Electric clocks for home use are run by tiny electric motors. The speed of these motors is controlled at the city's electric-power plant by regulating the frequency of the alternating current supplied to the power lines leading to the house. The master clock at the power house is frequently a pendulum clock.

Time and the Mean Solar Day. Three kinds of time are recognized by astronomers: first, *sidereal time;* second, *apparent solar time;* and third, *mean solar time.* The latter is the time used in civil life. If at any given point on the earth's surface we adjust the gnomon of a sundial to lie in the North-South vertical plane, the time interval between two successive transits of the sun's shadow over the twelve-o'clock mark is called the apparent solar day. For several reasons, one being that the earth's orbit around the sun is elliptical, this interval of time varies slightly from day to day. An apparent solar day in December is about one minute longer than an apparent solar day in September. It is clear, therefore, why in this day of accurate time pieces we do not regulate our clocks to apparent solar time.

The *average* length of all apparent solar days throughout a solar year is called the *mean solar day*. This is a satisfactory time interval, because it is invariable and can be kept by well-regulated clocks and watches. The time interval called the *second* is defined as 1/86400 part of a mean solar day.

$$1 \text{ sec} = \frac{1}{60} \times \frac{1}{60} \times \frac{1}{24}$$

$$= \frac{1}{86400} \textbf{ part of one day}$$

There are 365.2421 mean solar days in one solar year; that is, with respect to the sun, the earth makes 365.2421 rotations in making one complete revolution in its orbit.

For astronomical purposes, a different time scale known as sidereal time is used. There is one more sidereal day in one solar year than there are mean solar days. One solar year equals 366.2421 sidereal days. The reason for the additional day is that in making one complete turn around the sun in its orbit the earth has actually made 366.2421 rotations with respect to the fixed stars. The sidereal second as ticked off by an astronomical clock is, therefore, slightly shorter than the second given by an ordinary clock keeping mean solar time.

Metric Units. Nearly all scientific experiments, in the United States as well as abroad, are performed using metric units. In these units, distance is usually measured in millimeters, centimeters, meters, or kilometers; mass is measured in grams or kilograms; and time is measured in seconds, minutes, or hours. For metric units, the abbreviation *cgs* means *centimeter, gram, second;* and *mks* means *meter, kilogram, second.*

The English system, as already referred to, uses the foot, yard, and mile as units of length; the ounce, pound, and ton as units of force; and the second as the unit of time. Americans have inherited the English system with all of its cumbersome fractions, and because it is so firmly ingrained in our civil life, it will be a difficult task to change over completely to the simpler metric system. There is a strong movement today, however, advocating such a change.

The chief advantage of metric units over English units is that all metric units may be conveniently divided into parts that are powers of ten: one hundred, one thousand, and so forth. This enables fractional distances and masses to be expressed as decimals. Decimals, of course, are easier to manipulate mathematically.

It is useful in learning the metric system to memorize the meanings of the prefixes used as shown in Table 1. (See also Appendix.)

Table 1

mega	1,000,000
kilo	1,000
deci	$\frac{1}{10}$
centi	$\frac{1}{100}$
milli	$\frac{1}{1,000}$
micro	$\frac{1}{1,000,000}$

QUESTIONS

1. What are the fundamental units in the (a) mks system? (b) the cgs system? (c) Which is the "more fundamental"? Explain.
2. What is the advantage of the metric system over the English system?
3. Could science have developed just as far as it has without the metric system? Explain.
4. Is the metric system more accurate than the English system? Explain.
5. Why have some countries recently converted their monetary systems from the English to a decimal system?
6. An alternative definition of the meter is given in terms of a certain number of wavelengths of the green light from a mercury lamp. What advantage might this "atomic standard" have over the Paris standard?
7. (a) What is the legal definition of the standard yard? (b) Why do we still use the yard rather than the meter?
8. Our ordinary clocks are based on 24 hours per day. (a) Does this refer to an apparent solar day, a mean solar day, or a sidereal day? (b) Give your reason why the others are not used.
9. Make a list of (a) ten fundamental and (b) ten derived units of measurement.

PROBLEMS

1. The standard foot was originally defined as the length of a certain English king's foot. How long was his foot in meters?
2. English tailors used to measure a yard of cloth by the distance from their left shoulder to their right hand. How far is this in millimeters?
3. Find the number of meters in 1 mi.
4. Find the number of kilometers in 1 mi.
5. Find the number of miles in 1 Km.
6. How many millimeters are (a) in one kilometer? (b) in one inch?
7. Sixty mi/hr is equal to how many ft/sec?
8. How many cubic centimeters would a container hold if its inner dimensions were measured as follows:

    length: 3 m, 25 cm
    width: 60 cm, 5 mm
    depth: 1 m

9. To obey the road sign in Mexico that reads 35 Km/hr, what would your speedometer have to read?
10. A standard lead brick weighs 13 Kg. What is its weight in pounds?
11. (a) What is the mass of a cubic foot of water in grams? (b) What does it weigh in pounds?

12. Approximately what would the correction be to the sundial on the University of California campus on July 4?

13. Calculate the distance to the moon in meters if the distance is 239,000 mi.

PROJECTS

1. Make a set of models to show the development of the accurate measurement of time.

2. Make and use a sundial. Compare its accuracy with a standard timepiece.

3. Make a very accurate clock based on the oscillations of an accurately ground crystal.

4. Study the development of the chronometer and its importance to navigation.

Special Lessons

. . . inasmuch as they [the Pythagoreans] saw in numbers the properties and proportions of the different kinds of harmonies, and since all other things so far as their entire nature is concerned were modelled upon numbers, whereas numbers are prior to anything else in nature,—from all this they inferred that the first elements of numbers were the first elements of all things that exist, and that the whole heaven was a harmony and a number.

Charles M. Bakewell, *Source Book in Ancient Philosophy*, Scribner's, New York, 1909, pp. 36-37.

Philosophy is written in that very great book, which continually lies open before our eyes (I mean the Universe); but we cannot understand it, if we do not first learn the language, and comprehend the characters in which it is written. It is written in the mathematical language, and its characters are triangles, circles and other geometrical figures, without the aid of which it is impossible to understand a word of it, without which one wanders vainly through a dark labyrinth.

Galileo Galilei, *Il Saggiatore*, Florentine Edition, 1842, p. 171.

◄ The key to our understanding of the world in the study of physics is the knowledge of mathematics with which to manipulate the data acquired from measurement.

Mettler Instrument Corp.

Lesson 4 *THE SLIDE RULE*

Significant Figures. Before learning to use a slide rule, we should clearly understand the meaning of the term *significant figures*. The three lists of numerals in Table 1 will help to illustrate its meaning.

The first significant figure of a numeral is the first digit that is not zero. The last significant figure is the last digit that is not zero.

Table 1. Significant Figures

A Two significant figures	B Three significant figures	C Four significant figures
24	374	5279
6.9	21.5	63.08
0.37	6.05	0.1062
0.053	0.00328	0.04503
4600	546000	692700

Most slide rules are capable of handling the multiplication and division of numbers to three significant figures only. Furthermore, the answers are correct to three significant figures only.

If numerals like those in column C are to be used in any slide-rule calculation, they should be reduced to three significant figures. These particular numbers would, therefore, be assumed to have the values

5280, 63.1, 0.106, 0.0450, and 693000, respectively.

Many students are disturbed at first by what appears to be a drastic reduction of the accuracy afforded by a slide rule. However, problems in physics are usually based on experiments made with instruments of limited accuracy. Measurements are made with devices, such as the ruler, the protractor, the thermometer, and the hydrometer, the accuracy of which depends on the smallest unit marked on them. Suppose one is using a metric ruler whose smallest marked division is the millimeter. Fig. A is a magnified portion of it. Let the numbered divisions be centimeters.

Because the metric conversion factor is 10, let us further read to the nearest tenth of a millimeter. Our reading might well be 7.54 cm. Reducing the ruler back to actual size, we must concede that the 7 and the 5 are accurate, but that the 4 is only a fairly good guess. Because we are not sure of the 4, to try to read to thousandths is sheer folly! Some physics students would have read the ruler to be 7.5 cm. After all, the millimeter is very small. But then the 5 would be too low; the 5, therefore, is a doubtful figure.

Let us find the area of a rectangular piece of metal whose length turns out to be our 7.54 and whose width, found in the same manner, is 4.23. Before we multiply these numbers, note that the dubious 4 and

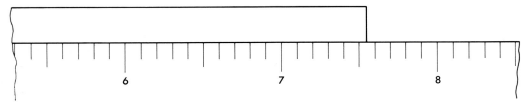

Fig. A. Magnified view of a metric ruler.

3 are printed in color to indicate the guess they involve. Now multiply:

$$
\begin{array}{r}
7.54 \\
4.23 \\
\hline
2262 \\
1508 \\
3016 \\
\hline
31.8942
\end{array}
$$

Note that the contamination of the two colored numbers affects the 6 and 2 in the first partial product, as well as the other colored figures as shown. If we are doubtful of the third figure of our product, why carry the 942? Let us round off the product to 31.9, and be done with it. Mathematicians have developed the rule: *The number of significant figures in the final product or quotient should not exceed the least number of significant figures in any one factor.* The student can prove this by taking examples involving numbers of different significance. The number of *significant figures is obtained by counting the figures that one is sure of and adding one more for the guessed one.* Thus our answer, 31.9, has 3 significant figures, even though the 9 may be a bit too big or too small. The same rules hold for division.

Addition and subtraction require a different treatment. The rule is: *In a column of addition or subtraction, in which the decimal points are placed one above the other, the number of significant figures in the final answer is determined by the first digit encountered going from left to right that terminates any one numeral:*

$$
\begin{array}{r}
5932.10\ 5 \\
26.10\ 78 \\
1.03\ 5984 \\
9.12 \\
432.16\ 5 \\
\hline
6400.53[3784]
\end{array}
$$

written 6400.53

In the example above, because 9.12 could not be read any more accurately than to three figures, one does not know what the fourth figure is. If this fourth figure is not known, the seventh figure in the answer and the ones following it cannot be given. In fact, to give the figures in the brackets has no meaning at all. One has as much right to place any digit from 1 to 9 in any of the four places in the brackets as [3784]. Therefore, the answer should be left 6400.53 even though the 3 is perhaps not the closest digit. If the 9.12 had been 9.123, which to three-figure accuracy is 9.12, the final answer would have been 6400.54.

If, in our multiplication problem, we had allowed ourselves an error in our readings of 0.02 cm, then 7.54 cm could represent a range of 7.52 to 7.56 and 4.23, a range of 4.21 to 4.25.

The maximum product would be—

$$
\begin{array}{r}
7.56 \\
4.25 \\
\hline
37\ 80 \\
151\ 2 \\
3024 \\
\hline
32.1300 \quad \text{or } 32.1
\end{array}
$$

The minimum product would be—

$$
\begin{array}{r}
7.52 \\
4.21 \\
\hline
7\ 52 \\
150\ 4 \\
3008 \\
\hline
31.6592 \quad \text{or } 31.7
\end{array}
$$

With the error assumed, our answer of 31.9 simply indicates that it might well be as low as 31.7 and as high as 32.1.

For extended problems such as—

$$
\frac{5732.50 \times 3.215}{62.51 \times 3.43}
$$

time can be saved by realizing that once the number of significant figures of the answer has been determined by the rules for multiplication and division, one need not carry (in intermediate products and quotients) more than one more significant figure than the answer can have. Doing so will make no significant difference to your answer.

We should also consider the numbers with zeros in them. These play a sort of double role in significant figures. Take the number 300.07. Zeros that lie between other numerals, as in this example, are significant; the numeral has five significant figures. Zeros between numerals are treated as the other digits.

What if the zero lies at the end of a numeral such as 2.310? This has four significant figures. If it had three significant figure, it would be written 2.31. The zero definitely indicates that it was possible to read to thousandths. Leaving it off would

two significant-figure number. These zeros indicate decimal point placement, not accuracy.

Because many of the measurements made in the science laboratory are accurate to only three significant figures, the use of a slide rule is usually, but not always, sufficient and justified.

The Slide Rule. A slide rule is a simple mechanical device used for carrying out the arithmetic processes of *multiplication* and *division*. Because slide rules are easy to use, and inexpensive ones are quite adequate for most purposes, every physics student should acquire a slide rule and learn how to use it.

The beginner should select a straight, inexpensive rule about ten inches in length and one that contains four, and not more than six, scales. The scales most commonly used are the *A, B, C,* and *D* scales as shown in Fig. B. Note that the slide rule consists of

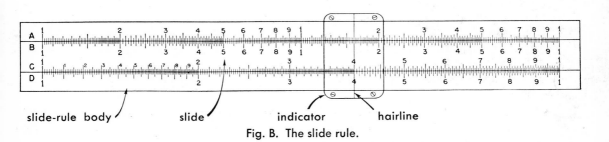

slide-rule body   slide   indicator   hairline

Fig. B. The slide rule.

indicate reading to hundredths. If, however, a numeral has a large number of zeros behind it such as 3,800,000, the meaning is ambiguous. It is not clear how many of the zeros are significant. In this case, one would assume that, unless stated otherwise, only the first two are significant. In the case of 3.700000 the zeros should be significant.

Now 0.0036 is different. Zeros appearing at the beginning of a numeral preceded by no other digit are not significant. This is a

the slide rule *body,* and two movable parts called the *slide* and the *indicator.*

The C and D Scales. In making the first critical examination of a slide rule, note that there are four fundamental scales, and that they are marked at the left end of the rule by *A, B, C,* and *D.* See Fig. B. Because multiplication and division are usually carried out with the two identical *C* and *D* scales, we will examine the entire length of these scales in three sections and see how to determine any position of the indicator hairline.

Consider the left-hand section of the C and D scales from the left index, 1, to the principal numeral 2, as shown in Fig. C.

sition in Fig. C, it could just as readily be placed before the first digit, after the second digit, or after the third digit, etc. In other words the left index, 1, can represent any of the numbers 1, 10, 100, 1000, or any power of ten, negative or positive. If we let this in-

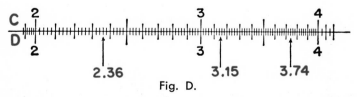

Fig. C.

Note that the interval is divided into ten divisions representing tenths, and each of these into ten divisions representing hundredths.

If the indicator hairline is located in the position shown by the arrow at the left, its position would be identified as 1.14. Similarly, the second arrow position represents the reading 1.37. The third arrow position appears to be halfway between 1.53 and 1.54; hence we *interpolate* and write 1.535. Interpolation is a process of inserting, or finding, intermediate values by making a reasonable estimate as to an exact value.

dex represent 10, the right-hand numeral 2 will represent 20, and the arrow positions would be read as 11.4, 13.7, 15.35, and 19.50. If we let the left index represent 100, the right-hand numeral 2 will represent 200, and the arrow positions would be read as 114, 137, 153.5, and 195.0.

Set the indicator of your rule at random between the principal numerals 1 and 2, and then practice reading its position until you feel confident you are reading it correctly.

We are now ready to examine the center section of the C and D scales between the index numerals 2, 3, and 4. Note in Fig. D,

Fig. D.

Because interpolation is nothing more than a good guess, the reading 1.535 is hardly better than three significant figures would indicate. Applying the interpolation process to the fourth arrow position we could write 1.950, with the understanding that the last figure, 0, may not be correct.

Although a decimal point has been inserted after the first digit of each arrow po-

and on your own rule, that each of the two intervals are divided into tenths, and each subdivision into fifths. In other words, the smallest intervals, as marked, each represent 2/10 of a subdivision. Suppose we wanted to locate the position 2.36 on these scales. The first significant figure indicates that the position lies between 2 and 3. Set the hairline on 2. The second significant figure, 3, indicates the position is between the third and fourth subdivision, while the third significant figure, 6, shows it is 6/10, or 3/5, of the distance between these two subdivisions. Hence, the left arrow is properly located at 2.36.

Because the index numerals 3, 4, and 5 can also represent the numbers 30, 40, and 50, or 300, 400, and 500, the arrow positions could represent 23.6, 31.5, and 37.4, or 236, 315, and 374, respectively.

Finally, we can examine the right-hand section of the *C* and *D* scales between the numerals 4, 5, 6, 7, 8, 9, and 1. See Fig. E.

ond numeral on the C scale. (4) *Read the answer on the D scale under the hairline.*

Suppose, for example, you want to find the product 3 × 2. While you don't need the slide rule to find the answer, the performance of such a simple operation will clarify the method. See Fig. F. (1) Set the hairline on 3 of the *D* scale. (2) Move the slide so that the left index, 1, of the *C* scale is on the hairline. (3) Move the indicator to the numeral 2 on the *C* scale. (4) Read the answer as 6 on the *D* scale.

A little study will show the slide-rule settings for the products 30 × 20, 3 × 20,

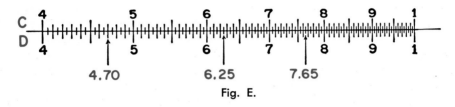

Fig. E.

Between each pair of numbers are ten subdivisions and each subdivision is divided into halves, or 5/10. Note carefully the positions of the arrows, and be sure you can read the position of the hairline when it is located any place on the *C* and *D* scales.

Multiplication. *To multiply two factors, carry out the four following steps:* (1) *Set*

30 × 2, 300 × 20, etc., would all be the same as the above. The numeral 6 is the correct first numeral for all answers, but the number of zeros to be added must be determined by inspection.

Consider the procedure for obtaining the product of 24.0 × 1.5. (1) Set the hairline exactly on the fourth subdivision line beyond the 2 of the *D* scale. This position

Fig. F.

the hairline at the first numeral on the D scale. (2) *Move the slide so the left-hand index, 1, of the C scale is exactly under the hairline.* (3) *Move the hairline to the sec-*

represents 24.0. (2) Move the left-hand index 1 of the *C* scale to the hairline. (3) Move indicator to the fifth subdivision between 1 and 2 on the *C* scale. (4) The answer is under the hairline on the *D* scale and appears exactly at the sixth subdivision beyond 3, or 360. To locate the decimal point, inspect the two original numerals. One-and-a-half times 24 cannot be as small as 3.60 nor as large as 360. Therefore it must be 36.0. Similarly, the product 24.0 × 2 is 48.0 as shown by the hairline position at the right in Fig. G.

imation. For example, in the last problem, round off 3.8 to 4, and 56.5 to 60. The product 4 × 60, by mental arithmetic, is 240, so the answer is 215 and not 21.5 or 2150.

Division. Division on the slide rule is just the reverse of multiplication. *To divide one number by the other, carry out the three following steps:* (1) *Set the hairline on the*

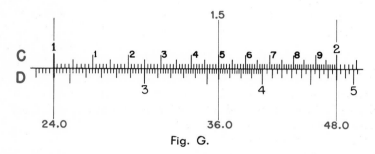

Fig. G.

Find the product 3.8 × 56.5. When the above steps are carried out for this product, the answer will be found to lie beyond the right-hand end of the *D* scale. In such cases, one moves the right-hand index, 1, of the *C* scale to the first number 3.8 on the *D* scale. See Fig. H. Moving the indicator to the left,

dividend, or numerator, on the D *scale.* (2) *Move the slide until the divisor, or denominator, on the* C *scale, lines up with the hairline.* (3) *The quotient, or answer, is under the* C *index at one of the two ends of the slide.* In simple terms, line up the numerator on the *D* scale with the denomi-

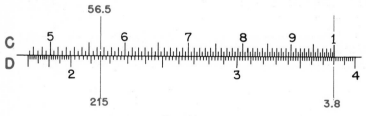

Fig. H.

until the hairline is on the second numeral, 56.5, on the *C* scale, the answer is read off the *D* scale as 215.

The Decimal Point. To find the decimal point in any problem, substitute round numbers for those in the problem and determine the position of the decimal point by approx-

nator on the *C* scale, and the answer is under the *C* scale index.

For example, find the quotient of 6/2. (1) Set the hairline on 6 of the *D* scale. See Fig. F. (2) Bring the 2 of the *C* scale to the hairline. (3) The answer 3 is now under the *C* index on the *D* scale. Note that the fraction 6/2 is just upside down on the rule.

As a second example, find the quotient of 215/56.5. See Fig. H. Set the hairline on 215 of the *D* scale, and then line up 56.5 of the *C* scale. The answer 3.8 is on the *D* scale under the *C* index at the right. Note again that the fraction is lined up, but inverted, at the hairline position.

To find the decimal point in the last problem, round off the numbers and use mental arithmetic. For 215 write 200, and for 3.8 write 4. The quotient for 200/4 is 50. The answer, therefore, is 56.5 and not 5.65 or 565.

Squares and Square Roots. To find the square of a number, one multiplies that number by itself. To find the square root of a number requires the carrying out of a complicated arithmetic process. With the slide rule these operations are relatively simple. *To find the square of a number, carry out the two following steps: (1) Set the hairline to the numeral on the* D *scale. (2) Read the answer under the hairline on the* A *scale.*

Inspection of Fig. B shows that directly above 2 on the *D* scale we find its square, or 4, on the *A* scale. Directly above 3 on the *D* scale is its square, or 9, on the *A* scale. Directly above 4 on the *D* scale (the position of the hairline shown) we find its square, or 16, on the *A* scale.

To find the square root of a number, the reverse steps are used: (1) Set the hairline at the numeral on the A *scale. (2) Read the square root on the* D *scale under the hairline.*

Because there are two identical parts to the *A* scale, some convention must be developed to decide whether to use the left or right half of the rule. In the number whose square root is to be found, pair off the digits on either side of the decimal point, starting at the decimal point. If one digit remains in the farthest-left pair, use the left half of the *A* scale; otherwise use the right half. Each digit you read off the *D* scale fits over a pair and automatically sets the decimal point. For example, find the square root of 820.

$$8 \ 20 \ . \ 00$$

Because one digit is left under the farthest-left pair, the left half of the *A* scale is used. The digits fit right over the brackets so that the answer is 28.6.

Another example might be the number 0.00545. Pairing this off gives—

$$.00 \ 54 \ 5$$

The farthest-left pair has two digits, 54, and so the right half of scale *A* is used. This gives an answer of 0.074.

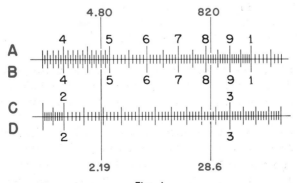

Fig. I.

In Fig. I, the hairline settings are shown for finding the square roots of 4.80 and 820. The two answers are shown on the D scale as 2.19 and 28.6.

Square Roots Without Slide Rule. One method for finding the square root of a number to an accuracy of three figures without a slide rule is the following: By inspection, a guess of the square root is made to two figures. For example, if the number is 685, inspection shows that it lies between $(20)^2 = 400$ and $(30)^2 = 900$, and that a reasonable guess might be 25. The original number is then divided by 25 and gives 27.4. The average of these two numbers, 26.2, is then the square root to three figures. If greater accuracy is desired, the averaged number may be assumed to be an original guess and the process repeated.

QUESTIONS

1. Which two scales of the slide rule should be used for (a) multiplication and (b) division?
2. Which two scales of the slide rule should be used for finding (a) the squares and (b) the square roots of numbers?
3. To how many significant figures can slide-rule calculations be depended upon?
4. Name the three principal parts of the slide rule.
5. Why should a long slide rule be more accurate than a shorter one?
6. Which end of the slide rule has the greatest accuracy as regards (a) significant figures and (b) percentage error? (*Note:* Can you interpolate any more accurately between 98 and 99 than between 101 and 102?)
7. Circular slide rules are available for those who want more accuracy in a small space. An 8-inch diameter circular rule would be equivalent to how large a straight rule?
8. What is the best method for determining where the decimal point belongs?
9. In finding square roots, how does one know which part of the A scale to use?

PROBLEMS

1. Express each of the following to three significant figures only: (a) 6497   (b) 38.27   (c) 0.43927   (d) 0.06008   (e) 349.8
2. Express each of the following to three significant figures only: (a) 2359   (b) 64.32   (c) 0.4953   (d) 0.007647   (e) 987.7
3. Find the product of each of the following: (a) 2.5×3 (b) 2.5×3.7 (c) 1.6×5.0 (d) 6×3.5 (e) 4.7×5.8
4. Find the product of each of the following: (a) 2.7×3 (b) 3.4×2.1 (c) 2.3×2.9 (d) 5.6×3.4 (e) 4.3×8.7
5. Find the product of each of the following: (a) 3×2.64 (b) 28×35 (c) 29×17 (d) 13.5×6 (e) 17.2×21.6
6. Find the product of each of the following: (a) 2.5×17 (b) 32×1.7 (c) 19×14 (d) 26.2×1.75 (e) 23.2×9.4

7. Find the quotient of each of the following: (a) 6/5   (b) 25/4   (c) 38/7
   (d) 64/3   (e) 72/2.7
8. Find the quotient of each of the following: (a) 7/2   (b) 32/5   (c) 56/4.2
   (d) 26/3.4   (e) 8.5/4.6
9. Find the quotient of each of the following: (a) 35/6.2   (b) 67/5.9   (c) 325/28
   (d) 430/270   (e) 675/780
10. Find the quotient of each of the following: (a) 49/37   (b) 72/26   (c) 260/15
   (d) 655/240   (e) 320/675
11. Find the square of each of the following: (a) 6.0   (b) 2.4   (c) 5.4   (d) 7.5
   (e) 25
12. Find the square root of each of the following: (a) 25   (b) 39   (c) 65.5
   (d) 420   (e) 4750

SPECIAL LESSONS

Lesson 5 ALGEBRA AND POWERS OF TEN

Algebra. Although you have studied algebra, you may feel that you have forgotten most of it. For this reason, it is well to review certain principles, even though only the very simplest manipulation of symbols will be used in the lessons that follow.

As the various subjects in physics are developed, we will see that an algebraic equation is nothing more than an abbreviated, but formal, way of expressing a principle or law, and that the equation is derived from a series of experimental measurements.

Example 1. As a simple illustration of the experimental process, suppose that we have a simple platform balance of the type shown schematically in Fig. A. On one pan, we place a 2-lb weight and, on the other pan, we add weights until balance is restored. Experimentally we then find that b must have a total of 2 lb. If a is increased to 5 lb, b must be 5 lb, and if a is changed to 21.5 lb, b must be 21.5 lb. In other words, we find experimentally that whatever may be the magnitude of the weight a, the total magnitude of b must be the same. Hence,

we bring mathematics into the problem and write—

$$a = b \qquad\qquad (1)$$

Having established this relation from many measurements, we now have confidence in this equation. We feel that if we put an unknown weight a on one pan and balance it with known weights on the other, Eq. (1) can be applied,

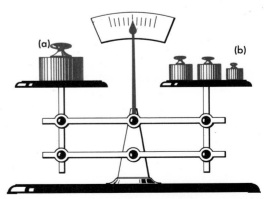

Fig. A. Only equal weights will balance the scale.

and we know that *a* weighs the same as *b*. The known, or measured quantity, *b*, is on the right, and the unknown quantity, *a*, is on the left.

Example 2. Let us imagine having performed an experiment in which we repeatedly measured three quantities, *x*, *y*, and *z*. We have established that the value of *x* is directly proportional to the product of *y* and *z*. As an algebraic equation, this would be written $x = kyz$, where *k* is the constant of proportionality. Wherever possible, the units in which *x*, *y*, and *z* are measured are chosen so as to make $k = 1$. Assuming this is the case, then this would give us—

$$x = yz \qquad (2)$$

as the final equation. It follows, therefore, that if we repeat the experiment and measure *y* and *z*, we need not measure *x* directly to find its value.

Our experimentally established Eq. (2) tells us that the unmeasured quantity *x*, which we call the *unknown*, is always equal to the product *y* × *z*.

Functions. Because the value of x depends on the value of y and z, then x is said to be a *function* of y and z. In this example, x, y, and z may have many different numerical vlaues. For this reason, they are called *variables,* as contrasted with quantities, such as π, which are *constant*.

Graphs. In almost all physics experiments, an attempt is made to simplify the interpretation of the results by keeping as many of the variables constant as possible. Then, one variable is changed, while its effect on another variable is noted by taking careful measurements. The algebraic relationship between these two variables is most easily discovered by plotting a geometrical curve. The most convenient way to represent a function of a single variable is to use *rectangular*, or *Cartesian*, *coordinates*. The

variable is plotted along the horizontal axis, while the *function*, which depends on the variable for its value, is plotted vertically.

Example 3. To illustrate the method, let us try to discover the relationship between the speed of sound in air and the temperature of the air. Of course, there are other factors, or variables, such as humidity and air pressure, that must be kept constant during the experiment. After establishing methods for measuring sound, speed, and air temperature, the following results are obtained.

Table 1
Air Temperature vs. Speed of Sound

Temperature °C	Speed of Sound, m/sec
0	332
5	335
10	338
15	341
20	344
25	347

Solution. A plot of the data is shown in Fig. B, with temperature on the horizontal axis

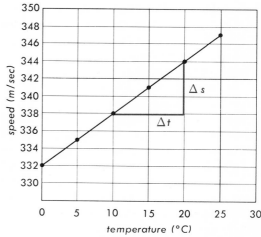

Fig. B. Graph of the speed of sound in air, as a function of the air temperature.

and the speed of sound on the vertical axis. The result shows a sloping straight line, which is always obtained when one plots an equation where one variable is directly proportional to another. The algebraic equation for this result can be written as follows:

$$s = kt + c$$

where s is the speed of sound in m/sec, t is the temperature in Celsius degrees, k is the proportionality constant, and c is a fixed constant.

The rate of change of speed with temperature is given by the *slope* of the graph. Any horizontal change, $\Delta t = t_2 - t_1$, will correspond to a vertical change, $\Delta s = s_2 - s_1$, as shown in Fig. B. For example, the change between 10° and 20° gives the slope:

$$\frac{\Delta s}{\Delta t} = \frac{344 - 338 \text{ m/sec}}{20 - 10°C} = 0.6 \text{ m/sec/°C}.$$

One says, "The speed of sound changes 0.6 m/sec per degree Celsius." Of course, not all experiments yield such simple results.

Example 4. Let us try to find the velocity an object attains as it falls vertically in space. Because it is difficult to measure velocity directly, we will measure the distance the object falls in different periods of time. The table gives data one might obtain under ideal conditions of no air friction and with accurate instruments.

Table 2. Time vs. Distance

Time, sec	Distance, m
0	0
1	4.9
2	19.6
3	44.0
4	78.3
5	123

Solution. As before, a plot will be made with time on the horizontal axis and distance traveled on the vertical axis. See Fig. C. The graph this time is not a simple straight line,

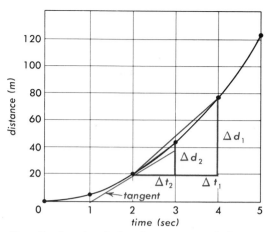

Fig. C. Graph of the distance traveled by a falling object, as a function of time.

but a *curve*. The average velocity between any two time intervals can be found by measuring the *chord* of the curve between these two points as follows: The slope is defined as the difference in vertical distance of the chord divided by the difference in horizontal distance of the chord. In the example shown, the change in distance (Δd_i) equals 34.3 m, and the time interval (Δt_1) is 2 sec. The slope of the chord, or average velocity, is therefore—

$$\bar{v} = \frac{58.7}{2} = 29.4 \text{ m/sec}$$

When $\Delta t = 1$ sec:

$$\bar{v} = \frac{24.4}{1} = 24.4 \text{ m/sec}$$

The bar over the v indicates average value.

If the time interval, Δt, is reduced to a very small value, the average velocity over a small distance will be obtained. If Δt is reduced almost to the vanishing point, then a very accurate slope is obtained. This will give the instantaneous velocity.

One way to estimate the slope is to draw a *tangent* to the curve. The slope of the curve in Fig. C at the point of tangency is then just the slope of the tangent, which can be measured at any point along the tangent. In our example—

$$v(\text{at } t = 2 \text{ sec}) = \frac{39.2 - 0}{3 - 1} = 19.6 \text{ m/sec}$$

Use of an Unknown (x). By thinking of x as a real number, one can usually set up an equation that will help solve the problem. Of course, familiarity with the physics of the problem is essential.

Example 5. Let us say we wish to find what percent of atoms in chlorine have atomic weight 35 and what percent are 37, its average atomic weight being 35.46. By inspection, it can be seen that, if there were 50 percent of each, the average weight would be 36.

Solution. Let $x = $ percent of 35. Then, $100 - x = $ percent of 37:

$$35x + 37(100 - x) = 35.46 \cdot 100$$
$$35x + 3700 - 37x = 3546$$
$$-2x = 3546 - 3700$$
$$-2x = -154$$
$$x = 77\% \text{ of } 35$$
$$\text{and } 100 - 77 = 23\% \text{ of } 37$$

Quadratic Equations. An equation that has an unknown squared term and no other terms of higher powers is a quadratic equation. If the equation can be factored, then its solution is fairly simple. For situations where this is not obvious, we use the general quadratic formula—

$$x = \frac{-b \pm \sqrt{b^2 - 4ac}}{2a}$$

where the quadratic equation has the general form—

$$ax^2 + bx + c = 0$$

Example 6. Solve for x:

$$3x^2 - 5x + 1 = 0$$
$$a = 3; b = -5; c = 1$$
$$x = \frac{5 \pm \sqrt{(-5)^2 - 4 \times 3 \times 1}}{(2)(3)}$$
$$= \frac{5 + \sqrt{13}}{6} \text{ and } \frac{5 - \sqrt{13}}{6}$$

These examples involve the algebraic principles of much of the mathematics we will encounter in this book. It would be well worthwhile to practice carrying out these same operations using different letters for the symbols.

Abbreviated System for Numbers. In speaking of the size and shape of an object or the time interval between the occurrence of two events, it is convenient to express very large numbers and very small decimals in an abbreviated form. This is done principally to conserve time and space. It is convenient for the astronomer in the study of stars and for the physicist and chemist in the study of atoms. The abbreviations in common use are based upon powers of ten as follows:

$10 = 10^1$	$1 = 10^0$
$100 = 10^2$	$0.1 = 10^{-1}$
$1{,}000 = 10^3$	$0.01 = 10^{-2}$
$10{,}000 = 10^4$	$0.001 = 10^{-3}$
$100{,}000 = 10^5$	$0.0001 = 10^{-4}$
$1{,}000{,}000 = 10^6$	$0.00001 = 10^{-5}$

The abbreviated form on the right side of each equation is mathematically correct. For example—

$$10^3 = 10 \times 10 \times 10 = 1000$$

and—

$$10^{-3} = \frac{1}{10^3} = \frac{1}{1000} = 0.001$$

In every case *the exponent is seen to give directly the number of digits the decimal point is moved from unity*, positive integers specifying the number of places the decimal point is moved to the right represent large numbers, and negative integers specifying the number of places it is moved to the left to represent small numbers. To illustrate the use of this system, suppose we say that a truck weighs three million grams. This can be written—

3,000,000 gm $= 3 \times 1,000,000$ gm
$\qquad\qquad = 3 \times 10^6$ gm

In the abbreviated notation, the mass is written 3×10^6 gm. If more than one numeral other than zero occurs, any one of several abbreviations might be written. For example, in the case of large numbers—

$840,000,000 = 84 \times 10,000,000$
$\qquad\qquad\quad = 84 \times 10^7$

or—

$840,000,000 = 8.4 \times 100,000,000$
$\qquad\qquad\quad = 8.4 \times 10^8$

In the case of small numbers, on the other hand—

$0.0024 = 2.4 \times 10^{-3},$ or 24×10^{-4}

To illustrate the advantages of this abbreviated notation, the mass of the *earth* and the mass of an *electron* are found by experiment to be as follows:

mass of the earth: $m = 5.97 \times 10^{24}$ **Kg**
mass of an electron: $m = 9.11 \times 10^{-31}$ **Kg**

If these are written in complete decimal form, they would appear as follows:

mass of the earth =
5,970,000,000,000,000,000,000,000 **Kg**
mass of the electron =
0.000,000,000,000,000,000,000,000,
$\qquad\qquad\qquad$ 000,000,911 **Kg**

Multiplication and Division of Large and Small Numbers. The multiplication and division of large and small numbers in the abbreviated notation involves the addition and subtraction of exponents.

Rule 1. When a power number is changed from numerator to denominator, or vice versa, the sign of the exponent is changed. For example—

$$\frac{5}{2 \times 10^{-6}} = \frac{5 \times 10^6}{2}$$

Rule 2. When two power numbers are multiplied, their exponents are added. For example—

$$3 \times 10^5 \times 2 \times 10^4 = 3 \times 2 \times 10^{5+4}$$
$$= 6 \times 10^9$$

Again—

$$3 \times 10^{17} \times 2 \times 10^{-12} = 3 \times 2 \times 10^{17-12}$$
$$= 6 \times 10^5$$

Rule 3. When two power numbers are divided, their exponents are subtracted. For example—

$$\frac{8 \times 10^9}{2 \times 10^4} = \frac{8 \times 10^{9-4}}{2} = 4 \times 10^5$$

Again—

$$\frac{6 \times 10^{-7}}{3 \times 10^{-2}} = \frac{6 \times 10^{-7+2}}{3} = 2 \times 10^{-5}$$

QUESTIONS

1. What do the symbols of an algebraic equation represent?
2. Why do we use algebra in physics?
3. Why do we express numbers in powers of ten?
4. If two numbers, expressed in powers of ten, are to multiplied, what mathematical operation is performed on the exponents?
5. If we are to find the quotient of two numbers, each expressed in powers-of-ten notation, what mathematical operation is performed on the exponents?
6. If a power number is moved from the denominator to the numerator, what change takes place in the exponent?
7. (a) What is a "factor"? (b) Can two factors be added?

8. (a) Do we use letters only when we don't know their numerical values? (b) If the values are known, why use letters for them?

9. In the equation for finding the volume of a sphere, $V = \frac{4}{3}\pi r^2$, which factors are constant and which are variables?

10. (a) What kind of graph would the equation $y = 3t + 4$ produce on Cartesian graph paper? (b) How can you be sure of your answer?

11. Why are experiments in economics usually more difficult to do than those in the physical sciences?

12. (a) What is meant by the slope of a curve? (b) What kind of a curve gives a constant slope?

13. How can you determine the slope at a given point on a curved line?

14. (a) Draw the graph of the function $y = 3x^2$. (b) At what point does the slope appear to be zero?

PROBLEMS

1. The following relation between three measurable quantities, v, a, and t, has been established experimentally: $v = at$. Solve this equation for (a) a and for (b) t.

2. The following relation has been established by experiment: $s = \frac{1}{2}at^2$. Solve this equation for (a) a and (b) t.

3. The following relation has been established by experiment: $v^2 = 2as$. Solve this equation for (a) a, (b) s, and (c) v.

4. Solve each of the following equations for x:

   (a) $\frac{x}{a} = \frac{y}{b}$ (b) $\frac{x}{a} = \frac{2y}{b}$ (c) $\frac{5x}{y} = \frac{2a}{b}$ (d) $\frac{a+b}{c} = \frac{y}{x}$

5. Solve each of the following equations for v:

   (a) $\frac{v}{w} = \frac{5s}{p}$ (b) $\frac{v}{p} = \frac{7q}{y}$ (c) $\frac{2s}{p} = \frac{v}{q}$ (d) $\frac{1}{a} + \frac{1}{b} = \frac{1}{v}$

6. Solve the following equations for z:

   (a) $x = y + z$ (b) $\frac{x}{a} = \frac{y+z}{b}$ (c) $\frac{x}{a} = \frac{y}{b} + \frac{z}{c}$ (d) $\frac{a}{x} = \frac{b}{y} + \frac{c}{z}$

7. Express each of the following in powers-of-ten notation: (a) 26,000   (b) 240,000   (c) 93,000,000   (d) 0.00037

8. Solve each of the following, and give the answer in powers-of-ten notation: (a) $5 \times 10^3 \times 10^5$ (b) $2 \times 10^6 \times 4 \times 10^7$ (c) $8 \times 10^{14} \div 2 \times 10^8$ (d) $4.2 \times 10^8 \times 2 \times 10^{-5}$

9. Solve each of the following, and give the answer in powers-of-ten notation: (a) $4 \times 10^6 \times 3.5 \times 10^{-3}$ (b) $2.5 \times 10^{-8} \times 6 \times 10^5$ (c) $2 \times 10^7 \times 8 \times 10^8 \div (4 \times 10^5)$ (d) $8 \times 10^{14} \times 2 \times 10^7 \div 10^3$

10. Solve problem 5(d) for v if $a = 5 \times 10^4$ and $b = 2 \times 10^5$.

11. Solve for x: $5x^2 + 4x - 2 = 0$

12. Solve for x: $7x^2 = -3x + 1$

SPECIAL LESSONS

Lesson 6 **TRIGONOMETRY**

Although you may never have studied trigonometry, you will find that the principles that will be introduced are not only simple but very useful. The word *trigonometry* means *triangle measurement*.

The Sine, Cosine, and Tangent. The measured sides and angles of a triangle are so related that from any three known parts, provided at least one of them is a side, one can determine the size and shape of the triangle. The relations we will consider will all be confined to right triangles, that is, to triangles in which one angle is 90°. As a result of the following treatment, we will see how it is possible to calculate the unknown sides of a right triangle from the numerical value of one known side and one of the acute angles. We will begin by drawing two straight lines, AP and AQ, to form any acute angle, θ, as shown in Fig. A. Next, we

choose points like B, D, and F, anywhere along the line AP and drop perpendiculars to the lower line intersecting AQ at C, E, and G, respectively. In this way we have formed a series of right triangles, similar in shape, and all with the common angle θ.

From geometry, you may remember that the ratios of the lengths of corresponding sides of similar triangles are equal. Therefore, in abbreviated notation, we may write—

$$\frac{BC}{AB} = \frac{DE}{AD} = \frac{FG}{AF}$$

$$\frac{AC}{AB} = \frac{AE}{AD} = \frac{AG}{AF} \qquad (1)$$

$$\frac{BC}{AC} = \frac{DE}{AE} = \frac{FG}{AG}$$

If the lengths of the sides are measured and these ratios computed, the answers will remain the same as long as the angle θ remains unchanged. Hence, for every value of an angle θ there are definite numbers that define that angle in any right triangle.

Let a, b, and c denote the lengths of the three sides of a right triangle and θ the value of one of the acute angles as shown in Fig. B. Starting with the equalities in Eq. (1), we take the first ratio BC/AB and call it *the sine of θ*, the second ratio AC/AB and call it *the cosine of θ*, and finally the third ratio BC/AC and call it *the tangent of θ*.

In abbreviated notation, these can be written—

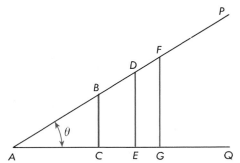

Fig. A. The ratios between corresponding sides of similar triangles are equal.

$$\sin \theta = \frac{a}{c} \qquad (2)$$

$$\cos \theta = \frac{b}{c} \qquad (3)$$

$$\tan \theta = \frac{a}{b} \qquad (4)$$

Example 1. Two lines *AP* and *AQ* make an angle of 35° with each other as shown in Fig. A. Find, by graphical construction, the sine, cosine, and tangent of this angle.

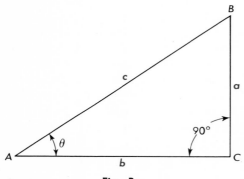

Fig. B.

Solution. In graphical solutions, we use a ruler and protractor. Two lines *AP* and *AQ* making an angle of 35° with each other are first drawn as shown in Fig. C.

Along *AP*, we next measure off a fixed distance, say 5 cm, and draw a perpendicular to

AQ. We then measure the lengths of the other two sides and find—

$$a = 2.87 \text{ cm}$$
$$b = 4.10 \text{ cm}$$

along with—

$$c = 5.00 \text{ cm}$$

If we now substitute these values in Eqs. (2), (3), and (4), we obtain—

$$\sin 35° = \frac{2.87}{5.00} = 0.574$$

$$\cos 35° = \frac{4.10}{5.0} = 0.820$$

$$\tan 35° = \frac{2.87}{4.10} = 0.700$$

These values are to be compared with the values tabulated in Appendix I. The student should repeat this construction and, in so doing, measure off an initial distance, *c*, of 8 to 10 cm. Using care, and a sharp pencil, the same values, 0.574, 0.820, and 0.700, should be obtained to within two or three integers in the third significant figure.

Example 2. If one angle of a right triangle is 42° and the length of the hypotenuse is 7.0 cm, find the lengths of the other two sides. See Fig. D.

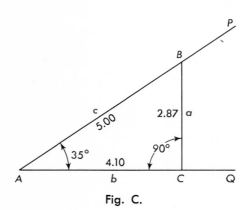

Fig. C.

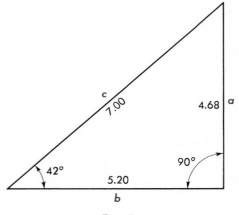

Fig. D.

Solution. The lengths of the sides a and b may be obtained graphically by using a centimeter rule and protractor, drawing the triangle to scale as described in Example 1, or they may be calculated by the use of the tables of sines and cosines in the Appendix.

First, we write down the sine relation from Eq. (2):

$$\sin \theta = \frac{a}{c}$$

Because $\theta = 42°$, we look in Appendix I. In the column headed "sin," we find opposite 42° the value 0.669. Substitute this for $\sin \theta$ and 7.0 cm for c, and we obtain—

$$0.669 = \frac{a}{7.0 \text{ cm}}$$

Now, solving for a, we obtain—

$$a = 7.0 \text{ cm} \times 0.669$$

or—

$$a = 4.683 \text{ cm}$$

which, to three significant figures, becomes—

$$a = 4.68 \text{ cm}$$

To find the length of the side b, we may now use either the cosine relation or the tangent relation, Eq. (3) or Eq. (4). Using the cosine relation, we write—

$$\frac{b}{c} = \cos \theta$$

Before substituting, it is well to solve the equation for b:

$$b = c \cos \theta$$

We now look up the value for the cosine of 42° in the table in Appendix I and find cos 42° = 0.743. Substituting the known quantities, we obtain—

$$b = 7.0 \text{ cm} \times 0.743 = 5.20 \text{ cm}$$

To three significant figures, 5.20 cm is the length of the side b.

As a check upon these two calculated re-sults for a and b, the student should look up the tangent of 42° in Appendix I and compare the value with the ratio a/b.

Functions of Angles Greater than 90°. An xy coordinate system is shown in Fig. E.

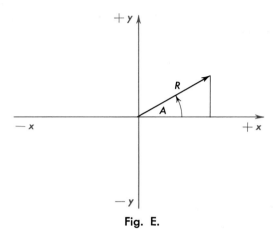

Fig. E.

A line R from the origin is rotated to an angle whose functions we wish to find. In this first quadrant, all values of x and y are positive, and all functions of angles from 0 to 90° are as we found before.

Angles between 90 and 180°, as shown in Fig. F, fall in the second quadrant. From

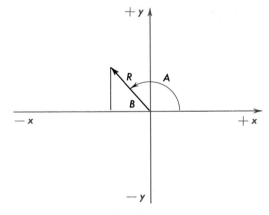

Fig. F.

the end of the line R, which generated the desired angle A, a perpendicular is drawn to the x axis. Angle B whose value is $(180° - \text{angle } A)$ has the following functions:

$$\sin B = \frac{+y}{R}$$

$$\cos B = \frac{-x}{R}$$

$$\tan B = \frac{+y}{-x}$$

To find the functions of an angle larger than 90°, therefore, we look up the function of its supplement, and apply the proper sign.

Example 3. Find the cosine of 120°.

Solution. The supplement of 120° = $(180° - 120°) = 60°$. The cos 60° = 0.50, but because a 120-degree angle is in the second quadrant, the cos 120° = −0.50.

Solution of a Right Triangle by the Pythagorean Theorem. Referring to Fig. G,

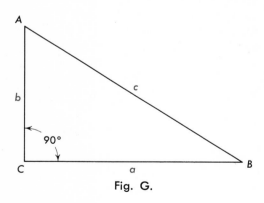

Fig. G.

it can be shown from geometric principles that the square of the hypotenuse is equal to the sum of the squares of the other sides.

In algebraic form, we get—

$$c^2 = a^2 + b^2 \qquad (5)$$

or

$$c = \sqrt{a^2 + b^2} \qquad (6)$$

Solution of Any Triangle by the Law of Cosines. The square of any side of a triangle is equal to the sum of the squares of the two other sides minus twice the product of these two sides multiplied by the cosine of their included angle.

In algebraic form, and referring to Fig. H, we get—

$$c^2 = a^2 + b^2 - 2ab \cos C \qquad (7)$$

which enables us to solve acute or obtuse triangles. When the cosine of C is 0 (for

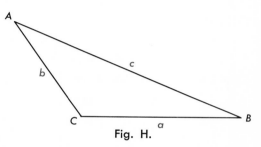

Fig. H.

90°), this formula becomes the Pythagorean Theorem.

Example 4. In Fig. H, what would the value of line c be if the sides a and b were 7 cm and 8 cm, respectively, and angle C were 110°?

Solution. By the Law of Cosines—

$$
\begin{aligned}
c^2 &= a^2 + b^2 - 2ab \cos C \\
&= 7^2 + 8^2 - 2 \times 7 \times 8 \times \cos 110° \\
&= 49 + 64 - 112(-0.342) \\
&= 151 \\
c &= 12.3 \text{ cm}
\end{aligned}
$$

Solution of Any Triangle by the Law of Sines. In any triangle, the sides are proportional to the sines of their opposite angles. In algebraic form (see Fig. H)—

$$\frac{a}{\sin A} = \frac{b}{\sin B} = \frac{c}{\sin C} \qquad (8)$$

Example 5. In the triangle of Fig. H, what would the value of angle A be if side a were

6 cm, side c were 15 cm, and angle C were 100°?

Solution. By the Law of Sines—

$$\frac{a}{\sin A} = \frac{c}{\sin C}$$

$$\frac{6}{\sin A} = \frac{15}{\sin 100°}$$

$$\sin 100° = \sin (180° - 100°)$$
$$= 0.985$$

$$\frac{6}{\sin A} = \frac{15}{0.985}$$

$$\sin A = \frac{6 \times 0.985}{15} = 0.394$$

angle $A = 23°$

QUESTIONS

1. Draw a right triangle. Label the sides a, b, and c, and the angles A, B, and 90°. Write down the symbol relations for sin A, cos A, and tan A. Write down the symbol relations for sin B, cos B, and tan B.
2. If you had a ruler and a protractor, how could you find the sine, cosine, and tangent of an angle of 25°?
3. If one of the two acute angles of a right triangle is known, how can you find the remaining angle?
4. If one angle of a right triangle is known and the length of hypotenuse is measured, what trigonometric relation would you use to find the length (a) of the opposite side? (b) of the adjacent side?
5. If the two sides of a triangle forming an angle of 90° with each other are known, what trigonometric relations would you use to find the other two angles?
6. What trigonometric relationship would you use to solve for the sides of an obtuse triangle?
7. Why does the law of cosines for right triangles become the Pythagorean Theorem?
8. (a) Under what conditions would you use the law of cosines, rather than the law of sines, to solve for a side of a triangle? (b) Under what conditions would you use the law of sines but could not use the law of cosines?
9. What is the minimum information needed in order to determine the size and shape of a triangle?

PROBLEMS

1. Find the number of degrees in each of the following angles: (a) $\sin \theta = 0.375$ (b) $\sin \theta = 0.839$ (c) $\cos \theta = 0.788$ (d) $\cos \theta = 0.242$ (e) $\tan \theta = 0.649$
2. The hypotenuse of a right triangle is 8.5 cm long, and one of the acute angles is 32°. Find, by graphical construction, the lengths of the other two sides.
3. One acute angle of a right triangle is 55°, and the length of the hypotenuse is 12 ft. Using trigonometry, calculate the lengths of the other two sides.
4. One acute angle of a right triangle is 38°, and the length of the adjacent side is 8.5 cm. Using trigonometry, find the lengths of the other two sides.

5. One acute angle of a right triangle is 48° and the length of the opposite side is 15.0 cm. Using trigonometry, calculate the lengths of the other two sides.

6. If the hypotenuse of a right triangle is 20 ft long and one side is 6 ft long, (a) what are the values of the two acute angles and (b) what is the length of the other side?

7. A right triangle has sides of 3 cm, 4 cm, and 5 cm. Make a diagram to scale and measure the three angles with a protractor.

8. If one side of a right triangle is 18 m long, and the other side is 12 m long, what are the values of (a) the two acute angles and (b) the hypotenuse?

9. The hypotenuse of a right triangle is 22 cm, and the sine of one of the acute angles is 0.345. What are the lengths of the two sides?

10. The hypotenuse of a right triangle is 33 cm, and the tangent of one of the acute angles is 1.45. What are the lengths of the two sides?

11. The sine of an acute angle of a right triangle is 0.5, and the length of the adjacent side is 12 in. What is the length of the hypotenuse?

12. Two sides of an acute triangle are 6.0 cm and 4.8 cm. The included angle between them is 35°. What is the length of the third side?

13. The two sides of a triangle are 10.0 cm and 12.5 cm, while the angle between these two sides is 135°. What is the length of the remaining side?

14. The angles of a triangle are 20, 50, and 110°. If the length of the side opposite the 50° angle is 15.4 cm, what are the lengths of the other two sides?

15. The angles of a triangle are 25, 75, and 80°. If the side opposite the 25° angle is 30.0 ft, what is the dimension of the side opposite the 80° angle?

16. Three sides of a triangle are 5, 6, and 9 cm. Find the three angles.

17. Use the Pythagorean Theorem to show that $(\sin \theta)^2 + (\cos \theta)^2 = 1$ for any θ.

18. Express $\tan \theta$ in terms of $\sin \theta$ and $\cos \theta$.

Mechanics

Law I. Every body continues in its state of rest, or of uniform motion in a right line, unless it is compelled to change that state by forces impressed upon it.

Projectiles continue in their motions, so far as they are not retarded by the resistance of the air, or impelled downwards by the force of gravity. A top, whose parts by their cohesion are continually drawn aside from rectilinear motions, does not cease its rotation, otherwise than as it is retarded by the air. The greater bodies of the planets and comets, meeting with less resistance in freer spaces, preserve motions both progressive and circular for a much longer time.

Law II. The change in motion is proportional to the motive forces impressed, and is made in the direction of the right line in which that force is impressed.

Law III. To every action there is always opposed an equal reaction; or, the mutual actions of two bodies upon each other are always equal, and directed to contrary parts.

Sir Isaac Newton's Mathematical Principles, F. Cajori, ed., Andrew Motte, trans., University of California, Berkeley, 1934, p. 13.

We cannot create mechanical force, but we may help ourselves from the general storehouse of Nature. The brook and the wind, which drive our mills, the forest and the coal-bed, which supply our steam-engines and warm our rooms, are to us the bearers of a small portion of the great natural supply which we draw upon for our purposes, and the actions of which we can apply as we think fit. The possessor of a mill claims the gravity of the descending rivulet, or the living force of the moving wind, as his possession. These portions of the store of Nature are what give his property its chief value.

Hermann Helmholtz, *The Interaction of Forces*

◄ **A volunteer floats for from twelve to fifteen seconds at a time in the cabin of an Air Force plane during zero gravity studies.**

Wright Air Development Center

Lesson 7 SPEED AND VELOCITY

Mechanics is defined as that branch of physics dealing with the motions or states of material bodies. It is generally divided into three parts: *kinematics, dynamics,* and *statics.* Some of the concepts and principles to be described and classified under each of these headings are as follows:

Kinematics
> *speed*
> *velocity*
> *acceleration*
> *angular velocity*

Dynamics
> *force*
> *impulse*
> *momentum*
> *kinetic energy*

Statics
> *equilibrium*
> *balanced forces*
> *composition of forces*
> *resolution of forces*

Kinematics is concerned with kinds of motion, but not with the properties of the object that is moving. Dynamics is concerned with causes for changes in motion, and it involves the masses of bodies and how they react to forces acting upon them. Statics deals with bodies in equilibrium. As an introduction to the kinematics of motion, the elementary concepts of *speed* and *velocity* will first be taken up.

Speed. Speed is defined as the time rate of change of position. By change of position is meant the distance traveled, and by time rate we mean the elapsed time. As an equation—

$$\text{speed} = \frac{\text{change of position}}{\text{elapsed time}} \qquad (1)$$

Change of position is illustrated in Fig. A. A car traveling with uniform speed along

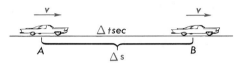

Fig. A. Diagram of a body moving with constant velocity.

a straight line passes the point A at one instant of time, t_1, and the point B at some later instant of time, t_2. If the positions of points A and B are measured from some point of origin, O, the distances can be expressed as s_1 and s_2, respectively.

With these symbols, the change in position, Δs, is equal to $s_2 - s_1$, and the elapsed time of travel, Δt, is equal to $t_2 - t_1$:

$$\Delta s = s_2 - s_1$$
$$\Delta t = t_2 - t_1$$

In symbols, we may therefore write Eq. (1) as—

$$v = \frac{\Delta s}{\Delta t} \qquad (2)$$

where v is the speed, Δs is the change in position, and Δt is the elapsed time, or time of travel.

If we measure distances and times from the point A as the origin, we see that $s_1 = 0$ and $t_1 = 0$, and Eq. (2) can be written $v = \dfrac{s_2}{t_2}$, or more simply—

$$v = \frac{s}{t} \qquad (3)$$

43

velocity

It is understood that s stands for Δs, the distance traveled, and t stands for Δt, the elapsed-time interval.

Example 1. A pilot takes 2 hr to fly his plane to a distant city 120 mi away. What is his speed?

Solution. Here the distance traveled is $s =$ 120 mi, and the time interval is $t = 2$ hr. The speed, therefore, is—

$$v = \frac{120 \text{ mi}}{2 \text{ hr}} = 60 \frac{\text{mi}}{\text{hr}} \qquad (4)$$

The answer is 60 *mi/hr*. The units are just as important as the numbers and must be included in the answer.

If, in the answer to the above example, the time, 1 hr, in the denominator is replaced by its equivalent of 3600 sec, a speed of 60 mi/hr becomes—

$$v = 60 \frac{\text{mi}}{\text{hr}} = 60 \frac{\text{mi}}{3600 \text{ sec}} = 0.0167 \frac{\text{mi}}{\text{sec}} \qquad (5)$$

If, at the same time, the distance, 1 mi, in the numerator is replaced by its equivalent of 5280 ft—

$$v = 60 \frac{\text{mi}}{\text{hr}} = 60 \frac{5280 \text{ ft}}{3600 \text{ sec}} = 88 \frac{\text{ft}}{\text{sec}} \qquad (6)$$

All three of the answers above—60 mi/hr, 0.0167 mi/sec, and 88 ft/sec—are exactly equal, although they are expressed in different units. This last derived result, 60 mi/hr is equivalent to 88 ft/sec, should be memorized, as it is very useful in the solving of many practical problems. A speed of 120 mi/hr, for example, is equivalent to 2×88 or 176 ft/sec, while a speed of 30 mi/hr is equivalent to $\frac{1}{2} \times 88$, or 44 ft/sec.

Example 2. A toy train running along a straight track at constant speed requires 8 sec to travel a distance of 20 m. Find the speed.

Solution. Because $s = 20$ m and $t = 8$ sec, the speed is—

$$v = \frac{20 \text{ m}}{8 \text{ sec}} = 2.5 \frac{\text{m}}{\text{sec}}$$

The answer is read *two point five meters per second*. To change this answer to centimeters per second, the unit 1 m in the numerator is changed to 100 cm, and the answer becomes—

$$v = 2.5 \frac{\text{m}}{\text{sec}} = 2.5 \frac{100 \text{ cm}}{\text{sec}} = 250 \frac{\text{cm}}{\text{sec}}$$

Distance Traveled. If the speed of a body is known, the distance traveled can be calculated for any given interval of time. For such problems Eq. (3) is conveniently changed by solving for s: *DISTANCE*

$$s = vt \qquad (7)$$

Example 3. If a body moves with a speed of 45 cm/sec, how far will it travel in 2 min?

Solution. The distance traveled can be determined by Eq. (7):

$$s = 45 \frac{\text{cm}}{\text{sec}} \times 2 \text{ min} = 90 \frac{\text{cm min}}{\text{sec}}$$

In order to eliminate the two time units in this answer, they must both be expressed in the same unit. To do this, the minutes may be changed to seconds as follows:

$$s = 45 \frac{\text{cm}}{\text{sec}} \times 120 \text{ sec} = 5400 \text{ cm}$$

Note that *sec* in the numerator cancels *sec* in the denominator, leaving *cm* in the answer as the unit of length. This illustrates a common practice that should be followed in the solving of all problems. Always express like quantities in the same units.

Dividing both sides of Eq. (7) by v gives— *TIME*

$$t = \frac{s}{v} \qquad (8)$$

which is an equation for the time of travel in terms of s and t.

Example 4. If a car travels with an average speed of 30 mi/hr, how long will it take to go 175 mi?

Solution. Using Eq. (8)—

$$t = \frac{s}{v} = \frac{175 \text{ mi}}{30 \text{ mi/hr}} = 5.83 \text{ hr}$$

Vectors and Scalars. Nearly all physical measurements, whether they are made with the simplest of instruments or with the most complex of apparatus, may be classified as *vector* or *scalar* quantities.

Measurable quantities that have magnitude and direction are called vectors. Examples of vector quantities are *displacement, velocity, acceleration,* and *force.*

Measurable quantities that have magnitude only are called scalars. Examples of scalar quantities are *volume, area,* and *mass.*

The distinction between quantities that have direction and those which do not may seem trivial. However, the sum of two such vector quantities may be any value from their arithmetic sum to their arithmetic difference.

No difficulty is generally encountered with scalars, because such quantities are added arithmetically. For example, in the addition of volumes, the sum of 2 gallons and 3 gallons is 5 gallons. The addition of two vectors, on the other hand, is more complicated. For example, a man who walked 1 mile east and then one mile north is not 2 miles from his starting point. The special process called *vector addition* will be treated in detail in Lesson 9.

Speed and Velocity. The terms *speed* and *velocity* are often used synonymously. They are both represented by the symbol *v.* Strictly speaking, however, *speed is a scalar quantity* and *velocity is a vector quantity.* In the last section, it was explained that vector quantities have magnitude and direction while scalars have magnitude only.

Speed is a term applied only to the magnitude of velocity and does not specify the direction of motion. In moving along a straight line, *speed* and *velocity* are numerically equal to each other. If, however, the speed along a curved path is constant, the velocity is not considered to be constant because of its changing direction.

When a body moves with constant speed along a straight line whose direction is specified, it is customary to speak of its *velocity.* When motion is along either a straight or curved path, with no reference being made to direction, it is proper to speak of *speed.*

Example 5. Change 30 mi/hr to kilometers per hour.

Solution. From Table 1, 1 mi/hr in the left-hand column is (read across to the fourth column) equal to 1.6093 Km/hr. Therefore—

$$30 \times 1.6093 = 48.279 \frac{\text{Km}}{\text{hr}}$$

Dropping off the last two figures gives the answer to three significant figures as—

$$30 \frac{\text{mi}}{\text{hr}} = 48.3 \frac{\text{Km}}{\text{hr}}$$

The *knot* is a nautical unit of speed about 15% greater than speed in miles per hour. It is *not* correct to say the speed of a ship is 10 knots/hr; it is correct to say the speed is 10 knots.

In mechanics, it is often convenient to neglect the size and shape of a body and to consider its motion as that of a small *particle* of neglible size. For example, in describing the motion of an airplane flying between two cities it is not necessary to give a detailed description of the plane to give its position and progress. Hence, it is customary to speak of the motion of a body as the motion of a particle.

Constant and Variable Velocity. If the statement is made that a particle travels 30 mi in 1 hr, it does not necessarily mean that

Table 1. Conversion Factors for Speed and Velocity

Velocity	m/sec	ft/sec	Km/hr	mi/hr	knots
1 m/sec =	1	3.281	3.600	2.240	1.940
1 ft/sec =	0.30480	1	1.0973	0.6818	0.5921
1 Km/hr =	0.27778	0.9113	1	0.6214	0.5396
1 mi/hr =	0.44704	1.4667	1.6093	1	0.8684
1 knot =	0.51480	1.689	1.853	1.152	1

its speed is constant. Moving in a straight line, the particle moved either with a *constant speed* or with a *variable speed*. A *constant speed is defined as one in which equal distances are traversed in equal intervals of time.* In other words, the distance traveled in any one second is equal to that traveled in any other second.

A particle has *variable speed* when, in equal intervals of time, its displacements are unequal. In such cases, the particle is said to be *accelerating* and it is customary to speak of the average speed. Average speed, $\bar{v}$, is defined by—

$$\bar{v} = \frac{s}{t} \qquad (9)$$

where t is the total time required to travel the total distance s.

A particle is said to have *constant velocity* of its *speed and direction* remain the same. If either the speed or the direction of a particle is changed, then its velocity is variable and the particle, again, is said to be accelerating. This means that, even though a particle is moving with constant speed in a circular path (curvilinear motion), its velocity is changing. See Fig. B.

Instantaneous Velocity. In describing the curvilinear motion of a particle, it sometimes becomes necessary to specify its *instantaneous velocity.* As shown in Fig. C,

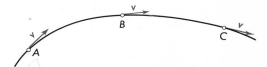

Fig. C. Arrows indicate instantaneous velocity.

the instantaneous velocity of a particle at any given point in its path is obtained by drawing a tangent to the curve at the point in question. The magnitude of the instantaneous velocity is equal to the speed of the particle as it passes that point, and the direction is that of the tangent to the curve at that point.

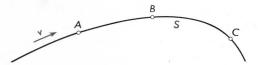

Fig. B. Motion along a curved path.

QUESTIONS

1. Which of the three branches of mechanics is being treated in this lesson?
2. In what way do the concepts of kinematics and dynamics differ?

3. If you know the velocity of an object, do you also know its speed? Explain.
4. Is it always important to distinguish between speed and velocity? Explain.
5. Give the units of velocity and speed in (a) the mks system and (b) the cgs system.
6. Classify the fundamental units given in Lesson 3, in terms of scalars and vectors.
7. You have just made a three-hour auto trip, and have stopped for gas. You calculate the distance you traveled per hour. What actually have you calculated?
8. What does the speedometer of your car tell you?
9. What kind of graph would you get if you plotted the distance a particle traveled against time for: (a) variable speed, (b) constant speed?
10. What is the difference between 60 mi/hr and 88 ft/sec?
11. Give an example of the motion of an object whose average velocity is zero, but whose average speed is not.
12. A car accelerates for a mile during a drag race, starting from rest. Is it meaningful to say that the instantaneous velocity is equal to the average velocity? Explain.
13. A train maintains a constant speed of 60 mi/hr as it rounds a curve. Is the velocity constant?
14. Which of the two units is the larger: (a) 1 mi/hr or 1 knot, (b) 1 Km/hr or 1 mi/hr, (c) 1 mi/hr or 1 ft/sec?

PROBLEMS

1. An airplane in a steep dive moves with a speed of 620 mi/hr. Compute its speed in (a) ft/sec, (b) Km/hr, and (c) knots.
2. A ship sailing from San Francisco to Hawaii makes the trip of 2300 miles in $4\frac{1}{2}$ days. What is its average speed in (a) mi/hr, (b) Km/hr, and (c) knots?
3. It takes a farmer $2\frac{1}{2}$ hr to walk the full length of the fence surrounding his farm, which is one mile square. Calculate his average speed in (a) mi/hr, (b) ft/sec, and (c) cm/sec.
4. A circular racetrack is 1600 ft in diameter. A car makes 100 laps around the track in 56 min. Calculate the average speed in (a) mi/hr, (b) ft/sec, and (c) Km/hr.
5. A boy walks to school with an average speed of 3.5 mi/hr. The school is 1.5 mi away. How long will it take him to get to school?
6. A track star runs the mile in 4 min 3 sec. What is his average speed in (a) ft/sec and (b) mi/hr?
7. How long would it take you to walk a distance of 50 mi, if you could average 2.75 mi/hr?
8. The escape velocity from the earth is 25,000 mi/hr. If a spacecraft could maintain this speed, how long would it take to go to Mars, which is 48.7 million mi away?
9. How fast would you have to go to go around the equator, if you wanted to take the same time the sun appears to take? Assume the earth's radius to be 4000 mi.

10. A spacecraft takes 5 days to reach the moon and return. What is the average speed of the spacecraft in Km/hr if the moon is 230,000 mi away?

11. The speed limit on a road in Mexico reads 100 Km/hr. Is this slower or faster than 65 mi/hr? By how much?

12. A car goes due north a distance of 6 mi in 12 min. It then turns around and goes due south for an equal amount of time. (a) What is its average speed? (b) Where is it now?

13. A driver of a car notices that his odometer reads 32,475 mi at 3:00 PM. When he stops for gas it is 6:30 PM, and his odometer reads 32,638 mi. What is his average speed in mi/hr?

PROJECT

Develop an apparatus that will make it possible for you to measure the speed of an electric train or car with considerable accuracy.

MECHANICS

Lesson 8 ACCELERATION

Uniform Acceleration. Whenever the velocity of a body changes, the motion is described as an acceleration. Acceleration is defined as *the rate of change of velocity.* A car "picking up speed" has a *positive acceleration,* while one slowing down has a *negative acceleration,* or *deceleration.* Standing still or moving with constant velocity, a car has no acceleration.

Consider as an illustration of accelerated motion the car shown in Fig. A. Owing to a constantly acting force, exerted by the motor through the drive wheels, this car is constantly accelerated as it moves along the straight line *AB*. As it passes *A*, it has a relatively low velocity, v_0, while farther along its path at a point *B* it is moving faster and has a velocity v. The *initial velocity* is called v_0, and the *final velocity* is called v.

If the time required to go from *A* to *B* is t, the acceleration, by the definition given above, is written—

acceleration =
$$\frac{\textbf{final velocity} - \textbf{initial velocity}}{\textbf{elapsed time}}$$

or algebraically as—

$$a = \frac{v - v_0}{t - t_0}$$

or in increment notation as—

Fig. A. A car undergoing constant acceleration.

accel.

$$a = \frac{\Delta v}{\Delta t} \qquad (1)$$

Example 1. Suppose at A, in Fig. A, that the velocity of the car is 20 ft/sec, that at B it has increased to 40 ft/sec, and that it takes 4 sec to go from A to B. What is the acceleration?

Solution. By direct substitution in Eq. (1), we obtain—

$$a = \frac{40 \text{ ft/sec} - 20 \text{ ft/sec}}{4 \text{ sec}}$$

$$= \frac{20 \text{ ft/sec}}{4 \text{ sec}} = 5 \frac{\text{ft}}{\text{sec sec}}$$

The answer is read *five feet per second per second* and means that the velocity increases 5 ft/sec every second of time. Initially, the velocity is 20 ft/sec. An increase of 5 ft/sec means that at the end of 1 sec the velocity is 25 ft/sec, at the end of 2 sec it is 30 ft/sec, at the end of 3 sec it is 35 ft/sec, and at the end of 4 sec it is 40 ft/sec. See

$$v = at \tag{3}$$

where v is the final velocity.

Example 2. An airplane, starting from rest at one end of a runway, acquires its take-off speed of 60 mi/hr in 8 sec. What is its acceleration?

Solution. The acceleration is obtained from Eq. (2):

$$a = \frac{60 \text{ mi/hr}}{8 \text{ sec}} = 7.5 \frac{\text{mi/hr}}{\text{sec}} = 7.5 \frac{\text{mi}}{\text{hr sec}}$$

The answer is read *seven point five miles per hour per second.*

Remembering that 60 mi/hr is equivalent to 88 ft/sec, this same acceleration can be expressed as—

$$a = \frac{88 \text{ ft/sec}}{8 \text{ sec}} = 11 \frac{\text{ft}}{\text{sec}^2}$$

read *eleven feet per second per second.*

20 ft/s   25 ft/s   30 ft/s   35 ft/s   40 ft/s

Fig. B. Diagram of accelerated car in Example 1.

Fig. B. *A body is said to move with constant acceleration when its velocity changes by equal amounts each equal unit of time.*

When a body is slowing down, the initial velocity is greater than the final velocity, and the acceleration, as given by Eq. (1) is negative.

Starting from Rest. When a body starting from rest undergoes a constant acceleration, the initial velocity, v_0, as given in Eq. (1) is zero, i.e., $v_0 = 0$. If the initial time is also taken to be zero, the acceleration, a, is then given by the special equation—

$$a = \frac{v}{t} \tag{2}$$

or—

Average Velocity. When the velocity of an accelerated body is continually changing, the distance traveled in any given time, t, may be described in terms of its *average velocity.* The average velocity of a particle moving with constant acceleration is given by—

$$v = \frac{v + v_0}{2} \tag{4}$$

For the special case of a body starting from rest, $v_0 = 0$, Eq. (4) becomes—

$$\bar{v} = \frac{v}{2} \tag{5}$$

The equation $s = vt$, already given as Eq. (7) in Lesson 7, will not hold true for accelerated motion unless v is replaced by the average velocity, $\bar{v}$. Thus, we may write $s = \bar{v}t$, or—

$$s = \frac{v}{2}t \qquad (6)$$

DISTANCE TRAVELED

Example 3. A car starting from rest undergoes uniform acceleration, acquiring a speed of 20 m/sec in 8 sec. Find (a) the acceleration and (b) the distance traveled.

Solution. The given quantities are $v = 20$ m/sec and $t = 8$ sec. For the answer to part (a), use Eq. (2):

$$a = \frac{v}{t}$$

and substitute—

$$a = \frac{20 \text{ m/sec}}{8 \text{ sec}} = 2.5 \frac{\text{m}}{\text{sec}^2}$$

For the answer to part (b), use Eq. (6) and substitute directly:

$$s = \frac{20 \text{ m/sec}}{2} \times 8 \text{ sec} = 80 \text{ m}$$

Distance Traveled During Uniform Acceleration. As a demonstration of the scientific method, we may perform an experiment of the kind shown in Fig. C. Here a toy

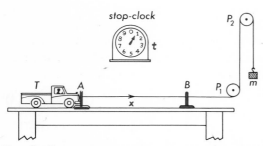

Fig. C. Demonstration experiment with a toy truck.

truck, T, with ball-bearing, steel-rimmed wheels, is shown free to roll with a minimum amount of friction along a level glass plate.

Uniform acceleration is brought about by a thin cord passing over two pulleys, P_1 and P_2, to a small mass, m. We now wish to accelerate the truck and to find the relation between the distance traveled and the time of travel. Markers A and B are located a short distance apart, and the distance, s, between them is measured with a meter stick. With the front bumper at marker A, the truck is released and the clock is started. As the truck reaches marker B, the clock is stopped and the time is recorded. This procedure is repeated with the markers farther and farther apart, and the data recorded in a table. Suppose this experiment has been performed at five different distances and the data recorded are as shown in Table 1.

Table 1. Recorded Data for Truck

Trial	Distance s (cm)	Time t (sec)
1	17.5	1.6
2	39.2	2.4
3	98.1	3.8
4	163.4	4.9
5	213.3	5.6

To find how s and t are related to each other, the measured quantities are plotted. If we plot s vertically and t horizontally as shown in Fig. D, we obtain the points marked $\times$. When a smooth line is drawn through these points, it is definitely not a straight line. The curve must be drawn through the origin, $s = 0$ and $t = 0$, because this is an observed point. In zero time, the distance traveled is zero.

Because the graph does not yield a straight line, s is not proportional to t. The problem then becomes one of seeing if either or both of the measured quantities can be modified to produce a straight-line graph. A few trials of plotting such quanti-

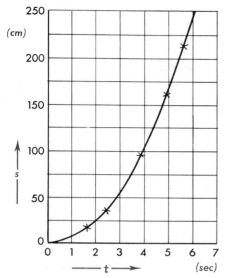

Fig. D. Graph of measurements made with a toy truck.

ties as $2s$, s^2, $\sqrt{s}$, $2t$, t^2, $\sqrt{t}$, etc., will show that if s is plotted against t^2, a straight line as that shown in Fig. E will be the result.

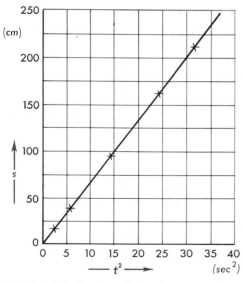

Fig. E. Straight-line graph for the toy-truck experiment.

From this graph, we can conclude that s is proportional to t^2:

$$s \propto t^2$$

To make an equation of this relation, the proportionality sign is replaced by an equal sign, and a proportionality constant inserted on the right. Calling this constant k, we can write—

$$s = kt^2 \qquad (7)$$

To find the value of k in this particular experiment, substitute the measured values of s and the square of the measured values of t, and solve for k. We find, in all cases—

$$k = 6.8\ \frac{\text{cm}}{\text{sec}^2}$$

This result, we will soon see, is just one-half the acceleration, a:

$$a = 2k = 13.6\ \frac{\text{cm}}{\text{sec}^2}$$

Derived Equations. All of the problems concerning acceleration from rest can be solved by one of the two basic equations derived earlier. Those two equations should be memorized:

$$v = at; \quad s = \frac{v}{2}\, t$$

Note that each equation involves only three of the four quantities v, a, t, and s. Problems often arise in which the two known quantities are not in the same equation and we wish to determine, as an unknown quantity, either one of the other two. For this purpose, it is convenient to combine these two equations as follows: Solve both Eq. (3) and Eq. (6) for the time, t:

TIME $$t = \frac{v}{a}; \quad t = \frac{2s}{v}$$

Because the left-hand sides of these equations are equal, the right-hand sides are equal to each other, and we can write—

$$\frac{v}{a} = \frac{2s}{v}$$

or finally—

$$v^2 = 2as \qquad (8)$$

Or, if we solve both Eq. (3) and Eq. (6) for the velocity, v, we obtain—

$$v = at; \quad v = \frac{2s}{t}$$

Because the left-hand sides are now equal, the right-hand sides are also equal, and we can write—

$$\frac{2s}{t} = at$$

or—

$$s = \tfrac{1}{2}at^2 \qquad (9)$$

The equations (8) and (9) are called *derived equations*. They give no additional information to that given by Eqs. (3) and (6); they are only more convenient arrangements of the same quantities. Because each of these four equations involves only three of the four quantities v, a, t, and s, in any observations of an object starting from rest and moving with uniformly accelerated motion, we can measure two of these four quantities, and the other two can be computed by using the appropriate equations. Because of their fundamental importance, all four equations, (3), (6), (8), and (9), will be used many times in the following chapters and, for this reason, they should be memorized.

Example 4. A plane starting at one end of a runway, undergoes an acceleration of 1.2 m/sec², for a distance of 1000 meters before taking off. Calculate the take-off speed.

Solution. The given quantities are $a = 1.2$ m/sec² and $s = 1000$ m, and the unknown quantity is v. These three factors are found in Eq. (8) only, and direct substitution gives—

$$v^2 = 2 \times 1.2\,\frac{m}{sec} \times 1000\ m$$

$$v^2 = 2400\,\frac{m^2}{sec^2}$$

Take the square root of both sides—

$$v = 49\,\frac{m}{sec}$$

The take-off speed is forty-nine meters per second.

QUESTIONS

1. (a) What are the mks units of acceleration? (b) What are the cgs units? (c) What are the English units?
2. (a) Could a body move with a variable acceleration? (b) Give an example.
3. Give two examples of negative acceleration.
4. What is meant by (a) the initial velocity, and (b) the final velocity of an accelerated body?
5. The units of acceleration involve the unit of time twice. (a) Why is this? (b) Can one of the units be in seconds and the other in minutes or hours?
6. Give an example in which an object is repeatedly accelerated positively and then negatively.
7. What is meant by a derived equation?
8. Is acceleration a vector quantity? Explain.

PROBLEMS

1. In a drag race, a car starting from rest acquires a speed of 140 ft/sec in 9 sec. (a) What is its acceleration, and (b) how far did it travel?

2. A falling bottle has a vertical acceleration of 32 ft/sec/sec. What is its acceleration in ft/min²?

3. A rock starts rolling down a hill at 0.8 ft/sec. One minute later it is rolling at 0.3 ft/sec. What is its acceleration?

4. A rocket starting from rest undergoes an acceleration of 0.6 m/sec² straight upward for 3 min, when the fuel gives out. (a) What is its final velocity, and (b) how high is it above the earth?

5. A jet plane starting from rest at one end of a runway undergoes a constant acceleration of 1.6 m/sec² for a distance of 1600 m before taking off. Calculate (a) the take-off speed and (b) the time required to take off.

6. A train starts from rest, and after a constant acceleration for 65 sec acquires a speed of 100 Km/hr. What is its acceleration in m/sec²?

7. A car changes its velocity as indicated by the speedometer from 10 mi/hr to 20 mi/hr in 0.5 sec. Find (a) the average velocity in ft/sec and (b) the acceleration in ft/sec².

8. A car traveling at 60 mi/hr (i.e., 88 ft/sec) suddenly has its brakes applied, bringing it to rest in 4 sec. Find (a) the acceleration and (b) the distance traveled during this time.

9. A uniformly decelerating sled, started at 18 ft/sec, has slowed to 9 ft/sec in 25 sec. How much longer will it slide?

10. You are traveling 65 mi/hr in a car when you see a child dart into your path about 200 ft ahead. You are able to stop the car in 5 sec. Did you have enough time to avoid the accident?

11. Starting from rest, a car undergoes a constant acceleration of 3.0 m/sec². Find the distance traveled during (a) the first second of time and (b) the fourth second of time.

12. A box accidentally falls from a truck traveling 45 mi/hr and slides along the ground for a distance of 100 ft. Find (a) the acceleration of the box and (b) the time before the box comes to rest.

13. A jet plane is rolling backward along the runway at 10 mi/hr. The plane becomes airborne at 150 mi/hr, 12 sec after the jet engine is turned on. What was the acceleration?

14. Starting with Eq. (1) and $s = vt$, derive the equations for a body not starting from rest:

$$\text{(a)} \quad s = v_0t + \tfrac{1}{2}at^2$$

and—

$$\text{(b)} \quad v^2 = v_0{}^2 + 2as$$

PROJECTS

1. Develop an apparatus for accurately measuring the distance a small car with roller bearings travels as it accelerates uniformly.
2. Make a timer to be used for timing track events at your school that would be more accurate than what is now being used.

MECHANICS

Lesson 9 *COMPOSITION OF VELOCITIES*

Because velocity has magnitude and direction, it is a vector quantity and, therefore, subject to the principles of vector addition.

Velocity Is a Vector Quantity. When a body moves with two velocities simultaneously, the process of vector addition is applied to find its equivalent resultant velocity. To see what is meant by *simultaneous velocities* and a *resultant velocity*, consider the following problem.

While an ocean liner is sailing eastward with a velocity of 12 mi/hr, a man walks around on the deck at the rate of 5 mi/hr. The problem is to find at all times the man's

velocity of 12 mi/hr to give a resultant of 17 mi/hr eastward. As the man walks aft, however, his velocity of 5 mi/hr is subtracted from the ship's velocity of 12 mi/hr to give a resultant of 7 mi/hr eastward.

In the first case, the vectors are parallel and in the same direction and they add arithmetically, while in the second case they are oppositely directed, or antiparallel, and they subtract arithmetically.

When the man walks across the deck at right angles to the ship's motion, his resultant velocity is 13 mi/hr in a direction 22.6° north of east. To show how this answer is determined, a *space diagram* of the problem is given in Fig. A. The diagram at the left

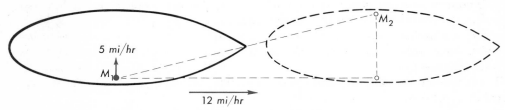

Fig. A. A body undergoes two simultaneous velocities.

velocity with respect to the water. When he walks in the direction of the ship's motion, his velocity of 5 mi/hr is added to the ship's

shows M_1 as the starting point of both the man and boat, while the diagram at the right shows the position of the boat when

(a)

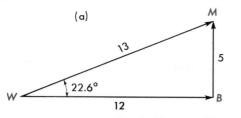

(b)

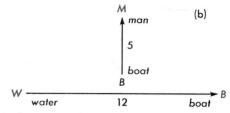

Fig. B. Vector addition of simultaneous velocities.

the man reaches M_2 on the port side. The plane of the page represents the water.

The vector addition of the two velocities is shown at the left in Fig. B. The arrow WB is first drawn 12 units long and pointing in the direction of the boat's motion. BM is next drawn upwards from B, 5 units long, and pointing in the direction the man is walking on the boat. The triangle is then completed, the length of the side WM is measured from the figure, and the angle is measured with a protractor. The resultant, $WM = 13$ mi/hr at 22.6°, represents both in magnitude and direction the velocity of the man with respect to the water.

A general procedure that can be applied to all problems involving simultaneous velocities is illustrated in Fig. B(b). Taking the above problem as an example, each vector is first drawn separately with its proper magnitude and specified direction. Each is then labeled with the moving body at the head of the arrow and the object with reference to which it is moving at the tail. The vectors are then put together in a single diagram with like labels together, as in Fig. B(a). This procedure is called the *domino method* because of its similarity to the game of dominos.

The principles of vector addition are particularly useful when applied to the motion of a body in a medium that is, itself, moving. The drift of an airplane in a wind or the drift of a boat on a moving body of water are good examples.

The preceding problem may alterna-

tively be solved mathematically. First, the resultant is found, using the Pythagorean Theorem:

$$WM^2 = WB^2 + BM^2$$
$$= 169 \text{ (mi/hr)}^2$$

or—

$$WB = 13 \text{ mi/hr}$$

The angle may be found by the trigonometric relation—

$$\tan \theta = \frac{BM}{WB} = \frac{5}{12} = 0.416$$

from which we find—

$$\theta = 22.6°$$

The River-Boat Problem. A small passenger boat is capable of making 2 mi/hr in still water. The pilot heads his boat straight across a river from a point where the river is one mile wide. What is his velocity, and how far downstream will he land at the other side if the water flows at 1 mi/hr?

A space diagram for this problem is shown in Fig. C. Note how the boat, starting from the point A on one bank and

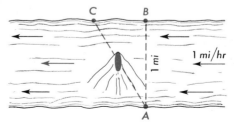

Fig. C. Diagram of the river-boat problem.

headed originally toward the point B on the opposite bank, drifts along with the water and arrives at point C.

Following the procedure outlined above, we draw two vectors to the same scale, representing the two given velocities, and label them as shown in Fig. D. The two vectors

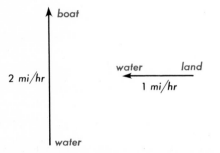

Fig. D. Velocity vectors of the river-boat problem.

are then combined with like words together, as shown at (a) in Fig. E.

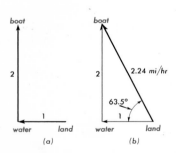

Fig. E. Composition of velocities for the river-boat problem.

Connecting the two end points with a straight line, one obtains a right triangle as shown at (b) in Fig. E. When the length of the hypotenuse is measured, it is found to be 2.24 units long. When the angle it makes with the base is measured with a protractor, it is found to be 63.5°. These represent the

magnitude and direction of the velocity of the boat with respect to the shoreline or bank.

To find the distance B to C along the shore, we notice that the distance AB is one mile. The time to cross at 2 mi/hr is therefore 0.5 hours. It follows that the distance BC is found from the water velocity:

$$BC = 1.0 \, \frac{\textbf{mi}}{\textbf{hr}} \times 0.5 \, \textbf{hr}$$

from which we find $BC = \frac{1}{2}$ mi. In other words, the boat travels 2.24 mi/hr along the line AC and arrives $\frac{1}{2}$ mi downstream at point C.

The problem may also be solved by trigonometry. First, the boat velocity is found by the Pythagorean Theorem:

$$v^2 = \left(\frac{\textbf{2 mi}}{\textbf{hr}}\right)^2 + \left(\frac{\textbf{1 mi}}{\textbf{hr}}\right)^2$$
$$= 5 \, \textbf{mi}^2/\textbf{hr}^2$$

or $v = 2.24$ mi/hr. The angle is found from the relation—

$$\tan \theta = \frac{\textbf{2 mi/hr}}{\textbf{1 mi/hr}} = 2$$

or—

$$\theta = 63.5°$$

The Airplane Problem. A pilot is in a plane having a cruising speed, or air speed, of 150 mi/hr. Aloft, a wind of 75 mi/hr is blowing. If the wind direction is parallel to his motion (a tailwind), his ground speed would be the sum of the two, or 225 mi/hr. If the wind direction is opposite to his motion (a headwind), his ground speed is the difference, or 75 mi/hr.

The present problem involves the wind blowing from the north. If the pilot sets his course due east, how far off his course will he be at the end of one hour? This problem involves two simultaneous velocities. The plane flies through the air with a velocity of

150 mi/hr and the air, thought of as a large mass, is itself moving southward. See Fig. F. Though the pilot starts from the land

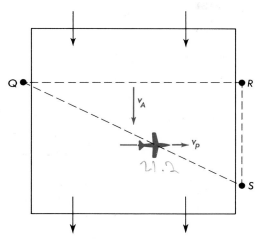

Fig. F. Space diagram for the airplane problem.

point Q and keeps the plane's nose headed directly toward the east, the plane is carried southward along the land line QS.

The graphical procedure to be followed in this problem is that given in italics in the seventh paragraph of this lesson. Vectors are first drawn as shown in Fig. G. With the

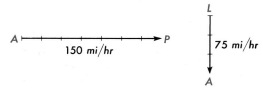

Fig. G. Velocity vectors for the airplane problem.

velocities known, each is measured off to the same scale in its proper direction and then labeled. The pilot and plane, P, are moving eastward at 150 mi/hr with respect to the air, A, while the air is moving southward at 75 mi/hr with respect to the land, L.

The next step is to combine the two vectors with their like labels, A, together as shown in Fig. H. The line LP is then drawn

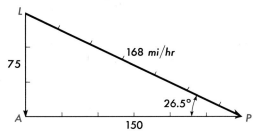

Fig. H. Vector diagram of velocities for the airplane problem.

in with an arrowhead at P and the length measured with the common scale. The vector LP of 168 represents the velocity of the plane, P, with respect to the land, L, while the angle of 26.5°, measured from the triangle, gives the direction in which the plane is traveling with respect to the land. Fig. F shows how the plane, headed due east, and flying through the air with a speed v_p of 150 mi/hr, follows a course 26.5° south of east with a ground speed of 168 mi/hr.

To find how far off course the plane is at the end of 2 hours, we note that the wind velocity of 75 mi/hr, acting for 2 hours, will put the plane off course a distance—

$$RS = 75\ \frac{mi}{hr} \times 2\ hr$$

The plane is off course 150 mi directly south.

This problem may be solved by trigonometry as follows. First, the angle may be found using the relation containing the known sides:

$$\tan \theta = \frac{75\ mi/hr}{150\ mi/hr}$$

$$= 0.5$$

Using Appendix 1, we find—

$$\theta = 26.5°$$

To determine the velocity, *LP*, we use the Pythagorean Theorem:

$$LP = \sqrt{150^2 + 75^2}$$
$$= 168 \text{ mi/hr}$$

Frames of Reference. As we have just seen, velocity is a vector quantity and, therefore, it has direction in addition to magnitude. It is fairly clear that the units of magnitude are quite arbitrary. Many units of length are in use today, some of which are cumbersome. Scientists have, to some extent, tried to simplify this problem by standardizing on the metric system. Even so, there is some argument as to whether the meter or centimeter is the more useful unit.

At first glance, it would appear that there is no problem associated with direc-

reference for us on the earth is to use the earth itself.

Now assume that two people are in the car moving in a straight line at 60 mi/hr. If we use the earth as the frame of reference, then the people are moving at 60 mi/hr. But if we use the car itself as the frame, then the people in the car are not moving at all.

What kind of motion do points on the wheel of a moving automobile make? The usual answer is that they move in circles. However, that is only true if we use the axle as the frame of reference, which in turn gives the simplest answer. With reference to the earth, the motion is quite complex, because as the wheel turns, it also moves forward. Such a path is called a *cycloid*. See Fig. I.

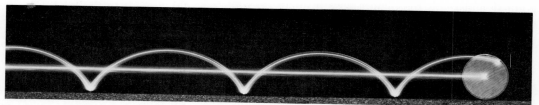

Fig. I. A point on the rim of a rolling wheel describes a cycloid to an observer standing at a right angle to its path. The axle, of course, traces a straight line.

tion. The description of the direction of a velocity also depends on an assumption as to the starting point. This is usually chosen so as to give the simplest result possible. This arbitrary zero, or starting point, is called the *frame of reference.*

What motion does a car have when it is standing still? Clearly, with respect to the ground, it has zero velocity. What kind of motion would the car have to an observer far out in space? With reference to himself, the car is revolving daily around an axis and also making a large elliptical path around the sun. Obviously the simplest frame of

A boy, for example, is in a train moving with uniform velocity, and he decides to play ball. He drops a ball from the highest position possible in the train. Where will the ball hit the floor? This is a confusing question if the frame of reference is not specified. If the front of the train is the point of origin, the ball will drop at the same distance from the origin as it was dropped. To an observer on the ground who is using the earth as his frame of reference, the ball will appear to move forward. Both answers are correct depending, of course, on which frame of reference is being used.

In our studies of motion, it will almost always pay to use the frame of reference in which the description of motion is the simplest.

QUESTIONS

1. (a) How is it possible for a body to move with two different velocities at the same time? Explain. (b) Give an example.
2. Give an example of a body moving with three simultaneous velocities.
3. (a) If two vectors at right angles are given, give three ways in which the resultant can be found. (b) Give two ways in which the other angles may be determined.
4. Under what circumstances do two vectors add arithmetically?
5. What is meant by (a) "add arithmetically" and (b) "add vectorially"?
6. Under what conditions could an airplane be flying with its engine at maximum power but still appear to be standing still?
7. Why do jet trips usually take longer to go from New York to San Francisco than to return?
8. (a) What is a frame of reference? (b) How many frames of reference can there be?
9. Why does traveling at 500 mi/hr in a jet airliner at 40,000 feet altitude give less sensation of movement than going 70 mi/hr in a car?
10. (a) What frame of reference is generally used in describing the motion of the planets? (b) Is this the only one possible? Explain.
11. (a) In what frame of reference will a spot on the rim of a wheel on a moving bicycle appear to move in a circle? (b) In a cycloid? (c) Not to move at all?

PROBLEMS

1. A plane flies 400 mi eastward in 1 hr and 20 min. Represent this velocity by a vector, and label the ends properly.
2. While a train is moving north at 55 mi/hr, a man walks from one side of the club car to the other at 3 mi/hr. (a) Draw the appropriate domino diagram. (b) Draw a domino diagram for the case in which the man walks the length of the club car.
3. An auto ferry is making 12 knots while pointed due east across a river that is moving south at 5 knots. A man, walking across the ferry toward the port side at 3 knots, was wondering what his velocity was with respect to the land. Draw a domino diagram to find out.
4. An ocean liner crosses the Atlantic, sailing directly eastward at 18 mi/hr. A man walks across the deck at right angles to the ship's keel at 3 mi/hr. Make a velocity vector-diagram, and compute the velocity of the man with respect to the water. Use the graphical method.
5. Evaluate the resultant velocity of the previous problem using a different method.

6. An Indian who can paddle a canoe at 3 m/sec heads straight across a river 400 m wide. If the water flows at 1.4 m/sec, how far down the river will he land on the other side?

7. A motorboat heads directly across a mile-wide river whose water is moving at 10 knots. (a) If the boat lands 3500 ft downstream, what was its speed with respect to the water? (b) With respect to the land?

8. A ship is sailing westward at 20 knots and a 15-knot wind is blowing from the north. (a) What is the velocity of the wind with respect to the ship? (b) What angle will the trail of smoke left by the funnels make with the ship's course?

9. A pilot with a plane having a cruising speed of 200 mi/hr wishes to fly to another airport 100 mi to the north and return. A steady 50 mi/hr wind is blowing from the south. (a) What is his time flying north? (b) Flying south? (c) What is his total flying time? (d) What would be his flying time if there were no wind?

10. A plane, with an air speed of 200 mi/hr is to fly to an airfield 100 mi due east. However, there is a 20 mi/hr wind from the north. Use a domino diagram to determine the angle at which the pilot must direct the plane so that his land course is due east. (a) What is his ground speed? (b) How long does the trip take?

11. A boat has a velocity of 4 mi/hr in a lake. If the boat is launched into a river that is moving at 2 mi/hr, which trip would take the most time, 1 mi upstream and return or 1 mi across and back?

PROJECT

Design and make a boat model with an electric motor. Also make a model river in which the boat could be made to operate. Show by actual measurements that a boat in a river follows the vector principles you have just studied.

MECHANICS

Lesson 10 RESOLUTION OF VELOCITIES

In the preceding lesson on *composition of velocities*, we have seen how two velocities can be added together as vectors to find their *resultant* velocity. We now take up the reverse process, the *resolution of velocities*.

Components of Velocity. Many of the problems in mechanics are most easily solved by a process called the *method of components*. The method of components is applied to vector quantities only, and when applied to velocities, is frequently referred to as the *resolution of velocities*.

Consider, as an illustration, a ship leaving New York harbor and sailing in a direction 30° north of east at a speed of 20 mi/hr.

The ship's velocity can be represented by a single vector, as shown in Fig. A.

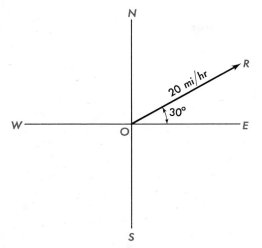

Fig. A. Velocity is a vector quantity.

We now proceed as shown in Fig. B to resolve the single velocity, *OR*, into two perpendicular components. This is done by dropping perpendiculars to the *NS* and the

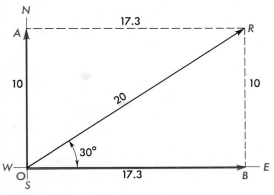

Fig. B. A single velocity vector is resolved into two components.

EW lines, respectively. Where the dotted lines intersect at *A* and *B*, arrowheads are drawn in, creating two vectors, *OA* and *OB*, at right angles to each other.

The components could be taken in many

directions. However, for many purposes those at right angles to each other are most useful.

The vector *OA*, when measured, is found to be 10 units long and represents the velocity of the ship toward the north, while the vector *OB*, when measured, is found to be 17.3 units long and represents the velocity of the ship toward the east. This means that the ship may be thought of as having two velocities simultaneously, a velocity of 10 mi/hr toward the north and one of 17.3 mi/hr toward the east. Note that the dotted lines have lengths of 10 and 17.3 units, respectively, and that the vector sum of *OB* + *OA* is equal to the original vector, *OR*. In other words, the *composition of velocities* refers to the combining of two velocities to find a single resultant velocity, while the resolution of a velocity refers to the breaking up of a single velocity into two velocities called *components*.

To find the solutions by trigonometry, we can use the relations—

$$\frac{OA}{OR} = \sin 30°$$

$$\frac{OB}{OR} = \cos 30°$$

The vectors are then found:

$$OA = 20 \text{ mi/hr} \times \sin 30°$$
$$= 20 \times 0.5 \text{ mi/hr}$$
$$= 10 \text{ mi/hr}$$

and—

$$OB = 20 \text{ mi/hr} \times \cos 30°$$
$$= 20 \times 0.866 \text{ mi/hr}$$
$$= 17.3 \text{ mi/hr}$$

Example 1. An object is given a velocity of 50 m/sec in a direction making 40° with the x-axis. Resolve this velocity into two components, one along the x-direction and the other at right angles along the y-direction.

Solution. By graphical methods, we draw

62   **MECHANICS**

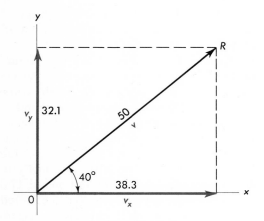

Fig. C. A velocity vector is resolved into x- and y-components.

x- and y-axes as shown in Fig. C. The velocity vector, v, is drawn to some convenient scale 50 units long and at an angle of 40° with the x-axis. From the tip of this vector, we draw the dotted lines parallel to the x- and y-axes, and where they cross the lines, they terminate the two components v_x and v_y. Upon measuring the lengths of these two lines with our chosen scale, we find 38.3 units and 32.1 units, respectively, representing the two velocities—

$$v_x = 38.3 \text{ m/sec}$$
$$v_y = 32.1 \text{ m/sec}$$

These two velocities are the components of $v = 50$ m/sec, with the subscripts denoting their x- and y-directions, respectively.

Alternatively, the velocity components may be easily found using the trigonometric relations—

$$v_x = v \sin \theta$$
$$v_y = v \cos \theta$$

RES OLUTION~ velocity

Relative Velocity. One of the principles upon which Einstein's theory of relativity is founded is that all motions are relative. A body moving with a specified velocity with respect to one frame of reference may be moving with a different velocity when referred to another. To illustrate, suppose two

seaplanes leave the same island base at the same time, one flying northeast with a velocity of 200 mi/hr, the other flying east with a velocity of 250 mi/hr.

A vector diagram of these velocities is given in Fig. D. Vector BA_1 represents the

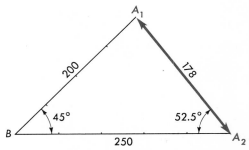

Fig. D. According to Einstein's special theory of relativity, all motions are relative.

velocity of plane A_1 with respect to the base B, while vector BA_2 represents the velocity of plane A_2 with respect to the same base. For both of these vectors, the page of the book with the fixed point B is the frame of reference from which the velocity of A_1 and A_2 are specified.

The vector joining A_1 and A_2 represents the relative velocities of the two planes. The navigator in A_2 observes plane A_1 receding from him with a velocity of 178 mi/hr in a direction 52.5 degrees north of west, while the navigator in A_1 observes plane A_2 receding from him with a velocity of 178 mi/hr in a direction 52.5 degrees south of east.

With respect to A_2 the base B is moving west with a velocity of 250 mi/hr. With respect to A_1 the base is moving southwest with a velocity of 200 mi/hr. *All motions are relative.*

Resolving velocities into components is illustrated in the following example:

Example 2. Solve the problem in the previous example of relative velocity for the angle

θ and the velocity v both graphically and by trigonometry by resolving the velocity into components.

Solution. See Fig. E. The x-component of the velocity vector BA_1 is found by dropping

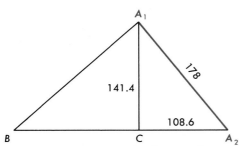

141.4
178
108.6
A_1
B   C A_2

Fig. E. The components of relative velocity are evaluated and combined.

a perpendicular from A_1 to the x-axis so that BC is the x-component. However, the other velocity, BA_2, already lies entirely along the x-axis. The x-component of relative velocity is just the difference $BA_2 - BC$ or A_2C. Notice that by taking components, the difference is just the numerical difference, and no vector rules are involved. The y-component of relative velocity is simply A_1C. These two components of relative velocity are measured to be 108.6 and 141.4 mi/hr, respectively.

The use of trigonometry allows us not only to solve for the components, but to calculate the angle θ and the relative velocity, v, as well. First, we determine the x-component of the relative velocity v_x:

$$v_x = v_{x_2} - v_{x_1}$$
$$= v_2 - v_1 \times \cos 45°$$
$$= 250 - 200 \times 0.707 = 108.6 \text{ mi/hr}$$

The y-component of the relative velocity is then found:

$$v_y = v_{y_1}$$
$$= v_1 \times \sin 45° = 141.4 \text{ mi/hr}$$

Using the known sides of the resultant triangle as in Fig. E, we can now find the relative angle:

$$\tan \theta = \frac{141.4 \text{ mi/hr}}{108.6 \text{ mi/hr}}$$
$$= 1.302$$

or

$$\theta = 52.5°$$

The relative velocity may be found by the Pythagorean Theorem:

$$v = \sqrt{v_x{}^2 + v_y{}^2}$$
$$= \sqrt{(108.6)^2 + (141.4)^2}$$
$$= 178 \text{ mi/hr}$$

QUESTIONS

1. (a) What are components of a vector? (b) What are components of a velocity?
2. What is meant by relative velocity? Give an example.
3. How does the composition of velocities compare with the resolution of a velocity?
4. (a) How many motions does the earth have relative to the universe? (b) Relative to the sun?
5. (a) Normally, what is your frame of reference when you are in a city? (b) When you are in a boat?
6. Explain why the perpendicular components always add up numerically to greater than the original vector.
7. The opposite of relative velocity is absolute velocity. What would absolute velocity mean?

8. Is it possible to have absolute motion? Explain.
9. Describe how you would add three vectors using the method of resolution of velocity.

PROBLEMS

1. On an x,y-coordinate system, find the x- and y-components of a 75 cm/sec vector that makes a direction of 70° with the x-axis. Solve graphically and by trigonometry.
2. Draw a vector of length 8 pointed toward the northeast, and resolve it into two components. Resolve it into a second set of components. Give an example in which one might want to resolve a vector into two or more sets of components.
3. An arrow is shot into the air with an initial velocity of 60 m/sec at an angle of 55° with the horizontal. Find the horizontal and vertical components of this initial velocity.
4. A ship making 30 knots is sailing in a direction 30° north of east. What is its velocity (a) toward the north and (b) toward the east?
5. A plane cruises at 375 mi/hr in a direction 35° south of west. What is its velocity (a) toward the south and (b) toward the west?
6. A rocket having a velocity of 18,000 mi/hr is traveling in a direction 42° east of south. What is its velocity (a) toward the east and (b) toward the south?
7. Two cars, one from the west and the other from the east, are traveling 60 mi/hr and 65 mi/hr, respectively. (a) What is their relative velocity? (b) What will their relative velocity be after they pass?
8. Two trains are headed due west, both at 55 mi/hr. If one is 35 mi northeast of the other, what is their relative velocity?
9. One ship moving southwest at 26 knots passes another ship moving northeast at 22 knots. What is their relative velocity after they pass?
10. One plane flies northeast at 230 mi/hr, while another that left the airfield at the same time flies southeast at 230 mi/hr. What is their relative velocity?
11. If you used the north and east directions as your y- and x-axes in Problem 10, you should recognize that there is a more convenient set of axes at right angles to each other. Define these axes and solve the problem using them.

PROJECT

Develop a working model, with at least two frames of reference, which would show that the measured velocity and position depend on the frame used.

MECHANICS

Lesson 11 *FALLING BODIES*

Neglecting friction, all bodies, large and small, fall with the same acceleration. This, the law of falling bodies, is a physical paradox, for it contradicts the conclusion the average person might derive *a priori*. This is not to be wondered at, for centuries ago, the great philosopher Aristotle* taught that heavy bodies fall proportionately faster than lighter ones.

It took the world nearly two thousand years to produce a challenger of Aristotle's scientific teachings. In the year 1590, Galileo† was pondering over the question of falling bodies and found apparent inconsistencies with Aristotle's teachings. He is said to have dropped various kinds of ob-

---

* Aristotle (384-322 B.C.), famous Greek philosopher, logician, moralist, political thinker, biologist, and founder of literary criticism, spent his early years as a student of and fellow worker with Plato. While practically all of Aristotle's teachings concerning physical principles are now known to be erroneous, his contributions to other fields of knowledge have placed him high among the great men of ancient Greece.

† Galileo Galilei (1564-1642), Italian mathematician, astronomer, and experimental physicist. At the age of twenty-four, Galileo wrote a treatise on the center of gravity of solids. This led the following year to his appointment as professor of mathematics at the University of Pisa. A rumor that a Dutch lens grinder had observed that two lenses used together make distant objects appear close at hand led Galileo to construct the first telescope. Successful telescopes of greater and greater magnification enabled him eventually to observe, for the first time, the mountains on the moon, the major satellites of Jupiter, and sunspots. While at Pisa, Galileo carried out many experiments and public demonstrations of principles that laid the foundations of mechanics and the laws of projectiles and falling bodies.

jects from different levels of the leaning tower of Pisa and to have timed their fall and measured their velocities.

On one occasion, Galileo is alleged to have attracted a large crowd to the leaning tower, where he climbed the spiral staircase to the bell chamber at the top and there through an open archway dropped two stones, one large and one small. These two bodies fell side by side and struck the ground together, thus sounding the death knell of an old hypothesis and the birth of a new era in science.

Whether this particular incident is true or not, the importance of Galileo's many authentic experiments lies not in the fact that they demonstrated the fallacy of Aristotle's reasoning, but that they presented to the world a new and more reliable scientific method, the method of experimentation.

Gravitation. The principle that all objects fall with the same acceleration can be demonstrated in various ways. One of these is illustrated, in Fig. A, where two steel balls, one large and one small, are supported in the groove of a wooden block 10 or 20 ft above the ground. When the block is tipped by pulling the cord, both balls fall together and strike the ground together. Dropped from a height of 16 ft, the time of fall is just 1 sec. The shaded circles in the figure show the position of the two bodies at the end of each quarter second.

If the balls in the experiment are replaced by two others of the same size, one steel and the other wood, they too will fall

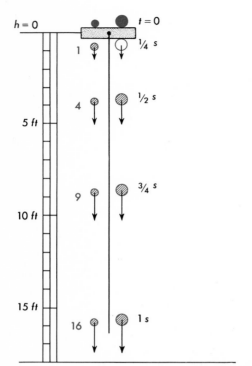

Fig. A. All bodies falling freely under constant gravity drop 16 ft in the first second.

fall with the acceleration of a solid steel ball. An experiment illustrating just this is shown in Fig. B. A long glass cylinder, con-

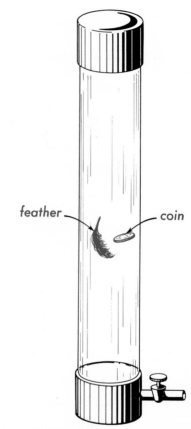

Fig. B. In a vacuum, a feather and a coin fall at the same acceleration and strike the bottom simultaneously.

side by side and strike the ground together. In this case the steel ball weighs fifteen times as much as the wood. (Density of steel, 7.6 gm/cm³; density of wood, 0.5 gm/cm³.)

The question of air friction usually arises in this latter experiment, for careful observation will show that the wooden ball lags slightly behind the steel ball. This lagging, due to air friction, increases the farther they fall and is even more pronounced when a still lighter object, like a piece of paper, is allowed to fall in comparison with a metal washer. If the sheet of paper is, however, crumpled into a small ball, so that it occupies a volume more closely related to the washer, and they are both dropped together, it will be found that they both strike the floor together.

In the absence of air, even a feather will

taining a feather and silver coin, is connected by flexible tube to a vacuum pump. If after evacuation the tube is turned upside down, the feather and the coin will be observed to fall together. When the air is once more admitted to the cylinder the feather will again flutter slowly to the bottom.

In the absence of air friction, all bodies fall with the same acceleration.

In the treatment of falling bodies given

in the remainder of this and following lessons, air friction is entirely neglected. The formulas presented and used in working problems are known to hold only approximately. In most practical cases, however, the calculated results are so nearly realized experimentally that corrections for air friction need only be made where the distances and velocities involved are large. A detailed discussion of the effects of air friction on falling bodies is given in Lesson 23.

Free Fall. Many laboratory experiments can be performed to demonstrate the well-established laws of falling bodies. One of these is the inclined plane experiment. If the angle a plane makes with the horizontal is increased, the acceleration of a ball down the plane will also increase. The velocities as well as the distances traveled will increase in the proper proportions to show that the equations relating these quantities in Lesson 8 are generally valid. This is true even for the limiting angle of 90° where the inclined plane becomes straight up and down, and the steel ball falls freely under the full force of gravity.

As indicated in Fig. C, the measured distance a body falls is 16 ft in the first second; four times sixteen or 64 ft in 2 sec, nine times sixteen or 144 ft in 3 sec, etc. Inserting these distances in the equation $s = \frac{1}{2}at^2$, the constant of acceleration is computed to be $a = 32 \ ft/sec^2$. If the distances are measured in centimeters, the same formula gives the equivalent acceleration as $980 \ cm/sec^2$ or $9.80 \ m/sec^2$.

The Acceleration Due to Gravity. Experiments carried on at many points over the earth show that the acceleration due to gravity is not everywhere the same; there are slight variations. While these variations are small and are not of any consequence in most practical problems, they do exist.

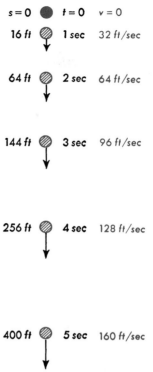

Fig. C. Illustrating the distance and velocity of freely falling bodies at the end of each of the first five seconds.

In general, the values of the acceleration due to gravity lie between a minimum of 32.09 ft/sec², or 9.7804 m/sec², at the equator, and a maximum of 32.26 ft/sec², or 9.8321 m/sec², at the North and South Poles. Referring here to the equator and the poles is still only a generalization, for not all points on the equator have the same values as quoted above, nor do all points on any one latitude have the same value. Irregularities of the earth's structure give rise to minute random differences.

The International Committee on Weights and Measures has adopted as a standard or accepted value, 9.80665 m/sec², or 32.174 ft/sec². For practical purposes, however, it is customary to round off the values to 9.80 m/sec² and 32 ft/sec², and in formulas for free fall to use the small letter g in place of a as given previously. For freely falling bodies, then—

$$g = 9.80 \text{ m/sec}^2$$
$$g = 980 \text{ cm/sec}^2$$
$$g = 32 \text{ ft/sec}^2$$

and equations developed in Lesson 8, to be used for a body falling from rest are—

$$v = gt \tag{1}$$

$$s = \frac{v}{2}\, t \tag{2}$$

$$v^2 = 2gs \tag{3}$$

$$s = \tfrac{1}{2} g t^2 \tag{4}$$

Example. A boy standing on a high bridge drops a stone into the water below. Looking at his watch, he notes that it takes just 3 sec for the stone to fall. Calculate (a) the speed of the stone as it hits the water and (b) the height of the bridge.

Solution. To find the speed, it is convenient to use Eq. (1) and substitute the known quantities $g = 32$ ft/sec² and $t = 3$ sec:

$$v = 32 \,\frac{\text{ft}}{\text{sec}^2} \times 3 \text{ sec} = 96 \,\frac{\text{ft}}{\text{sec}}$$

To find the height, use Eq. (4) and substitute the same quantities as follows:

$$s = \frac{1}{2} \times 32 \,\frac{\text{ft}}{\text{sec}^2} \times 9 \text{ sec}^2 = 144 \text{ ft}$$

The answers are: (a) the stone hits the water with a speed of 96 ft/sec, and (b) the height of the bridge is 144 ft.

QUESTIONS

1. What is meant by a freely falling body?
2. Why does a leaf or feather fall more slowly than a stone?
3. If air friction were eliminated, what could you say about all falling bodies?
4. How much farther does a freely falling body fall during two seconds than it does during one second? Assume it falls from rest.
5. After falling for one second, a body acquires a velocity of 32 ft/sec. How then do you account for the fact that it falls only 16 ft during that time?
6. What new approach to the scientific method is attributed to Galileo?
7. What reasons might Aristotle have had for contending that heavy bodies fell faster than light bodies?
8. Describe a simple experiment that anyone can perform to determine the value of g.
9. A paratrooper delays the opening of his parachute and soon acquires a maximum velocity of 160 mi/hr. Why is he no longer accelerated?
10. Without the use of an air pump or other elaborate machinery, how could you prove that very light objects fall as rapidly as heavy objects?
11. Will a helicopter crash if its engine fails? Explain.
12. Would a parachute be helpful to an astronaut if he were in difficulty in outer space? Explain.

PROBLEMS

In the following problems, air friction is to be ignored.

1. A workman accidentally drops a hammer while working on a tall building. If it requires 8 sec to reach the ground, (a) how high is the building, and (b) with what speed does the hammer strike the ground?
2. A rock dropped from a certain height strikes the ground in 2 sec. How long would it take the rock to fall from the same height above the surface of the moon, where g is only one-sixth of that on earth?
3. A sandbag dropped from a balloon hits the ground with a speed of 180 mi/hr. (a) How high is the balloon, and (b) how long did the sandbag fall?
4. An object falls from a bridge 225 ft above the water. (a) With what speed does it hit the water, and (b) how long is it in the air?
5. What is the value of g (a) in mi/hr²? (b) In mm/min²?
6. In diving from a high platform, a swimmer is moving with a downward velocity of 48 ft/sec when he enters the water. Find (a) the height from which he dives, and (b) the time it takes to reach the water.
7. A lead brick takes 2 sec to fall to the ground. A gold brick takes 3 sec to fall to the ground. What was the difference in heights from which they were dropped?
8. A pillow is found to fall 16 ft in 1 sec, 64 ft in 2 sec, 128 ft in 3 sec, and 144 ft in 4 sec. Use Fig. C to estimate how fast it is falling when air friction starts to become significant.
9. A rock takes a time T to fall a distance S. How long would it take to fall a distance $2S$?
10. A golf ball has a velocity V when it is dropped from a height H. If it had a velocity $2V$, from how high had it fallen?

PROJECTS

1. Make a long tube that can be evacuated with a pump at will. Put in a feather and a small steel ball to demonstrate that heavy and light objects fall uniformly if air friction is removed.
2. Using a pendulum whose length and period can be accurately measured, measure the acceleration due to gravity in a number of high and low places.

MECHANICS

Lesson 12 **PROJECTILES**

Horizontal Projection. If one body falls freely from rest at the same time another is projected horizontally from the same height, the two will strike the ground simultaneously. An experimental proof of this fundamental observation may be verified by an experiment of the type diagrammed in Fig. A.

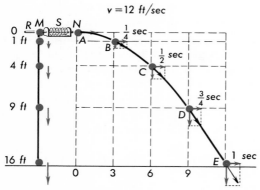

Fig. A. A body dropped from rest simultaneously with another projected horizontally will strike the ground at the same time as the projected body.

Two identical marbles, M and N, are supported by a rod and trough, respectively, in such a way that when the compressed spring, S, is released, the rod, R, springs to the right, dropping M and projecting N horizontally. Marble M falling with the acceleration of gravity, g, and marble N traversing the longer path $ABCDE$ strike the ground at the same time. Repetition of the experiment, with higher or lower projection velocities and from different heights, ends always with the same result: both marbles hit the ground together.

The first conclusion that may be drawn from this experiment is that the downward acceleration of a projectile is the same as a freely falling body and takes place independently of its horizontal motion. Furthermore, an experimental measurement of *times* and *distances* shows that the horizontal velocity of projection continues unchanged and takes place independently of the vertical motion.

In other words, a projectile carries out two motions independently: (1) a constant horizontal velocity, v, *and (2) a vertically downward acceleration,* g.

Projection Straight Upward. When a body is projected straight upward, its speed will rapidly diminish until at some point it comes momentarily to rest and then falls back toward the earth, acquiring again at the ground the same speed as it had upon projection. Experiment shows that the time taken to rise to the highest point of its trajectory is equal to the time taken to fall from there to the ground. This implies that the upward motions are just the same as the downward motions, but in reverse, and that the time and speed for any point along the path are given by the same equations for free fall from rest. See Lesson 11.

$$v = gt \tag{1}$$

$$s = \frac{v}{2}\,t \tag{2}$$

$$v^2 = 2gs \tag{3}$$

$$s = \tfrac{1}{2}gt^2 \tag{4}$$

In Fig. B, a particle is shown projected upward with a velocity of 128 ft/sec. After each second, its speed on the way up is shown to be the same as its speed at the same level on the way down. It is convenient, therefore, in solving problems of upward projection, to start at the top where the object is at rest and apply the equations for free fall.

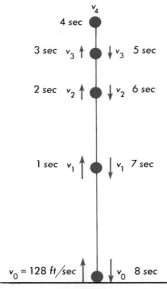

Fig. B. Neglecting air friction, the upward motion of a body is the same as the downward motion in reverse. A stone thrown upward returns to the ground with the same speed.

Example 1. A ball is thrown straight upward with a speed of 128 ft/sec. Neglecting friction, find (a) the time taken to reach the top of its flight and (b) the maximum height reached.

Solution. Since the time to rise equals the time to fall, we can apply Eq. (1) for free fall. By substituting directly into the equation we obtain (a)—

$$128 \ \frac{ft}{sec} = 32 \ \frac{ft}{sec^2} \times t$$

By solving for t and canceling units, we find—

$$t = \frac{128}{32} \ sec = 4 \ sec$$

By applying Eq. (4) we obtain (b) by direct substitution—

$$s = \frac{1}{2} \times 32 \ \frac{ft}{sec^2} \times (4 \ sec)^2 = 256 \ ft$$

It, therefore, takes 4 sec to rise to the highest point, 256 ft above the ground, and another 4 sec to return, or a total of 8 sec.

Projectiles. Many missiles projected into the air follow a parabolic path. In practical cases, air friction may be considered negligible only for slowly moving objects with high densities, like a large stone, a block of metal, or a solid ball. For high-speed projectiles the air continually slows the projectile down and the path departs from a parabola somewhat in the fashion shown in Fig. C.

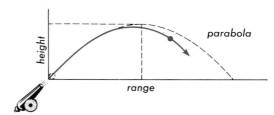

Fig. C. Projectiles tend to follow a parabolic path, but fall short owing to air friction.

The interesting and important information to be obtained from a study of projectiles is the *maximum height*, the *range*, and the *time of flight*.

The maximum height is defined as the greatest vertical distance reached by the projectile as measured from the ground up. The range is defined as the horizontal distance from the point of projection to the point where the projectile returns again to the same level. The time of flight is defined as the time required for the projectile to

again reach the level of its initial projection.
Experiment shows that all three of these
factors will depend upon two things: first,
the *initial velocity* of the projectile, and
second, on the projectile's *angle of projec-*

maximum height in the same time and return to strike the ground simultaneously.

Since the component v_y is directed
straight up, the formulas for fall from rest
may be used.

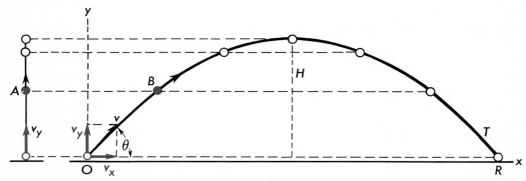

Fig. D. The range R, maximum height H, and the time of flight T of a projectile depend
upon the initial velocity, v, and the elevation angle, θ.

tion. The latter is always measured from the
horizontal and is called the *elevation angle.*
See Fig. D.

If v is the velocity of projection and θ is
the elevation angle, the maximum height,
H, the range, R, and the time of flight, T,
are found by trigonometry. We first resolve
the initial velocity into components, as
shown in Fig. D:

$$v_y = v \sin \theta$$
$$v_x = v \cos \theta \qquad (5)$$

where v_y is the component of velocity in
the upward direction, and v_x is the component of velocity in the horizontal direction. We then visualize the projectile as
having two motions at the same time: one is
the motion of a body moving horizontally
with a velocity v_x and the other the motion
of a body projected upward with the velocity v_y. In other words, if one projectile, A, is
projected straight upward with a velocity v_y
and simultaneously another projectile, B, is
projected with the velocity v at the elevation angle θ, the two will rise to the same

(a) The time for fall from rest, T, is
given by Eq. (1). Therefore, the time for
rise and fall is just twice this, or—

$$T = 2\frac{v_y}{g}$$

$$T = \frac{2v \sin \theta}{g} \qquad (6)$$

(b) The height, H, may be found from
Eq. (2):

$$H = \frac{1}{2} gt^2$$

$$= \frac{1}{2} g \times \left(\frac{v \sin \theta}{g}\right)^2$$

$$H = \frac{(v \sin \theta)^2}{2g} \qquad (7)$$

(c) The range, R, is found by using the
constant horizontal-velocity component, v_x,
to determine the horizontal distance traveled:

$$s = v_x t$$

If we now use the time of flight already determined, we find—

$$R = v_x T$$

$$= (v \cos \theta) \times \frac{2v \sin \theta}{g}$$

$$R = \frac{2v^2}{g} \sin \theta \cos \theta \qquad (8)$$

To see how to apply the above equations, consider the following example.

Example 2. In May, 1966, Randy Matson of the United States broke the world shot-put record, set earlier by himself. Assuming an initial velocity of projection of 14.5 m/sec and an elevation angle of 45°, find (a) the record distance thrown and (b) the time of flight.

Solution. The known quantities are v = 14.5 m/sec, θ = 45°, and g = 9.8 m/sec². Using the range formula, we have—

$$R = \frac{2v^2}{g} \sin \theta \times \cos \theta$$

$$= \frac{2 \times (14.5 \text{ m/sec})^2}{9.8 \text{ m/sec}^2} \times 0.707 \times 0.707$$

$$= 21.5 \text{ m}$$

The time of flight is found by using the appropriate formula—

$$T = \frac{2v \sin \theta}{g}$$

$$= \frac{2 \times 14.5 \times .707 \text{ m/sec}}{9.8 \text{ m/sec}^2}$$

$$= 2.09 \text{ sec}$$

Maximum Range. It is often useful to know what elevation angle to use to obtain the greatest projectile range. From the range formula, Eq. (8), we see that for constant initial velocity, we must pick θ so that—

$$\sin \theta \times \cos \theta = \textbf{a maximum}$$

A quick examination of Appendix I shows a value of zero for 0° and 90°, whereas the maximum occurs roughly in the center of the table. By multiplying out several products, we find the optimum angle to be 45°.

Maximum Height. From the height formula, Eq. (7), it is seen that the greatest height is reached for—

$$\sin \theta = \textbf{a maximum}$$

This is satisfied for—

$$\theta = \textbf{90}°$$

or straight up, as would be expected.

An interesting demonstration of projectile motion may be made using a large flat

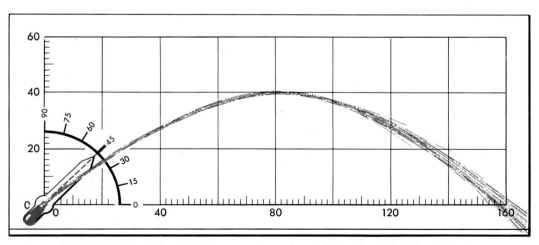

Fig. E. Diagram of a water-jet experiment for studying the paths of projectiles.

board as shown in Fig. E. At the lower left corner, a small nozzle producing a narrow stream of water is mounted so that it is free to turn about a horizontal axis. Waterdrops, therefore, become the projectiles in our experiment. Not only does the water stream permit one to see the entire trajectory at a glance but also to observe continuously how the shape changes with the elevation angle. From this type of demonstration, it is easy to show why the range is zero for 0° and 90°, and maximum for 45°.

QUESTIONS

1. When a projectile is thrown straight upward, how does its upward motion compare with its subsequent downward motion?
2. If a ball is thrown horizontally, what can you say about its (a) horizontal motion and (b) downward motion?
3. Do the horizontal and vertical motions of a projectile affect one another? (Neglect friction.)
4. (a) Does a 12-lb shot-put follow a parabolic path? (b) Does a hard-driven golf ball follow a parabolic path?
5. How does the impact velocity depend upon elevation angle? The impact velocity is the total velocity just preceding impact.
6. (a) Does the shape of a projectile have anything to do with its path? (b) Will it make any difference if a projectile is fired in space or from the surface of the moon?
7. If you fire buckshot straight up on a calm day, is it safe to stay where you are without any protection? Explain.
8. (a) Why does an object that is given a forward velocity fall to the ground at the same time as another object that is released at the same time from the same point? (b) Would this also be true on the moon?
9. A cannon is fired horizontally from a high cliff. (a) What type of motion describes the horizontal component of velocity? (b) The vertical component?
10. At what elevation angle will the time of flight be a maximum?
11. If the initial velocity of a projectile is doubled, how will the time of flight be affected?

PROBLEMS

1. An arrow is shot straight upward with a speed of 22.4 m/sec. Find (a) the height to which it rises and (b) the time required to return to the ground.
2. A stone is thrown vertically upward with speed of 60 mi/hr. Find (a) the height to which it rises and (b) the total time to reach the ground. (*Note:* 60 mi/hr = 88 ft/sec.)
3. A mail plane in straight and level flight, moving 100 mi/hr at 1500 ft above the ground, releases a mailbag to be picked up on the ground. How long does the mailbag take to fall?

4. A shot-put is thrown with a speed 35 ft/sec at an elevation angle of 45°. Find (a) the range, (b) the maximum height, and (c) the time of flight.

5. An arrow is shot upward with a speed of 180 ft/sec at an elevation angle of 60°. Find (a) the range, (b) the maximum height, and (c) the time of flight.

6. A shot-put is thrown with a speed of 40 ft/sec at an elevation angle of 40° on earth. (a) How far would it go? (b) How much farther would it go on the moon where the acceleration of gravity is $\frac{1}{6}$ that on earth?

7. Using the trigonometric functions table in Appendix I, plot the product of the sine and cosine for 5° intervals from 0° to 90°. At what angle is the product a maximum?

8. If the initial velocity of a projectile is doubled, how will the time of flight be affected?

9. Use Equations (7) and (8) to find the elevation angle for which the range is equal to the height.

10. (a) What elevation angle yields the maximum flight time? (b) What angle yields half the maximum flight time?

11. What elevation angle yields half the maximum height?

12. A firehose pointed with an elevation angle 35° plays water for a certain distance. (a) How many other angles yield the same range? (b) What are their values?

PROJECT

Set up a water jet experiment as suggested in Fig. E. Calculate the velocity of the water by at least two different methods to check the results obtained.

MECHANICS

Lesson 13 *NEWTON'S FIRST LAW OF MOTION*

In a preceding lesson, the motions of bodies have been described in terms of *speed*, *velocity*, and *acceleration*. The definitions of these quantities, and the laws and formulas relating to them, belong to that branch of mechanics called "kinematics." In this lesson, the cause of motion is treated. Such a treatment involves the introduction of *mass* and *force* into the equations already presented.

To Isaac Newton* goes the credit of

* Sir Isaac Newton (1642-1727), English physicist and mathematician, was born in England on Christmas Day, 1642. He obtained his education at Trinity College, Cambridge, where in 1665 he was awarded the Master of Arts degree. At just this time, the prevalence of the black plague forced him into retirement at his old home in Woolsthorpe, where in the two years 1665 and 1666 his genius developed. In this period, he invented the calculus, discovered the composition of white light, and conceived the idea of universal gravitation. In the years

having been the first to introduce these concepts into mechanics systematically and to formulate the fundamental laws governing all motion. These laws constitute the fundamental principles of that branch of mechanics called "dynamics" and resolve them-

Newton's First Law of Motion. Why does the earth continue to revolve about the sun? The reason is that there is nothing to stop it. *A body at rest or in uniform motion will remain at rest or in uniform motion unless some external force is applied to it.*

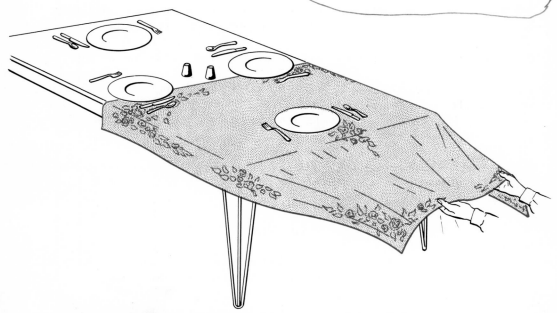

Fig. A. A tablecloth can be pulled from a table without dislodging the dishes.

selves into three laws commonly referred to as "Newton's Laws of Motion."

that followed, he published much of his work on optics and developed his ideas on gravitation, which were published in 1687 in his "Principia." At the age of fifty he suffered from a nervous breakdown and never again did any extensive scientific work.

His "Principia" is considered to be one of the greatest monuments of the human intellect. In it, Newton lays the foundations of mechanics, which are broad enough to include all future developments, and these he applies to the motions of heavenly bodies under the law of gravitation. He was elected to Parliament, was president of the Royal Society for twenty-five years, and was knighted by Queen Anne in 1705. The greatness of this modest man is illustrated by a remark he made on his deathbed, "If I have seen farther than others, it is by standing on the shoulders of giants."

This law can be demonstrated by many simple experiments. In Fig. A a tablecloth is shown in the process of being removed from under the dishes and silverware on a table without disturbing their original setting. In Fig. B a small car is shown free to move on a smooth hard track. If the track is jerked quickly to right or left, the wheels of the car will turn, but the car itself will tend to remain at rest.

In these experiments, both the dishes and the car are at rest. They tend to remain at rest, because the sudden motions of the objects on which they are resting exert no large force for any appreciable length of time. Actually, the dishes and the car do

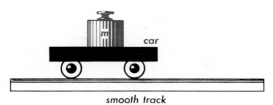

Fig. B. The smooth track can quickly be moved so as not to set the car in motion.

A body in uniform motion will remain in uniform motion unless some external force is applied to it.

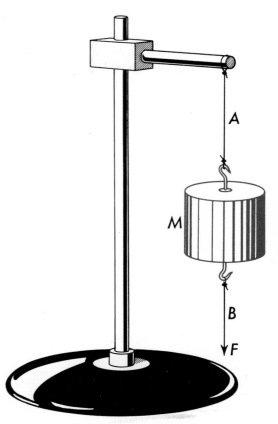

Fig. C. A slow, steady pull at F breaks the thread at A, while a quick pull at F breaks the thread at B.

move slightly due to small frictional forces between the moving parts in contact. The tendency for each body to remain at rest is due to the property of *inertia*, which is common to all material bodies. *The inertia of a body may be defined as that property of a body that tends to resist a change in its state of rest or motion. Mass is defined as a quantitative measure of inertia.*

A third experiment illustrating inertia, and Newton's First Law, is shown in Fig. C. A small mass, *M*, of 1000 gm is suspended by a fine thread, *A*, and then pulled downward by another piece of the same kind of thread, *B*. If the force *F* is a slow, steady pull, the thread will always break at *A;* whereas if the force is a sudden jerk, the thread will always break at *B*. In the first case, the tension in the upper thread is the greater and is equivalent to the force, *F*, plus the weight of the mass, *M*. In the second case, the force, *F*, is momentarily very large, causing the thread to break before the mass, *M*, has had time to move down far enough to stretch and break the upper thread. It is the inertia of *M* that permits the very large force, *F*, to be momentarily applied to the lower thread only.

Inertia and Motion. The three preceding demonstrations are concerned with bodies at rest. The second part of Newton's first law of motion is concerned with moving bodies, and a restatement of the law confined to this aspect would read:

This aspect of Newton's first law was first recognized by Galileo. In order to study the acceleration due to gravity, he used an inclined plane to reduce the acceleration due to gravity, thereby permitting better measurements. He observed that a ball, after rolling down one incline, would roll up another incline to approximately the same height at which it started on the first, regardless of the inclination of the second plane. Furthermore, if the ball were allowed to roll out on a level plane when it reached the bottom of the incline, it could never achieve its original height but tended to roll on and on. Due to friction it would eventually stop.

A most striking demonstration of this property of inertia is provided by a "dry-ice disk" as shown in Fig. D. Here, friction is

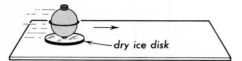

Fig. D. Demonstration of the inertia of a body moving with uniform acceleration.

reduced to practically zero by a metal disk that rides over a glass plate and literally floats on a thin layer of carbon dioxide gas. When this body is given a very slight push, it rides across the plate and seems to keep going on and on, with constant velocity, as if by magic. What keeps the body moving in the same straight line is its inertia.* The above law, of course, neglects friction, for

* A cross-section diagram of this dry ice disk is shown in Fig. E. A thin-walled, brass or copper ball about 10 cm in diameter is soldered to a flat, circular brass disk about 2 cm thick and 15 cm in diameter. Thin-walled vessels of this kind are used as a float in bathroom flush tanks and may be purchased in most hardware stores. Dry ice is available at almost every soda fountain, and one loading will last a couple of hours. The bottom surface of the disk is undercut several thousandths of a centimeter, and a hole about 0.5 cm in diameter is drilled through the center. A short section of metal tubing is mounted directly above this center and prevents the dry ice from clogging the hole. A larger hole in the top is provided for the insertion of dry ice, and a tight-fitting cork closes the opening.

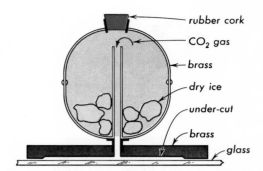

Fig. E. Cross-section diagram of a dry-ice disk.

we know that, left to itself, friction will eventually bring the body to rest. The greater the friction, the sooner it will stop. The smaller the friction, the longer it will move. If friction could be entirely eliminated, the *inertia* of the body would keep it moving indefinitely with constant velocity.

Inertia and Mass. Mass is a measure of inertia. In the metric system, inertia and mass are measured in *grams* and *kilograms*. In the English system, they are both measured in *slugs*, which are defined in Lesson 14. Fig. F is a diagram illustrating the rela-

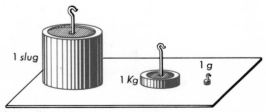

Fig. F. Units of mass are also units of inertia.

tive size of these three units. They are shown in a hooked-weight form convenient for use in experiments.

QUESTIONS

1. Give two of your own examples illustrating Newton's First Law of Motion.
2. (a) What concept does this law introduce? (b) What measurable quantity is involved? (c) In what units is it measured?

3. A fisherman gives a sharp tug on the line to retrieve a fish, but the line breaks. Why?

4. Does Newton's First Law apply to the case of a car moving along a straight road at 60 mi/hr?

5. Does Newton's First Law apply to an elevator car moving upward at constant speed?

6. What keeps a satellite moving after the jet booster turns off?

7. A space ship attains a velocity of 30,000 mi/hr in deep space. How could it continue to go at this speed?

8. Two railroad cars on a level track are being pulled together by a yardman standing on one car pulling a cable attached to the other. (a) In what sense is the tension in the cable referred to as an external force? (b) As an internal force? (c) How does. Newton's First Law apply?

9. A Mexican jumping bean has no external forces applied, but moves as a result of a worm inside it. Does the bean violate Newton's First Law? Explain.

10. Can you think of ways in which the principles developed in this lesson are involved in things happening in the world around us?

PROJECTS

1. Make a dry ice disk using the copper float of a bathroom flush tank. Demonstrate how long an object like this will move on a level glass or other smooth surface.

2. Make a little device of your own to show that matter has inertia. The principle to be demonstrated will be similar to that shown in Fig. A, but will not be as expensive as that experiment if it doesn't work.

MECHANICS

Lesson 14 *NEWTON'S SECOND LAW OF MOTION*

Newton's Second Law of Motion. Newton's First Law, concerning bodies at rest or moving with constant velocity, assumes that no forces are acting to change their state. Newton's Second Law, however, assumes that such a force is acting and describes the resulting *change in motion*. In Fig. A, for example, a small car of mass m is acted upon by a constant force, F. The force is produced by the pull of gravity on the mass M and is transmitted to the car by a cord passing over pulleys as indicated. If the car is initially at rest, this force will start it moving; if it is already moving with a velocity v_0, the force will increase its velocity. Thus the car is accelerated. More-

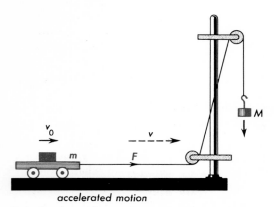

accelerated motion

Fig. A. A small car being accelerated by a constant force.

over, it is found that the acceleration is increased either by increasing the applied force or by decreasing the mass:

$$a = k \frac{F}{m}$$

If the force units are properly chosen so that $k = 1$, the law can be written as the equation—

$$a = \frac{F}{m}$$

Thus, the so-called "force equation," which forms the basis of so many principles in mechanics, is obtained:

$$F = m \times a \qquad (1)$$
$$\textbf{force} = \textbf{mass} \times \textbf{acceleration}$$

Example 1. Neglecting friction, what constant force will give a mass of 50 gm an acceleration of 5 cm/sec²?

Solution. By substituting directly into the force equation, Eq. (1), we obtain—

$$F = 50 \text{ gm} \times 5 \frac{\text{cm}}{\text{sec}^2} = 250 \frac{\text{gm cm}}{\text{sec}^2}$$

The answer is a force of 250 gm cm/sec². Thus, force is not as simple a concept as it might seem at first hand; it involves all three

of the fundamental units, *length, mass,* and *time.*

By definition, 1 gm cm/sec² is a unit of force called the *dyne.* According to this definition the answer to the above problem could have been written 250 dynes. *The dyne is a force that, acting on a 1-gm mass, will give it an acceleration of 1 cm/sec².* In the cgs system (centimeter-gram-second system), the units of Eq. (1) become—

$$1 \text{ dyne} = 1 \text{ gm} \times 1 \frac{\text{cm}}{\text{sec}^2}$$

There is a widespread preference among scientists and teachers of physics to use the kilogram and meter in place of the gram and centimeter as units of mass and length. According to the mks system (meter-kilogram-second system), a unit force is called the newton in honor of Sir Isaac Newton. *The newton is defined as the force that, applied to a 1-Kg mass, will give it an acceleration of 1 m/sec².*

In the mks system of units, the units of Eq. (1) become—

$$1 \text{ newton} = 1 \text{ Kg} \times 1 \frac{\text{m}}{\text{sec}^2} \qquad (2)$$

Example 2. Neglecting friction, what constant force in newtons will give a mass of 4 Kg an acceleration of 3.8 m/sec²?

Solution. By applying the force equation, $F = ma$, we obtain—

$$F = 4 \text{ Kg} \times 3.8 \frac{\text{m}}{\text{sec}^2}$$
$$= 15.2 \frac{\text{Kg m}}{\text{sec}^2} = 15.2 \text{ newtons}$$

The answer is a constant force of 15.2 newtons.

Dynes and *newtons* are absolute units of force. They arise from the force equation when the absolute units of *mass* and *time* are used as they are above.

Because 1 Kg = 1000 gm, and 1 m = 100 cm—

1 newton = 100,000 dynes

The engineer seldom uses the metric system of units described above; he has traditionally measured *force* in *pounds*. To apply Newton's Second Law of Motion, as expressed by the force equation, $F = ma$, it is necessary to introduce a unit of mass called the *slug*. See Fig. B. *One slug is defined as*

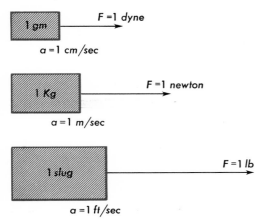

Fig. B. Unit force acting on unit mass produces unit acceleration.

the mass that, when acted upon by a 1-lb force, is given an acceleration of 1 ft/sec²:

$$1 \text{ lb} = 1 \text{ slug} \times 1 \frac{\text{ft}}{\text{sec}^2} \qquad (3)$$

Weight and Mass. When a mass, m, is allowed to fall freely, it is the constant downward force of gravity on the mass that gives rise to its constant acceleration. If Newton's Second Law is applied to this motion, see Eq. (1), the force, F, is none other than the weight, W, of the body, and the acceleration, a, is the acceleration due to gravity, g. For falling bodies the force equation, $F = ma$, is written in different symbols:

$$W = mg \qquad (4)$$
weight = mass × acceleration
due to gravity

As we have seen in a preceding lesson, weight *and* force *have both magnitude and direction and are, therefore, vector quantities.* Mass, on the other hand, is a scalar quantity, because it has only magnitude. The distinction between *weight* and *mass* is illustrated by imagining a given body to be carried out into free space far removed from other bodies and their gravitational attraction. There, a body at rest will still have its mass, but it will have no weight. That such a body has its mass would be demonstrated if another mass were to bump into it. The smaller the mass of the incoming body, the less would be the recoil of the first mass from the impact.

Weight here on the earth is due to the gravitational attraction of the earth upon a mass at its surface. In the equation $W = mg$, we may define g as the *weight per unit mass*. W is the *mass* times the *weight per unit mass*.

Example 3. Calculate the weight of a body having a mass of 1 Kg.

Solution. By direct substitution in Eq. (4) we obtain—

$$W = 1 \text{ Kg} \times 9.80 \frac{\text{m}}{\text{sec}^2}$$

$$= 9.80 \frac{\text{Kg m}}{\text{sec}^2} = 9.80 \text{ newtons}$$

To find the weight of an object, multiply its mass by g, the acceleration due to gravity. To find the mass of any object, divide its weight by g:

$$g = 9.80 \frac{\text{m}}{\text{sec}^2}$$

$$g = 980 \frac{\text{cm}}{\text{sec}^2}$$

$$g = 32 \frac{\text{ft}}{\text{sec}^2}$$

The mass of a body in slugs may be obtained by dividing the weight of that body in pounds by 32, when the weight is measured at the surface of the earth.

Example 4. What horizontal force, in pounds, applied to the tongue of a small wagon weighing 176 lb will give it an acceleration of 6 ft/sec²?

Solution. By applying Newton's Second Law, Eq. (1), we obtain—

$$F = \frac{176}{32} \text{ slugs} \times 6 \frac{\text{ft}}{\text{sec}^2}$$

$$F = 5.5 \text{ slugs} \times 6 \frac{\text{ft}}{\text{sec}^2} = 33 \text{ lb}$$

The answer is a constant force of 33 lb.

To illustrate how Newton's Second Law may always be relied upon, consider the following paradox. A spool of thread is placed upon the table as shown in Fig. C.

Fig. C. If the thread is pulled to the right, which way will the spool roll?

With the thread leading off the underside of the spool, a horizontal force, *F*, will cause the spool to move. Will it roll to the right and wind up the thread, or will it roll to the left and unwind? The performance and explanation of this experiment are left as a problem for the student.

Measurement of Weight as a Force. Everyone knows that, when he weighs himself, he is measuring the downward force he exerts on the foot board of the scales and that this force causes some mechanism within the scales to indicate his weight. The greater the downward force, the greater is the indicated weight. We are not interested here in the system of levers, weights, or springs within the scales, but rather with the downward force we call our *weight.*

Weight, as has been explained, is due to the gravitational attraction of the earth for all bodies.

As illustrated in Fig. D, gravitational

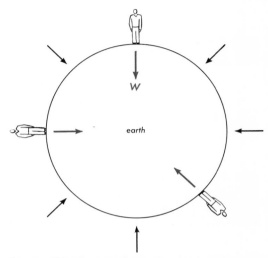

Fig. D. Weight is a force due to gravitational attraction. Gravitational force acts along a line joining the center of the body to the center of the earth.

forces always act in the direction of a line joining the body and the center of the earth and are, therefore, perpendicular to the earth's surface at the body.

The term *force* is not confined to weight alone, but describes the action of any one body upon another. For example, in towing an automobile as shown in Fig. E, there are

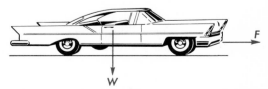

Fig. E. Illustrating two independent forces acting on the same body.

two forces acting: (1) a downward force, W, due to gravity and (2) a horizontal force, F, due to a pull on the tow line. The latter force is supplied by some external object or machine.

Regardless of the direction in which a force may act, its magnitude may be expressed in *dynes, newtons,* or *pounds.*

Use of Mass Units as Weight. One often hears of a weight referred to in grams or kilograms. This is confusing usage because grams and kilograms are mass units, not weight units. A kilogram in outer space weighs nothing. When a person says that an object weighs 3 kilograms, he means that it weighs the same amount as any 3 kilogram mass would on the surface of the earth at sea level. The expression of weight in mass units should be avoided until the distinction between mass and weight is clearly understood.

QUESTIONS

1. Is the pound a unit of mass? Explain.
2. (a) If an astronaut were to land on the moon, where the acceleration of gravity is less than on earth, would his mass be different? (b) His weight? Explain.
3. (a) How does the acceleration of a body depend upon the force? (b) If the force is doubled, how does the acceleration change? (c) How does the distance traveled in one second change?
4. If the mass of a body is doubled and the force remains the same, what change takes place in the acceleration?
5. How is the weight of a body related to its mass?
6. (a) Does a set of balances measure mass or weight? (b) Do bathroom scales measure mass or weight? Explain.
7. (a) Which is the largest of the three forces: 1 newton, 1 dyne, or 1 lb? (b) Which is the largest: 1 lb, 10 newtons, or 2000 dynes?
8. Which way does the spool roll in Fig. C? Explain.
9. Should the mass M in Fig. A be added to the mass m when applying Newton's Second Law to the system? Explain.
10. A 10-lb weight and 1-lb weight are dropped side by side. Because the earth pulls downward on one with a ten-times greater force, why do the two have the same acceleration?
11. What would be the weight of a 1-Kg mass if it were out in free space far removed from all astronomical bodies?
12. Why does a man in a satellite in orbit around the earth weigh nothing?
13. What could you do to acquaint yourself with the force of 1 lb, 1 newton, 1 dyne?
14. Assuming that you apply a constant pedal pressure to the accelerator on your car, will the car continue to go faster according to Newton's Law?
15. A car weighs 1600 lb. Another car with an identical motor has a weight of 3200 lb. Which car would have the greater acceleration? Explain.

PROBLEMS

1. Your mass expressed in Kg is 60 Kg. What would your weight be (a) in newtons? (b) In dynes?

2. A mass of 4 Kg is given in acceleration of 2.5 m/sec². Calculate the force required in (a) newtons and (b) dynes.

3. A racing car weighing 1650 lb is moving with an acceleration equal to the acceleration of gravity. What force is being applied to the road by the wheels?

4. A car weighing 1800 lb has an acceleration of 2.5 ft/sec². Find the effective force on the road in pounds.

5. A force of 120 lb is applied to a car weighing 2200 lb. Find (a) the mass of the car in slugs and (b) the acceleration.

6. A locomotive weighing 60 tons is capable of an acceleration of 2 ft/sec². Calculate (a) the mass of the locomotive in slugs and (b) the force it develops in pounds.

7. Let us define the *irk* to be the unit of force in a meter-gram-second system, and the *irf* to be the unit of force in a centimeter-kilogram-second system. How is the *irk* related to the *irf*?

8. If the mass *M* in Fig. A is 300 gm, and the mass *m* is 400 gm, what is the acceleration of the car?

9. An 8-lb weight is allowed to fall freely under the constant downward pull of gravity. Find the acceleration.

10. A 14-ton passenger plane, starting from rest at one end of a runway, acquires its take-off speed of 88 ft/sec in 20 sec. Calculate (a) the acceleration and (b) the total average thrust of its propellers.

11. A force of 50 newtons is applied to a mass of 15 Kg. Find (a) the acceleration and (b) the speed acquired at the end of 5 sec.

12. A car weighing 2800 lb is moving along a level road at a speed of 100 ft/sec. Calculate the force required to stop it in 5 sec.

13. Develop a formula for converting slugs to newtons.

14. Look up the acceleration due to gravity for Jupiter, Saturn, Mars, and the sun. Assuming that you could exist in these places, calculate your weight on these planets and on the sun.

15. What is the magnitude of your own inertia? (a) In the metric mks system of units? (b) In the English system of units?

PROJECT

Set up a demonstration experiment that will show that the acceleration a body experiences is directly proportional to the applied force and inversely proportional to the mass of the object. Try to avoid friction to get good results.

MECHANICS

Lesson 15 NEWTON'S LAW OF GRAVITATION AND THIRD LAW OF MOTION

Newton's Law of Gravitation. Nearly everyone has heard the story of how young Isaac Newton, while sitting under an apple tree one day, was struck on the head by a falling apple. This incident set Newton to thinking about falling bodies and led him, at the early age of twenty-three, to the discovery of the law of gravitation.

It has often been incorrectly said that Newton discovered gravity. What Newton discovered was the *universal law of gravitation.*

Any two bodies attract each other with a force that is proportional to the product of their masses and inversely proportional to the square of the distance between them.

Written in algebraic symbols—

$$F \propto \frac{m_1 m_2}{d^2}$$

As illustrated in Fig. A, F is the force of attraction, m_1 and m_2 are the two masses, and d is the distance between them. Mass

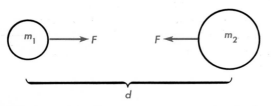

Fig. A. The gravitational attraction of a body of mass m_1 for another of mass m_2.

m_1 pulls on m_2 with a force, F, to the left, and m_2 pulls on m_1 with a force, F, to the right. To make an equation of this symbolism it is necessary only to replace the pro-

portionality symbol above by an equal sign and insert a constant on either side of the equality:

$$F = G \frac{m_1 m_2}{d^2} \qquad (1)$$

Experiment shows that if F is measured in newtons, m_1 and m_2 in kilograms, and d in meters, the "Newtonian Constant of Gravitation," G, has the value—

$$G = 0.000,000,000,0666 \ \frac{\text{m}^3}{\text{Kg sec}^2}$$

or in shorthand notation—

$$G = 6.66 \times 10^{-11} \ \frac{\text{m}^3}{\text{Kg sec}^2} \qquad (2)$$

If F is measured in pounds, m_1 and m_2 in slugs, and d in feet—

$$G = 3.41 \times 10^{-8} \ \frac{\text{ft}^3}{\text{slug sec}^2} \qquad (3)$$

Example. Two locomotives, weighing 64 tons each, stand beside each other with their centers 10 ft apart. Calculate the gravitational attractive force between them.

Solution. First, find the mass of each locomotive in slugs as follows:

$$m = \frac{64 \times 2000}{32} = 4000 \text{ slugs}$$

Direct substitution in Eq. (1) now gives—

$$F = 3.41 \times 10^{-8} \frac{4000 \times 4000}{10^2} = 0.00546 \text{ lb}$$

This force of 0.00546 lb is extremely small and would be difficult to detect, much less measure.

If we now consider the attraction between a very large object, like the earth, and another object like our own body, the force becomes one that is quite measurable, for it is none other than our own weight. It is the force that keeps all of us on the earth. It is also the force that keeps man-made satellites in orbit.

To go one step further, gravitational attraction is the force that keeps the moon in its orbit around the earth, and the earth in its orbit around the sun. Such forces have magnitudes of billions of billions of tons. See Fig. B.

Newton's Third Law of Motion. Of Newton's three laws of motion, the third is perhaps the least understood. This is probably because it is seldom used in solving problems, and often, when it is used, it is incorrectly applied.

Newton's Third Law of Motion states that to every action force there is an equal and opposite reaction force.

The principle of action and reaction may be illustrated by a bat striking a ball, Fig. C. During impact, the bat exerts a force, *F*, on the ball, and the ball exerts an equal but

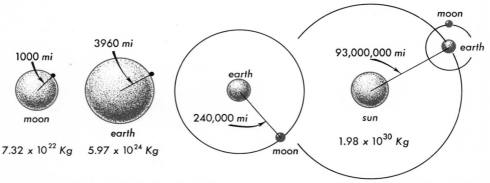

Fig. B. Gravitational attraction keeps the moon in its orbit around the earth and the earth in its orbit around the sun.

If we now let m_1 represent the mass of the earth, *M*, and m_2 represent a small mass, *m*, on earth, *d* becomes the earth's radius, *R*, and we can write—

$$F = G \frac{Mm}{R^2}$$

Now if we let the mass fall freely from a few feet above the ground, its acceleration is *g*. By Newton's Second Law of Motion $F = mg$. Therefore—

$$mg = G \frac{Mm}{R^2}$$

or—

$$g = \frac{GM}{R^2} \qquad (4)$$

opposite force, *G*, on the bat. The force *F* being exerted on the ball gives the ball an acceleration to the right, while the force *G* being exerted on the bat gives the bat an acceleration to the left. The ball speeds up during the impact and acquires a high velocity, while the bat in the same interval slows down to a lower velocity.

Consider the second example of a block hanging by a cord as illustrated in Fig. D. The weight of the block, *W*, is the force with which the earth pulls downward on the block, while the equal and opposite force, *X*, is the upward force exerted by the block on the earth.

In addition to this pair of forces, the

Fig. C. A bat at all times exerts a force on the ball equal in magnitude to the force that the ball exerts on the bat.

block exerts a downward force, G, on the cord, while the cord pulls upward with the reaction force F. If the block is not being accelerated, the force of the earth on the block happens to be equal and opposite to the force that the cord exerts on the block. However, this is not the action-reaction pair implied by the third law of motion.

Although many people find these forces

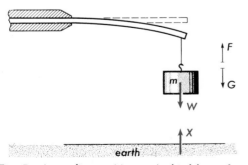

Fig. D. According to Newton's third law of motion, forces always exist in pairs.

confusing, it should be pointed out that Newton himself had some difficulty in applying his third law to certain problems. The difficulty arises from trying to apply action and reaction forces to the same body when in reality they apply to different ones.

The action force and the reaction force in Newton's Third Law of Motion act on different bodies. In particular, if the action force is the force that A exerts on B, the reaction force is the force that B exerts on A.

The Train-and-Track Experiment. Another illustration of Newton's Third Law is that of a train on a track, both of which, the track as well as the train, are free to move. The drive wheels push back on the track with a force, B, and the track pushes forward on the wheels with an equal and opposite force, F. These two form an action and reaction pair.

In Fig. E, the track is mounted on a

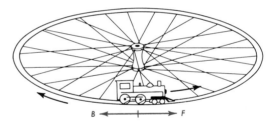

Fig. E. Demonstration of Newton's third law. The train moves forward and the track, if free to move, moves backward.

large wheel whose axis of rotation is vertical. With the track free to move, both forces of the pair are seen to be real, the track moves backward and the train moves forward. The track moves backward, because the wheels exert a force, B, upon it in that direction, and the train goes forward because the track exerts a force, F, upon it in that direction. If, when the train acquires a

certain velocity, the power is shut off, the
force F vanishes—so also does B—and the

train and track continue to move with constant speed.

QUESTIONS

1. (a) Is the value of G the same on the surface of the moon as on earth? (b) Is g the same? Explain.
2. Would the acceleration of gravity be less on top of a mountain than at sea level? Explain.
3. (a) Would the acceleration be less at the bottom of a deep mine shaft than at the surface? Explain. (b) What would be the acceleration of gravity at the center of the earth?
4. A book is at rest on a table. Make a diagram, and show the three pairs of action and reaction forces involved.
5. An automobile moves along a straight and level road with constant velocity. What horizontal pairs of forces are acting here?
6. A car crashes into a stone wall. What horizontal forces are involved? Make a diagram.
7. A horse pulls a wagon along a level road. According to Newton's Third Law of Motion, the wagon pulls back on the horse with a force equal to the forward force of the horse on the wagon. Because these forces must always be equal and opposite, explain why the wagon ever moves at all.
8. A stone is allowed to fall freely. (a) Neglecting air friction, what action and reaction forces are involved? (b) What can you say about the earth's motion while the stone falls?
9. (a) What happens to the earth's rotational motion when a heavy train starts from a station? (b) What happens when the train stops?
10. What is the value of g at a distance of 12,000 miles from the surface of the earth? (Assume the earth's radius = 4,000 miles.)

PROBLEMS

1. Two metal spheres, each having a mass of 3 million Kg, are located with their centers 4 m apart. Calculate the force of attraction between them in newtons.
2. The moon has a mass of 7.3×10^{22} Kg, and the earth a mass of 6.0×10^{24} Kg. Find the attractive force between these two bodies in newtons if their centers are 3.9×10^8 m apart.
3. A man weighing 150 lb stands on scales to weigh himself. What is the direction and magnitude of the force he exerts on the scale board?
4. A 20-lb stone is dropped from a bridge. What is the direction and magnitude of the force exerted by the stone on the earth?
5. A man weighing 200 lb sits in a chair. (a) What are the directions and magni-

tudes of the two forces acting on him? (b) Do these two forces represent action and reaction?

6. An elephant weighing 3000 lb is being lifted at constant velocity by an elevator. What are the directions and magnitudes of the two forces acting on the elephant?

7. The diameter of the moon is 2000 mi, whereas the diameter of the earth is 8000 mi. Using the masses in Problem 2, calculate the value of *g* on the surface of the moon in cm/sec².

8. Mt. Everest is 29,000 ft high. What is the acceleration of gravity at the top in cm/sec²?

9. (a) What is the acceleration of gravity at the center of the earth? (b) Which way does it point?

10. A man weighing 180 lb makes a trip to the moon. Using data given in previous problems, determine the force that the earth exerts on the man while he is on the moon.

11. An 8 Kg meteorite weighs 19.6 newtons. How high above the surface of the earth is it?

PROJECT

Make an apparatus as suggested by Fig. E. The track should be mounted so that it is free to move. A reversing electric train should be used to show the two forces that exist.

MECHANICS

Lesson 16 *BALANCED AND UNBALANCED FORCES*

Forces Are Added Vectorially. Because forces have both magnitude and direction, they are vector quantities and, therefore, subject to the rules of *vector addition*. Consider the diagram in Fig. A, illustrating a heavy trunk being pulled along the floor by two ropes. With steady pulls of 25 lb each exerted in directions at 60° from each other, the trunk moves in a direction indicated by the dotted arrow.

By vector addition, a resultant force can be found that, upon taking the place of the two forces shown, will produce the same motion.

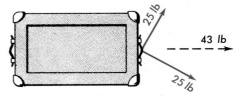

Fig. A. Two forces acting at an angle to each other are equivalent to a single force acting in a direction between them.

When this *resultant* is determined by vector addition, it is found to have a magnitude of 43 lb and a direction making an angle of 30° with each force.

To illustrate the common methods employed in the vector addition of two forces, consider the illustration shown in Fig. B,

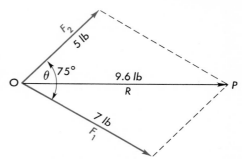

Fig. C. Illustrating the parallelogram method of vector addition.

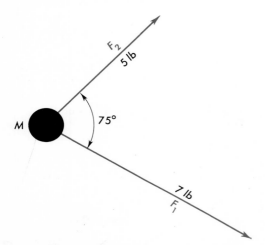

Fig. B. Force diagram of two forces acting on the same body in different directions.

where forces of 7 lb and 5 lb are applied to a body at the common point, *M*. In addition to using trigonometry, there are two graphical methods for finding the resultant: first, the *parallelogram method;* and second, the *triangle method.*

The parallelogram method of vector addition is shown in Fig. C. First, a line, F_1, is drawn in the proper direction to represent the 7-lb force. The length of the line is made to be 7 cm to represent the magnitude of the force, and the arrowhead is inserted at the right end to indicate its direction. In a similar way, the line F_2 is drawn 5-cm long and in the proper direction to represent the 5-lb force.

From the head of the vector representing the 5-lb force a dotted line is drawn parallel to the 7-lb vector, and from the

head of the 7-lb vector a dotted line is drawn parallel to the 5-lb vector. Starting from the origin, *O*, the resultant, *R*, is drawn to the point, *P*, where these two dotted lines intersect. Using the same scale that was used to mark off the 7-lb and 5-lb vectors, the length of *R* can be read directly as 9.6 lb, and the angle it makes with either F_1 or F_2 can be read in degrees with a protractor. In other words, the length of *R* gives the magnitude of the resultant force, and the direction of *R* gives the direction of the force. As a vector equation, we write—

$$\vec{F_1} + \vec{F_2} = \vec{R}$$

This resultant force, if acting on the body, will produce exactly the same effect as, and is equivalent to, the two original forces. The construction of a few vector diagrams like these, but with larger and smaller angles between the two, will show that when the forces are in the same direction, $\theta = 0$, or in opposite directions, $\theta = 180°$, the resultant, *R*, is equal, respectively, to the arithmetical sum and difference. Thus, the magnitude of *R* may have any value from the arithmetic difference, 2 lb, up to the arithmetic sum, 12 lb, depending solely upon the relative directions of the two original forces.

The triangle method of vector addition, as shown in Fig. D, follows directly from

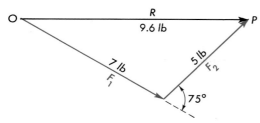

Fig. D. Illustrating the triangle method of vector addition.

the parallelogram method just described. Only half of the parallelogram need be drawn. For example, the 7-lb vector is first drawn to some scale. Second, the 5-lb vector is started at the arrowhead of the 7-lb vector and drawn in its true direction and to the same scale. The resultant is finally drawn starting at the origin O and ending at P, the second arrowhead. For convenience alone, this triangle method is to be preferred over the parallelogram method.

The trigonometric method of solution requires that the two forces first be resolved along perpendicular axes according to the methods of Lesson 10. Their components are then added. The final result is found by combining these added components.

Taking the x-axis to lie along the 7-lb vector (see Fig. E), the x-component of force is calculated—

$$F_x = F_1 + F_2 \cos \theta$$
$$= 7 + 5 \cos 75°$$
$$= 8.294 \text{ lb}$$

The y-component is just—

$$F_y = F_2 \sin \theta$$
$$= 5 \sin 75° = 4.830 \text{ lb}$$

The total force is found from the Pythagorean Theorem:

$$R = \sqrt{F_x^2 + F_y^2}$$
$$= 9.598 \text{ lb}$$

Conditions for Equilibrium. When one or more forces act upon a body at rest, and their resultant sum is not zero, the body will be set into motion. Under such conditions, there is an *unbalanced force* acting, and this force alone accounts for the acceleration. If, however, the vector sum of all the forces acting is zero, the body is in equilibrium and the body will remain at rest.

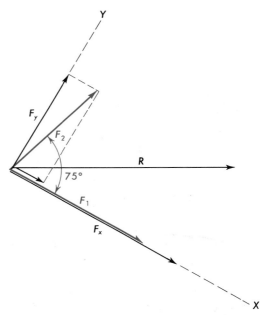

Fig. E. Illustrating the trigonometric method of vector addition.

Whether a body is at rest or in motion, the state of that body depends upon the forces acting on it and not upon the forces it exerts on something else. So far as the body is concerned, the latter do not determine its motion.

The condition for equilibrium may be reworded as follows: *Any object remaining at rest is in equilibrium, and the resultant of all forces acting upon it is zero.*

If two, and only two, forces act upon a body in equilibrium, a little study will show that they must be equal in magnitude and opposite in direction. A book lying on the

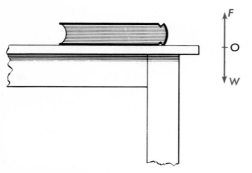

Fig. F. A book lying on a table is in equilibrium.

table or a lamp hanging from the ceiling are good examples of dual forces in equilibrium. See Figs. F and G.

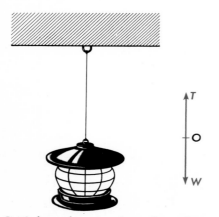

Fig. G. A lamp hanging from the ceiling is in equilibrium.

The two forces acting on the book are W, the downward pull of the earth, called the *weight*, and F, the upward thrust of the table. Because the book is in equilibrium, the force, F, is equal in magnitude to the weight, W:

$$\vec{F} + \vec{W} = 0$$

For the lamp, the downward force, or weight, is counterbalanced by the upward tension in the cord:

$$\vec{T} + \vec{W} = 0$$

Here again, the forces are equal in magnitude and opposite in direction. A body moving with constant velocity is in equilibrium; because there is no acceleration, there is no unbalanced force.

Concurrent and Coplanar Forces. Concurrent forces are those forces whose lines of action intersect at a common point, while the term "coplanar" specifies that they all lie in the same plane. Most common force problems, but by no means all of them, are of this type.

Three Forces in Equilibrium. Consider three concurrent, coplanar, forces acting on a single body. If we make vector diagrams for these three forces, they should be drawn to scale as shown in Fig. H. If the forces are

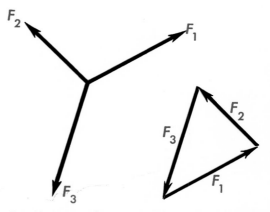

Fig. H. Vector diagrams of three forces in equilibrium.

in equilibrium, their vector sum, as shown in Fig. H, will form a closed triangle with a zero resultant.

Starting now with the left-hand diagram, apply the parallelogram method of vector addition to F_1 and F_2 alone, and find their resultant. As shown in Fig. I, this vector resultant, R, is equal in magnitude but opposite in direction to F_3. This must be true, because R is equivalent to $\overrightarrow{F_1} + \overrightarrow{F_2}$ and can replace them. With R and F_3 acting on

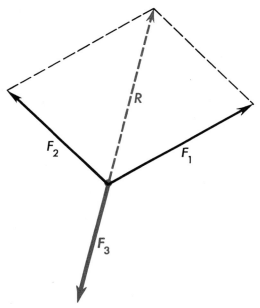

Fig. I. The resultant force R is equal to and opposite the equilibrant force F_3.

a body alone, these two forces could only produce equilibrium if they are equal and opposite. R is therefore called a *resultant*, and F_3 can be thought of as the *equilibrant*.

By making similar diagrams, it can be shown that the resultant of $\overrightarrow{F_2} + \overrightarrow{F_3}$, when reversed in direction to become the equilibrant of these two forces, is just the remaining force F_1.

As an illustration, consider a street light of 50 lb suspended from two points as shown in Fig. J.

The three forces acting through the common point O are W, the weight of the lamp, 50 lb acting straight downward; F_1, the pull

of one rope at 45° up and to the left; and F_2, the pull of the other rope at 30° up and to the right. The force diagram is shown to the right of the lamp.

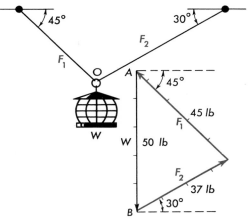

Fig. J. Three forces produce equilibrium if their vector sum is zero.

The force W is first drawn downward and 50 units long to represent 50 lb. The force F_2 is added up to the right and at 30° with the horizontal. The force F_1 is drawn in, starting at A at 45° with the horizontal.

Where F_1 and F_2 intersect, the vectors are terminated, and the arrowhead drawn as indicated. When the lengths of the two lines are measured, F_2 has a length of 37 units, representing 37 lb, and F_1 has a length of 45 units, representing 45 lb. As vectors—

$$\overrightarrow{W} + \overrightarrow{F_2} + \overrightarrow{F_1} = 0$$

Four or More Forces in Equilibrium. Any number of concurrent forces may be added by the graphical method described. The method would be to add each force, in turn, to the previous resultant. In equilibrium, the force vectors form a closed polygon, and need not be coplanar.

QUESTIONS

1. Briefly describe the process of vector addition as it applies to two forces making an angle of 90° with each other.
2. (a) What is the significance of a resultant force? (b) What does it represent by comparison with the original forces?
3. (a) Explain why, in the case of two forces, the resultant is always numerically equal to or smaller than the arithmetic sum of the components. (b) When is it equal to the sum?
4. (a) What is an equilibrant? (b) What is its magnitude and direction?
5. You are standing on a table. Assuming that the table is capable of holding you up, what forces must be balanced in order for you to keep your equilibrium?
6. If two forces act upon a body, what are the conditions for equilibrium?
7. If three forces act upon a body, what are the conditions for equilibrium?
8. If five forces act on a body, what are the conditions of equilibrium?
9. Are the two equal but opposite forces in Fig. F an action-reaction pair described by Newton's Third Law? Explain.
10. If two forces act upon a body and it is not in equilibrium, what single force can be applied to bring it into a state of equilibrium? Explain.
11. (a) Sketch an example illustrating three concurrent but noncoplanar forces acting on a body. (b) Illustrate three coplanar but not concurrent forces.
12. Can you think of any examples of where the principles developed in this lesson are involved in the world around us?

PROBLEMS

1. Make a scale diagram of the vector addition of two forces of 3 lb and 4 lb applied at right angles to each other. Find the resultant force (a) graphically and (b) by calculation.
2. A 60-lb force and an 80-lb force act to move a boulder. Make sketches showing these forces acting at (a) 0°, (b) 90°, and (c) 180° with each other. Calculate the resultant in the three cases.
3. Two forces of 60 newtons each make an angle of 50° with the other. Find by graphical construction (a) their resultant and (b) a third force that will produce equilibrium.
4. Two forces of 5 lb and 7 lb act on the same body. If the angle between them is 120°, calculate the magnitude of the resultant.
5. A canal boat is being pulled by two ropes making an angle of 45° with each other. If the forces are 150 lb and 175 lb, respectively, what is the magnitude of the resultant force?
6. Use trigonometry to solve for the angle between F_1 and R in Fig. E.
7. Two horses exert a force of 100 lb and 75 lb, on a plow. The angle between

them is 40°. Make a sketch, and use trigonometry to find the net force on the plow.

8. Three coplanar forces, applied from the north, east, and south, respectively, are applied to a body. If all forces are 80 lb, what is the magnitude and direction of the resultant?

9. Show how three noncoplanar forces can make a 90° angle with each other. If each force is 10 newtons, what is the resultant?

10. Three forces act on an object, but do not move it. If the magnitudes of the three forces are equal, what are the angles between them?

PROJECT

Put nails in the corners of a rectangular piece of wood. Place three spring balances tied together so they all exert forces on each other. Measure the direction and magnitudes of each. Add any two of the forces vectorially, and check with the third force.

MECHANICS

Lesson 17 *RESOLUTION OF FORCES*

Resolution of a Force into Components. Many of the force problems in mechanics are most easily solved by the so-called *method of components*. To apply this method to typical problems, it is necessary that we first review how a single vector may be resolved into two components. Consider, for example, the known force F, making an angle of θ degrees with the x-axis, as shown in Fig. A.

By dropping lines from A, perpendicular to the x- and y-axes, the component forces F_x and F_y are obtained. These two components are equivalent to the original force, F, because when added vectorially, they give F as a resultant.

With F_x and F_y perpendicular to each

other, triangles OAB and AOC are congruent right triangles with corresponding sides equal: $F_y = BA$ and $F_x = CA$.

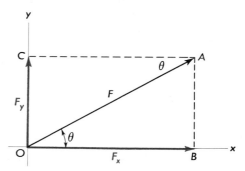

Fig. A. Illustrating the resolution of a vector into two rectangular components.

By trigonometry, then—

$$\frac{F_y}{F} = \sin \theta$$

$$\frac{F_x}{F} = \cos \theta \qquad (1)$$

$$\frac{F_y}{F_x} = \tan \theta$$

Because F and θ are usually the known quantities, the first two equations are the

The vertical component of force F_y can also be calculated.

Example 2. A force of 50 lb is applied to the handle of a 150-lb lawn roller. See Fig. C. Calculate (a) the horizontal and vertical components of this force, if the handle makes an angle of 40° with the horizontal and (b) the force exerted by the roller on the ground.

Solution. The graphical solution to (a) is shown at the lower right in Fig. C. The magni-

Fig. B. Illustration of force components.

most useful in finding the magnitudes of force components. These become—

$$\begin{aligned} F_y &= F \sin \theta \\ F_x &= F \cos \theta \end{aligned} \qquad (2)$$

Example 1. A force of 750 lb is applied at an angle of 30° with the horizontal to pull a heavy truck across a plowed field. What is the effective horizontal force?

Solution. As shown in Fig. B, the applied force F of 750 lb can be resolved into two components, F_x and F_y. To find the magnitude of F_x, we use Eq. (2) and substitute the known quantities directly:

$$F_x = 750 \text{ lb} \times \cos 30°$$

Looking up the cosine of 30° in the Appendix I, we find—

$$\cos 30° = 0.866$$

Upon substitution in the above equation, we obtain—

$$\begin{aligned} F_x &= 750 \text{ lb} \times 0.866 \\ F_x &= 649 \text{ lb} \end{aligned}$$

tudes of the two components, F_x and F_y, are calculated by direct substitutions in Eq. (1):

$$F_x = 50 \text{ lb} \times \cos 40°$$
$$F_y = 50 \text{ lb} \times \sin 40°$$

From tables of sines and cosines, substitution gives—

$$F_x = 50 \times 0.766 = 38.3 \text{ lb}$$
$$F_y = 50 \times 0.643 = 32.1 \text{ lb}$$

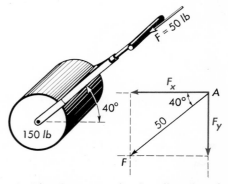

Fig. C. The force on the handle of a lawn roller is resolved into two components.

The horizontal component, $F_x = 38.3$ lb, is the force causing the roller to move, while the vertical component, $F_y = 32.1$ lb, acting straight downward must be added to the weight of the roller to find the total force exerted by the roller on the ground:

$$\text{total downward force} = 150 + 32.1$$
$$= 182.1 \text{ lb}$$

Consider the following example of the resolution of a force into two rectangular components. A boy is pulling a small 40-lb wagon up a 50 percent grade as illustrated in Fig. D. A 50 percent grade means that for

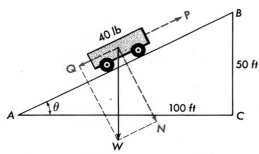

Fig. D. A wagon on an inclined plane.

every 100 ft traveled in the horizontal direction there is a vertical rise of 50 ft. (This is not equivalent to an angle of 50°.) The angle may easily be determined using the relation—

$$\tan \theta = \frac{50 \text{ ft}}{100 \text{ ft}}$$
$$= 0.50$$

from which we find—

$$\theta = 26.6°$$

To find how hard the boy must pull on the wagon, the weight of the wagon, W, is resolved into two components, one parallel to the incline and the other perpendicular to it. As shown in Fig. E, the 40-lb vector, W, is first drawn vertically downward. Dotted

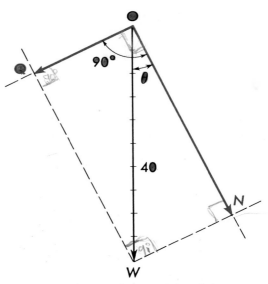

Fig. E. Resolution of the weight of the wagon into two components.

lines are next drawn, one parallel and the other perpendicular to the incline, from both ends of W. Where these lines intersect at Q and N, the vector components Q and N are terminated. The magnitudes of these two components are found from Eq. (2):

$$Q = W \sin \theta$$
$$= 40 \times 0.447$$
$$= 17.9 \text{ lb}$$
$$N = W \cos \theta$$
$$= 40 \times 0.894$$
$$= 35.8 \text{ lb}$$

The force N is the force the wheels of the wagon exert against the incline and, being perpendicular to it, neither aids nor hinders the motion. To pull the wagon, the boy must exert a force, P, equal to or greater than 17.9 lb, the magnitude of the component Q down the incline.

An experiment may be set up to measure the force components of an object on an inclined plane. A toy automobile, for example, whose mass has been determined by weighing, is supported on an inclined board by a single cord passing over a pulley, B, to a weight as shown in Fig. F. With the incline angle, θ, set at some value, the right-hand

one parallel and the other perpendicular to the boat, the force, B, responsible for the boat's motion, is found.

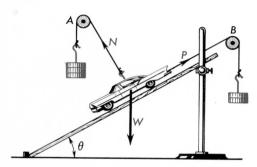

Fig. F. Experimental arrangement for measuring force components on an inclined plane.

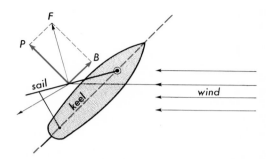

Fig. G. A boat sailing into the wind is an example of the resolution of a force F into two rectangular components, P and B.

weights are adjusted until the car accelerates neither up nor down the incline.

A second cord is now hooked to the top of the car and over a pulley to another set of hooked weights. These weights are changed until the wheels just barely lift from the incline, and the direction of N is at right angles to the surface of the board.

Under these conditions, the inclined plane can be removed if desired. In any case, one can measure the angle θ and the magnitudes of P and N.

The Sailboat. A problem that puzzles many people, particularly those more or less familiar with sailboats, is that of sailing across the water into the wind. This technique, commonly known as *tacking*, is another illustration of the resolution of a force into rectangular components.

As shown in Fig. G, the wind is from the east and the boat is headed NE. When the sail is properly set, the wind, in blowing across the canvas, is deflected away in such a way that it exerts a force, F, normal to the surface of the sail, as shown. By resolving this force into two rectangular components,

The other component, P, has little effect upon the boat, because it is perpendicular to the motion. It is a useless force, which tends to tip the boat and move it to leeward. To prevent tipping or being pushed sideways, sailboats are equipped with a deep, heavy keel. By increasing the angle between the sail and the wind, the force F will increase, but the forward component will decrease. If the boat is headed more directly into the wind, without changing the relative position of the sail, the useful component B will again decrease. Most rapid progress upwind is attained when the wind and keel make an angle of 45° and the rudder is parallel to the keel.

Constraints. The force on the cart in Fig. D must be resolved into two components as described, because those particular components affect the motion in different ways. The component parallel to the inclined surface produces acceleration, whereas the normal component cannot affect its motion. The surface is a constraint, a feature other than the applied forces that determines the motion.

In analyzing problems involving constraints, the forces and velocities must be resolved into components whose directions are determined by the constraints.

QUESTIONS

1. (a) Why does the resolution of a force into components help in solving a problem? (b) Under what circumstances wouldn't it help?
2. Can either of two components of a force be larger than the original force itself, if the components are at right angles to each other?
3. Imagine a car on the side of a hill with the brakes set. (a) Show how to resolve the weight of the car into two components, one parallel to the hillside and one perpendicular to it. (b) Why would we resolve the force into these components rather than some other components?
4. (a) Into how many different components can a force be resolved? (b) Which are usually the most useful?
5. A heavy picture is hung by two cords making a V between them. To minimize the tension of the cords, what angle should be used between the cords?
6. Explain why a clothesline can never be absolutely horizontal when clothes are on it.
7. If you wanted to push a lawnmower with the minimum of effort, what angle should there be between the handle and the lawn?
8. From an examination of Fig. G, can you explain why a sailboat requires a large keelboard for stability?
9. Two men, a short and a tall one, both rent the same lawn roller to prepare a seed bed. One comes back and complains that it was too difficult to push, while the other one is satisfied. Explain.
10. (a) Describe the constraints involved in Figs. B, C, F, and G. (b) In each case, what motion would occur if the constraints were suddenly removed?
11. Think of a situation in which it would be useful to resolve a force into components which are not at right angles to each other.

PROBLEMS

1. Compute the magnitudes of the x- and y-components of a force of 24 lb acting in a direction that forms an angle of 28° with the x-axis.
2. The car on a 30°-incline weighs 1.5 tons. Calculate the tension in the cable required to keep it moving with uniform speed up or down the incline.
3. A concrete bucket weighing 1500 lb is mounted on wheels and pulled up a 40 percent grade. Calculate the force required if the cable is parallel to the incline.
4. Two men are trying to lift a trunk. One is exerting 80 lb at 60° from the horizontal, and the other is exerting 90 lb at 50° from the horizontal. If the trunk is barely raised, how much does it weigh?

5. The men in the previous problem are on opposite sides of the trunk, so that the horizontal components are oppositely directed. What force is trying to move the trunk across the floor?

6. A force of 30 newtons is to be resolved into two components at right angles to each other. If one is to be 3 times the other, what are their magnitudes?

7. A long rope, making an angle of 30° with the horizontal, has the upper end tied to the top of a tree. (a) If the tension in the rope is 100 lb, what are the components of this force parallel and perpendicular to the ground? (b) Which component tends to pull the tree over?

8. A force of 50 lb is exerted on the handle of a 400-lb lawn roller. If the handle makes an angle of 30° with the horizontal, what is the total downward force on the ground?

9. One end of a rope is tied to a log and the other end to an elephant. If the rope makes an angle of 55° with the ground and a tension of 480 lb exists in the rope, what horizontal force is applied to drag the log?

10. A picture and frame weighing 5 lb are hung with a single cord to two nails spaced horizontally on a wall. Each angle formed by the parts of the cord is 30°. (a) What is the force trying to break the cord? (b) How much greater will the force be if the angle is increased to 60°?

11. A clothesline capable of holding 50 lb of force before it breaks is loaded at its center with a weight of 25 lb. Will the line break if the angle between the parts of the line is 170°?

12. A man who weighs 200 lb gets on a hammock. His weight causes the ropes holding the hammock to make an angle between them of 150°. Will the hammock hold him, if the rope is able to sustain a force of 300 lb?

13. A V-shaped trough was installed in which to roll metal balls from one end of a factory to another. The angle between the sides is 45°. What would be the total force tending to push the sides apart, in a 10-ft section, if there were 6 balls moving there, each weighing 10 lb?

14. A sailboat is sailing into the wind at an angle of 45°. What percent of the total force produced on the sail will be useful in driving the boat in the direction of its bow?

PROJECTS

1. Make an apparatus that would be adjustable and would show the forces on a truck as it attempted to climb hills with a variety of grades.

2. Make an apparatus that would show the forces of tension and compression on a sign supported at right angles to the side of a building.

MECHANICS

Lesson 18 *EQUILIBRIUM*

We have seen, in preceding lessons, how a body, acted upon by a number of forces, is in equilibrium if the vector sum of all the forces is zero. We have also seen how any force can be resolved into x- and y-components. We will begin this lesson by seeing how the conditions of equilibrium may be applied to the force components rather than to the forces themselves. To do this, we simply resolve each force into x- and y-components and then apply the conditions of equilibrium to each of the two sets of components separately.

Translational Equilibrium. In Fig. A we see three forces, F_1, F_2, and F_3, acting

$$\overrightarrow{F_1} + \overrightarrow{F_2} + \overrightarrow{F_3} = 0 \qquad (1)$$

Indeed, if there were four, five, six, or any number of forces acting on a body, and that body were in equilibrium, the vector sum of all the forces would have to be zero. In general, then, we can write—

$$\Sigma \overrightarrow{F} = 0 \qquad (2)$$

where the Greek Σ means *summation,* and $\Sigma \overrightarrow{F}$ means the *vector sum* of all the F's. This is referred to as the *first condition of equilibrium,* or the *condition of translational equilibrium.*

In Fig. B, the three forces of Fig. A have each been resolved into x- and y-compo-

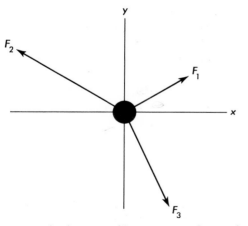

Fig. A. A body in equilibrium is acted upon by three forces.

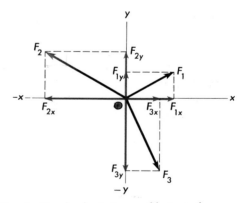

Fig. B. If a body is in equilibrium, the sum of all the x-components of force is zero and the sum of all the y-components is also zero.

on a body in equilibrium. If a vector diagram is made of these forces, we know that a complete triangle will be formed, and we can write—

nents. The x-components of all three forces are horizontal, while the y-components are all vertical. We now state that the sum of all the x-components is zero and the sum of all the y-components is zero. These two statements can be written as follows:

$$\Sigma F_x = 0 \qquad (3)$$

$$\Sigma F_y = 0 \qquad (4)$$

Notice that these statements need not be considered vector sums, but rather, arithmetic sums. That is, all the components of the same kind may be added in magnitude only. The x-components of F_1 and F_3 are to the right and are said to be *positive*, while the x-component of F_2 is to the left, and, therefore, is *negative*. In other words, to have a vector sum of zero, $F_{1x} + F_{3x}$ must be just equal and opposite to F_{2x}. Similarly, the sum of the upward components $F_{1y} + F_{2y}$ must be equal to the downward component, F_{3y}. We see, therefore, that for a body to be in equilibrium, Eqs. (3) and (4) must be satisfied. These equations, too, are referred to as the *first condition of equilibrium*.

Torque. When a single force acting on a body tends to produce rotation, it is said to exert a *torque*. *Torque is synonymous with* force-moment *and is defined as* the product of force times lever arm, the lever arm being the perpendicular distance from the pivot point to the force. In Fig. C, a body is shown acted upon by a torque. The

force, F, is applied at the point A, while the body is pivoted at the point P. The perpendicular distance, r, is equal to the line PQ, and the torque, L, is given by—

$$L = F_1 \times r \qquad (5)$$

If $F_1 = 5$ newtons, and $r = 3$ m—

$$L = \ \textbf{5 newtons} \times \textbf{3 meters}$$
$$L = \textbf{15 newton meters}$$

Rotational Equilibrium. Consider the rigid body in Fig. D, pivoted by a pin at the

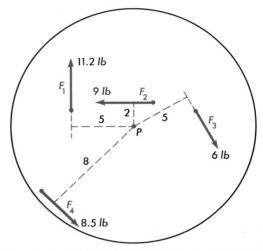

Fig. D. A rigid body in rotational equilibrium under the action of four torques.

point P and acted upon by four forces, F_1, F_2, F_3, and F_4. With lever arms of 5, 2, 5, and 8 ft, respectively, these four forces constitute torques L_1, L_2, L_3, and L_4. For this body to be in translational equilibrium, the summation of all the forces, or the sums of all their x- and y-components, must be zero. In other words, the first condition of equilibrium must be satisfied.

To be in rotational equilibrium, the summation of all the torques must be zero. This latter, the *second condition of equilibrium*, can be expressed symbolically as—

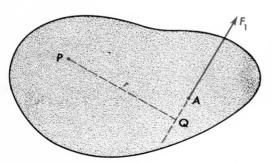

Fig. C. A single force acting on a rigid body that pivots at some point, *P*, exerts a torque $L = F_1 \times r$.

$$\Sigma L = 0 \qquad\qquad (6)$$

It is customary to assign a positive sign to all torques acting to turn a body counter-clockwise and a minus sign to all torques tending to turn it clockwise.

Let us now see how to apply the second condition of equilibrium to Fig. D. The first torque L_1 is given by the product of the force 11.2 lb and the lever arm distance 5 ft, or -56 lb ft. The minus sign indicates that the torque acts in a clockwise direction. If we calculate all four torques and list them, we obtain—

$$
\begin{aligned}
L_1 &= 11.2 \times 5 = -56 \text{ lb ft}\\
L_2 &= 9 \times 2 = +18 \text{ lb ft}\\
L_3 &= 6 \times 5 = -30 \text{ lb ft}\\
L_4 &= 8.5 \times 8 = +68 \text{ lb ft}\\
\hline
&\qquad\qquad\quad \Sigma L = 0
\end{aligned}
$$

The pin at P serves two purposes. First, it serves as a reference point from which to calculate torques. If the sum of the torques is zero about this point, however, it will be zero about any point. Second, the pin constrains the body not to move, in case the first condition of equilibrium is not satisfied. If the pin were removed in this example, the body might move, but it would still not rotate.

The sum of the clockwise torques $L_1 + L_3 = 86$ lb ft is just equal to the sum of the counterclockwise torques $L_2 + L_4$. Because the sum of all the torques is zero, rotational equilibrium is assured.

Demonstration Experiment. A rigid body is defined as one whose various parts do not change their relative positions when forces are applied at different points. Actually, no known bodies strictly satisfy this condition, but for practical purposes, most solid bodies may be regarded as rigid.

Because a rigid body may have any size or shape, a thin piece of one-quarter-inch plywood, cut in the shape of a dog as shown in Fig. E, will be used as a demonstration experiment. Two pulleys are mounted on a pegboard, and the rigid body is pivoted free to rotate on a fixed pin, P, near the center.

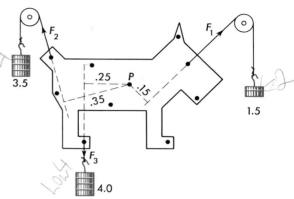

Fig. E. Demonstration experiment on rotational equilibrium.

Three cords and three sets of weights are now attached to any three of the several holes drilled through the body.

Whatever weights have been selected, the dog will turn to some equilibrium position. If the pin is now removed, the dog will move as a whole to some new equilibrium position; and such a position, for example, could be the one shown in the diagram.

While the body is in this equilibrium condition, imagine the pin inserted at P and fastened to the pegboard. Such a pin cannot exert forces or torques upon the body, but it may be thought of as a pivot. Next, we draw dotted lines on the dog, extending the lines of action of each of the three forces, until we can measure the lengths of the perpendicular lever arms. The lever arms shown in the diagram are in meters, and the masses are in kilograms.

Remembering that torque is given by Eq. (5) as force times lever arm, the three torques may be calculated as follows:

$$L_1 = 1.5 \times 9.8 \times 0.15$$
$$L_2 = 3.5 \times 9.8 \times 0.35$$
$$L_3 = 4.0 \times 9.8 \times 0.25$$

The products of the first two numbers give, in each case, the three forces in newtons. These are multiplied by the three lever arms at the right. Multiplying out and assigning a minus sign to the clockwise torque L_2, we obtain—

$$L_1 = \quad +2.2 \text{ newton meters}$$
$$L_2 = \quad -12.0$$
$$\underline{L_3 = \quad +9.8}$$
$$\Sigma L = 0$$

Because the position of P was chosen at random, we are free to relocate the pivot P anywhere in the body. Upon measuring the lengths of the lever arms to the new pivot point and calculating torques, we again find the sum to be zero.

In the illustration just described, translational equilibrium conditions are also satisfied because the body is at rest. A vector diagram of the three forces, F_1, F_2, and F_3, would form a closed triangle. If this were not true, there would be a resultant force acting on the body, and it would move in the direction of that force with an acceleration given by Newton's Second Law of Motion. Hence, both the first and second conditions of equilibrium are satisfied.

QUESTIONS

1. (a) What are the conditions for translational equilibrium? (b) If a body moves with constant velocity, is it in translational equilibrium?
2. (a) What are the conditions for rotational equilibrium? (b) If a body rotates with constant angular velocity, is it in rotational equilibrium?
3. (a) Define torque. (b) Make a diagram to show three torques acting on a body. Assign forces and lever arms to each torque. (c) Write down the magnitude and direction of each torque.
4. When three forces act on a body that is in equilibrium, the vector diagram of the three forces is a closed triangle. What would be the result for five forces?
5. If an object is standing still, does this necessarily mean there are no forces acting on the object? Explain.
6. (a) How many lines can be drawn from a point to a line? (b) Which one of these lines is used as the lever arm? (c) Why?
7. A picture hangs from a nail in the wall, by a cord fastened to the two top corners of the frame. Make a diagram of the three forces acting on the picture frame.
8. Sketch a wheel. (a) Show two forces of equal magnitude applied so that there is rotational equilibrium, but no translational equilibrium; (b) translational equilibrium but no rotational equilibrium; (c) neither translational nor rotational equilibrium.
9. What examples can you think of in the world around us to which the principles developed in this lesson are applicable?

PROBLEMS

1. A force of 6 lb is applied to a rope that is wound around the rim of a wheel 30 in. in diameter. Calculate the applied torque if the wheel is free to rotate around the center.
2. A uniform timber 8 ft long is pivoted to turn freely about its center in a horizontal plane. A 50-lb load is placed on one end and a 20-lb load at the other. Find the resultant torque.
3. Suppose the lever arms in Fig. D were to remain unchanged, but the forces were altered as follows: $F_1 = 9$ lb, $F_2 = 4$ lb, and $F_3 = 7$ lb. To what value would F_4 have to be changed to maintain rotational equilibrium?
4. Suppose the lever arm of F_3 in Fig. D were reduced to 3 ft, and we altered the magnitude of F_4 to restore equilibrium. Find the magnitude of the new force F_4.
5. Two 10-newton forces are applied to the rim of a wheel. This results in translational equilibrium but a 3-newton-meter torque about the center. Sketch the wheel and the forces and indicate the radius of the wheel.
6. A 30-lb boy and a 60-lb boy are sitting on opposite sides of a 6-m seesaw. Neglecting the weight of the seesaw, where is the pivot point if the seesaw is balanced?
7. A sheet of metal 2 ft square is supported by a pivot at one corner. A 5-lb weight hangs from each of the two nearest corners. Make a diagram of this problem, and show the magnitudes of the three forces acting on the body, as well as the two torques. Neglect the weight of the metal.
8. A uniform wooden plank 12 ft long is pivoted to turn freely about its center. A boy weighing 100 lb is to sit on one end. Where should a boy weighing 150 lb be located to produce balance?

PROJECTS

1. Set up a simple lever with a movable fulcrum to show how the lengths of the lever arms determine the equilibrium of the system.
2. Make a model of a small bridge and arrange spring balances or other means to measure the forces involved in the equilibrium of the bridge. A scale model of an actual bridge would be even more interesting.

MECHANICS

Lesson 19 CENTER OF MASS AND CENTER OF GRAVITY

In the kinematics and dynamics of motion, one often neglects the size and shape of a body and speaks of the object as if it were located at a point. Of course, this is done for convenience only and is justified as long as one's interests are not centered on structural details. Under certain conditions, it is necessary to take into account the structural details and still make use of the simplest forms of Newton's laws of motion. How this is accomplished is the subject of this lesson.

Center of Mass. *The center of mass of any given body, or system of bodies, is a point such that if any plane is passed through it, the mass moments on one side of the plane are equal to the mass moments on the other.*

Consider, for example, two spheres of mass m_1 and m_2, as shown in Fig. A. The

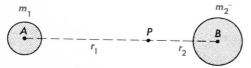

Fig. A. The center of mass of a two-body system is located at some point on a line joining the centers of mass of the two bodies.

center of mass, or *c of m*, P lies on a line connecting the centers of the two bodies and in a position such that—

$$m_1 \times r_1 = m_2 \times r_2 \qquad (1)$$

For a vertical plane through P, perpendicular to the plane of the page, $m_1 \times r_1$ is the mass moment of m_1, and $m_2 \times r_2$ is the

mass moment of m_2. The mass moment of a body about any chosen plane is given by the mass of the body multiplied by its perpendicular distance to the plane.

Example. Find the c of m of two bodies $m_1 = 2$ gm, and $m_2 = 5$ gm, placed 14 cm apart.

Solution. Because the distance $r_1 + r_2 = 14$ cm, we obtain—

$$r_2 = 14 - r_1$$

By substituting all known quantities in Eq. (1), we obtain—

$$2r_1 = 5(14 - r_1)$$

or—

$$2r_1 = 70 - 5r_1$$

giving—

$$7r_1 = 70$$

or—

$$r_1 = 10 \text{ cm}$$

By substituting this value of r_1 in Eq. (1), we find—

$$r_2 = 4 \text{ cm}$$

The c of m of a three-body system is found by an extension of the above principle. See Fig. B. To illustrate, two of the masses, for example, A and B, are first selected and their c of m found by use of Eq. (1). These two bodies are then treated as though they were one body located at P. With one mass $(m_1 + m_2)$ located at P and a second mass m_3 located at C, Eq. (1) is applied to find P', the resultant c of m. If a system consists of more than three bodies,

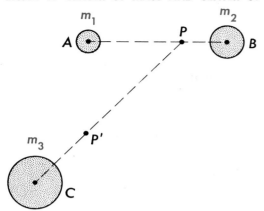

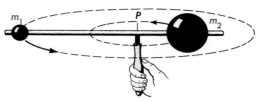

Fig. D. Illustrating the smooth rotation of two bodies around their center of mass.

Fig. B. The method for finding the center of mass of a three-body system.

the above process is continued until all masses have been included.

The c of m of all regularly shaped bodies, like those shown in Fig. C, is at their

ence an unbalanced force on his hand, tending to make the system wobble.

Should the two-body system be thrown spinning into the air, as shown in Fig. E, it will be observed to rotate about its c of m while the c of m traces out the smooth trajectory of a projectile.

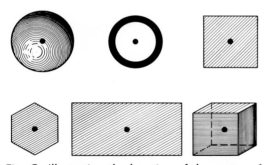

Fig. C. Illustrating the location of the center of mass of regularly shaped bodies.

geometrical center. A plane passed through the center of any of these figures will divide the body into two equal parts.

Rotation about the Center of Mass. In Fig. D, two masses m_1 and m_2 are shown supported at the ends of a thin rod and rotating smoothly around a pin through the c of m. If the pin is located at any other point, for example, half way between the two masses, the experimenter will experi-

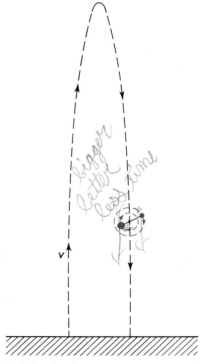

Fig. E. A body thrown spinning into the air rotates smoothly about its center of mass, while the center of mass traces out the smooth trajectory of a projectile.

The moon traverses its orbit once around the earth approximately every four weeks. Actually, the earth and the moon rotate around their common center of mass, a point on the line between their centers about 1000 mi below the earth's surface and about 3000 mi from its center.

Center of Gravity. The center of gravity or *c of g* of the two bodies in Fig. A is the one and only point about which the two bodies will, if pivoted, balance under the earth's gravitational pull. The downward pull of the earth on m_1 is given by m_1g and the downward pull on m_2 is given by m_2g. To be in rotational equilibrium—

$$m_1g \times r_1 = m_2g \times r_2 \qquad (2)$$

where each product $mg \times r$ is a force times a lever arm and is called a *force moment*, or *torque*. Eq. (2), then, states that the clockwise torque about the c of g always cancels the counterclockwise torque. Therefore, a single upward force applied at the c of g is equal in magnitude to the weight of the two bodies and will maintain equilibrium; the system will not tend to move in any direction, and it will not tend to rotate. The c of g is, therefore, a point at which all of the weight can be considered to be concentrated.

Because g in Eq. (2) is common to both sides, this relation becomes Eq. (1). For this reason the c of m is identical with the c of g.

The c of g of a regularly or irregularly shaped body of uniform or nonuniform density can be found by suspending it from one pivot point and then another, as shown in Fig. F. With each suspension from a point *P* near the periphery, the body will hang with its c of g directly under that point. Lines drawn along the string supporting the plumb bob for each suspension will all cross at the common point, the c of g.

If pivoted at this point and set turning, or thrown spinning into the air, the rotation will be smooth about the c of g. (*Note:* Because the force of gravity decreases with altitude, the c of g of a body is not always at exactly the same point as the c of m. The lower part of a mass, for example, is closer to the earth's center than the upper part, and, therefore, has a greater weight per unit mass. Therefore, the c of g of an extended

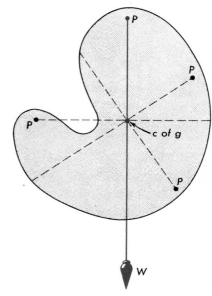

Fig. F. The center of gravity of any freely suspended object lies at or directly beneath the point of suspension.

body lies slightly below the c of m. For all practical purposes, however, the two terms, c of g and c of m, are considered synonymous.)

Notice that, in the preceding discussion, the c of m of a body is defined in terms of inertial properties, whereas the c of g is defined in terms of its gravitational properties. The equality of the inertial and gravitational properties of mass is called the *principle of equivalence.*

QUESTIONS

1. What is the distinction between the center of mass and the center of gravity?
2. How can one find the center of gravity of an irregularly shaped body?
3. If you have found the center of gravity of a body, how can you find the center of mass?
4. (a) Approximately where is the center of mass of the moon and earth as a system? (b) Of what significance is this center of mass?
5. (a) Does the center of mass always lie somewhere within the substance of which a body is composed? (b) Where is the center of mass of a uniform hoop?
6. An astronaut in a spacecraft is far from any planets or stars. (a) Could he determine the center of mass or the center of gravity of an irregularly shaped object? (b) If so, how?
7. (a) Where is the center of gravity of a sports car compared with a truck? (b) What effect does this have on the driving characteristics?
8. The distinction between c of m and c of g is almost never important. Can you, however, think of a hypothetical example in which the two points are significantly separated?
9. In what ways are the principles developed in this lesson involved in things we can observe in the world around us?

PROBLEMS

1. Two meteorites in free space have masses of 5 Kg and 9 Kg, respectively. Where is their center of mass if they are 8 meters apart?
2. Two bodies, 16 lb and 21 lb, respectively, are located 3 ft apart. Find their center of gravity.
3. A uniform bar 8 m long has a mass of 4 Kg. Find the center of mass if a 10-Kg mass is fastened to one end.
4. A uniform bar 6 ft long has a mass of 20 lb. Find the center of gravity if a 10-lb weight is fastened to one end and a 40-lb weight is fastened to the other.
5. A plywood board is 2 ft square and weighs 20 lb. A 5-lb weight is fastened to one corner. Find the center of gravity.
6. Two stones with masses of 2 Kg and 4 Kg are tied 60 cm apart at opposite ends of a wire and then thrown whirling into the air. About what point do these two rotate smoothly?
7. Five 2-Kg spheres are equally spaced around the periphery of a semicircle. If the diameter is 2 m and the two end spheres are diametrically opposite each other, find their center of mass.
8. A solid cube, 0.6 meters on a side, has a mass of 88 Kg. If a 22-Kg mass is fastened to one corner, find the center of mass.
9. A plastic sheet is 3 ft square and weighs 12 lb. If 2-lb weights are fastened to three of the four corners, where is the center of gravity?

PROJECTS

1. Make an apparatus similar to that shown in Fig. D, with adjustable weights, to show how rotation is influenced by the center of mass.
2. Make a number of irregularly shaped metal shapes such as is shown in Fig. F. Locate the center of gravity by balancing the object and drawing a line from a point of rotation to the center of the earth. The intersection of two of these lines will be the center of gravity. Try balancing the object at this point.

MECHANICS

Lesson 20 *EQUILIBRIUM OF RIGID BODIES*

We have seen how the entire weight of a body may be considered as concentrated at a single point called its *center of gravity.* In this lesson, we will apply this concept, along with the principles of equilibrium, to a specific problem. The methods by which this problem is solved are typical of many problems in mechanics and, therefore, are of fundamental importance.

Consider the case of a simple crane,

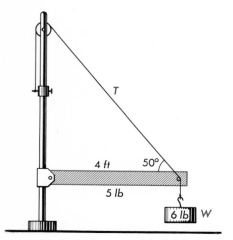

Fig. A. The crane problem.

composed of a uniform wooden timber and mounted as shown in Fig A. Because this arrangement lends itself to being set up in the laboratory as a demonstration experiment, we will assume that the boom has a length of 4 ft and a mass of 5 lb, that a load of 6 lb is supported at the end, and that the tie rope makes an angle of 50° with the horizontal.

We now propose to find the magnitudes and directions of all the forces acting on the boom. This is accomplished by applying the *first* and *second conditions of equilibrium.*

The first step in all such problems is to make a diagram of the rigid body itself and then to show all forces that must be acting on that body, whether their magnitudes and directions are known or not. Such an isolation diagram for the boom is shown in Fig. B.

Because the boom is uniform, its total weight of 5 lb can be assumed concentrated at the center of gravity, 2 ft from either end. The other known quantities are the direction of *T*, the load of 6 lb acting straight downward at the right, and the length of the boom, 4 ft.

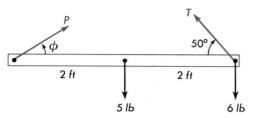

Fig. B. Isolation diagram of a crane boom showing all forces acting upon it.

The unknown quantities are three in number: (1) the magnitude of T, the tension in the rope, (2) the magnitude of P, and (3) the direction angle ϕ that P makes with the boom. The force P is the force exerted by the king post on the left end of the boom.

While there are several methods of attack on the problem, we will proceed to resolve T and P into x- and y-components, replace T and P by their respective components, and relabel the isolation diagram as shown in Fig. C. All forces are now hori-

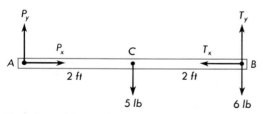

Fig. C. Isolation diagram of a crane boom showing all force components.

zontal or vertical and we can apply the first condition of equilibrium, as given in Lesson 18—

$$\Sigma F_x = 0 \tag{1}$$
$$\Sigma F_y = 0 \tag{2}$$

In the x-direction, there are but two forces, P_x to the right and T_x to the left. Taking forces to the right as positive and applying Eq. (1), we obtain for the vector sum—

$$P_x - T_x = 0$$

or—

$$P_x = T_x \tag{3}$$

This equation tells us that these two forces are equal in magnitude, but it does not give us their numerical value.

In the y-direction, there are four forces. Taking upward forces as positive and summing them up according to Eq. (2), we obtain—

$$P_y + T_y - 5 \text{ lb} - 6 \text{ lb} = 0$$

or—

$$P_y + T_y = 11 \text{ lb} \tag{4}$$

We next apply the second condition of equilibrium, as explained in Lesson 18:

$$\Sigma L = 0 \tag{5}$$

Because equilibrium exists, we can choose any pivot point about which to compute torques. If we select the point A, we observe that forces P_x, P_y, and T_x act in a direction through that point and have no lever arms. Having no torques about A, these forces are temporarily eliminated, and in summing up the remaining torques according to Eq. (5), we obtain—

$$T_y \times 4 \text{ ft} - 6 \text{ lb} \times 4 \text{ ft} - 5 \text{ lb} \times 2 \text{ ft} = 0$$

or—

$$4T_y \text{ ft} = 34 \text{ lb ft}$$

from which—

$$T_y = 8.5 \text{ lb} \tag{6}$$

If, in a similar way, we select B as a pivot, the forces T_y, T_x, and P_x, and 6 lb have no lever arms; and applying Eq. (5), we obtain—

$$5 \text{ lb} \times 2 \text{ ft} - P_y \times 4 \text{ ft} = 0$$

or—

$$10 \text{ lb ft} = 4 P_y \text{ ft}$$

from which—

$$P_y = 2.5 \text{ lb} \tag{7}$$

To find the magnitude of T_x, we now reconstruct a resolution diagram for the original force T as shown in Fig. D. Because

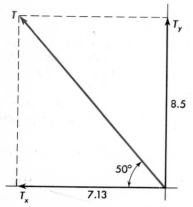

Fig. D. Force components of the tie-rope tension, T.

we know $T_y = 8.5$ lb and the angle is $50°$, we can write for the lower right triangle—

$$\frac{8.5 \text{ lb}}{T_x} = \tan 50°$$

or—

$$T_x = \frac{8.5 \text{ lb}}{\tan 50°} \qquad (8)$$

Upon looking up $\tan 50°$ in the tables, we find 1.192, and Eq. (8) becomes—

$$T_x = \frac{8.5 \text{ lb}}{1.192} = 7.13 \text{ lb}$$

From Eq. (3), we know that—

$$P_x = 7.13 \text{ lb}$$

We have now found all force components, and they are the following:

$$P_x = 7.13 \text{ lb}$$
$$P_y = 2.5 \ \text{ lb}$$
$$T_x = 7.13 \text{ lb}$$
$$T_y = 8.5 \ \text{ lb}$$

Observe from these answers that half the weight of the boom, 2.5 lb, is carried by P_y, and the other half by T_y, where the 6-lb load and the 2.5 lb of the boom make 8.5 lb.

To find the original force, T, we apply the Pythagorean Theorem for right triangles and write—

$$T^2 = (7.13)^2 + (8.5)^2$$

from which—

$$T = 11.1 \text{ lb}$$

We finally draw a component diagram for P, as shown in Fig. E, and again apply

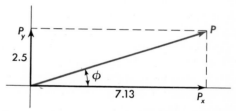

Fig. E. Force components of the force P.

the Pythagorean Theorem to the lower right triangle:

$$P^2 = (7.13)^2 + (2.5)^2$$

from which—

$$P = 7.56 \text{ lb}$$

To find the angle ϕ, we write—

$$\tan \phi = \frac{2.5}{7.13}$$

We divide and, upon looking up the value in the tables, we find—

$$\phi = 19°$$

All unknowns in this problem have now been determined. The forces and their directions have been computed from basic principles in mechanics, and the results are consistent with reason.

QUESTIONS

1. What two conditions must exist in order for a rigid body to be in equilibrium?
2. Explain why it is safer to climb a ladder that is closer to the wall than one whose base is at some distance from the wall.
3. Show in a diagram how two forces, equal in magnitude, may be applied to a body so that there is (a) a net torque but no net force, (b) a net force but no net torque, (c) a net force and a net torque, (d) neither net force nor net torque.
4. A construction worker is standing on the end of an I-beam, which is being lifted by a cable attached near its center. Make a diagram illustrating the situation. Also make an isolation diagram showing all forces acting.
5. Make a diagram of a simple crane with the boom in a horizontal position. Show a load, W, supported at the far end and the tie rope making an angle of 60° with the horizontal.
6. Make a diagram of a simple crane with the boom making an angle of 30° with the horizontal and the tie rope making an angle of 60° with the horizontal. Show a load, W, supported at the far end.
7. (a) Make an isolation diagram for the boom in Question 5 and show all forces acting. (b) Make a second diagram showing all forces resolved into components.
8. Make an isolation diagram for the boom in Question 6 and show all forces acting. (b) Make a second diagram showing all forces resolved into components.
9. (a) Make a diagram of a uniform ladder leaning against a smooth wall. (b) Make an isolation diagram showing all forces. Assume that the force on the upper end is perpendicular to the wall. weight in kilograms not measured in kilograms

PROBLEMS

1. A uniform rod, 2 m long and weighing 15 Kg, is suspended by a single rope. A weight of 5 Kg is suspended 0.2 m from one end. Where must the rope be attached to assure equilibrium of the rod?
2. A uniform rod, 16 ft long and weighing 40 lb, is supported on a fulcrum, with weights of 35 lb and 45 lb suspended on its ends. Where must the fulcrum be to produce equilibrium?
3. A uniform ladder, 18 ft long and weighing 120 lb, is supported by two men, one 2 ft from one end and the other 4 ft from the other end. How much weight does each man carry?
4. A wheelbarrow that weighs 70 lb has its center of gravity 2 ft from the wheel axis. The handles are 5 ft long, measured from the wheel axis. How much of the weight of the wheelbarrow does each arm support?
5. A boy is chinning himself at home on a clothes bar that is 6 ft long. He weighs 180 lb. At first his hands are holding the bar at 3 and 4 ft from one end, and all goes well. He shifts his hands to 1 and 2 ft from one end to make room for

his friend, but before his friend can join him, the support breaks. Solve the problem to explain exactly why this happened.

6. The uniform boom of a crane has a length of 10 ft and weighs 50 lb. The tie rope makes an angle of 60° with the horizontal boom, and a load of 100 lb is supported at the end. See Fig. A. Find all forces acting on the boom.

7. A uniform pole, 8 ft long and weighing 80 lb, is used as the boom of a simple crane. A load of 200 lb is applied at the end. Find all the forces acting on the horizontal boom if the tie rope makes an angle of 40° with the horizontal. See Fig. A.

8. A uniform ladder, 10 ft long and weighing 100 lb, leans against a smooth wall and makes an angle of 60° with the horizontal. Find all forces on the ladder. Assume that the force of the wall on the top end of the ladder is horizontal.

9. The uniform boom of a crane has a length of 20 ft and weighs 350 lb. The boom makes an angle of 30° with the horizontal and supports a 600-lb load at the far end. Find the tension in the tie rope if it makes an angle of 60° with the horizontal.

PROJECT

Make a small and inexpensive crane for measuring the various forces acting on the boom that were calculated in this lesson.

MECHANICS

Lesson 21 *LEVERS*

The great philosopher Archimedes* once said, "Give me a place to stand, and I will move the earth." In making this boast Archimedes was undoubtedly referring to the principle of the lever. It must have been common knowledge at the time of Archi-

* Archimedes (287-212 B.C.), Greek mathematician and inventor, was born at Syracuse in Sicily. He was the son of Pheidias, an astronomer, and was on intimate terms with, if not a relative of, Hiero, King of Syracuse. Archimedes is said to have set one end of a lever to a ship that was just ready to be launched and King Hiero himself, upon pushing lightly upon the other end, moved the ship into the water.

At another time, King Hiero, suspecting that his goldsmith had not made his crown of pure gold, as instructed, gave Archimedes the task of learning the truth without harming the crown. Just when he felt he would have to tell the king it couldn't be done, Archimedes stepped into the bath and

noticed how the water ran over the edge. Springing from the bath he ran naked through the streets shouting "Eureka." To find the volume of the metal had stumped him, but now he knew that by submerging the crown in a vessel previously filled with water, the volume of the overflow water would equal the volume of metal. Knowing the actual weight of the crown and its volume, he calculated the density and found it to be less than the density of pure gold. A confession from the goldsmith confirmed the king's suspicions and Archimedes' experimental observations.

medes that, when some heavy object had to be lifted or a huge stone had to be loosed from the ground, a long straight pole could be used to do it.

Levers. Three classes of levers are shown in Fig. A. In each illustration, P is the *ful-*

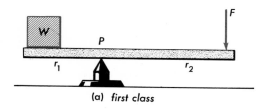

(a) *first class*

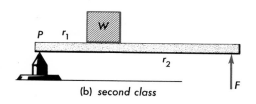

(b) *second class*

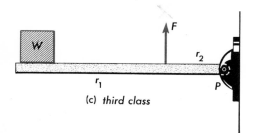

(c) *third class*

Fig. A. Illustrating three classes of levers commonly used for lifting heavy objects.

crum, or *axis,* about which the lever is made to pivot; W is the *weight,* or *load,* to be lifted; and F is the *applied force,* or *effort.* The distance r_1 is called the lever arm of the load, and the distance r_2 the lever arm of the applied force. As can be seen, the only difference between the levers is the relative

positions of the fulcrum, the load, and the effort.

The lever arm of any force is defined as the perpendicular distance between the force direction and the fulcrum. *The moment of a force is defined as the product of force times lever arm:*

$$\text{moment} = \text{force} \times \text{lever arm} \quad (1)$$

To operate a lever, a force, F, of a certain magnitude must be applied to maintain equilibrium or balance, and then the force must be increased ever so slightly to cause motion and lift the weight, W. To maintain equilibrium, the moments of both forces must counterbalance. In other words, the moment of the force tending to produce a clockwise rotation must equal the moment of the force tending to produce a counterclockwise rotation:

clockwise moment
$$= \textbf{counterclockwise moment}$$

For each of the three classes of levers in Fig. A—

$$W \times r_1 = F \times r_2 \quad (2)$$

These products, $W \times r_1$ and $F \times r_2$, called the force moments, are simply counterclockwise and clockwise torques, respectively, acting on the rigid body, the lever. Eq. (2) is simply another way of expressing the second condition of equilibrium, which was discussed in Lesson 18. For the lever in Fig. A(a), the force may be a second weight. In this case, we can express W and F of Eq. (2) as m_1g and m_2g, respectively:

$$m_1g \times r_1 = m_2g \times r_2$$

Because g is on both sides of the equation, we obtain—

$$m_1r_1 = m_2r_2 \quad (3)$$

These products, m_1r_1 and m_2r_2, are mass moments, and we recognize the relation as one locating the center of mass.

Example. How great a load can be lifted by a lever if the downward force applied is 150 lb? Assume the lever to be 10 ft long with the fulcrum 2 ft from the load.

Solution. Referring to Fig. A(a) and Eq. (2)—

$$W \times 2 = 150 \times 8$$

or—

$$W = \frac{150 \times 8}{2} = 600 \text{ lb}$$

Note that the closer W is to the fulcrum, P, the greater is the load that can be lifted by any given force, F. This is undoubtedly what Archimedes had in mind when he said, "Give me a place to stand, and I will move the earth."

Diagrams of three common devices are shown in Fig. B, which illustrates the different ways in which levers may be used.

The loaded shovel in Fig. B(c) shows a different location of the fulcrum, being located in the man's left hand.

Cog wheels in a machine, a crank shaft in an engine, and pulley wheels in a block and tackle are additional examples of levers.

Anatomical Mechanics. In preceding lessons we have seen that, to obtain a solution to many problems in mechanics, it is customary to neglect certain minor details such as the weight of a beam or the friction in a bearing, in order to simplify a problem and arrive at some approximate, yet practical, numerical answer.

Although complicated, the general principles of muscle function in animals, as well as in living human beings, may also be simplified in much the same way by neglecting certain minor parts. As a result of such simplification, the bones of the body and the

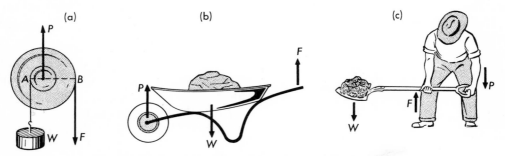

Fig. B. Illustrating devices employing the principles of levers.

In the wheel and axle of Fig. B(a), P is the fulcrum, AP is one lever arm and PB is the other. The weight, W, is lifted by one rope wound around the axle, while the smaller force, F, is applied to another rope wrapped around the wheel.

The wheelbarrow in Fig. B(b) rotates around the axle of the wheel, so its pivot is as shown at P. The heavily loaded barrow is lifted to a rolling position by applying a smaller force, F, at the handles.

muscles that move them form the compression and tension members, respectively, of mechanical systems already classified as levers. It is, therefore, interesting to see in what way some of the principles of mechanics may be found in, and applied to, the human anatomy.

Mechanics of the Lower Jaw. The *mandible*, or lower jawbone, is a large, strong, horseshoe-shaped bone, forming the lower third of the facial skeleton. See Fig. C. A pair of *condyles* at the ends fit into sockets, one on either side of the skull just in front of the auditory canal, and act as hinges about which the lower jaw pivots.

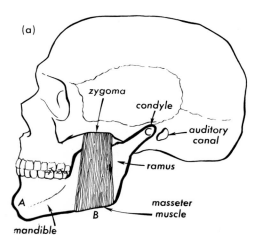

(a)

Fig. C. Diagram of the human skull.

The *masseter*, or "chewing muscle," is one of the strongest muscles in the body. As illustrated in the figure, it is located in the back part of the side of the face. Originating on the lower margin of the *zygoma*, the masseter passes downward to where it terminates on the lower edge of the *ramus* of the mandible.

The action of the two masseters, one on either side of the face, is such as to lift the lower jaw and, at the same time, draw it slightly forward. In principle, this is a lever action with a pivot at C, an upward force at B, and a load force at A, introduced when chewing takes place between the teeth of the upper and lower jaws.

A schematic diagram of the lever action is shown at the right in Fig. D, with selected values of the dimensions given in inches. When the lever is isolated as a rigid body, all of the acting forces, due to symmetry, are reduced to three, W, T, and P. To cal-

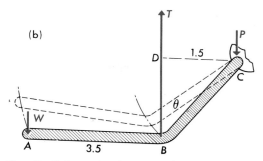

(b)

Fig. D. Schematic diagram showing the mechanics involved in chewing.

culate the magnitude of these forces, at least one of them must be known.

As a problem, assume that the lower jaw, in chewing with the front teeth, is able to exert a measured force of 20 lb. To calculate the tension, T, exerted by the two masseters, the point C is assumed as pivot and the torques are equated as follows:

$$W \times 5 \text{ in.} = T \times 1.5 \text{ in.}$$

Inserting $W = 20$ lb and solving for T—

$$T = \frac{20 \text{ lb} \times 5 \text{ in.}}{1.5 \text{ in.}} = 66.7 \text{ lb}$$

Equating downward forces to upward forces—

$$P + W = T$$

from which—

$$P = T - W = 66.7 - 20 = 46.7 \text{ lb}$$

Each masseter, therefore, exerts one half of 66.7 lb, or 33.3 lb, while the condyles each press against their sockets with a force of one-half of 46.7 lb, or 23.3 lb.

The Biceps. The above procedure of solution can be applied to the muscle problem involved in the flexion of the lower arm. In Fig. E, a skeleton of the forearm is shown in a horizontal position supporting a stone in the palm of the hand. With a pivot point at the elbow joint, the forearm and hand

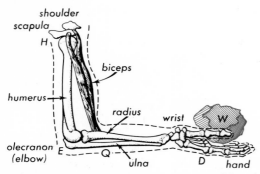

Fig. E. Skeleton diagram of the arm and hand showing the biceps used in lifting a load, W.

form a compression member, like the boom of a crane, while the *biceps*, assuming the duty of prime mover in any flexor movement, become the tension member.

The biceps originate on the *scapula*, or shoulder, from where they pass downward and forward to terminate on the *radius* near the elbow.

A schematic diagram of this force problem is shown in Fig. F: the vertical member, *EH*, represents the *humerus*. The horizontal member, *ED*, 14 in. in length, represents the forearm and hand; and the tension member, *T*, the biceps. Assume that a

weight of 10 lb is held in the hand, while the weight of the forearm and hand is taken to be 2 lb and applied at the center of mass 8 in. from the elbow.

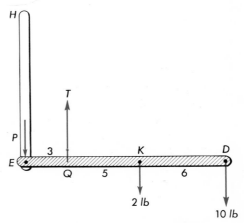

Fig. F. Mechanics of the forearm.

The problem to be solved resolves itself into one of calculating (a) the upward force, *T*, exerted by the biceps and (b) the downward force, *P*, exerted by the humerus on the elbow. The solution of this problem is left as an exercise for the student. See Problem 3.

QUESTIONS

1. What is a lever? Give an example.
2. Is a wheel and axle a lever? Explain.
3. (a) What is the fulcrum of a lever? (b) How is its position related to the load? (c) To the applied force?
4. Is the load lifted by a lever lighter, heavier, or equal to the applied force? Explain.
5. (a) Make a diagram of the lower jaw as a lever. (b) What muscles are involved in producing the primary force? (c) Where is the pivot?
6. (a) Make a diagram of the lever action involved with the forearm horizontal and the upper arm vertical. (b) With a weight in the palm of the hand, what large muscles are brought into play? (c) With the lower arm as a lever, where is the pivot?
7. Which is the larger of the two forces brought into action in chewing: the muscle tension or the pivot force?

8. With the forearm in the position shown in Fig. E, which force is the larger, the tension in the biceps, or the load lifted by the hand?

9. (a) What are the advantages of having the tendons attached as far from the joints as possible? (b) What are the disadvantages?

PROBLEMS

1. A pole 5 m long is used as a lever to lift a mass of 600 Kg. Where must the load be placed if the maximum upward applied force available is 750 newtons?

2. A plank 16 ft long is used as a lever to lift a 1200-lb load. Where must the pivot be located if the downward applied force is 130 lb?

3. Solve the problem as it is stated in the last paragraph of this lesson (see Fig. F.)

4. If the heaviest load a strong man can lift in his one hand in the median position shown in Fig. E is 25 Kg, what is the required tension in the biceps? Assume the distance $EQ = 6.0$ cm and the distance $ED = 38$ cm. Neglect the weight of the forearm.

5. A 10-lb weight is held as in Fig. E by an arm 16 in. long. If the arm weighs 3 lb and the biceps exert a tension of 75 lb, what is the distance from the elbow to the tendon termination?

6. A 12-Kg object is held by an arm 40 cm long. If a compression force of 600 newtons is exerted on the humerus, what is the distance from the elbow to the tendon termination?

7. A weight lifter found he could support 300 lb when his forearm made an angle of 90° with respect to his humerus. What weight could he lift if the angle were 45°?

8. In biting down to crack a nut with his front teeth, a man exerts a force of 22 lb. Calculate the tension in the masseter muscles if the mandible has the following dimensions (see Fig. D): $AB = 9$ cm, $BC = 6.6$ cm, and $\theta = 52°$.

9. If each masseter muscle of a man is capable of exerting a maximum force of 65 lb, calculate the maximum force he can exert at his front teeth if the mandible has the following dimensions (see Fig. D): $AB = 3.6$ in., $BC = 2.5$ in., and $\theta = 48°$.

PROJECTS

1. Make a working model of the human arm using Fig. E as a guide. Make measurements of the forces involved in the mechanics of the arm.

2. Make a working model of the human jaw using Fig. D as a guide. Make measurements of the forces involved in chewing.

MECHANICS

Lesson 22 *FRICTION*

Newton's Laws of Motion were introduced in earlier lessons with the provision that friction can be neglected. In this lesson, we will study sliding friction and see how Newton's Laws of Motion can be extended to include frictional forces.

The general statement can be made that wherever you see motion there is friction. All forms of friction may be classified as one of three kinds: *sliding friction, rolling friction,* and *fluid friction.*

Sliding and rolling friction are concerned with solids, while fluid friction is concerned with liquids and gases. Generally speaking, sliding friction is greater than fluid friction at low speeds, while the reverse is true at high speeds.

Sliding Friction. Whenever one body slides over another, frictional forces opposing the motion are developed between them. Such forces are due largely to the atomic and molecular attractive forces at the small *contact areas.* See Fig. A. Within

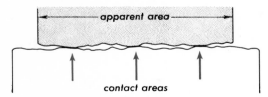

Fig. A. Illustrating the relatively small contact areas between two bodies having a much larger apparent contact area.

limits, the smoothness of the surfaces does not greatly affect *f,* the force of sliding friction. If the surfaces are smooth, there

will be many small areas in contact; while if they are rough, there may be fewer but larger ones. It is well known that surfaces of the same material in contact with one another show greater friction than do surfaces of different materials. This is one of the reasons why machine bearings are often made of one metal, like bronze, while their rotating shafts are made of another, like steel.

Experiments show that to start a body sliding often requires a greater force than that needed to keep it moving. In other words *static friction,* or *starting friction,* is greater than *kinetic friction.* Once a body is moving, however, the force of sliding friction increases only slightly with increasing speed and then remains nearly constant over a moderate range of speeds.

Recent experiments with metals in contact show that, when one surface is pressed against another and sliding is brought about, the enormous pressures existing at the tiny contact areas cause a kind of welding together of the two materials. With all materials, in general, the atoms and molecules are so close together at the contact areas that strong mutually attractive forces often pull microscopic bits of material from one body to the other as the parts move along. To start a body moving is to break these bonds instantly, while to keep it moving is to break them continuously and smoothly.

A quantitative treatment of sliding friction here is based on the result of a simple laboratory experiment illustrated in Fig. B. In diagram (*a*), a block of wood of mass

500 gm is shown being pulled with uniform speed across a table top by the tangential force of a 100-gm weight. The latter force has been determined by trying different

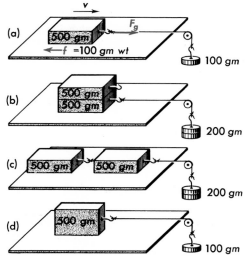

Fig. B. Sliding friction is proportional to the normal force pushing the surfaces together and independent of area of contact.

loads on the hook at the right. A load greater than 100 gm will accelerate the block, while a load smaller than 100 gm will not cause the block to move. Moving with constant speed, the applied force, F, is just counterbalanced by f, the force of sliding friction.

In diagram (b), a second block of mass 500 gm is added to make the sliding mass 1000 gm. By experiment, the force required to pull the two with constant velocity is now found to be a 200-gm weight. Should a third and then a fourth block be added successively, 300- and 400-gm weights, respectively, will be found necessary to pull them. In other words, the force of sliding friction, f, is directly proportional to the total downward force, N.

$$f \propto N \qquad (1)$$

When the two blocks in diagram (b) are connected in tandem, one behind the other as in diagram (c), the force of friction is still that of a 200-gm weight.

Again, if the single block in diagram (a) is turned on edge as in diagram (d), the force of a 100-gm weight is just enough to slide it with constant speed. These observations, along with the results of other similar experiments, may be explained largely in terms of molecular attractive forces. In general, the total contact area where molecular attraction is effective (see Fig. A) is small compared with the total apparent area. When a greater force is applied normal to the surfaces, the contact areas increase in size and number, and the following relation is found to hold reasonably true:

The force of sliding friction is proportional to the total normal (perpendicular) force and independent of the area of contact.

Introducing the Greek letter μ as a constant of proportionality, Eq. (1) becomes

$$f = \mu N \qquad (2)$$

μ is called the *coefficient of sliding friction,* and is defined as the ratio—

$$\mu = \frac{f}{N} \qquad (3)$$

By knowing the value of μ for a given pair of surfaces, one is able to calculate the force of friction, f, in terms of the normal force, N. Average values of μ for a number of surfaces are given in Table 1, page 122.

As an illustration of the general use of the coefficient of friction, consider the problem diagramed in Fig. C.

Example. What force is required to pull an iron box weighing 60 lb across a smooth oak floor?

Solution. From Table 1, μ for metals on oak is 0.55. The normal force, N, is the weight of

Table 1. Coefficients of Sliding Friction for a Few Common Materials (Average values for dry surfaces)

Material	μ
oak on oak......................	0.25
pine on pine.....................	0.35
maple on maple..................	0.28
wood on concrete................	0.55
smooth rubber on oak............	0.25
rubber on concrete..............	0.70
metals on oak...................	0.55
metals on elm...................	0.20
hemp on oak.....................	0.53
steel on steel..................	0.18
greased surfaces................	0.05
iron on concrete................	0.30
leather on metals...............	0.56
steel on babbit.................	0.14

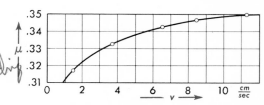

Fig. D. Experimental graph showing how the coefficient of sliding friction increases with speed, yet becomes nearly constant at relatively slow velocities.

Motion as $F = ma$, is therefore modified by friction and becomes—

$$F - f = ma \qquad (4)$$

resultant force = mass × acceleration

The Angle of Uniform Slip. If a block of a certain material is placed on a plane and the plane is slowly tilted, an angle will ultimately be reached at which the block slides down with constant velocity. See Fig. E. When this condition exists, Eq. (3) can

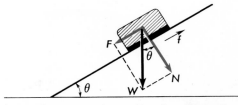

Fig. E. Illustrating the angle of uniform slip for a block on an inclined plane.

the box, or 60 lb. Substituting in Eq. (2), the force of friction is found to be

$$f = 0.55 \times 60 \text{ lb} = 33 \text{ lb}$$

The graph in Fig. D illustrates the general observation that sliding friction increases with speed only slightly at low speeds and levels off to become practically constant at higher speeds.

If the force, F, applied to a body is greater than that required to overcome friction, f, the resultant force, $(F - f)$, is effective in producing acceleration. The force equation, given by Newton's Second Law of

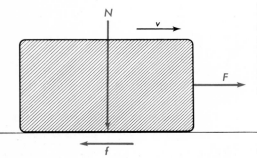

Fig. C. Sliding friction, f, is proportional to the normal force, N, pushing the surfaces together.

be imposed directly upon the components of the weight, W. The component F is equal in magnitude to f, the sliding friction, and the component N is the normal force pushing the two surfaces together. If θ is the angle of the incline, then—

$$\mu = \frac{f}{N}$$

or—

$$\mu = \frac{F}{N}$$

From the right triangle in Fig. E, it is clear that—

$$\frac{F}{N} = \tan \theta$$

Therefore, we can write—

$$\mu = \tan \theta \qquad (5)$$

where θ is the so-called *angle of uniform slip*.

An apparatus for measuring the angle of uniform slip may be made of a number of smooth, straight boards of different kinds of wood, and several smooth wooden blocks. Various materials, such as sheet rubber and metal, can be fastened or glued to the flat surfaces of some of the blocks and used in the experiment.

A board, such as walnut, is selected and tilted up against a support as shown in Fig. F. Any block is then placed on the

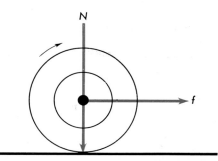

Fig. G. The coefficient of rolling friction depends upon *f* and *N*.

ing friction is defined in the same way as that of sliding and is given by the same formula, Eq. (3). For the illustration in Fig. G, f is the horizontal force pulling the wheel along, and N is the normal force pushing the wheel down against the road.

A comparison of the force required to slide a heavy box along the ground with the force required to move it on rollers shows that sliding friction is many times greater than rolling friction. It is for this reason that wheels are used on vehicles instead of runners and that ball bearings are employed in some machines in place of sleeve bearings.

A comparison of the sleeve-type bearing with a ball bearing is made in Fig. H. The rotating axle, as shown in (a), slides on the bottom of the sleeve at low speeds and climbs part way up the side as the speed increases. The purpose of lubricating such

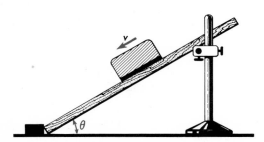

Fig. F. Apparatus for determining the coefficient of sliding friction.

board, and the angle θ increased or decreased until the block slides down with a slow but uniform speed. Although the sliding surfaces are not perfectly uniform, and the block will slow down and speed up, careful observation enables one to set the angle with considerable precision. The angle θ is then measured.

A shoe placed on any one board should give an interesting result.

Rolling Friction. The coefficient of roll-

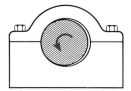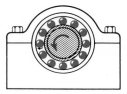

Fig. H. Sleeve bearing and ball bearings illustrate the two kinds of friction: (a) sliding friction and (b) rolling friction. (*Note:* the clearance in the sleeve bearing is exaggerated.)

bearings with oils and greases is to keep the two metal surfaces from coming into direct contact. Properly lubricated, the axle rides on a thin film of oil. In diagram (b), it may be seen how the axle rolls around on the balls with little or no possibility for sliding. The balls themselves roll in a groove called a "race."

The harder a rolling wheel or ball, and the harder the surface over which it rolls, the less is the force of rolling friction.

The same equations that hold for sliding friction also hold for rolling friction, the only difference being that the coefficients for rolling friction are exceedingly small:

$$f = \mu N \qquad (6)$$

Table 2. Coefficients of Rolling Friction

cast iron on rails...............	$\mu = 0.004$
rubber tires on concrete.........	$\mu = 0.030$
ball bearing on steel...........	$\mu = 0.002$

QUESTIONS

1. (a) How does the frictional force of an object depend upon its velocity? (b) On its contact area?
2. What do recent experiments indicate as to the principal cause of sliding friction?
3. A plane is inclined to an angle θ, at which time an object resting on it starts to slip. (a) How do you determine the coefficient of friction? (b) What kind of friction does this coefficient represent?
4. How would you use an inclined plane to measure the coefficient of sliding friction of an object?
5. How would you use an inclined plane to measure the coefficient of rolling friction of an object?
6. Would a bronze shaft in a bronze bearing have a low coefficient of friction? Explain.
7. If a body is given a certain velocity and then released, friction would slow it down and finally bring it to rest. How would you use the force of friction to calculate the negative acceleration?
8. (a) What everyday events can you think of in which the existence of friction is of great importance? (b) Where is friction a nuisance?
9. What are the general methods used to reduce friction where it is not wanted?
10. What common utility devices are designed to increase friction?
11. A boy on a sled is sliding down a hill at a constant velocity. If the boy gets off, will the sled accelerate, remain at the constant velocity, or slow down? Explain.
12. Explain what would happen to an ordinary frame house if all friction were suddenly to disappear.
13. Why does a hill that is stable when it is dry produce a slide when it has been saturated with a great deal of rain?

PROBLEMS

1. A horizontal force of 38 lb is required to pull a 120-lb trunk across the floor. Find the coefficient of sliding friction.
2. A driver, in bringing a car to a stop, skids all four tires. If the car weighs 3500 lb, what is the force of friction between the tires and the concrete pavement?
3. An oak box weighing 192 lb is pulled across an oak floor by a horizontal force of 56 lb. Find its accelerations. (*Note:* The mass must be in slugs.)
4. What horizontal force is required to pull a 2500-lb car with constant speed along a level concrete road?
5. A horizontal force of 36 lb is required to pull a 76-lb trunk across the floor. If 48 lb are added to the trunk, what force is required to pull it?
6. A boy exerts a horizontal force of 2 lb to pull his 20-lb sled over the snow. If a boy weighing 140 lb sits on the sled, what force must now be exerted?
7. A 20-lb wooden box falls from a truck traveling at 45 mi/hr (66 ft/sec). If the coefficient of sliding friction between wood and concrete is 0.55, how far will the box slide along the pavement in coming to a stop?
8. A force of 76 lb is exerted on a 200-lb box to move it across the floor. The force is applied at 45° above the horizontal. What is the coefficient of sliding friction?
9. What would be the angle of slip between two blocks of pine wood?
10. (a) What would be the angle of slip between two steel surfaces? (b) How many degree of change would occur if grease were applied to the two surfaces?
11. A steel axle was run in a babbit bearing lubricated with grease. (a) If this bearing were replaced with a ball bearing of steel, what would be the percentage change in the force required to turn this wheel? (b) Do you think this would be worthwhile?
12. A large steel drill press, which weighs 1500 lb, has to be dragged across a concrete floor. How many pounds force will be needed?

PROJECTS

1. Measure the coefficient of friction of an object by pulling on it with uniform force and by the method of uniform slip. Compare results. Which method do you consider more accurate? Why?
2. Devise an apparatus with which you could determine accurately the coefficient of friction and the effect of different lubricants.

MECHANICS

Lesson 23 *FLUID FRICTION*

Friction in a gas or liquid manifests itself when the fluid is made to flow around a stationary obstacle or an object is made to move through a previously stationary fluid. Such friction is involved in the propulsion of ships through the water, and of automobiles, trains, and airplanes through the air. In any discussion or treatment of fluid friction, it makes no difference whether the fluid is considered as moving and the object as standing still, or vice versa. It is only necessary to specify that there is a relative motion between the two.

Experiments show that, at relatively low speeds, the flow of fluid around an object is smooth and regular and that fluid friction, unlike sliding friction, is proportional to the velocity. See Fig. A(a).

$$f = Kv \qquad (1)$$

where K is a constant of proportionality.

The above equation holds only for *laminar flow*, that is, for the smooth flow that occurs at relatively low velocities.

If, initially, $v = 0$, frictional resistance to motion is zero, and an applied force is entirely effective in producing acceleration. As the speed increases, however, friction increases proportionally so that less and less force is available for acceleration. Newton's Second Law, applied to motion through a fluid, therefore takes the same form as Eq. (4) in Lesson 22:

$$F - Kv = ma \qquad (2)$$

where f has been given by Eq. (1) above. In this equation, v and a represent instantaneous values of speed and acceleration.

As the speed increases, a point is reached where *turbulence* sets in and the

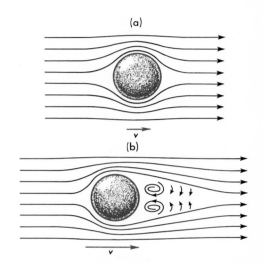

Fig. A. (a) Low-velocity fluid showing laminar flow. (b) High-velocity fluid showing turbulent flow.

force of friction increases rapidly and becomes proportional to the square of the velocity:

$$f \propto v^2$$

or, putting in a proportionality constant, T—

$$f = Tv^2 \qquad (3)$$

Turbulent flow is characterized by small eddy currents that form behind the object as shown in Fig. A(b). Not only does the fluid have to move out and around the obstacle quickly, but considerable energy is taken up by the eddies. This, of course, results in greater loss of energy and, therefore, greater friction. When the velocity is increased still further, the eddies, instead of forming symmetrical pairs, form alternately on one side and then the other, leaving a long trail of vortex motions such as those shown in Fig. B. These strings of

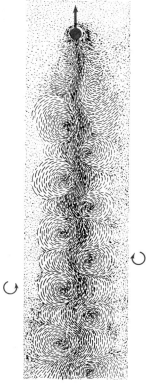

Fig. B. Eddies, set up by drawing an obstacle through still water, form a Kármán trail.

whirlwinds or whirlpools are commonly referred to as *Kármán trails*. The existence of such trails is illustrated by the flapping of the rope on a flagpole. The waving of the flag at the top of the pole is direct evidence of the whirlwinds that follow each other alternately along the sides.

As the velocity of a streamlined body

approaches the velocity of sound, friction again increases rapidly, becoming proportional to the cube of the velocity: $f \propto v^3$.

Terminal Velocity. It is well known that raindrops fall with a speed that depends upon their size and not upon the height from which they fall. Starting from rest, a particle falling in a gas or a liquid increases in velocity until the retarding force of friction becomes as great as the downward force of gravity. When this condition is reached, the body is in equilibrium and falls with a constant velocity called its *terminal velocity*.

The terminal velocity for small particles, like fog drops, is so low that the air stream around them is one of *laminar flow*. It was Stokes who first discovered that the terminal velocity of small particles is proportional to their weight. This relation is known as *Stokes' Law.**

For increasingly larger bodies terminal velocity increases, and turbulent flow sets in to eventually be the predominating part of frictional resistance.

If a parachutist delays the opening of his chute long enough, he will attain a terminal velocity of from 130 to 150 mi/hr. At such speeds, wind resistance pushes upward with a total force equal to his weight with the result that he is no longer accelerated.

Streamlining. By shaping a body to the streamlines of the fluid through which it is moving, the retarding force of friction may be greatly reduced. This is particularly effective at high velocities where the con-

* Sir George G. Stokes (1819-1903), British mathematician and physicist, is well known for his fundamental contribution to hydrodynamics, diffraction, double refraction, and the polarization of light. He received the Rumford Medal in 1852 and the Copley Medal in 1893, and was at one time president of the Royal Society.

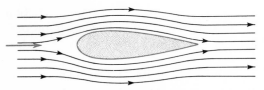

Fig. C. The flow of air around a properly shaped body may be smooth and steady.

ditions of turbulent flow would otherwise predominate.

Referring to Fig. A(b), it may be seen that, by adding a tail to an object, so that its cross section has the form shown in Fig. C, the tendency to form eddy currents can be reduced and the body made to slip

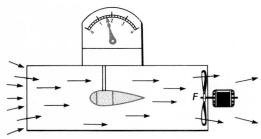

Fig. D. Diagram of a tunnel used for testing the air friction of an airfoil or streamlined body.

through the fluid with a minimum disturbance.

The experiment diagramed in Fig. D

shows that a long pointed tail and a rounded or pointed nose are both effective in cutting down resistance. The diagram pictures a small wind tunnel through which a stream of air is drawn by a fan, F. Objects for which wind resistance is to be measured are suspended from a support connected at the center to a spring balance.

The bodies of airplanes, torpedoes, and ships are streamlined to cut down resistance and, hence, permit higher speed with the same forward thrust of the propellers. Bombs are streamlined to enable them to acquire higher terminal velocities. Automobiles, if they are to travel at high speeds, should be streamlined to make more efficient use of gasoline.

Airplanes. The necessity for streamlining all outside structures of an airplane where high speeds must be maintained is quite clear. For land planes, *solid friction* is of importance only during take-off. Once a plane is in the air, friction is almost entirely due to turbulent flow and is approximately proportional to the square of the velocity.

In Fig. E, a streamlined plane is shown in a climb. Rising with constant velocity, the conditions of equilibrium exist, and all forces acting form a closed triangle. The

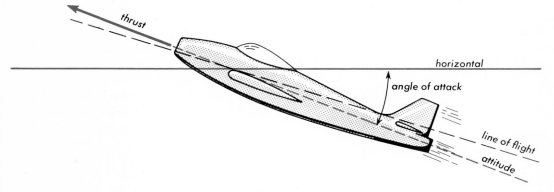

Fig. E. Diagram of a plane in a climb.

external forces acting on an airplane are three in number: they are *weight, thrust,* and *friction.* See Fig. F.

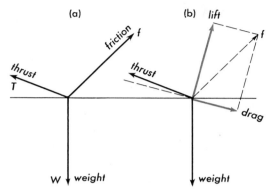

(a)   (b) lift

friction *f*

thrust
T

thrust

f

drag

W ↓ weight   ↓ weight

Fig. F. Force diagrams for an airplane, showing the origin of lift and drag.

The weight, W, may be assumed to act vertically downward through the center of gravity of the plane. The thrust, T, is the result of the reaction of the plane to the ejection of hot gas by the jet. The force acts in the direction of the jet-nozzle axis. The angle between this direction, the plane's *attitude,* and the horizontal is called the *angle of attack.* The friction, f, is the resultant force of air friction on the plane and acts in a direction upward and back as shown in Fig. F(a). Note that the line of flight, the path along which the plane is flying, is not quite the same as the plane's attitude.

It is customary to resolve the frictional force into two components: one, a useful component perpendicular to the line of flight and called *lift,* and the other a hindering component parallel to the line of flight and called the *drag.*

Supersonic Velocities. The rapid development of rockets and jet-propelled planes capable of acquiring and maintaining speeds greater than the velocity of sound

has increased the importance of studying high-speed air flow around bodies of different size and shape. The flow of air around missiles moving with *supersonic velocity,* that is, a velocity greater than the velocity of sound, is characterized by the existence in the air of discontinuities known as *shock waves.*

These sudden discontinuities are the result of sudden encounters of the air with an impenetrable body. At subsonic velocities, the fluid is forewarned and begins its outward flow in advance of the arrival of the leading edge. With supersonic velocity, however, the fluid in front of the missile is absolutely undisturbed, while immediately behind, it is moving sideways. The sudden impulse at the nose creates a high-pressure region which, traveling outward with the velocity of sound, creates the conical-shaped shock wave that changes the direction of air flow. See Fig. G.

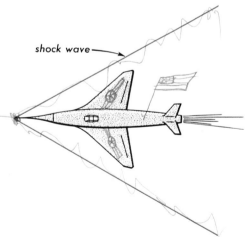

shock wave ——►

Fig. G. Shock wave produced by jet or rocket plane at supersonic velocity.

It is customary in supersonic studies to specify the velocity of a body relative to the velocity of sound in the immediate vicinity of the object. The ratio between these two velocities is called the *Mach number:*

$$\text{Mach number} = \frac{\textbf{velocity of body}}{\textbf{velocity of sound}}$$

The speed of sound in air at sea level is approximately 750 mi/hr. A missile of Mach number 2.0 is, therefore, moving with twice the speed of sound, or 1500 mi/hr.

QUESTIONS

1. (a) What is Stokes' Law regarding small particles? (b) Is the terminal velocity of a ping-pong ball greater or less than that of a fog drop? Explain.
2. Does a flapping flag represent laminar flow? Explain.
3. Is a body falling at terminal velocity forcing the fluid around it into laminar or turbulent flow? Explain.
4. What is meant by streamlining a body?
5. What are Karman trails?
6. Does the thrust of a jet plane result from the ejected gas pushing on the air? Explain.
7. Give an example in which fluid friction is useful.
8. (a) What is a shock wave? (b) What are the conditions necessary to produce a shock wave?
9. Why is the air "forewarned" by an object moving at a subsonic velocity, but not at a supersonic velocity?
10. Will it ever be possible to design supersonic planes that will not produce sonic booms? Explain.
11. An astronaut circles the earth at a supersonic speed. Why doesn't his vehicle create a continuous sonic boom?
12. You are asked to design a milk-delivery van. Would you have to think of streamlining your design? Explain.
13. What is the major reason that the consumption of fuel goes up so markedly as a car is made to travel at high speeds?

PROBLEMS

1. The frictional force due to turbulent flow around a certain automobile traveling at 20 mi/hr is found to be 45 lb. What is the frictional force when the car is making (a) 60 mi/hr and (b) 75 mi/hr?
2. The frictional force due to turbulent flow around a certain racing car traveling at 50 mi/hr is 65 lb. If the maximum force the car can exert is 500 lb, what is its top speed?
3. A boat moving at 20 knots requires a force of 150 lb to propel it. At 30 knots, it needs 225 lb. Is the water flow laminar or turbulent?
4. If the boat in the preceding problem needs 350 lb to propel it at 40 knots, what type of flow is involved?

5. A missile has a Mach number of 3.75. What is its speed in mi/hr?

6. The frictional force on a baseball, thrown with a speed of 50 ft/sec, is 0.15 lb. What will the force be when it is thrown at a speed of 110 ft/sec? Assume turbulent flow.

7. The frictional force on a golf ball traveling at 40 m/sec is 0.5 newton. What will be the speed when the force of friction is 2.5 newtons? Assume turbulent flow.

8. A tennis ball, with a mass of 0.05 Kg, has a terminal velocity of 30 m/sec when dropped from an airplane. What is the force of air friction at (a) terminal velocity and (b) at 10 m/sec? Assume turbulent flow.

9. Find the Mach number of a car traveling at 65 mi/hr.

10. What is the Mach number of a bullet traveling 200 ft/sec?

11. A paratrooper, with all his gear, weighs 230 lb when he jumps from a plane. If he delays opening his parachute and the force of friction becomes 30 lb when he is falling at 45 mi/hr, what will be his terminal velocity? Assume turbulent flow.

12. A car of a certain design when traveling at 50 mi/hr sets up considerable turbulence. How much greater will the force of friction be in this car if the speed is increased to 70 mi/hr?

PROJECTS

1. Set up a small wind tunnel where you could measure the air resistance of differently shaped objects and air foils.

2. Develop an apparatus that could be used to measure the terminal velocity of a number of differently shaped objects.

3. Look up and report on the use that was made by Millikan of Stokes' Law in determining the charge on the electron.

4. Make a simple and inexpensive device for demonstrating laminar flow and turbulent flow.

MECHANICS

Lesson 24 *WORK AND ENERGY*

There is little doubt that the most important concept in all nature is energy. It is important because it represents a fundamental entity common to all forms of matter in all parts of the known physical world. Closely associated with energy is another concept, *work,* a term used to describe the expenditure of one's stored up bodily energy. Because energy is most easily described in terms of work, this latter will first be treated in detail.

Work. In its simplest mechanical form, *work* is defined as *a force times the distance through which the force acts:*

$$\text{work} = \text{force} \times \text{distance}$$

Algebraically—

$$\text{work} = F \times \Delta s \qquad (1)$$

It is important to understand that, in the mechanical sense, unless the force produces motion, no work has been done. A student pushing with great force on an immovable desk accomplishes no work in this sense, although he may be very tired after his effort.

Consider the general problem of calculating the work done in lifting a mass, m, to a height, s, above the ground. See Fig. A.

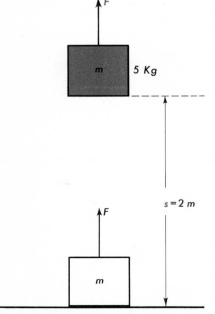

Fig. A. To raise a body vertically, work must be done against the pull due to gravity.

By Newton's Second Law of Motion, $F = ma$, the force required to lift any mass, m, is equal to its own weight:

$$W = mg$$

Substitute the weight mg for F in Eq. (1):

$$\text{work done} = mg \times \Delta s \qquad (2)$$

To give numerical values, assume that a mass of 5 Kg is lifted vertically a distance of 2 m. By direct substitution in Eq. (2)—

$$\text{work} = 5\,\text{Kg} \times 9.8\,\frac{\text{m}}{\text{sec}^2} \times 2\,\text{m} = 98\,\frac{\text{Kg m}^2}{\text{sec}^2}$$

Because *force*, in *newtons*, has the units Kg m/sec², the answer can also be written

$$\text{work done} = 98\ \text{newton meters} \qquad (3)$$

Work in the mks system is seen to have the absolute units *Kg m²/sec²*, which are equal to the derived units, *newton meters*. In the cgs system the corresponding absolute units are *gm cm²/sec²*, which are equal to the derived units, *dyne centimeters*.

In the English, or engineering, system, the units of work are *foot-pounds*, or *ft-lb*.

Example 1. Find the work done in lifting a weight of 5 lb to a height of 10 ft.

Solution. By substituting directly in Eq. (1) we obtain—

$$\text{work} = 5\,\text{lb} \times 10\,\text{ft} = 50\ \text{ft-lb}$$

Note that, because the weight of the object is given, rather than its mass, the force needed to lift it is directly given. If the mass of an object had been given as so many slugs, then its weight would have been found first by multiplying its mass by g.

Ergs and Joules. In the cgs system, the *dyne cm*, as a unit of work, is called the *erg:*

$$1\ \text{dyne cm} = 1\ \text{erg} \qquad (4)$$

A force of 1 dyne acting through a distance of 1 cm in the same direction does 1 erg of work.

In the mks system of units, a force of *1 newton* acting through a distance of *1 m* in the same direction performs an amount of work equivalent to *1 joule:*

$$\textbf{1 newton meter = 1 joule} \qquad (5)$$

Because the *newton*, as a unit of force, $= 1 \text{ Kg} \times 1 \text{ m/sec}^2 = 1000 \text{ gm} \times 100 \text{ cm/sec}^2 = 10^5$ dynes, the newton meter $= 10^5$ dynes $\times 100$ cm $= 10^7$ dyne cm. In other words—

$$\textbf{1 joule} = 10^7 \textbf{ ergs} \qquad (6)$$

The *joule*, as a unit of work is, therefore, much larger than the *erg* and, in many practical problems, is to be preferred because of the smaller numbers involved in calculations.

Example 2. Calculate the work done in lifting a mass of 4.0 Kg to a height of 2.5 m.

Solution. The known quantities are $m = 4.0$ Kg, $\Delta s = 2.5$ m, and $g = 9.8$ m/sec^2

By substitution in Eq. (2), we obtain—

$$\text{work} = 4.0 \text{ Kg} \times 9.8 \frac{\text{m}}{\text{sec}^2} \times 2.5 \text{ m}$$

$$\text{work} = 98 \text{ joules}$$

Work Done Against Friction. In sliding a mass of 5 Kg along a horizontal plane for a distance of 2 m, the work done *will not*, in general, be as great as that required to lift the same mass 2 m vertically.

As shown in Fig. B, the weight of a 1-Kg mass is large enough to overcome friction and slide the 5-Kg mass along the table. Direct substitution in Eq. (2) shows that the—

$$\textbf{work done = 1 Kg} \times 9.8 \frac{\textbf{m}}{\textbf{sec}^2} \times \textbf{2 m}$$

$$= \textbf{19.6} \frac{\textbf{Kg m}^2}{\textbf{sec}^2}$$

or—

19.6 newton meters (joules)

This is only one-fifth as much work as that required to lift the same 5-Kg mass an equal vertical distance of 2 m. See Eq. (3). By reducing the friction between the block and plane, the force, F, can be reduced still further. Such a reduction can be accomplished by smoothing and lubricating the sliding surfaces, or, better, by mounting the block on wheels. Were the friction to be eliminated entirely, the work done in moving any object in a horizontal direction would be practically zero, for, once started it would continue moving with constant velocity. A vertical lift, however, requires at least an amount of work equal to the weight, mg, times the height, s.

When a force, applied to an object, makes an angle with the direction of motion, only the component of the force in the direction of motion is effective in doing work. This is illustrated in Fig. C where a force, F, is applied to a heavy trunk to pull it across the floor. In the diagram, F is shown resolved into vertical and horizontal components, F_y and F_x. The upward force, F_y, has a lifting effect and helps to reduce friction, while the horizontal force, F_x, is the one that does the work. This force mul-

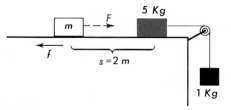

Fig. B. To slide a body along a level plane, work must be done against friction.

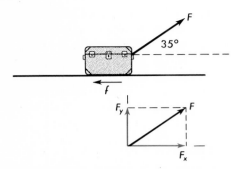

Fig. C. The force required to pull a heavy trunk across a floor is resolved into components.

tiplied by the horizontal distance moved is equal to the work done:

$$\textbf{work done} = F_x \times \Delta s$$

Potential Energy. Mechanical energy is divided into two categories, *potential energy* and *kinetic energy*. *A body is said to have potential energy if, by virtue of its position or state, it is able to do work.* Water at the top of a fall and a wound clock spring are examples of objects with potential energy. The clock spring may keep a clock running for a certain length of time, and the water may, by falling, turn a paddle wheel. Potential energy is measured by the

amount of work that is available. It is, therefore, measured in *ergs, joules,* or *foot-pounds.*

If a given mass, m, is raised to a specified height, s, as illustrated in Fig. D, it then has potential energy, $F \times \Delta s$, by virtue of its position above the ground level from which it has been lifted. The *work done* in lifting it has been stored up as potential energy in the block. This energy can be regained by dropping the mass back to the ground, for in so doing it can be made to perform some kind of work. By definition—

$$\textbf{potential energy} = F \times \Delta s \qquad (7)$$

or, in weight units, Eq. (2)—

$$\textbf{P.E.} = mg \times \Delta s \qquad (8)$$

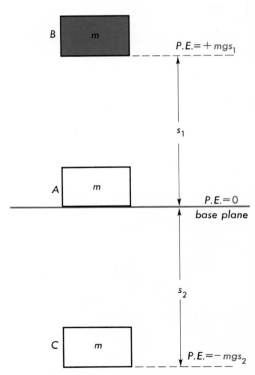

Fig. E. Potential energy with respect to a base plane may be plus or minus.

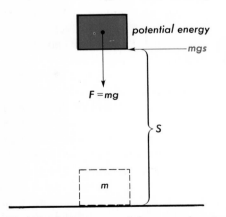

Fig. D. A body has potential energy by virtue of its position.

Example 3. A mass of 5 Kg is raised to a height of 2.5 m above the ground. Calculate its potential energy.

Solution. By substituting the known quantities in Eq. (7), we obtain—

$$P.E. = 5 \text{ Kg} \times 9.8 \frac{m}{sec^2} \times 2.5 \text{ m} = 122.5 \text{ joules}$$

If a body is lifted straight upward, carried up a staircase, or pulled up an inclined plane, the potential energy acquired is given by the *weight × vertical height* to which it is raised.

The meaning of *positive, zero,* or *negative potential energy* is illustrated in Fig. E. Located at any point above the *base plane*, a body has positive potential energy, while at points below that line, it has negative potential energy. In lifting the mass, m, from A to B, work is done and the mass acquires potential energy to the amount of mgs_1.

In returning from B to A, the mass loses potential energy, performing $work = mgs_1$ on some other body. Similarly, in going from A to C the body loses energy and ends up at C with, mgs_2, less energy than it had at A. To raise it again to A, an equivalent amount of work, mgs_2, will have to be done on the body.

The choosing of a *base plane* as a zero energy level is a purely arbitrary selection. In most practical applications, it is customary to select the lowest point to be reached by a body as the zero level so that all displacements from there will be positive in sign.

If we do not wish to refer to a particular base plane at all, Eq. (8) will refer to the change in potential energy:

$$\Delta P.E. = mg\Delta s \qquad (9)$$

In the engineering system of units, *potential energy*, like *work*, is expressed in *foot-pounds*, i.e., *pounds × vertical distance in feet*.

QUESTIONS

1. (a) When a force is applied to pull a trunk across a level floor, what is the work done? (b) Is the work done stored as potential energy? (c) If not, where is the energy?
2. Suppose a heavy box is raised to a platform by sliding it up a plank. (a) Is all of the work done stored as potential energy? (b) If not, explain why.
3. When a track star runs a mile in four minutes, has he done some work? Explain.
4. What is the difference between the concepts of work and energy?
5. A bowling ball is resting on the ground floor of a house, which has an attic and a basement. Does the ball have positive, negative, or zero potential energy? Explain?
6. A spring has zero potential energy when no forces are exerted on it. (a) Does it have positive or negative potential energy if it is stretched? (b) If it is compressed?
7. Equations (2) and (8) appear identical. Give an example that shows how they actually differ.
8. A block is moved across a rough floor, which has a coefficient of friction $\mu = 2$.

Is the work done in moving the block over a certain distance more than the work done in lifting it the same distance? Explain.

9. Could the work required to push an object ever be greater than that required to lift it? Explain.
10. An object is on the ground. What two ways could be used to give it positive potential energy?
11. A boy is holding a heavy weight in his hand. Is he doing a considerable amount of work while he is doing this? Explain.
12. Why is it more difficult to run up a hill than to run on a level spot of ground?
13. Why are the formulas for work different for the metric and English systems?
14. Assume that a compressed metal spring could be slowly dissolved in an acid solution without being released. What would happen to the potential energy it had?

PROBLEMS

1. A mass of 10 Kg is lifted 3 m in 2 sec. (a) What work was done on the object? (b) What is its potential energy?
2. A force of 12 lb acts through a distance of 6 ft parallel to the force. What is the work done?
3. A 160-lb boy goes up a flight of 24 steps, each 7 in. high. (a) How much work does he do? (b) His girl friend who weighs 110 lb does how much work if she is with him?
4. In the auto shop, a motor weighing 600 lb is pulled up from a car by an elaborate pulley system a height of 4 ft. How much potential energy does the motor have, assuming it was 3 ft above the ground when it was in the car?
5. One foot-pound is equal to how many joules?
6. A 100 lb trunk is moved 20 ft along a floor. One man helped lower the friction by lifting with 30 lb, while the other man pushed it along with 20 lb. (a) How much work was done? (b) How much potential energy was gained?
7. A funicular weighing 800 lb is pulled 1000 ft up a mountainside at an angle of 45°. What is the potential energy gained?
8. A car of 2000 Kg is pulled up an incline to a vertical height of 200 m. Find the potential energy in joules.
9. A trunk weighing 100 lb is pulled 15 ft across the floor. How much work is done if the coefficient of sliding friction is 0.50?
10. A block of ice with a mass of 30 Kg slides down a plank 10 m long that makes an angle of 25° with the horizontal. How much energy is lost?
11. A fallen tree weighing 2 tons is pulled through the forest by elephants for a distance of 500 ft. If the coefficient of sliding friction is 0.55, what is (a) the applied force and (b) the work done?
12. An oak box weighing 150 lb is pulled 12 ft up an oak plank by a force of 80

lb. If the plank makes an angle of 30° with the horizontal, how much energy is
(a) stored as potential energy and (b) lost in overcoming friction?

13. Ten inches of snow fall at an elevation of 7000 ft over an area of approximately 200 square miles. Assuming that this is equivalent to one inch of water, what potential energy does this amount of snow represent?

PROJECTS

1. Develop a machine that would use a very small motor to lift a fairly large weight. Calculate the efficiency of your device.
2. Develop a machine that would distinguish between the work done to slide an object along a level plane and the work done to lift it.

MECHANICS

Lesson 25 *ENERGY AND POWER*

In Lesson 24 it was stated that mechanical energy is of two kinds: *potential energy* and *kinetic energy*.

There it was said that *a body has potential energy if, by virtue of its position or state, it is able to do work*. In other words, potential energy does not involve motion. In this lesson we will consider kinetic energy and find that it does involve motion. Kinetic energy is often referred to as *energy of motion*.

Kinetic Energy. *The kinetic energy of a moving body is defined as its ability to do work by virtue of its motion.* A car moving along the highway has kinetic energy of translation, and a rotating wheel on a machine has kinetic energy of rotation.

A moving body has energy because, in being brought to rest, it must exert a force, F, on some other object, and this force act-

ing through a distance, Δs, does work. In other words, work can be done by a moving body. Conversely, by applying a constant horizontal force, F, on a body of mass, m, for a distance, Δs, it will be given a kinetic energy equal to the work done:

$$\text{work} = F \times \Delta s$$

The force may be stated according to Newton's Second Law:

$$F = ma$$

and the acceleration may be stated, in terms of the final velocity, by Eq. (7) in Lesson 8,

$$v^2 = 2a \, \Delta s$$

or

$$\Delta s = \frac{v^2}{2a}$$

Therefore, the work exerted on a body to

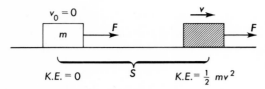

Fig. A. A body has kinetic energy by virtue of its motion.

accelerate it through a distance s is $\frac{1}{2}mv^2$. See Fig. A.

$$F \times \Delta s = \tfrac{1}{2}mv^2 \qquad (1)$$

This is known as the "work equation." In it, friction is entirely neglected, and the body is presumed to start from rest. In this case, the work is transformed into kinetic energy instead of potential energy.

In Fig. B, a car of mass m is shown mov-

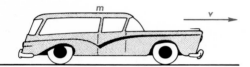

Fig. B. A moving body has kinetic energy equal to ½ mv².

ing along the road. As it moves along with a constant velocity, v, it possesses kinetic energy given by the formula—

$$K.E. = \tfrac{1}{2}mv^2 \qquad (2)$$

To see how to use this formula, consider the following example.

Example 1. Calculate the kinetic energy of a 20-Kg mass moving with a velocity of 4 m/sec.

Solution. By direct substitution in Eq. (2), we obtain—

$$K.E. = \frac{1}{2} \times 20 \text{ Kg} \times \left(4\,\frac{m}{sec}\right)^2 = 160\,\frac{Kg\ m^2}{sec^2}$$

This answer has exactly the dimensions of *work* and *potential energy* and can be written in the same derived units:

$$K.E. = 160 \text{ joules}$$

Example 2. A constant horizontal force of 25 lb acts for a distance of 20 ft on a 500-lb midget racing car. If friction is neglected and the car starts from rest, (a) how much work is done and (b) what is the car's velocity?

Solution. The known quantities are $F = 25$ lb, $\Delta s = 20$ ft, and $m = 500/32$ slugs. To find the answer to (a) we use the formula—

$$\text{work} = F \times \Delta s$$

By direct substitution, we obtain—

$$\text{work} = 25 \text{ lb} \times 20 \text{ ft}$$
$$\text{work} = 500 \text{ ft-lb}$$

(b) To find the car's velocity, we use Eq. (2). The unknown quantity, v^2, is brought to the left-hand side of the equality and all other factors to the right:

$$v^2 = \frac{2(F \times \Delta s)}{m}$$

By direct substitution, we obtain—

$$v^2 = \frac{2 \times 500 \text{ ft-lb}}{500/32 \text{ slugs}}$$

$$v^2 = 64\,\frac{\text{ft-lb}}{\text{slugs}}$$

Because slugs have the units lb sec²/ft, we may substitute and write—

$$v^2 = 64\,\frac{\text{ft}^2}{\text{sec}^2}$$

and, taking the square root, obtain for the velocity:

$$v = 8\,\frac{\text{ft}}{\text{sec}}$$

Power. *Power is defined as the rate of doing work, or the rate at which work is being done:*

$$\text{power} = \frac{\text{work}}{\text{time}}$$

$$P = \frac{F \times \Delta s}{\Delta t} \qquad (3)$$

The faster a given amount of work is done, the greater is the power.

In the metric system, with work measured in *ergs* or *joules,* power is expressed either in *ergs per second* or in *joules per second.* One joule per second is called the *watt,* a unit of power:

$$1\,\frac{\textbf{joule}}{\textbf{sec}} = 1\ \textbf{watt} \qquad (4)$$

The *kilowatt* is another unit of power and is equal to 1000 watts.

Example 3. A small hoist raises a 160-Kg bucket of concrete to a height of 30 m in 8 sec. Find the power required in (a) joules per second and (b) in kilowatts.

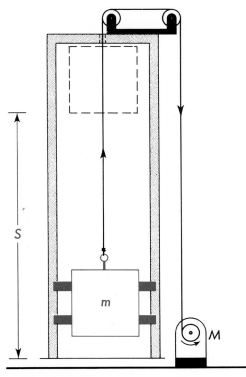

Fig. C. Demonstration of a concrete hoist. See Example 3.

Solution. This example is diagramed in Fig. C. To find the power, use Eq. (3), $P = F \times \Delta s / \Delta t$. Because the force must be in newtons, $F = mg$, on substitution we obtain—

$$P = \frac{160\ \text{Kg} \times 9.8\ \text{m/sec}^2 \times 30\ \text{m}}{8\ \text{sec}}$$

$$P = 5880\ \frac{\textbf{newton meters}}{\textbf{sec}}$$

(a) $$P = 5880\ \frac{\textbf{joules}}{\textbf{sec}}$$

   $$P = 5880\ \textbf{watts}$$

(b) $$P = 5.88\ \textbf{kilowatts}$$

In the engineering system, with work measured in *foot-pounds,* power is expressed in *foot-pounds per second,* and, in some cases, *horsepower* or *hp. 1 hp is defined as the power that can do 550 ft-lb of work in 1 sec.*

Example 4. Find the power of an engine capable of lifting 200 lb to a height of 55 ft in 10 sec.

Solution. By direct substitution in Eq. (3), we obtain—

$$P = \frac{200\ \text{lb} \times 55\ \text{ft}}{10\ \text{sec}} = 1100\ \frac{\textbf{ft-lb}}{\textbf{sec}}$$

Dividing this answer by 550 to get horsepower, we find—

$$\frac{1100}{550} = 2\ \textbf{hp}$$

If 550 ft-lb/sec is changed to metric units (1 ft = 0.305 m and 1 lb = 0.454 Kg), we find—

$$1\ \textbf{hp} = 746\ \frac{\textbf{joules}}{\textbf{sec}}$$

or—

$$1\ \textbf{hp} = 746\ \textbf{watts}$$

QUESTIONS

1. Give an example of how a single force may be applied to an object to do work that is transformed into potential, kinetic, and heat energy simultaneously.
2. (a) Give an example of how a force may be applied to an object to do work that is transformed into only potential energy. (b) Only kinetic energy. (c) Only heat energy.
3. (a) Can potential energy take on negative values? (b) Can kinetic energy?
4. Using the formula for work, explain what would be meant by negative work.
5. A hiker walks along a level trail. Is he doing work? Explain.
6. A box accelerates down a rough plank. Describe which energy is increasing and which is decreasing.
7. An object is dropped to the ground from a height h. Show that the kinetic energy it has when it reaches the ground is exactly equal to the potential energy it had at the top.
8. Why do the brakes of a modern automobile sometimes "fade" after too long a sustained use?
9. (a) Does the distance required to stop a moving car have anything to do with its weight or velocity? (b) Which, if either, is the more important factor?
10. Electricity for home use is sold by the kilowatt-hour. Is this a unit of work or power? Explain.
11. (a) Explain the reason a car that is full of passengers drives differently from one with only the driver. (b) Would this effect be more pronounced in a light or heavy car?
12. What happens to most of the energy of the gasoline that is put into an automobile tank?
13. Why is it so difficult to design the mechanisms and equipment necessary to bring an astronaut back to earth after being in orbit?

PROBLEMS

1. A mass of 200 Kg is given a velocity of 2.5 m/sec. Find its kinetic energy in joules.
2. A car weighing 3200 lb is traveling along the highway with a speed of 50 ft/sec. Find its kinetic energy in ft-lb.
3. Starting from rest, a 180-Kg mass acquires a speed of 5 m/sec in a distance of 15 m. Find the force in newtons.
4. An elevator car weighing 1200 lb rises 100 ft in 5 sec. What is the horsepower developed?
5. A bucket of concrete having a mass of 3000 Kg is hoisted up an elevator shaft

a distance of 50 m in 8 sec. (a) Find the power in kilowatts. (b) Find the work done in joules.

6. A coal elevator in a mine shaft weighs 6 tons when loaded. What is the minimum power realized by a motor that could lift this car 400 ft in one minute?

7. A 3-Kg box slides down a 10-m plank, which is inclined at 45°. If the coefficient of friction is 0.5, how much potential energy is lost?

8. An automobile weighing 3800 lb and moving with a velocity of 45 mi/hr, or 66 ft/sec, is brought to rest in a distance of 200 ft. Find (a) the initial kinetic energy and (b) the average force provided by the brakes.

9. How heavy a load can a 30-hp hoist lift at a steady speed of 568 ft/min?

10. A person weighing 160 lb is in a jet traveling at 30,000 ft at a velocity of 400 mi/hr. (a) What is the kinetic energy that the person has? (b) Where did he get this energy?

11. An electron has a mass of 9.11×10^{-31} Kg. (a) With what kinetic energy does it strike the inside of a TV tube if it is moving with a speed of 2×10^6 m/sec? (b) What happens to this energy?

12. In the Bohr model of the hydrogen atom, the electron is assumed to be in an orbit 0.53×10^{-8} m from the nucleus when in the ground state. What would the kinetic energy of the electron be if its mass is 9.11×10^{-31} Kg and its velocity is 2.18×10^6 m/sec?

13. The mass of the earth is approximately 6×10^{24} Kg. Its average distance to the sun is 149,500,000 Km. Assume a circular orbit and that there are 365¼ days in a year, what is the average kinetic energy of the earth?

PROJECT

Develop an experiment to measure the kinetic energy of a toy truck.

MECHANICS

Lesson 26 *CONSERVATION OF ENERGY*

Most important of all the laws of nature is the law of the conservation of energy. While the law has been stated in almost as many different ways as there are books written on the subject, they all have in reality the same meaning. The following three examples are typical statements: (1) *in transforming energy from one form to another, energy is always conserved*, (2) *energy is never created nor destroyed*, or (3) *the sum total of all energy in the universe remains constant.*

Everyone should be aware of the fact that there are many forms of energy. To illustrate, we should take a look at them.

Forms of Energy

Mechanical	Light
Electrical	Atomic
Chemical	Molecular
Heat	Nuclear

In this lesson, we are concerned with the law of conservation of energy only as it applies to the two forms of mechanical energy, *potential* and *kinetic*. The law will again be encountered in connection with the other forms in the lessons on heat, electricity, and atomic structure.

As an illustration of the transformation of one form of mechanical energy into another, consider the demonstration experiment shown in Fig. A.

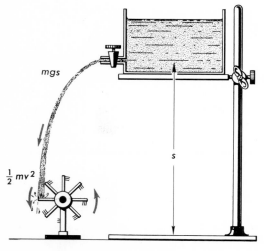

Fig. A. Demonstration of energy transformation.

Water in a tank escapes through an outlet pipe and falls on the blades of a paddle wheel. The water in the tank has potential energy mgh. As it falls with ever-increasing speed, that energy is converted into kinetic

energy $\frac{1}{2}mv^2$. In turning the paddle wheel, this energy of motion can be utilized to do mechanical work of one kind or another. On the other hand, it might well be made to turn an electric generator and convert mechanical energy into electrical. The electrical generator, in turn, may be connected to a toaster and convert electrical energy into heat.

In this example, as in all practical examples, a fraction of the original energy is transformed into heat energy. This generally occurs as a result of friction, but it is produced here by the turbulence of the water striking the wheel. Maximum conversion to kinetic energy, and minimum production of heat energy, is achieved by shaping the vanes so that the water flows smoothly over them.

Consider the energy involved in a waterfall as shown in Fig. B. The water at the top

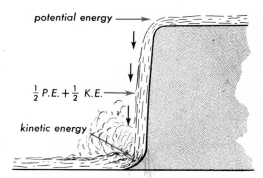

Fig. B. All the available energy at the top of a waterfall is potential. At the bottom it is kinetic.

of the fall has potential energy by virtue of its position above the base. As it falls over and then downward with ever-increasing speed, the kinetic energy $\frac{1}{2}mv^2$ increases, while the potential energy decreases. At the bottom of the fall, the potential energy approaches zero, and the kinetic energy approaches its maximum value. At the top the energy was practically all potential, while near the bottom it is mostly kinetic. Assuming the water to start from rest at the top and that no energy is lost in falling, the *P.E.* at the top of the falls equals the *K.E.* at the bottom:

(P.E. at top) = (K.E. at bottom)   (1)

or—

$$mg\Delta s = \tfrac{1}{2}mv^2 \qquad (2)$$

Dividing both sides of the equation by *m* and solving for *v* gives—

$$v^2 = 2g\Delta s$$

or—

$$v = \sqrt{2g\Delta s} \qquad (3)$$

This is the special Eq. (3) derived for falling bodies, in one of the preceding lessons, from the laws of accelerated motion. Here, the equation has been derived from the law of conservation of energy.

Example. A mass of 25 Kg is dropped from a height of 5 m. Find the kinetic energy and velocity just as it reaches the ground.

Solution. Because the *P.E.* at the top is equivalent to the *K.E.* at the bottom—

$$P.E. = 25 \text{ Kg} \times 9.8 \frac{m}{sec^2} \times 5 \text{ m}$$

$$= 1225 \text{ joules} = K.E.$$

The velocity is found by Eq. (3):

$$v = \sqrt{2 \times 9.8 \times 5} = 9.9 \text{ m/sec}$$

When the falling body in the above problem is part way down, it has some *P.E.* and some *K.E.* Its total energy, *E* is, therefore, of two kinds:

$$E = \tfrac{1}{2}mv^2 + mg\Delta s \qquad (4)$$

At the instant the body reaches the ground, it is suddenly stopped and all of the energy is quickly transformed into heat. The transformation of mechanical energy into heat is often demonstrated in the physics laboratory by an experiment in which a

quantity of lead shot is dropped from a height of several feet and its temperature measured before and after falling. By raising the shot and dropping it many times, the rise in temperature amounts to several degrees.

The Inclined Plane. Consider the demonstration experiment shown in Fig. C, in

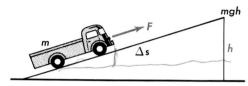

Fig. C. Conservation of energy.

which a small truck is pulled up an incline. The work done to reach the top is given by the product of force, *F*, times the distance, *s*. By conservation of energy, this must be equal to the stored-up potential energy *mgh* at the top. Therefore—

$$F \times \Delta s = mgh \qquad (5)$$

Now if the truck is released, it will accelerate back down the incline, thereby converting the potential energy, *mgh*, into kinetic energy $\tfrac{1}{2}mv^2$. By conservation of energy, we can write—

$$mgh = \tfrac{1}{2}mv^2 \qquad (6)$$

Because the *m* on both sides refers to the same mass, we obtain—

$$gh = \tfrac{1}{2}v^2$$

or—

$$v^2 = 2gh$$

from which—

$$v = \sqrt{2gh} \qquad (7)$$

It is important to note that the velocity at the bottom of the incline depends only on the height, *h*. This means that no matter how steep the incline may be, the velocity at the bottom will be the same if the height, h, is the same.

The Simple Pendulum. A similar energy treatment can be given for the swinging of a simple pendulum. At the extreme ends of each swing, see Fig. D, the bob comes mo-

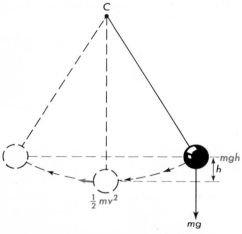

Fig. D. Potential energy of a pendulum changes to kinetic energy and back again.

mentarily to rest and the energy, E, is all potential and equal to mgh. At the bottom of the swing, the energy, E, is all kinetic and equal to $\frac{1}{2}mv^2$.

The motion of the pendulum bob is like that of a body sliding, without friction, down an inclined plane of changing angle. The kinetic energy acquired in going down one side is just sufficient to carry it up to an equal height on the other.

At any intermediate point, the kinetic energy may be calculated from the conservation law:

$$E = K.E. + P.E.$$

or—

$$mgh = \tfrac{1}{2}mv^2 + mgy$$

where y is the height above the lowest point

of the swing. The kinetic energy at any point is, therefore, given by

$$\tfrac{1}{2}mv^2 = mg(h - y)$$

The Brachistochrone. In 1696, Jean Bernoulli addressed a letter to the mathematicians of Europe challenging them to solve within six months the following problem in mechanics. Along what path should a body move in order to descend from one point, A, to a lower and horizontally displaced point, B, in the least possible time? See Fig. E. After some months had passed, Leibnitz,

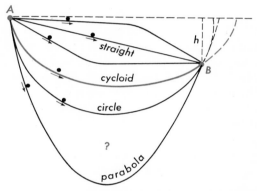

Fig. E. The brachistochrone. Which path should the ball take to reach B in the least time?

Jacques Bernoulli, and L'Hopital arrived at the answer. On January 29, 1697, Newton received from France a copy of the printed paper containing the problem and the following day sent the solution to the President of the Royal Society.

The curve of the shortest time, and now called the "Brachistochrone," is a cycloid. See Fig. E. The cycloid is the path traversed by a point on the rim of a wheel when it is rolled along a horizontal plane. It is interesting to note that, although the cycloid is the path of least time for a body starting from rest at A and sliding without friction from A to B, the velocity of arrival at B is

the same for all paths. By the law of conservation of energy, this final velocity is

given by Eq. (7), where h is the vertical
height between A and B.

QUESTIONS

1. A body falls from rest. What form of energy does it have (a) before it falls, (b) just before it hits the ground, and (c) halfway down?

2. Assume that a child slides without friction down a playground slide. (a) Upon what factors does his velocity at the bottom depend? (b) Does his velocity depend upon his weight or the length of the slide?

3. Cut a disk about 2 in. in diameter from a piece of cardboard. Roll this disk along the edge of a sheet of paper, and trace out the path of a point on the rim. What kind of curve is this?

4. Give an example in which kinetic energy is converted into: (a) potential energy, (b) heat energy, and (c) heat and potential energy.

5. A lead weight is dropped onto a concrete floor. (a) At what point does it have only kinetic, only potential, and only heat energy? Explain if and when it simultaneously has (b) potential and kinetic energy, (c) potential and heat energy, and (d) kinetic and heat energy.

6. A box slides down a frictionless plank from a fixed height. (a) What angle should the plank make with the horizontal if the kinetic energy at the bottom is to be a maximum? (b) Answer the same question if the plank is not frictionless. Explain.

7. A boy is jumping along on a pogo stick. Describe the various conditions in which the potential energy and kinetic energy are maximum and minimum.

8. Describe an apparatus that would transform kinetic energy into some form of energy other than potential or heat.

9. Why is electricity the most useful form of energy in the home? Name at least five places where electricity is transformed into kinetic energy in the average house.

10. Because energy is conserved, why do most scientists contend that a perpetual-motion machine is impossible and many inventors persist in trying to make them?

11. (a) Is a windmill "free" power? (b) Where does its energy ultimately come from?

12. It is seriously proposed that the energy of the ocean waves be utilized. What would be the ultimate energy source this would be tapping?

PROBLEMS

1. A 5-Kg stone is dropped from a height of 6 m. Find the kinetic energy just before it strikes the ground.

2. An 8-lb weight is raised to a height of 40 ft and then dropped. Find (a) the

potential energy acquired at its highest point and (b) the maximum velocity acquired in falling.

3. A boy weighing 64 lb slides for 20 ft down a slide inclined 30° with the horizontal. Neglecting friction, what is (a) his velocity and (b) his kinetic energy when he reaches the bottom of the slide?

4. A boy pulls a 2-Kg wagon up a 30° hill. If he gained 80 joules potential energy, how far did he walk?

5. The boy in the previous problem rode the wagon to the bottom of the hill, but took a route which was sloped at 20°. What was his kinetic energy when he reached the bottom?

6. At the top of a hill, a car has 950 joules of potential energy and 450 joules of kinetic energy. Near the bottom it has 500 joules of potential energy and 525 joules of kinetic energy. (a) Has the driver been using the brake or the accelerator? Explain. (b) Is energy "lost" in the process? Explain.

7. A simple pendulum 1 m long has a 2-Kg bob. If the bob is raised until the string makes an angle of 45° with the vertical and is then released, find (a) the potential energy before release and (b) the maximum velocity acquired as it swings.

8. A 5-Kg mass is raised to a height of 16 m and then dropped. Find (a) the potential energy at the top, (b) the time of fall, and (c) the maximum velocity acquired.

9. Four hundred joules of energy are expended in projecting a 5-Kg mass straight upward. What is (a) its initial velocity and (b) its maximum height reached?

10. A 2-Kg mass is to be projected upward with a velocity of 10 m/sec. Find (a) the energy required and (b) the maximum height reached. Employ energy principles only.

11. If all the energy of a 650-lb shell, having a velocity of 2000 ft/sec, could be spent in raising an 8000-ton ship, how high would it lift it?

PROJECTS

1. Investigate the many different types of "perpetual-motion machines," and make a working model of the one that looks the most promising.

2. Make a working model of a hydroelectric plant.

3. Develop a generator attached to your bicycle with lights or meters to measure how much electricity your friends can produce. This also might be used to measure the average horsepower of your friends.

MECHANICS

Lesson 27 *MACHINES*

A mechanical machine constitutes a device wherein mechanical energy is applied at one point and mechanical energy in a more useful form is delivered at another.

The Lever. The lever, as described in detail in Lesson 21, is one of the simplest of all mechanical devices that may rightfully be called a machine. By applying a downward force at one end of a lever, as shown in Fig. A, a heavy load may be lifted at the

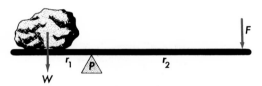

Fig. A. A lever.

other. The principle of the lever requires that the moment on one side of the fulcrum, P, be equal to the moment on the other side:

$$W \times r_1 = F \times r_2 \qquad (1)$$

When the two moments are exactly equal, the lever is in equilibrium, that is, all parts are at rest or moving with uniform speed. If the lever is at rest, then, neglecting friction, any small additional force added to F will produce the necessary lifting motion.

Mechanical Advantage. *The mechanical advantage of a machine may be defined as the ratio of the output force delivered by the machine to the input force.* With a simple machine such as the lever, as shown in Fig. B, W represents the *output force*, and F represents the *input force;* and the me-

chanical advantage, or M.A., is given by—

$$M.A. = \frac{W}{F} \qquad (2)$$

By rearranging Eq. (1), the mechanical advantage is also expressed as the ratio of the lever arms:

$$M.A. = \frac{W}{F} = \frac{r_2}{r_1} \qquad (3)$$

Suppose, for example, that a man weighing 150 lb wishes to lift a heavy stone

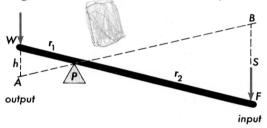

Fig. B. A lever is classified as a machine.

weighing 1500 lb by means of a lever. The mechanical advantage required of the lever must, therefore, be—

$$M.A. = \tfrac{1500}{150} = 10$$

Eq. (3) shows that, to obtain this mechanical advantage, the lever arm, r_2, must be 10 times as long as r_1. Although 1500 lb can be lifted by the application of a force only one-tenth as large, energy relations show that the operator is not getting "something for nothing." The law of conservation of energy requires that the work done *by* the machine be no greater than the work done *on* the machine. As illustrated in the diagram, the work done on the machine by the operator is equal to the product of *force*

148

MECHANICS

× *distance*, $F \times s$, while the work done by the machine is equal to the product of *weight × distance*, $W \times h$.

By conservation of energy—

$$W \times h = F \times s \qquad (4)$$
$$\text{output} \quad \text{input}$$

or—

$$\frac{W}{F} = \frac{s}{h} \qquad (5)$$

which shows that the mechanical advantage, defined as the ratio of the forces W/F, is also given by the inverse ratio of the distances, s/h.

Efficiency. In arriving at the above relations for the mechanical advantage, it was assumed that the lever, as a machine, operates without friction. As a practical matter, such ideal conditions are never actually attained. It is customary, in engineering practice, to neglect friction at first by applying the above equations and then to make corrections where necessary by taking into account the efficiency of the machine.

Friction in a machine is not always a desirable feature, for by its presence, energy is continually wasted in all moving parts by being transformed into heat. By the law of conservation of energy,

input work = output work
+ wasted energy

The efficiency of a machine is defined as the ratio of output work to input work:

$$\text{efficiency} = \frac{\text{output work}}{\text{input work}} \qquad (6)$$

This ratio is always less than unity and is usually multiplied by 100 to express the efficiency in percent:

$$\text{percent efficiency} = \frac{\text{output}}{\text{input}} \times 100 \qquad (7)$$

The smaller the amount of energy lost

through friction, the greater is the efficiency of a machine and the nearer is the efficiency to 100%. In all cases where friction is assumed to be so small that it can be neglected, the efficiency is taken to be 100%, and the mechanical advantage is given by Eqs. (2), (3), and (5).

If friction is appreciably large and must be taken into account when making calculations, the mechanical advantage is still given by Eq. (2), but not by the ratio of the lever arms, r_2/r_1, nor by the distances moved, s/h.

Wheel and Axle. The wheel and axle is a simple machine involving the principle of the lever. As shown in Fig. C, a heavy load, W, is lifted by a rope wrapped around an axle of radius r by pulling down on an-

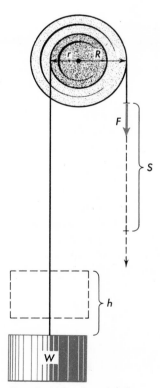

Fig. C. Wheel and axle.

other rope wrapped around an attached wheel of larger radius, R. By exerting the force F through a distance s, the load, W, is lifted a distance, h. Neglecting friction, the input work, $F \times s$, is equal to the output work, $W \times h$.

In one revolution of the wheel, the force, F, moves down a distance, s, equal to the circumference of the wheel, $2\pi R$, and the load, W, moves up a distance, h, equal to the circumference of the axle, $2\pi r$. By conservation of energy—

$$\underset{\textbf{output}}{W \times 2\pi r} = \underset{\textbf{input}}{F \times 2\pi R} \qquad (8)$$

Rearranging F to the left side of the equation and $2\pi r$ to the right, the mechanical advantage, W/F, is given by—

$$\frac{W}{F} = \frac{2\pi R}{2\pi r} = \frac{R}{r} \qquad (9)$$

Pulleys. The action of a pulley is the same as that of a lever having equal arms.

Singly, pulleys may be used in one of two ways, either as a *fixed pulley* or as a *movable pulley*. In Fig. D, a fixed pulley is shown being used to lift a load, W, by means of an applied force, F. With the pivot at the center of the pulley, the two forces have equal arms, each equal to the radius, r. Having equal arms, the forces, neglecting friction, must be equal, and the theoretical mechanical advantage is unity.

Although a mechanical advantage of unity obtained with a fixed pulley may be looked upon as no mechanical advantage at all, it often happens that a downward force is more conveniently applied to lift a body than is an equal upward force.

A movable pulley, on the other hand, see Fig. E, has a mechanical advantage of 2. To move the load W upward a distance h, both of the supporting cords must be shortened by this same amount. To take up the

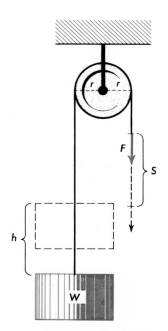

Fig. D. A fixed pulley.

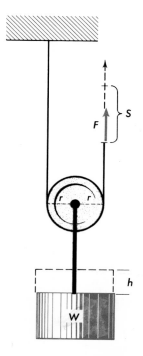

Fig. E. A movable pulley.

slack, the force F must move up a distance $s = 2\,h$. By energy conservation—

$$W \times h = F \times (2h)$$
output   input

from which the mechanical advantage can be computed: $M.A. = W/F = 2$.

Block and Tackle. The block and tackle is a contrivance with a large mechanical advantage, employing the use of any number of movable and fixed pulleys. One form is shown in Fig. F. The pulleys, it may be seen, are in two blocks with two pulleys, or sheaves, in each block. The fixed end of the rope is attached to the lower end of the

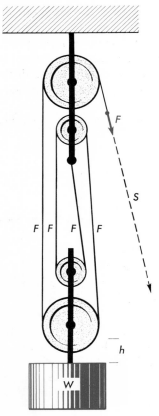

Fig. F. A block and tackle.

upper block and after passing around each pulley, as shown, goes to the prime mover.

In some blocks the pulleys are all of the same size and mounted side by side, while in others they are of different size and mounted one below the other as shown. Regardless of size, the function of each pulley is simply to reverse the direction of the force, F, so that the same tension exists throughout the supporting rope.

Neglecting friction in the pulleys and the weight of the rope, the tension in each of the four sections of rope holding up the lower block and weight, W, in the diagram is equal to F. For the block and weight to be in equilibrium, therefore, the total upward force $4F$ must be equal to the downward force W. This gives for the mechanical advantage—

$$M.A. = W/F = 4$$

The same result is derived from energy considerations as follows. In raising the load, W, a height h, each of the four ropes supporting it must be shortened by this amount, and hence the force F must act through a distance $s = 4h$. Because $F \times s = W \times h$, the mechanical advantage $W/F = s/h = 4$.

In general, the mechanical advantage of any block and tackle is given by the number of parallel ropes supporting the load. The load, W, includes the weight of the lower block:

$$M.A. = \textbf{number of supporting ropes}$$
$$(10)$$

The above relations give only the theoretical mechanical advantages of pulleys and blocks and tackles. Because of friction such mechanical advantages are never realized, and the efficiency is less than 100%. To determine the efficiency and the actual mechanical advantage, weights can be applied as loads, and the actual force required to operate the machine can be measured The latter is readily performed as an ex- periment by establishing equilibrium of weights for both W and F.

QUESTIONS

1. (a) What is meant by the mechanical advantage of a machine? (b) What is meant by efficiency?
2. If a lever has a mechanical advantage of 5, what can you say about (a) the forces involved and (b) the lever arms?
3. If the efficiency of a machine is 90 percent, what can you say about (a) the work done and (b) the forces involved?
4. (a) Name a very common vehicle whose mechanical advantage is considerably under one and yet is built this way on purpose. (b) What is gained by making it this way?
5. Why are perpetual-motion machines a dream that will never be realized?
6. If it were possible, would it be a good idea to eliminate all friction in the operation of an automobile? Explain.
7. What advantage is gained by using a four-speed transmission in a sports car as compared to the standard three-shift pattern commonly used?
8. Some high-school boys replace the rear tires of their cars with larger diameter ones. This makes their car slant downward toward the front. What mechanical reason can you see for doing this?
9. Are simple machines becoming gradually obsolete as the world's machinery becomes more sophisticated? Explain.

PROBLEMS

1. A plank 16 ft long is used to lift a 900-lb load. Where must the pivot be located if the applied force is 130 lb?
2. A wheel and axle have radii of 45 cm and 10 cm, respectively. What force on the wheel cord will raise an 80-Kg mass fastened to the axle cord?
3. What force must be applied to the handles of a wheelbarrow if the handles are 4 ft from the axle of the wheel, and the 300-lb load to be lifted is 18 in. in from the axle?
4. A screwdriver is used to pry the lid from a tin can. If the distance between the tip of the lid and the rim of the can is 8 mm and the applied force of 18 newtons is 20 cm from the rim, what force is applied to the lid?
5. An oarlock is 28 in. from the handle of a 10-ft oar. If a force of 45 lb is used on each of two oars, what will be the force acting to move the boat through the water? (Assume pivots at the oarlocks.)
6. A wheel and axle have diameters of 24 in. and 1.5 in., respectively. (a) What is the mechanical advantage? (b) What force is required to lift a load of 600

lb? (c) What would be the mechanical advantage if the load was suspended from the wheel and the force applied to the axle?

7. A farmer raises a bucket of water weighing 35 lb from the bottom of a well. To do this he has the rope wound around a 10-in. diameter wooden drum. The handle of the crank on the drum is 18 in. from the center of rotation. Find (a) the mechanical advantage and (b) the required force on the handle.

8. A horizontal force of 60 lb is applied to the top of the tire on one wheel of an automobile stuck in the mud. (a) What is the effective force on the automobile? (b) What is the mechanical advantage?

9. In a garage, a block and tackle is used to lift a 320-lb motor out of a car. If the upper and lower blocks each contain four sheaves and one end of the rope is connected to the upper block, (a) What is the mechanical advantage? (b) What force must be applied? (Neglect friction.)

10. A wheel and axle are 30 cm and 20 cm in diameter, respectively. To lift a 20-Kg mass suspended from the axle, it was found that 150 newtons must be exerted on a rope suspended from the wheel. (a) What is the mechanical advantage? (b) What is the efficiency?

11. A block and tackle is used to pull tree stumps out of the ground. Each block contains three pulleys. One block should be fastened to the tree stump and the other to the anchor. (a) To which of the two blocks should the rope be fastened to obtain the greatest mechanical advantage? Make a diagram. (b) If a force of 120 lb is applied to the free end of the rope, and the efficiency is 50%, what force is applied to the stump?

12. A painter hoists himself up the side of a tall building by means of a block and tackle having two pulleys in the upper block and one in the lower block. The man and his equipment weigh 220 lb. What is the tension in the rope? (Note: The man himself does the pulling.)

13. Show how to hook up a block-and-tackle system that has a mechanical advantage of $\frac{1}{4}$. Why might such a small mechanical advantage be helpful?

14. An inventor built a machine that should have a mechanical advantage of 0.9, but found that, owing to friction, the mechanical advantage was only 0.7. What was the efficiency?

PROJECTS

1. Design a machine that would enable one to measure the mechanical advantage and efficiency of a block-and-tackle rig.

2. Work out the plans for a project in which you would construct a simple and inexpensive device for demonstrating the mechanical advantage of a machine involving two levers.

MECHANICS

Lesson 28 **CONSERVATION OF MOMENTUM**

When two or more objects collide, momentum is conserved, although many of the physical quantities involved are changed. For example, the sum of velocities following a collision will usually be changed, but, as a result of Newton's Second Law, the sum of the momenta does not change. In this lesson, we shall see how such a "conserved" quantity proves to be useful.

The momentum of a moving object is defined as the product—

$$\text{momentum} = mv$$

where v, and therefore momentum, is a vector quantity. In this lesson, we will study the total momentum of a group of particles both before and after they interact with each other. We shall see that the total momentum does not change.

Consider, as an example, the "head-on" encounter of two balls as shown in Fig. A.

By similar reasoning it is clear that after impact, m_1 and m_2, with their new velocities v_1 and v_2 have a total momentum $m_1v_1 + m_2v_2$. While these two bodies are in collision, they are mutually accelerated according to Newton's Second Law—

$$F = ma \qquad (1)$$

According to Eq. (1) in Lesson 8, the acceleration is given by the change in velocity per unit time:

$$a = \frac{\Delta v}{\Delta t} \qquad (2)$$

Combining Eqs. (1) and (2), we have the impulse equation—

$$F\Delta t = m\Delta v \qquad (3)$$

The product, $F\Delta t$, is called the *impulse*, whereas the quantity on the right is the change in momentum.

During impact, two equal but opposite

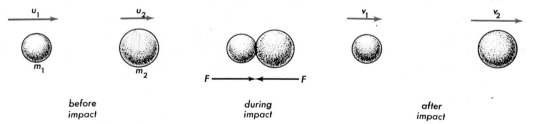

before impact   during impact   after impact

Fig. A. The total momentum of two bodies before impact is equal to the total momentum after impact.

Before impact, the mass m_1 is moving with a velocity u_1 and has a momentum m_1u_1, while m_2 is moving with a velocity u_2 and has a momentum m_2u_2. The total momentum before impact is, therefore, equal to the sum of the two momenta, $m_1u_1 + m_2u_2$.

forces are set up between the bodies, one the force exerted by m_1 on m_2 and the other the force exerted by m_2 on m_1. These two equal but opposite forces are an action and reaction pair, explained by Newton's Third Law of Motion. Each force acts for the same short interval of time, giving equal impulses, Ft, to both bodies. Therefore—

$$F\Delta t = m_1(v_1 - u_1)$$

and—

$$-F\Delta t = m_2(v_2 - u_2)$$

After multiplying both sides of the first equation by (-1), the right sides are seen to be equal:

$$-m_1(v_1 - u_1) = m_2(v_2 - u_2) \qquad (4)$$

One body gains as much momentum as the other loses.

Rearranging the terms, so that the initial momenta occur on the left and the final momenta occur on the right, the previous equation may be written—

$$m_1u_1 + m_2u_2 = m_1v_1 + m_2v_2 \qquad (5)$$

momentum before impact =
momentum after impact

In other words, when two or more bodies collide with each other, momentum is conserved.

The law of conservation of momentum applies to all collision phenomena and states that *the total momentum before impact equals the total momentum after impact*. The total momentum, therefore, remains constant.

Example 1. An ivory ball of mass 5 gm, moving with a velocity of 20 cm/sec, collides with another ivory ball of mass 10 gm, moving in the same direction along the same line, with a velocity of 10 cm/sec. After impact, the first mass is still moving in the same direction, but with a velocity of only 8 cm/sec. Calculate the velocity of the second mass after impact. Apply Eq. (5).

Solution. By direct substitution in Eq. (5)—

$$(5 \times 20) + (10 \times 10) = (5 \times 8) + (10 \times v_2)$$
$$200 = 40 + 10v_2$$
$$10v_2 = 160; \quad v_2 = 16 \text{ cm/sec}$$

After impact, the second mass has a velocity of 16 cm/sec.

If in Example 1 the total kinetic energy after impact is calculated and compared with the total kinetic energy before impact, the two will not be found equal. Employing the equation $K.E. = \frac{1}{2}mv^2$—

$$K.E. = \tfrac{1}{2}(5 \times 20^2) + \tfrac{1}{2}(10 \times 10^2)$$
$$= 1500 \text{ ergs, before impact}$$
$$K.E. = \tfrac{1}{2}(5 \times 8^2) + \tfrac{1}{2}(10 \times 16^2)$$
$$= 1440 \text{ ergs, after impact}$$

The difference in energy, to the amount of 60 ergs, has disappeared as mechanical energy and gone into heat. During impact, both masses were slightly deformed in shape owing to the mutually acting forces, and a small amount of heat was generated internally. This heat goes to raise the temperature of the two colliding bodies. It is only by including this heat energy of 60 ergs with the mechanical energy after impact that one can show the applicability of the law of conservation of energy. This is just another way of stating that collisions in general are not perfectly elastic. If they were perfectly elastic, conservation of mechanical energy would hold as well as conservation of momentum. Perfectly elastic collisions are known to occur between the *ultramicroscopic* atoms and molecules of a gas but not with the *macroscopic* bodies encountered in everyday life. The more inelastic the colliding bodies, the more energy is transformed into heat.

The most inelastic collision possible is one in which the objects stick together after colliding. A treatment of elasticity and its application to collision problems will be given in Lesson 35.

It is important to note, from the discussion above, that, *for all impact problems whether perfectly elastic or not, the law of conservation of momentum should be applied.*

An interesting experiment illustrating conservation of momentum is shown in Fig. B. Two small cars of equal mass, $m_1 = m_2$,

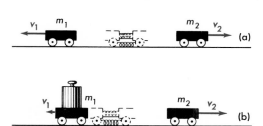

Fig. B. Conservation-of-momentum demonstration experiments.

are tied together with a compressed spring between them. When the cord tie is burned with a match, releasing the spring, the two cars fly apart with equal velocities. Before the spring is released, the cars are at rest and total momentum is zero. After the spring is released, the total momentum is still zero, because the two velocities are oppositely directed. Momentum being a vector quantity—

$$m_1 v_1 + m_2 v_2 = 0 \qquad (6)$$

With motions to the right taken as positive, v_2 is positive and v_1 negative, and the two momenta cancel.

If the experiment above is repeated with one of the cars heavily loaded as shown in diagram (b), the two fly apart as before but with unequal velocities. The lighter mass moves away with a high velocity while the heavier mass recoils with a low velocity. The product $m_1 \times v_1$, however, is equal in magnitude to the product $m_2 \times v_2$, and the sum of the two momenta is zero.

Example 2. A 60-Kg shell is shot with an initial velocity of 500 m/sec from a gun having a mass of 2000 Kg. What is the initial velocity with which the gun recoils?

Solution. Applying Eq. (6) and substituting directly the known quantities—

$$60 \text{ Kg} \times 500 \text{ m/sec} + 2000 \text{ Kg} \times v_2 = 0$$
$$30{,}000 \text{ Kg m/sec} + 2000\,v_2 \text{ Kg} = 0$$

$$v_2 = \frac{30{,}000 \text{ Kg m/sec}}{-2000 \text{ Kg}} = -15 \text{ m/sec}$$

The gun recoils with a velocity of 15 m/sec.

An experiment illustrating the recoil velocity of a heavy mass is shown by two pendulums in Fig. C. A U-shaped spring, compressed and tied with a cord, K, rests against a heavy iron ball, m_2, and a small wooden ball, m_1. When the cord, K, is burned through by a lighted match, the spring is released and the two masses fly apart with equal but opposite momenta. The small mass acquires a high velocity and swings up to a considerable height, while the large mass is barely perceived to move.

Another interesting experiment illustrating conservation of momentum may be performed with eight or nine duckpin balls and a grooved board, as shown in Fig. D. When one ball is rolled up to the others, it will be stopped by collision with the end ball, and the ball on the opposite end will roll out with almost the same speed. If two balls are rolled up, as indicated in the diagram, two will roll out on the other end, and if three are rolled up, three will roll out, etc. Glass or steel marbles work best in this experiment as they are highly elastic; however, duckpin balls or billiard balls produce a more spectacular effect.

Example 3. When two balls are rolled up to collide with the others, why doesn't just one ball roll off on the other side with twice the velocity, thus conserving momentum?

Solution. The answer to this involves the conservation of energy as well as momentum. If only one ball came off with twice the velocity to conserve momentum, its kinetic energy would be twice the energy available from the two incident balls.

The propelling force of a jet plane or

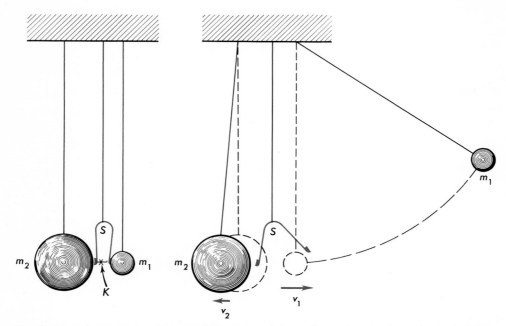

Fig. C. Experiment with a light and heavy pendulum, illustrating the law of conservation of momentum.

rocket is derived from the principle of conservation of momentum. See Fig. E.

As the gases are burned within the combustion chambers of the engine, they exert a large forward force, $-F$, on the plane and an equal and opposite force, $+F$, on the exhausting gases. As a result of the backward force, the gases acquire a very high velocity, v, and a momentum, mv. Flying at constant speed, the forward thrust, $-F$, just balances the frictional resistance, f, of the air. To relate the thrust with the exhaust gas momentum, we write Eq. (3):

$$F\Delta t = m\Delta v$$

To apply this, the *impulse equation*, to

the jet or rocket engine, m represents the mass of gas exhausted in any chosen number of seconds, Δt. The impulse $F \times \Delta t$ exerted on the gases is just equal and opposite to the impulse $-F \times \Delta t$ exerted on the plane.

Ballistics. The term ballistics is applied to the science of hurling missiles from a gun or launching device. One of the major problems in this science is concerned with the determination of the muzzle velocity of shells as they leave the end of the gun barrel.

Of the many methods that have been employed for determining the muzzle ve-

Fig. D. Experiment with the duckpin balls, illustrating the law of conservation of momentum.

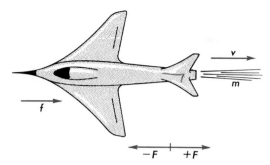

Fig. E. Conservation of momentum accounts for the forward thrust on a rocket plane or missile.

$$v = \frac{M + m}{m} V \qquad (8)$$

To find the recoil velocity, V, we measure the height, h, to which the block rises,

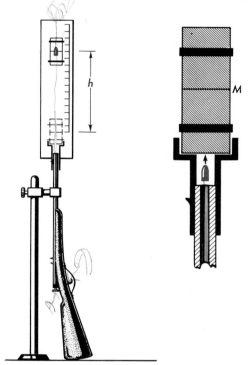

Fig. F. Rifle arrangement with attachments for ballistics experiment.

locity of shells from guns, consider the one shown in Fig. F. A rifle is clamped with its barrel pointing straight upward and the stock resting against the floor.

As the bullet leaves the barrel, it becomes imbedded in the wood block resting on the small platform. Together, the bullet and block rise to a height, h, as shown. Because this is an impact, or collision, problem, we can apply the law of conservation of momentum.

With the wood block initially at rest, the total momentum before impact is just that of the bullet, mv. After impact, the bullet and block, with a total mass of $M + m$, recoil upward with a velocity and total momentum of $(M + m)V$. Therefore, we can write—

$$mv = (M + m)V \qquad (7)$$

Solving for v, we obtain—

and apply the law of freely falling bodies. See Lesson 11.

$$V = \sqrt{2gh} \qquad (9)$$

QUESTIONS

1. Is the total kinetic energy before the impact of two bodies the same as the total energy after impact? Explain.
2. (a) When a shell is fired from a large gun, what can you say about the momentum of the shell? (b) The gun?
3. A man in a heavy boat pulls on a rowboat by means of a rope. (a) What can

you say about the momentum of each boat? (b) Which will have the greatest speed?

4. Two billiard balls of equal mass each have zero velocity after colliding. (a) Were their velocities equal before collision? (b) Does conservation of momentum apply? (c) Does conservation of energy apply?

5. A ball of putty is dropped. Before it strikes the floor, it has a velocity, but after it strikes the floor, it does not. Explain how the law of conservation of energy applies.

6. Write the law of conservation of momentum as it applies to three colliding masses.

7. (a) How does conservation of momentum apply to a rocket? (b) Will a rocket work in a vacuum, or must it have air to push on?

8. If one freight car bumps into another that is at rest and the two lock together, will conservation of momentum apply?

9. Is there a good scientific reason for the belief that, in a head-on collision between a light-weight car and a heavier one, the occupants of the lighter one would be in greater physical danger? Explain.

10. When one ball strikes the first of a row of identical balls, the one at the other end rolls off. Similarly when two balls strike, two balls roll away. What happens when four balls strike three stationary ones? Why.

11. In a jet engine what two things might be done to increase the force produced by the engines?

12. (a) Why is a jet plane more efficient at high altitudes than it is close to the ground? (b) Why can't it be used to go to the moon?

13. In the discharge of a rifle, the momentum of the rifle is supposed to be equal to the momentum of the bullet. Why is the bullet possibly lethal when it strikes someone, but the rifle doesn't injure the person firing it?

14. A boy is near the middle of an almost frictionless ice-coated pond. All attempts to get off fail due to lack of friction. (a) What should he do to get off? (b) Would it be easier if a friend were with him?

15. (a) Why is momentum a vector quantity? (b) In shooting billiards, does it seem at times that momentum is not conserved? Explain.

PROBLEMS

1. A gun weighing 500 lb fires a 4-oz shell with a muzzle velocity of 2000 ft/sec. If the gun is free to move, what is the recoil velocity?

2. How large is the impulse produced by a 400-newton force for 7 sec?

3. How large is the impulse that gives a 9.00-Kg mass a velocity change of 3.00 m/sec?

4. A boy weighing 80 lb and running at the rate of 15 ft/sec jumps on a sled that weighs 8 lb. What is their common speed just after the boy lands on the sled?

5. A 2-lb hammer is moving 3 ft/sec when it strikes a 1-oz nail and drives it ½

in. into a block of wood. (a) What was the average force on the nail? (b) For how long was the nail moving?

6. Two lumps of putty, each weighing 20 gm, are moving at 90° to each other, each with a speed of 15 m/sec. After colliding, they stick together. (a) What are the momentum and velocity of the single lump after the collision? (b) How much heat is liberated?

7. A 6-Kg mass moving with a constant speed of 4 m/sec overtakes and bumps into a 3-Kg mass moving in the same direction with a constant velocity of 1 m/sec. If after impact the 3-Kg mass has a velocity of 3.4 m/sec, calculate (a) the velocity of the 6-Kg mass and (b) the energy lost in the form of heat.

8. A 400-gm block of wood lying on a fence post is hit by a rifle bullet of 35-gm mass. If the bullet enters the block with a velocity of 600 m/sec and leaves the other side with a velocity of 200 m/sec, find the recoil velocity of the block.

9. A 30-gm bullet moving with a velocity of 800 m/sec enters and becomes embedded in a block of wood weighing 3.6 Kg. With what velocity will the block recoil if it was at rest before the impact?

10. An 8-Kg block of wood hangs as a pendulum by a long string. When a 15-gm bullet is fired at close range into the block and becomes embedded there, the block swings to a height of 20 cm above its rest position. Find (a) the recoil speed of the block and (b) the muzzle velocity of the bullet.

11. Three marbles are moving along a straight line, one to the right and the others to the left. Their masses are 4, 8, and 12 gm and their speeds are 5, 4, and 1 m/sec, respectively. After they collide, the total momentum is zero, but the total kinetic energy is 0.1 joule. (a) Which marble was moving to the right? (b) How much energy was lost as heat?

PROJECTS

1. Arrange a set of balls in a smooth groove to demonstrate the conservation of momentum.

2. Use two heavy carts with ball-bearing wheels to demonstrate the conservation of momentum and the changes that take place during a slow and during a rapid collision.

MECHANICS

Lesson 29 *CIRCULAR MOTION*

Angular Speed. The speed with which a body rotates is called its *angular speed* or *frequency of rotation.* Either of these terms refers to the number of complete revolutions a body makes in unit time and is designated by the letter f:

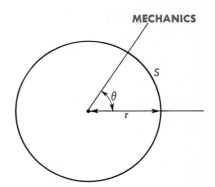

Fig. B. The radian is a unit of angular measure. When the arc s equals the radius r, the angle θ equals one radian.

f = number of revolutions per second

$$(1)$$

A flywheel, for example, might be said to have an angular speed of 10 revolutions per second, or $10r/sec$. The velocity of any point on the flywheel depends on the angular speed and its distance from the center of rotation.

Consider a body mass m fastened to the end of a string and whirling in a circle of radius r. See Fig. A. It is moving along the

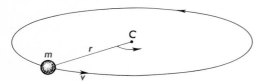

Fig. A. A mass, m, moving in a circle of radius, r, with a uniform speed, v.

circumference of a circle with a velocity v. Because v, the speed of the body along its path, is defined as the distance traveled per unit time, then—

$$v = \frac{\Delta s}{\Delta t} \qquad (2)$$

But because s is the circumference of a circle, $2\pi r$, and f is the number of revolutions per second, we can write Equation (2) as—

$$v = 2\pi rf \qquad (3)$$

The Radian. Angular speed can also be expressed in degrees or radians per second. Because all formulas for rotary motion are simpler when the radian measure is used, it will be studied now. The radian is defined as the angle subtended by the arc of a circle whose length is equal to the radius of the same circle. Referring to Fig. B, the distance, s, measured along the arc is equal to the radius, r, and the angle $\theta = 1$ radian.

Because the entire circumference of a

circle is just 2π times the radius, r, there are 2π radians in one complete circle:

$$2\pi \text{ radians} = 360°$$

Because $\pi = 3.1416$—

$$1 \text{ radian} = \frac{360°}{6.283} = 57.3°$$

It follows, from the above relations, that the angle θ in radians between any two points on the circumference of a circle is given by s, the length of the arc between the two points, divided by the radius r, or—

$$\text{angle in radians} = \frac{\text{arc length}}{\text{radius}}$$

or, in algebraic symbols—

$$\theta = \frac{s}{r} \qquad (4)$$

Consider the speed of a ball being whirled on the end of a string, as shown in Fig. C. The angular velocity of the motion is defined as the angle turned through divided by the elapsed time:

angular velocity

$$= \frac{\text{angle turned through}}{\text{time}}$$

In algebraic symbols—

$$\omega = \frac{\Delta\theta}{\Delta t} \qquad (5)$$

and is to be compared with the corresponding definition of linear velocity—

$$v = \frac{\Delta s}{\Delta t}$$

Angular velocity, ω, corresponds to linear velocity, v; angular displacement, θ,

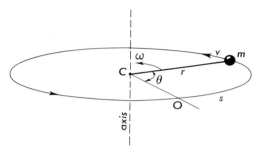

Fig. C. Illustrating circular motion.

corresponds to linear displacement, s. With θ measured in radians and t in seconds, the angular velocity, ω, has the units of radians per second or *rad/sec*.

The relation between the velocity and angular velocity of a rotating point may be found by combining Eqs. (3), (4), and (5) to give—

$$v = \omega r \qquad (6)$$

Example 1. Suppose a stone, when it is whirled on the end of a string 50 cm long, makes 8 complete revolutions in 2 sec and we wish to find the angular velocity in radians per second.

Solution. To employ Eq. (5), the angle $\Delta\theta$ is first calculated as follows. Because 1 revolution = 2π radians, 8 revolutions are equivalent to—

$$\Delta\theta = 2\pi \times 8 = 50.2 \text{ rad}$$

Substitution in Eq. (5) gives—

$$\omega = \frac{\Delta\theta}{\Delta t} = \frac{50.2 \text{ rad}}{2 \text{ sec}} = 25.1 \frac{\text{rad}}{\text{sec}}$$

The velocity of the stone along its path can now be easily found by substituting in Eq. (6)—

$$v = \omega r$$
$$= 25.1 \frac{\text{rad}}{\text{sec}} \times 50 \text{ cm} = 1255 \frac{\text{rad cm}}{\text{sec}}$$

but because—

$$\text{radian} = \frac{\text{arc length in cm}}{\text{radius in cm}}$$

we have—

$$v = 1255 \text{ cm / sec}$$

Centripetal Force. When a ball is whirling on the end of a string, there is an inward force exerted by the string on the ball. This force is called the *centripetal force* and is illustrated in Fig. D. Because the only force

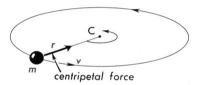

centripetal force

Fig. D. A mass, *m*, moving in a circle experiences an acceleration toward the center.

acting on the ball is inward, the ball is not in equilibrium but is being continually accelerated in the direction of the force, i.e., toward the center.

This appears to be a physical paradox, for here is a body moving with constant speed in a circle and yet being accelerated toward the center of the circle without getting any closer to it. If the string were to break suddenly, the ball would fly off on a tangent to the circle and move with constant velocity according to Newton's First Law.

Centripetal force is defined as the constant force that, when acting continuously at right angles to the motion of a particle, causes it to move in a circle with constant speed.

To obtain a clearer picture of centripetal force and acceleration toward the center, motion in a circle, as illustrated in Fig. E(c), is to be compared with the motion of

$$\frac{s}{r} = \frac{v'}{v}$$

Because the velocity v' is changing and is due to an acceleration, it can, by the

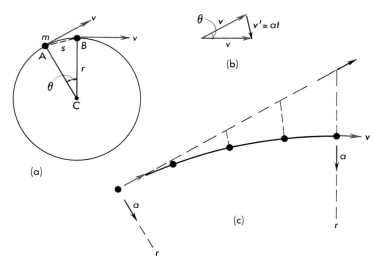

Fig. E. A body moving in a circle is continually being accelerated toward the center.

a projectile accelerated downward by the pull of gravity, described in Lesson 12. Because of the earth's attraction of all bodies, a projectile is continually accelerated downward away from the straight line of its original projection. In circular motion, the mass is continually accelerated toward the center, always at right angles to its instantaneous velocity and away from any straight-line tangent along which it would travel if suddenly released.

The instantaneous velocity is shown at two points, A and B, in Fig. E(a). The velocity, as indicated by the vectors, v, is seen to be changing in direction but not in magnitude. Diagram (b) is a velocity diagram showing v' as the change in velocity that occurs in going from A to B. Because this velocity triangle is similar to triangle ABC in diagram (a), corresponding sides are proportional to each other, and the following can be written—

equation $v = at$, be replaced by at. During the time t, the body moves, from A to B, a distance $s = vt$. For small angles θ, the distance measured along the arc AB is approximately equal to the chord s, so that, to a close approximation, s can be replaced by vt. These two substitutions made in the equation above give—

or

$$\frac{vt}{r} = \frac{at}{v}$$

$$a = \frac{v^2}{r} \qquad (7)$$

This acceleration of a body toward the center of the circle in which it is moving is called the *centripetal acceleration*.

Because by Newton's Second Law of Motion, $F = ma$, centripetal force is given by—

$$F = m\,\frac{v^2}{r} \qquad (8)$$

Example 2. A mass of 5 Kg is moving with a speed of 6 m/sec in a circle of 2 m radius. Find the centripetal force.

Solution. The known quantities can be substituted directly into Eq. (8):

$$F = 5 \text{ Kg} \frac{(6 \text{ m/sec})^2}{2 \text{ m}} = 90 \frac{\text{Kg m}}{\text{sec}^2}$$

or—

$$F = 90 \text{ newtons}$$

Experiments Demonstrating Centripetal Force. Many interesting experiments can be performed to illustrate centripetal force. In Fig. F, mercury and water have been placed in a dish and the dish set rotating rapidly about a vertical axis. From Eq. (8) it is observed that r and v will be similar for both water and mercury and that m is different. Because mercury is 13.6 times heavier than an equal volume of water, the centripetal force, F, is 13.6 times greater for mercury. The mercury, therefore, takes the outermost position in the dish.

Although the earth is often said to be spherical, it is in reality an oblate spheroid, i.e., a slightly flattened sphere. Accurate

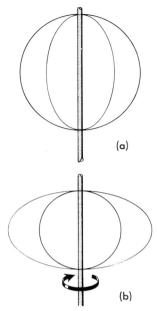

Fig. G. The flattening of the earth at its poles is owing to its rotation about the polar axis.

measurements show that the earth's diameter is 28 mi greater through the equator than it is through the poles. The cause for this flattening is illustrated in Fig. G by two circular metal strips. Diagram (a) shows the strips round when at rest, while (b) shows the flattening due to rapid rotation. The flattening of the earth is due to its own rotation of 2π radians every 24 hr. It is the enormous size of the earth and its lack of greater rigidity that makes it behave as though it were soft and semiplastic.

The opening of the loop in a lariat as whirled and thrown by a cowboy is also due to centripetal force. See Fig. H. Because of rotation, each small section of the rope, acting as an individual mass, m, tends to fly off on a tangent and thus get as far from the center of rotation as possible. The average distance from the center of all sections of the rope is a maximum when the loop takes the form of a circle rotating

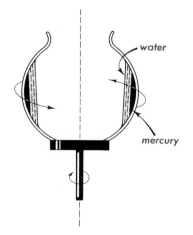

Fig. F. When mercury and water rotate in a dish, the water is inside the mercury. Centripetal force, like gravitational force, is greater for the substance of greater density.

Fig. H. A lariat takes a circular form because each small part tries to fly off on a tangent, thus getting as far from the center as possible. Centripetal force is responsible for keeping it in a circle.

about an axis perpendicular to the plane of the loop.

Centrifugal Force. By Newton's Third Law of Motion, centripetal force must induce an equal and opposite force, called the *centrifugal* force. For a mass moving in a circle at the end of a string, as in Fig. D, the centrifugal force is the outward force the mass exerts on the *string* and on the *pivot*. The centrifugal force cannot be described as a balancing or equilibrium force, because it does not act on the moving mass, as does the centripetal force.

QUESTIONS

1. How is angular velocity related to angular speed?
2. What is the advantage of measuring angles in radians instead of in degrees?
3. (a) Can you explain how each link of a fast-rotating circular loop of chain obtains its required centripetal force to keep it moving in a circle? (b) Is such a chain under tension when it is rotating?
4. (a) How can centripetal force be used to separate molecules of different molecular weights? (b) Does this have some practical value?
5. How does one explain the fact that the diameter of the earth is 28 mi shorter through the poles than through the equator?
6. A car going around a curve tends to continue going in a straight line according to Newton's First Law of Motion. What provides the centripetal force needed to make the car accelerate toward the center of the curve?
7. (a) Why is it usually possible for a sports car to negotiate a tight curve at a higher speed than a regular passenger car? (b) Can you think of some circumstance that would cause a seemingly safe situation to become very hazardous?
8. When an airplane makes a turn while flying, it always banks its wings. (a) What is the reason for this? (b) What would happen if the pilot forgot to do it?
9. In light planes, pilots speak of flying by "the seat of their pants." Can you explain the scientific meaning of this?
10. Suppose you are riding on a merry-go-round. (a) Describe where the centripetal and centrifugal forces are acting. (b) Are you in equilibrium? Explain.

PROBLEMS

1. An emery wheel rotates with a speed of 6000 r/min. What is the speed in (a) r/sec and (b) rad/sec?

2. A stone at the end of a string 50 cm long is whirled in a circle with a speed of 31.4 m/sec. Calculate the angular speed.

3. A mass of 2 Kg is fastened to the end of a wire 40 cm long and whirled in a circle with an angular speed of 720 r/min. (a) Calculate the speed of the 2-Kg mass. (b) Find the centripetal force.

4. A small lead weight of 2 lb is fastened to one end of a fine wire and whirled in a circle of 8-ft radius with a speed of 16 ft/sec. Find the centripetal force.

5. A weight of 2 lb is whirled at 60 r/min in a horizontal circle at the end of a cord 5 ft long. Neglecting gravity, what is the tension in the cord?

6. A 0.5-Kg stone is whirled at the end of a string with an angular velocity so low that the circular path lies considerably below the pivot point. If the radius of the circular path is 2 m, and the weight is equal to the centripetal force, what angle does the string make with the vertical? What is the tension in the string?

7. A 30-lb dumbbell is tossed into the air so that it is spinning end-over-end with an angular speed of 3 r/sec. What is the tension in the 9-inch rod that separates the 15-lb weights?

8. A 3200-lb car traveling at 60 mi/hr rounds a curve of 800-ft radius. What is (a) the angular velocity in rad/sec, (b) the centripetal acceleration, and (c) the centripetal force?

9. A boy weighing 128 lb sits on the floor of a merry-go-round 25 ft from the center. If the coefficient of friction is 0.5, at what angular speed will he start to slide?

10. A motorcycle and rider going 80 Km/hr round a curve of 100-m radius. (a) What is the centripetal acceleration? (b) At what angle will they lean from the vertical?

11. A pail held at arm's length is swung overhead in a circle of 0.8-m radius. What is the minimum speed at the top to assure that no water spills out?

12. A car that weighs 3200 lb requires a certain centripetal force to travel in a given radius at 20 mi/hr. What force would be needed to follow the same curve at 60 mi/hr?

13. (a) In the car described in Problem 12, if the radius of the curve were reduced by one-half and the speed were doubled, what would the required force be then? (b) What would happen if the required force were not available?

14. A car weighing 4000 lb is making a turn of 200 ft radius at 40 mi/hr. Assuming a coefficient of friction of 0.6 between the tires and the road, will the car safely negotiate the turn?

PROJECTS

1. Make a simple inexpensive centrifuge that would be suitable for analysis in a chemical laboratory.

2. Make a working model of the earth showing why its shape departs from a perfect sphere.

MECHANICS

Lesson 30 *PLANETARY MOTION AND SATELLITES*

According to astronomical history, it was the early Greek philosopher Pythagoras (530 B.C.) who said "the world is round and hangs in space." "The earth," he said, "does not stand still but revolves around a central fire, called Hestia. This fire is not the sun, for the sun is illuminated, as are the planets, by reflection from Hestia."

This idea lay dormant for two thousand years before Copernicus, at the beginning of the 16th century, said "the sun stands still, and the earth and planets move in orbits around it." The observational and mathematical proof that all the planets move in elliptical orbits was first presented in 1609 when John Kepler[*] published a book containing two of his three laws, which are now known as Kepler's Laws of Planetary Motion.

Kepler's First Law. The planets move *in elliptical orbits with the sun at one of the foci.*

An ellipse can be constructed by fasten-

[*] John Kepler (1571-1630), German astronomer and philosopher, was born in Weil of a poor but noble family. Kepler was educated at the University of Maulbroon. It was in his position as professor of astronomy at Gratz that he first became interested in the planets. When he heard that Tycho Brahe had recorded great quantities of data on the motions of hundreds of stellar objects, Kepler went to Prague. There he became a close and devoted friend of Tycho Brahe, and promised this grand old man that he would tabulate and publish the recorded observations. In 1609 Kepler published his *Commentaries on Mars,* in which his first two laws of planetary motion are to be found. The third law came a little later. Kepler was a religious, but sickly, man for most of his 59 years. He was twice married, but had no children of his own, and he died penniless.

ing the two ends of a piece of string to two pins, F_1 and F_2, as shown in Fig. A. By

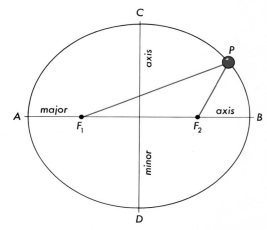

Fig. A. An ellipse can be drawn with two pins, a string, and a pencil.

keeping the string tight with a pencil at P, the complete arc can be swung around, much the same as one draws a circle with a compass.

If the length of the string remains unchanged, and the foci, F_1 and F_2, are brought closer and closer together, the major axis AB and the minor axis CD become more and more equal; at the limit when the foci coincide, the axes are equal and the ellipse becomes a circle. The real orbits of the planets are so nearly circular that, if they were drawn with a compass, the ellipse would differ from the circle by less than the thickness of the line.

The eccentricity, e, of an ellipse (see Fig. B) is defined as the ratio of the distance SQ and AQ:

$$e = \frac{SQ}{AQ} \qquad (1)$$

where AQ is the semimajor axis, a, and SQ is equal to ea. With the sun at one focus, the point, A, of closest approach is called *perihelion*, and the point, B, at the greatest

six months later at aphelion. All the areas between vectors in Fig. C are equal to each other.

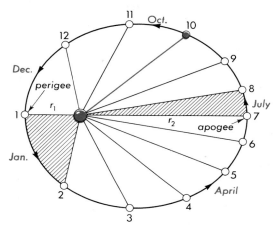

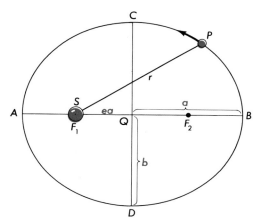

Fig. B. Elliptical orbit with an eccentricity e = 0.5.

Fig. C. Elliptical orbit of a planet, or satellite, showing equal areas swept out by the radius vector in equal intervals of time.

distance is called aphelion. A little study of Fig. B will enable the reader to find that—

$$\textbf{aphelion} = a(1 + e)$$
$$\textbf{perihelion} = a(1 - e)$$
$$\textbf{semiminor axis, } b, = a\sqrt{1 - e^2}$$

Kepler's Second Law. *The straight line joining the sun and any planet sweeps out equal areas in equal intervals of time.*

As shown in Fig. C, the straight line referred to is called the *radius vector;* it varies in length from a minimum at perihelion to a maximum at aphelion. Although the orbit of the earth is nearly circular, the numbers 1, 2, 3, 4, etc., correspond to the position of the earth at the end of each of 12 equal months.

To cover these unequal orbital distances in equal intervals of time, the speed must be a maximum at perihelion and minimum

As the earth moves along its orbit in September, October, November, etc., the attractive force of the sun causes it to speed up. Upon reaching perihelion at the end of December, its speed is a maximum and too fast to remain at this distance r_1 from the sun. During the months of March, April, May, etc., the earth is receding from the sun, and the attractive force of the sun slows the earth down. Upon reaching aphelion at the end of June, the speed of the revolving earth is a minimum, too slow to keep it at this greater distance r_2 from the sun. The average distance from the sun is 92,900,000 mi while the average orbital speed of the earth is 18.5 mi/sec.

Satellites. When a space vehicle takes off from the ground to orbit the earth as a satellite, its initial take-off direction is vertically upward. As the rocket gains height, control fins or jets are set to make it turn slowly, so that, at the moment the fuel in the last stage is exhausted, it has proper orbit speed and direction. The required precision with which this is done is extremely difficult to obtain.

To find the velocity that a space vehicle must acquire to circle the earth, consider the details of Fig. D. Imagine a tower

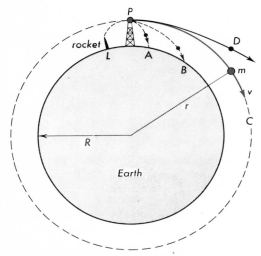

Fig. D. Horizontal projection from P with a high velocity, v, can cause a projectile, m, to circle the earth.

several hundred miles high, from the top of which projectiles are launched in a horizontal direction. With a low initial velocity, the projectile will follow a nearly parabolic path as shown at A. At a somewhat higher velocity, the trajectory will be that of path B. At a still higher velocity, the projectile in falling toward the earth will follow a circular path of radius r. This particular velocity is called the *orbiting velocity*. At still higher velocities, such as shown at D, the projectile will follow an elliptical path, or escape from the earth completely following a hyperbolic path.

For simplicity we will assume that the orbit of the satellite is circular, as shown

in Fig. E. In this diagram, M is the mass of the earth, m is the mass of a satellite, and r is the distance between their centers.

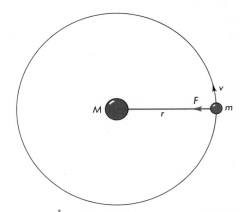

Fig. E. The gravitational force of attraction, F, is the centripetal force that keeps the satellite in its nearly circular orbit around the earth.

The centripetal force, F, as given by Eq. (8) in Lesson 29, is just the force of gravitational attraction given by Eq. (1) in Lesson 15.

$$F = m\,\frac{v^2}{r} \qquad\qquad F = G\,\frac{Mm}{r^2}$$

centripetal   Newton's law
force   of gravitation

where

$$G = 6.66 \times 10^{-11}\,\frac{m^3}{\text{Kg–sec}^2}$$

Because these two equations are different expressions for the same force F, the right-hand sides may be placed equal to each other, which gives—

$$G\,\frac{Mm}{r^2} = m\,\frac{v^2}{r}$$

Upon simplifying, this equation becomes—

$$\frac{GM}{r} = v^2 \qquad\qquad (2)$$

or—

$$v = \sqrt{GM/r} \qquad\qquad (3)$$

Note that the velocity needed at a given distance from the earth is independent of the mass of the satellite.

Example. If the earth's mass is 5.95×10^{24} Kg, and its radius is 6360 Km, what horizontal speed must be imparted to a satellite to cause it to orbit in a circle 800 Km (about 500 mi) above the earth's surface? What will be its period?

Solution. Direct substitution in Eq. (3) gives—

$$v = \sqrt{6.66 \times 10^{-11} \times 5.95 \times 10^{24} / (6360 + 800) \times 10^3}$$

$$v = \sqrt{55.4 \times 10^6 \, \frac{m^2}{sec^2}}$$

$$v = 7450 \, \frac{m}{sec}$$

This is equivalent to 16,700 mi/hr.

The distance it travels in one orbit is given by the circumference of its orbit:

$$c = 2\pi r$$

or—

$$= 2 \times 3.14 \times 7,160,000 \, m$$

Dividing this by the velocity of $7450 \, \frac{m}{sec}$ gives the time in seconds:

$$t = \frac{2 \times 3.14 \times 7,160,000 \, m}{7450 \, \frac{m}{sec}}$$

$$t = 6060 \, sec$$

or—

$$101 \, min$$

Escape Velocity. For a satellite to escape from the earth and never return, it must be launched with a velocity greater than that required to make it orbit. To find the minimum escape velocity, we make use of the concept of gravitational potential.

The work done in lifting a body from the surface of a planet of radius R, to a distance r from the center of the planet, is shown graphically in Fig. F.

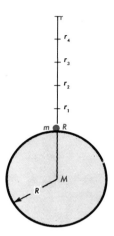

Fig. F. Diagram showing how to calculate the work done in lifting a mass, m, from the surface of a planet like the earth to a height r.

Imagine that we divide the distance from R to r into a number of small equal intervals, so that over each interval the gravitational force will be practically constant and given by a kind of average force over that interval. We can then calculate the work done for each interval and add to get the total.

At the surface, the force is $F_0 = GMm/R^2$ while at r_1 it is $F_1 = GMm/r^2$. We may, therefore, write for the average force in the first interval R to r_1—

$$F_1 = G \frac{Mm}{Rr_1}$$

and for the work done—

$$W_1 = G \frac{Mm}{Rr_1} (r_1 - R)$$

or—

$$W_1 = GMm \left(\frac{1}{R} - \frac{1}{r_1} \right)$$

In a similar way, the work done lifting

the mass through the second interval, r_1 to r_2, is found to be—

$$W_2 = GMm \left(\frac{1}{r_1} - \frac{1}{r_2} \right)$$

and, similarly, for the third interval—

$$W_3 = GMm \left(\frac{1}{r_2} - \frac{1}{r_3} \right)$$

If we add all these W's from R to r, all intermediate values cancel out, and we obtain the total:

$$W = GMm \left(\frac{1}{R} - \frac{1}{r} \right)$$

If we now choose r to be at infinity, $r = \infty$, the value $1/r = 0$, and we obtain—

$$W = G \frac{Mm}{R}$$

We can see from this simple result that, to carry a mass, m, from any point, A, at a distance r as shown in Fig. G, to infinity where

To lift a mass, m, from any point at a distance r from the center of M to infinity requires the expenditure of energy given by Eq. (4). (See Fig. G.) If we impart this energy by giving the mass a velocity, the total energy expended will be kinetic, $\frac{1}{2}mv^2$. By direct substitution in Eq. (4) of $\frac{1}{2}mv^2$ we obtain—

$$\frac{1}{2}mv^2 = m \frac{GM}{r}$$

Upon solving for v, we find that this equation gives—

$$v = \sqrt{2 \frac{GM}{r}} \qquad (6)$$

escape velocity

If we launch the mass, m, from the earth's surface, where $r = R$, we write—

$$v = \sqrt{2 \frac{GM}{R}} \qquad (7)$$

If we wish to express this escape velocity

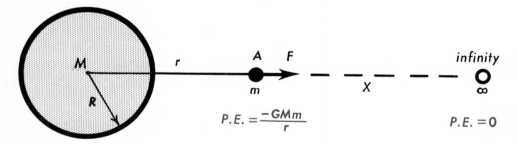

Fig. G. The potential energy of a mass, m, near the earth is negative with respect to its potential energy at infinity.

$r = \infty$, the energy expended is given by—

$$W = G \frac{Mm}{r} \qquad (4)$$

Because the work done is stored as potential energy, the potential energy of a mass, m, at any point, A, is—

$$P.E. = -G \frac{Mm}{r} \qquad (5)$$

in terms of g at the earth's surface, we can equate the force, F, given by Newton's Law of Gravitation with the force, F, given by his Second Law of Motion:

$$G \frac{Mm}{R^2} = mg$$

from which we obtain—

$$G = g \frac{R^2}{M} \qquad (8)$$

Upon the substitution of this expression for G in Eq. (7), we obtain—

$$v = \sqrt{2gR} \qquad (9)$$

where v is escape velocity from the earth's surface.

Note that this escape velocity is the square-root-of-two greater than the orbiting velocity:

$$v_{escape} = 1.41 v_{orbit} \qquad (10)$$

This relation holds for any value of r.

QUESTIONS

1. Explain how an orbiting satellite can be continuously accelerated toward the earth and still maintain the same distance from the earth's center.
2. What effect does the mass of a satellite have on the velocity required to maintain an orbit? Explain.
3. Which trip will require less fuel, a trip to the moon or the reverse? Explain.
4. What would the velocity of a satellite have to be in order to appear to be motionless in the sky?
5. Would a projectile escape the earth if it had engines capable of giving it a constant velocity of 100 mi/hr away from the center of the earth?
6. At a certain height, a satellite was supposed to have a velocity v_0 in order to remain in a circular orbit. Owing to a miscalculation, the actual velocity is 50% higher than expected. What will happen? Explain.
7. Two astronauts, Alan and John, are in satellites that are side by side in circular orbits around the earth. Alan decides to "slow down" by firing retrorockets. After one revolution around the earth Alan is ahead of John. Explain why.
8. Halley's comet appears every 75 years for several months and then departs. What sort of trajectory does it follow?

PROBLEMS

1. An ellipse is drawn with two pins placed 6 cm apart and a string 10 cm long. Find (a) the major axis, (b) the minor axis, (c) the eccentricity, (d) the apogee distance, and (e) the perigee distance.
2. An ellipse is to be drawn with a major axis of 8 m and a minor axis of 4 m. Find (a) the eccentricity, (b) the apogee distance, (c) the perigee distance, and (d) the distance between foci.
3. An ellipse is to be constructed with a major axis of 10 cm and a minor axis of 4 cm. Find (a) the eccentricity, (b) the apogee distance, (c) the perigee distance, (d) the distance between foci, and (e) the length of the string to be used.
4. A satellite is to orbit the earth at a height of 141 mi. Calculate (a) its speed, and (b) its period of revolution in min.
5. A satellite is to orbit the earth 1000 mi above the surface. Calculate (a) its speed, and (b) its period of revolution in min.

6. A satellite orbits the earth 440 mi above the surface. Find (a) its speed, and (b) its period in min.

7. (a) What must be the speed of a satellite if it is to orbit the earth 800 mi above the surface? (b) What will be its period?

8. Calculate the speed of a satellite orbiting the planet Mars at a distance of 100 Km above the surface.

9. Calculate the speed of a satellite orbiting the planet Jupiter at a distance of 200 Km above the surface.

10. Find the speed of a satellite orbiting the planet Venus at a distance of 100 mi above the surface.

11. Find the speed of a satellite orbiting the earth at a distance of 50 mi above the surface.

12. Calculate the speed of a satellite launched into a circular orbit 200 mi above the earth's surface. Assume the earth's radius to be 4000 mi.

13. What is the speed of an earth satellite launched into a circular orbit 2000 mi above the earth's surface? Assume the earth's radius to be 4000 mi.

14. Find the escape velocity of a space missile as it leaves a point 700 mi above the earth's surface.

15. Find the escape velocity from the surface of Mars.

16. Communication satellites are designed to appear to stand still in one spot in space relative to the earth. At what height and velocity must they be placed in orbit?

PROJECTS

1. Make a chart showing the actual elliptical orbit of the earth as compared to a circular one.

2. Calculate and then make a dramatic chart showing the escape velocities for the several planets.

MECHANICS

Lesson 31 *DYNAMICS OF ROTATION*

When a rigid body is acted upon by an unbalanced torque, it is set into rotation. Free to turn about an axis, such a body increases in angular velocity acquiring, when the torque ceases to act, some final speed. See Fig. A.

Angular Acceleration. Just as the acceleration of a body in linear motion is defined as the rate of change of velocity, so *the angular acceleration of a body in rotation is defined as the rate of change of angular velocity.*

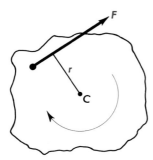

Fig. A. A rigid body is acted upon by a torque, $F \times r$.

By comparison, these two definitions are expressed the same mathematically:

$$a = \frac{\Delta v}{\Delta t} \qquad \alpha = \frac{\Delta \omega}{\Delta t}$$

linear   **angular**

The angular acceleration, α, is analogous to the linear acceleration, a, while the change in angular velocity, $\Delta \omega$, is analogous to the change in linear velocity, Δv.

If objects start from rest, these two defining equations reduce to—

$$a = \frac{v}{t} \qquad \alpha = \frac{\omega}{t} \qquad (1)$$

linear   **angular**

Upon rearranging each equation, we obtain—

$$v = at \qquad \omega = \alpha t \qquad (2)$$

linear   **angular**

A similar comparison between linear velocity and angular velocity is to be noted in the equations—

$$v = \frac{s}{t} \qquad \omega = \frac{\theta}{t} \qquad (3)$$

linear   **angular**

The following example will illustrate the meaning of, as well as an application of, the above angular formulas.

Example 1. A flywheel, starting from rest, acquires a speed of 240 r/min in 10 sec. Find the angular acceleration.

Solution. The final velocity, in radians per second, is calculated by use of Eq. (3). Since there are 2π radians in 1 revolution—

$$\omega = \frac{2\pi \times 240}{60} = 25.1 \frac{\text{rad}}{\text{sec}}$$

To find the angular acceleration, use Eq. (1):

$$\alpha = \frac{25.1 \text{ rad/sec}}{10 \text{ sec}} = 2.51 \frac{\text{rad}}{\text{sec}^2}$$

This is read two point five one radians per second per second.

It is clear from the above formulas that the quantities s, v, and a in the linear equations have only to be replaced by the corresponding angular quantities θ, ω, and α to obtain the angular equations. This direct correspondence is the result of using the radian as a unit of angular measure and holds throughout all of the formulas in mechanics.

The relation between linear quantities measured around any given circle to the angular quantities describing the same mo-

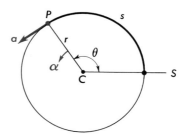

Fig. B. A wheel free to rotate about its center is given an angular acceleration.

tion are shown in Fig. B and given by the following interrelations:

$$s = r\theta \qquad (4)$$

$$v = r\omega \qquad (5)$$

$$a = r\alpha \qquad (6)$$

Kinematics of Rotation. The term kinematics of rotation refers to a quantitative description of motion such as that given above. To complete the customary set of formulas for circular motion, we need write down only the four linear equations for acceleration from rest, used so many times in the preceding lessons, and the rotational counterparts as follows:

$$v = at \qquad \omega = \alpha t \qquad (7)$$

$$s = \frac{v}{2}t \qquad \theta = \frac{\omega}{2}t \qquad (8)$$

$$v^2 = 2as \qquad \omega^2 = 2\alpha\theta \qquad (9)$$

$$s = \tfrac{1}{2}at^2 \qquad \theta = \tfrac{1}{2}\alpha t^2 \qquad (10)$$

Example 2. An automobile engine, starting from rest, is given an angular acceleration of 20 rad/sec^2 for 10 sec. Find (a) the angular velocity acquired, (b) the total angle turned through, and (c) the total number of revolutions.

Solution. The given quantities are $\alpha = 20$ rad/sec, and $t = 10$ sec. To find the angular velocity, ω, use Eq. (7):

(a) $\qquad \omega = 20 \dfrac{\text{rad}}{\text{sec}^2} \times 10 \text{ sec} = 200 \dfrac{\text{rad}}{\text{sec}}$

To find the angle θ, use Eq. (8) or Eq. (10). Using Eq. (8), we find—

(b) $\qquad \theta = \dfrac{200 \text{ rad/sec}}{2} \times 10 \text{ sec}$

$\qquad \theta = 1000 \text{ rad}$

To find the number of revolutions, divide by 2π:

(c) $\qquad \theta = \dfrac{1000 \text{ rad}}{2\pi} = 159 \text{ rev}$

Dynamics of Rotation. In the treatment of angular acceleration given in the preceding sections of this lesson, neither the torques causing the acceleration nor the mass of the rotating body entered into the calculations. When these two factors are introduced into the equations, the treatment is referred to as the *dynamics of rotation.*

When a specified torque is applied to a body free to rotate about some axis, the angular acceleration produced depends not only upon the size and shape of the body but also upon the distribution of the mass with respect to the axis of rotation.

To see how these factors are taken into account, consider the simplest kind of an example, namely, two identical masses, m, on a crossbar, free to rotate about a vertical axis as shown in Fig. C. The cord wrapped

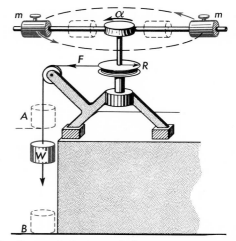

Fig. C. An experimental demonstration of moment of inertia.

around the drum, R, and passing over a pulley to the weight, W, gives rise to a constant force, F, and hence a constant torque to angularly accelerate the system.

When the masses are clamped at equal distances from, and half way out on, the arms, the angular acceleration is relatively large, and the weight, W, exerting the constant torque, L, quickly drops from A to B. When the masses, m, are moved to the outer ends of the arms where their distance, r, is doubled, the angular acceleration is reduced to ¼ and the weight W takes twice as long to go from A to B.

Moment of Inertia. We see by this experiment that, under the action of a constant torque, the angular acceleration depends upon the distribution of the mass with respect to the axis of rotation. This is not analogous to linear motion, because a constant force, F, applied to a mass, m, will produce a constant acceleration, a, independent of the shape of the body. To retain the similarity between linear and rotational formulas we write—

$$F = ma \qquad L = I\alpha \qquad (11)$$
$$\text{linear} \qquad \text{angular}$$

and thereby introduce a new quantity, I, called the *moment of inertia. The moment of inertia, I, in rotary motion takes the shape and mass into account and is analogous to* m *in the force equation.*

Example 3. Find the moment of inertia of a mass, m, which is a distance r from the axis of rotation.

Solution. Let us try to relate the linear and angular forms of Eq. (11). First, note that, from the definition of torque—

$$F = L/r$$

Then using the relation—

$$a = \alpha r$$

these formulas may be substituted into Newton's Second Law—

$$F = ma$$

to obtain—

$$\frac{L}{r} = m\alpha r$$

or—

$$L = mr^2 \times \alpha$$

According to the angular form of Eq. (11)—

$$I = mr^2$$

The moment of inertia of a body, with respect to any axis, is the sum of the products obtained by multiplying each elementary mass by the square of its distance from the axis. To illustrate, consider the uniform ring and the thin rod as shown in Fig. D.

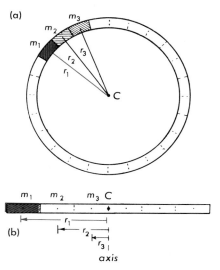

Fig. D. Diagram showing the division of (a) a ring, and (b) a rod, into small masses for calculating their moments of inertia.

Both the ring and the rod are divided into small parts, as shown by the dotted lines and shaded areas, and the moment of inertia, I, is calculated from the formula—

$$I = m_1 r_1^2 + m_2 r_2^2 + m_3 r_3^2 + \cdots \quad (12)$$

where m_1, m_2, m_3, ... represent the masses of each small part, and r_1, r_2, r_3, ... , their respective distances from the axis of rotation.

Because r has the same value for all masses around the ring, the subscripts on the r's can be dropped:

$$I = m_1 r^2 + m_2 r^2 + m_3 r^2 + \cdots$$

and the common factor, r^2, taken out as follows:

$$I = (m_1 + m_2 + m_3 + \cdots)r^2$$

Because the sum of all the masses $m_1 +$

$m_2 + m_3 + \ldots$ equals M, the total mass of the ring—

$$I_{\text{ring}} = Mr^2 \qquad (13)$$

This is the same as the formula for a mass on the end of a string.

When the same procedure is applied to the rod in Fig. D, the values of r vary from mass to mass, and the calculations, using Eq. (12), give only an approximate value of its moment of inertia. It is not difficult to show that the larger the number of parts into which the rod is divided, the more nearly will Eq. (12) give the true moment of inertia. A derivation of the formula by which the true moment of inertia is usually calculated requires the integral calculus and gives—

$$I_{\text{rod}} = \frac{1}{12} Ml^2 \qquad (14)$$

where M is the total mass of the rod and l its total length. Because the calculus method is beyond the scope of this book, this formula should be assumed to be correct. To illustrate the approximate method and to compare it with this correct formula, consider the following example:

Example 4. A uniform rod, 12 m long and having a mass of 30 Kg, is pivoted to turn about an axis through its center, perpendicular to its length. Calculate its moment of inertia by (a) the true formula, and (b) the approximate formula.

Solution. (a) Direct substitution in Eq. (14) gives—

$$I = \frac{1}{12} \times 30 \text{ Kg} \times (12)^2 \text{ m}^2 = 360 \text{ Kg m}^2$$

as the true moment of inertia.

(b) By dividing the rod into six equal parts as shown in Fig. D, six masses are yielded of 5 Kg each with distances 5 m, 3 m, 1 m, 1 m, 3 m, and 5 m, respectively. Applying Eq. (12), we obtain—

$$I = 5 \times 5^2 + 5 \times 3^2 + 5 \times 1^2 + 5 \times 1^2 \\ + 5 \times 3^2 + 5 \times 5^2 = 350 \text{ Kg m}^2$$

a value nearly 3% lower than the true value.

Should the rod in part (b) have been divided into twelve equal parts, the same summation process would give 357.5 Kg m^2, a value less than 1% lower than (a). Confirm this last result as an exercise.

The true moments of inertia of a number of regularly shaped solid bodies are given in Fig. E. Diagram (a) represents a thin

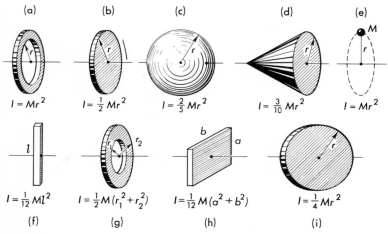

(a)   (b)   (c)   (d)   (e)

$I = Mr^2$ $I = \frac{1}{2}Mr^2$ $I = \frac{2}{5}Mr^2$ $I = \frac{3}{10}Mr^2$ $I = Mr^2$

$I = \frac{1}{12}Ml^2$ $I = \frac{1}{2}M(r_1^2 + r_2^2)$ $I = \frac{1}{12}M(a^2 + b^2)$ $I = \frac{1}{4}Mr^2$

(f)   (g)   (h)   (i)

Fig. E. Formulas for the moment of inertia of certain regularly shaped bodies.

ring, or hoop, of radius r, (b) a disk of uniform density, (c) a solid sphere with an axis through the center, etc.

Kinetic Energy of Rotation. When a body is in a state of rotation, it possesses kinetic energy. It possesses this energy because, in being brought to rest, it may be made to do work. To calculate the amount of energy stored up in a rotating body, an equation analogous to the linear equation is used:

$$K.E. = \tfrac{1}{2}mv^2 \qquad K.E. = \tfrac{1}{2}I\omega^2 \quad (15)$$
$$\text{linear} \qquad\qquad \text{angular}$$

As might well be expected, the moment of inertia enters into the rotational energy.

Example 5. A large grindstone, with a mass of 20 Kg and radius 50 cm, is rotating with an angular speed of 300 r/min. Calculate its kinetic energy.

Solution. To use Eq. (15), we must first calculate I and then ω. From diagram (b) in Fig. E we find—

$$I = \tfrac{1}{2}Mr^2$$
$$I = \tfrac{1}{2}\ 20\ \text{Kg} \times (.5\ \text{m})^2$$
$$I = 2.5\ \text{Kg m}^2$$

Dividing 300 r/min by 60, we obtain an angular speed of 5 r/sec. Multiplying by 2π, we find $\omega = 31.4$ rod/sec. Using Eq. (15), we can now substitute, to find—

$$K.E. = \tfrac{1}{2}I\omega^2$$
$$K.E. = \tfrac{1}{2}\ 2.5\ \text{Kg m}^2 \times (31.4\ \text{rod/sec})^2$$
$$K.E. = 1230\ \frac{\text{Kg m}^2}{\text{sec}^2}$$
$$K.E. = 1230\ \text{joules}$$

QUESTIONS

1. What is the difference between the kinematics of rotation and the dynamics of rotation?

2. What are the angular counterparts of the following linear quantities: (a) acceleration, (b) force, (c) mass, and (d) distance? Give the appropriate mks units.

3. (a) Why is the moment of inertia of the body in Fig. E(a) the same as that in Fig. E(e)? (b) Why is that in Fig. E(b) less?

4. Without altering its mass, (a) how can the moment of inertia of a body be increased? (b) How can it be decreased?

5. A uniform disk, a solid ball, and a metal hoop all have the same mass and diameter. (a) Which one has the largest moment of inertia? (b) Which one has the smallest?

6. (a) Sketch a picture of a door, and indicate the central axis about which the door would have the greatest moment of inertia. (b) About which central axis would the door have the smallest moment of inertia?

7. State Newton's three laws using only angular quantities.

8. In the cases illustrated in Fig. E, which factor is more important in relation to rotational inertia, mass or size of the object?

9. If you drew a graph of the relation between rotational inertia and the radius of a sphere, (a) what would the shape of the graph be? (b) Do it if you are not sure.

10. (a) In a one-cylinder gasoline engine, what physical property of the flywheel

is being used? (b) Would a large diameter flywheel be better than a smaller, thicker one of identical mass?

11. When a car is in motion, (a) what parts of the car have rotational inertia? (b) What part has linear inertia?

PROBLEMS

1. Starting from rest, the large flywheel of a steam engine acquires a speed of 650 r/min in one min. Find the angular acceleration in rad/sec².

2. An automobile engine is idling at 400 r/min. Upon acceleration, it acquires a speed of 3000 r/min in 2 sec. Calculate the angular acceleration.

3. An emery wheel 1 ft in diameter is making 3600 r/min. Find (a) the tangential velocity of a point on the rim, and (b) the distance traveled in 8 sec by a point midway between the rim and center.

4. A uniform ring of 6-Kg mass has an internal diameter of 16 cm and an external diameter of 20 cm. Find its moment of inertia.

5. A solid ball, with a mass of 150 Kg and radius of 50 cm, rotates about an axis through its center at 4 r/sec. Find its kinetic energy in joules.

6. An emery wheel, 30 cm in diameter and of 2-Kg mass, rotates at 4000 r/min. Find (a) its moment of inertia and (b) its kinetic energy.

7. Starting with the linear expression for kinetic energy, derive the angular expression (Eq. 15). Use a mass whirled at the end of a string in this derivation.

8. A jack is an object consisting of three rods intersecting each other at 90°. If the jack has mass m, and the rods each have length r, what is its moment of inertia about one of the rods as an axis? Assume the rods to be very thin, and consider Fig. E(f).

9. A 2-Kg disk of uniform density has a 15-cm radius. If it is rolling along at 2 m/sec, what is its kinetic energy? Remember that it has both linear and angular energy.

10. A 3-Kg emery wheel, rotating at 3200 r/min, is turned off. Assuming that it has a diameter of 40 cm, what is the frictional torque of its bearing if it takes three minutes to come to a stop?

PROJECT

Make a variety of balls and hoops of the same diameter and mass. Roll them down an inclined plane and try to predict which will roll down the fastest.

MECHANICS

Lesson 32 *CONSERVATION OF ANGULAR MOMENTUM*

In our previous lessons on rotating bodies, we have seen that, by expressing all angles in radian measure rather than in degrees, the various formulas for angular motion became identical in form with the corresponding linear formulas. It is the purpose of this lesson to extend our study of the mechanics of rotation to include angular momentum.

Angular Momentum. We have seen that, when a constant force, F, is applied to a mass, m, for a period of time, t, the velocity, v, it acquires is given by the impulse equation:

$$Ft = mv \qquad (1)$$

A comparison of such motion with its rotational counterpart is shown in Fig. A. If

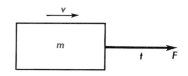

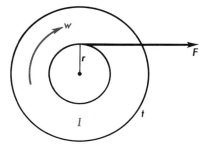

Fig. A. Comparison of linear motion with rotational motion.

we replace the linear symbols in Eq. (1) by those for rotational motion, we obtain—

$$Lt = I\omega \qquad (2)$$

where ω is the angular velocity, I is the moment of inertia, and L is the torque given by $F \times r$. In linear motion, Ft is the impulse, and mv the momentum. In rotational motion, Lt is the angular impulse and $I\omega$ the angular momentum.

Example. The wheel of a grindstone (see Fig. A) has applied at its axle, 2 cm in radius, a constant tangential force of 600 newtons. Find the angular momentum acquired at the end of 8 sec.

Solution. Begin by calculating the torque, L:

$$L = F \times r$$
$$L = 600 \times 0.02$$
$$L = 12 \text{ newton meters}$$

By direct substitution in Eq. (2), we obtain—

$$Lt = 12 \times 8 \, I\omega$$
$$I\omega = 96 \text{ newton m sec}$$

Consider the case of a mass, m, on the end of a string, rotating in a circle, as shown in Fig. B. The moment of inertia of this mass is given by Mr^2. (See Fig. E(e) in Lesson 31.)

$$I = Mr^2$$

In a previous lesson, we have also seen that the angular velocity, ω, is given by v/r:

$$\omega = \frac{v}{r}$$

Therefore, the angular momentum, $I\omega$, of this special case is given by—

$$I\omega = Mr^2 \times \frac{v}{r}$$

$$I\omega = Mvr \qquad (3)$$

Conservation of Angular Momentum.
Just as there is a law of conservation of mo-

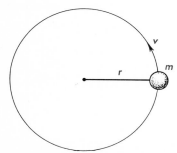

Fig. B. A ball of mass, *m*, whirling in a circle at the end of a string has an angular momentum *mvr*.

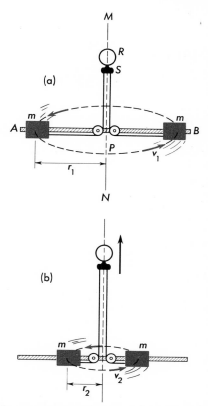

Fig. C. Experimental demonstration of the conservation of angular momentum.

mentum for bodies moving in a straight line, so also is there a law of conservation of angular momentum for bodies in rotation. *In an isolated system, on which no external torques act, angular momentum is conserved.* This law can best be illustrated by an experiment as shown in Fig. C.

Two equal masses, *m*, mounted on a rod, *AB*, are capable of rotation about a vertical axis, *MN*. Cords fastened to each mass and leading over pulleys at *P* to the ring, *R*, enable the radial distance to be changed from r_1 in (*a*) and to r_2 in (*b*) by simply pulling up on the ring *R*. The swivel, *S*, prevents the cords from twisting.

When the system is first set rotating, as in (*a*), with an angular velocity ω_1, the angular momentum of each mass is $I_1\omega_1$. On pulling up on the ring, *R*, the radius decreases to r_2 and the angular velocity ω_2 increases. Conservation of angular momentum requires that—

$$I_1\omega_1 = I_2\omega_2 \qquad (4)$$

Because this particular demonstration involves masses rotating as shown in Fig. B, Eq. (3) can be invoked, and we can write—

$$Mv_1r_1 = Mv_2r_2 \qquad (5)$$

Conservation of angular momentum, therefore, requires the product of these three quantities to remain constant. We can readily see that, if *r* decreases, *v* must increase, while if *r* increases, *v* must decrease. More specifically, the angular velocity is inversely proportional to the moment of inertia.

An interesting experiment illustrating the same principle is diagramed in Fig. D. An observer stands on a turntable with weights in each hand. With arms fully extended horizontally, he is first set rotating slowly. Upon drawing the hands and weights in toward the chest as shown, the angular speed is considerably increased. This experiment is best appreciated by the turning observer who feels himself speeded up by what seems to be a mysterious force.

Fig. D. Experiments illustrating conservation of angular momentum.

The kinetic energy of rotation in each of these two experiments increases as the masses are pulled in closer to the center of rotation. This increase is due to the fact that work, equal to force times distance, must be done to pull them in.

This principle is used by expert figure skaters on the ice. They start into a whirl with their arms and perhaps one leg extended, and then upon drawing the arms and leg in, they obtain a greatly increased angular speed. Again, by decreasing the moment of inertia, the angular velocity must increase, because conservation of angular momentum requires the product of these quantities to remain constant.

Angular Momentum a Vector. Angular momentum, as illustrated by the rotating wheel in Fig. E, may be treated as a vector quantity. To obtain an angular momentum

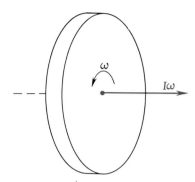

Fig. E. Angular momentum may be represented by a vector.

vector, imagine grasping the axis of rotation with the right hand, the fingers pointing in the direction of rotation, the thumb then pointing in the direction of the vector. The length of the vector is given by the magnitude of $I\omega$.

Because the angular momentum, $I\omega$, is the result of an applied angular impulse, Lt, the vector for $I\omega$ in Fig. E also represents Lt. In other words, Lt is a vector quantity, and its direction and magnitude is that of $I\omega$. Torque is likewise a vector quantity. Its magnitude is given by $r \times F$, and its direction is given by the right-hand rule above.

The advantage of representing angular momentum and angular impulse by vectors becomes apparent when attempting to determine the resultant motion of a body that undergoes rotation about two or more axes simultaneously. The gyroscope in some of its varied forms serves as a good illustration of this.

Gyroscopic Stability. If a balanced gyroscope wheel is mounted in gimbal rings as shown in Fig. F, it will exhibit a property

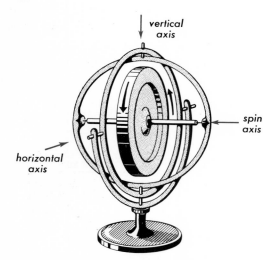

Fig. F. Gyroscope mounted in gimbal rings for demonstrating gyroscopic stability.

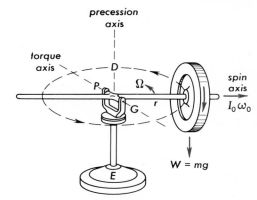

Fig. G. Experimental gyroscope for demonstrating precession.

called *gyroscopic stability* when set spinning at high speeds. When the gyro is picked up and carried about, the base can be turned in any direction without altering the direction of the spin axis relative to the earth. In other words, the plane of the gyro wheel seems to have assumed a rigidity in space.

To change the direction of the *spin axis* a torque must be exerted upon it. It is the function of the gimbal ring mounting to allow the base support to be turned in any way without exerting any torque whatever upon the wheel.

Newton's First Law of Motion, involving the inertia of a body, has its rotational counterpart in the above experiment. *A body in rotation about some fixed axis will continue to rotate about that same axis with constant angular momentum unless it is acted upon by an unbalanced torque.*

Precession. A fundamental study of gyroscopic precession may be readily made as diagramed in Fig. G. The wheel, W, is designed to have a large moment of inertia,

and is often ball-bearing mounted. Free rotation in any direction is permitted by the double pivot at the top of the stand, E.

When the wheel is set spinning at high speed and released with its axis in a horizontal position, a smooth *precession* takes place around the vertical axis. That is, one end of the axis falls away from starting position and describes a cone around that position. This precessional motion is due to the external force exerted by the earth's gravitational pull downward on the wheel. Acting through the wheel's center of gravity, this downward force, W, equal to mg, exerts a torque about a horizontal axis through PG. This torque, L, given by $r \times W$, and acting for a time t, constitutes a torque impulse Lt and gives rise to a corresponding angular momentum $(I\omega)'$ about the same axis.

The wheel, therefore, has two angular momenta, one $I_0\omega_0$ due to spin and the other $(I\omega)'$ about a horizontal axis PG. Combining these vectorially, as shown in Fig. H we obtain a resultant, R, equal in magnitude to the original $I_0\omega_0$ and now making an angle ϕ with its direction. In other words, there has been a precession, a change in the direction of the spin axis.

By analogy, the treatment above is similar to that of circular motion given in Fig.

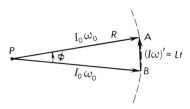

Fig. H. Vector diagram for precession of a gyroscope.

E in Lesson 29. There, a mass moves in a circle at constant speed, because a constant inward force is exerted upon it. Although the acceleration is toward the center, the radius remains constant, while only the direction of v changes.

In precessional motion, the magnitude of the angular momentum remains constant while its direction changes smoothly and continuously.

The Spinning Top. A common top, set spinning like the one shown in Fig. I, is a good illustration of angular momentum. It is but one of the many forms of gyroscopes. Spinning about its axis, the top precesses about its peg, or pivot point, the line AB describing an inverted cone about the vertical line AC. If, when observed from above,

such a top is spinning in a clockwise direction, the precession is clockwise; spinning counterclockwise, the precession is counterclockwise.

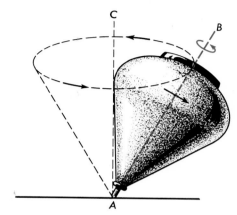

Fig. I. A spinning top precesses around a vertical axis.

Under certain circumstances, the spin axis follows a scalloped circle, rather than the smooth circle shown in Fig. I. This additional motion is called *nutation*. On the other hand, if the top is spinning fast enough, it will not nutate or precess at all, but will "sleep" with its axis vertical.

QUESTIONS

1. (a) What is an angular impulse? (b) What are its units?
2. Under what conditions does the law of conservation of angular momentum apply?
3. (a) What is inertia? (b) What is rotational inertia? (c) Because mass is a quantitative measure of inertia, what quantity is a measure of rotational inertia?
4. (a) What is a gyroscope? (b) Should a gyroscope have a large moment of inertia? If so, why? (c) Why should the wheel of a gyroscope be well balanced?
5. (a) Is an astronaut in a space capsule an "isolated system"? (b) To what does conservation of angular momentum apply: the astronaut, the capsule, or the whole system? Why?
6. (a) How could an astronaut apply an external torque to his capsule? (b) An internal torque? (c) How could he make the capsule rotate using internal torque only?

7. A space pilot in a rocket ship starts a top spinning and then drops it over-board. Does this action start the rocket ship rotating? Explain.

8. Two equal weights are tied to the ends of a string and a bowknot tied in the string. Shortly after the two are thrown spinning into the air the bowknot comes untied. What happens to the angular velocity and the angular momentum?

9. (a) How can a rapidly spinning ice skater slow down? (b) Having once slowed down can he speed again without adding additional energy? Explain.

10. (a) Explain how a gyroscope could be used to make a ship go on a more even keel in heavy seas. (b) Is your idea a practical one?

11. A helicopter has a spinning wing to provide lift. (a) How is it possible to prevent the helicopter from spinning in the opposite direction? (b) Because there is no propeller in front or a jet to cause forward motion, how does a heli-copter gain forward velocity?

PROBLEMS

1. A 4-Kg ball at the end of a wire 5 m long is whirled in a circle with a speed of 20 m/sec. Calculate its (a) moment of inertia and (b) angular momentum.

2. A 500-gm stone at the end of a string 50 cm long is whirled in a circle with a speed of 3 m/sec. Calculate its angular momentum.

3. A solid ball of mass 5 Kg and diameter 20 cm is rotating about an axis through its center. If the angular speed is 5 r/sec, find the angular momentum.

4. The rotating parts of an automobile motor have a moment of inertia equivalent to that of a uniform disk 1 ft in diameter and weighing 64 lb. (a) What is its moment of inertia in slugs ft²? (b) Find its angular momentum when rotating at 6000 r/min.

5. A 200-gm top, shaped like a cone, has a 6-cm diameter as measured across its face. To spin it, a string is wrapped around it halfway down, where the diameter is 3 cm, and it is pulled by a 2-newton force for 3 sec. (a) What is its angular momentum? (b) Its angular velocity?

6. A gyroscope in a rocket ship has a moment of inertia of 12 Kg m² and an angular speed of 18,000 r/min. The rest of the rocket ship has a moment of inertia of 150 Kg m². (a) What is the angular momentum of the system? (b) If the pilot brings the gyroscope to a stop, relative to the ship, what is the angular velocity of the rocket ship?

7. A 300-Kg space capsule is spherically shaped with roughly uniform density, and 2.5-m diameter. A total of 10 gm of gas can be discharged tangentially from two jets attached to the outer surface. What must be the exhaust velocity of the gas, if the astronaut is to stop the capsule from tumbling at 0.5 rad/sec?

8. A free-spinning disk, 22 ft in diameter, weighs 240 lb and is rotating at 0.3 r/sec. A boy weighing 100 lb jumps onto the wheel and skids to a stop 5 ft from the edge. What is the angular velocity of the boy and the wheel?

PROJECTS

1. Make a rotating chair that will enable a person to rotate while sitting in it. Have the person hold two heavy weights in his hands and set him in rotation. Watch the effect on his rotation as he moves his arms and weights away from and toward his body.
2. Make a demonstration gyrocompass and test its effectiveness compared to a magnetic compass.

Properties of Matter

Proposition 7. *A solid heavier than a fluid will, if placed in it, descend to the bottom of the fluid, and the solid will, when weighed in the fluid, be lighter than its true weight by the weight of the fluid displaced.*

Archimedes, On Floating Bodies, Book I

Proposition 1. *If a solid lighter than a fluid be at rest in it, the weight of the solid will be to that of the same volume of the fluid as the immersed portion of the solid is to the whole.*

Archimedes, On Floating Bodies, Book II

Or take a Wire string of twenty, or thirty, or forty foot long, and fasten the upper part thereof to a nail, and to the other end fasten a Scale to receive the weights: Then with a pair of Compasses take the distance of the bottom of the scale from the ground or floor underneath, and set down the said distance, then put in weights into the said scale in the same manner as in the former trials, and measure the several stretchings of the said string, and set them down. Then compare the several stretchings of the said string, and you will find that they will always bear the same proportions one to the other that the weights do that made them.

Robert Hooke, *POTENTIA RESTITUTIVA, or Spring,* London, 1678.

◀ **The properties of materials and the forces of wind and rushing water have helped to shape the picturesque valley of Crooked Creek, California.**

U.S. Geological Survey

Lesson 33 *ATOMIC THEORY OF MATTER*

In dealing with the physical properties of matter, it is convenient to divide substances into three forms or states: (1) *the solid state*, (2) *the liquid state*, and (3) *the gaseous state*. Most substances may be made to take on any one of these three forms simply by altering the temperature.

The atomic theory of matter assumes that all matter in the universe is made up of ultramicroscopic particles, called atoms, and that these are at all times in a rapid state of motion. The nature of this motion and its activity depends upon the temperature and the state of the matter, as well as upon the kinds of atoms of which it is composed.

Kinds of Atoms. Although there are thousands of different substances known to the scientific world they all, when broken down into their smallest component parts, are found to be composed of one or more kinds of atoms. A substance that contains atoms of one kind only is called an *element*, while those containing more than one kind are called *compounds* or *mixtures*. Iron, aluminum, platinum, mercury, hydrogen, and helium are examples of elements; whereas water, salt, brass, wood, and air are examples of compounds and mixtures.

The technical names and chemical abbreviations of a few of the more commonly known elements are given in Table 1. A complete table of the more than one hundred known elements is given in the Appendix.

With each element, it is customary to associate two numbers: one is the *atomic number*, the other the *atomic weight*. The atomic number, given at the left in the tables, specifies the position that element always occupies with respect to all the others, while the atomic weight, on the right, gives the average weight of one atom

Table 1. Some of the Chemical Elements

Atomic No.	Element	Symbol	Atomic Weight*
1	hydrogen	H	1.0080
2	helium	He	4.003
3	lithium	Li	6.94
4	beryllium	Be	9.01
6	carbon	C	12.01**
7	nitrogen	N	14.01
8	oxygen	O	16.00
10	neon	Ne	20.18
13	aluminum	Al	26.98
26	iron	Fe	55.85
50	tin	Sn	118.69
78	platinum	Pt	195.09
79	gold	Au	196.97
80	mercury	Hg	200.59
82	lead	Pb	207.19
88	radium	Ra	225.95
92	uranium	U	238.03
94	plutonium	Pu	239.18

* Based on the weight of the carbon-12 isotope having a mass of 12.0000.

** Natural carbon contains a small amount of the isotope carbon-13 (See Lesson 99).

of that element relative to the weight of the carbon-12 atom, taken as exactly 12. On this basis, the atom of the lightest known element, hydrogen, has an average weight of approximately unity.

Atomic weights increase with increasing atomic number, the four exceptions being 19, potassium; 28, nickel; 53, iodine; and 91, protoactinium.

To illustrate the minuteness of individual atoms, the actual masses in grams and approximate diameters in centimeters of the lightest element, hydrogen, and the very heavy element, plutonium, are as follows:

1. hydrogen $\begin{cases} \text{mass} = 1.66 \times 10^{-24} \text{ gm} \\ \text{diameter} = 1 \times 10^{-8} \text{ cm} \end{cases}$

94. plutonium $\begin{cases} \text{mass} = 3.9 \times 10^{-22} \text{ gm} \\ \text{diameter} = 6 \times 10^{-8} \text{ cm} \end{cases}$

The actual mass of any atom in grams can be obtained by multiplying the atomic weight of that element by the unit atomic mass, 1.66×10^{-24} gm.

Although the intricate structure of each atom plays an important part in its physical and chemical behavior, we will neglect this detailed structure for the time being and think only of each atom as being a tiny sphere-like particle with a very small mass.

In other lessons the structure of individual atoms will be considered in detail.

Molecules. One of the most important properties of atoms is their ability to act upon one another at a distance. Some atoms, when they come close together, attract each other, while others exhibit a force of repulsion. When, at the close approach of two or more atoms, attraction occurs, the atoms may combine to form a molecule. Once a molecule has formed, it will move about and behave as a unit particle under various physical conditions.

Molecules in general may contain almost any number of atoms. Those having but one atom are *monatomic molecules,* those with two are *diatomic molecules,* and those with three, *triatomic molecules.*

Examples of monatomic molecules are helium (He), neon (Ne), and krypton

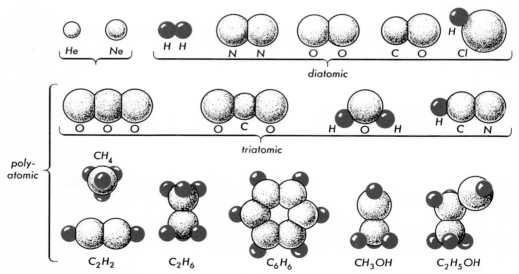

Fig. A. Schematic diagrams of a few common molecules. First Row: helium, neon, hydrogen, nitrogen, oxygen, carbon monoxide, hydrochloric acid. Second Row: ozone, carbon dioxide, water, hydrocyanic acid. Third Row: methane, acetylene, ethane, benzene, methyl alcohol, ethyl alcohol.

(Kr); of diatomic molecules are hydrogen (H_2), nitrogen (N_2), oxygen (O_2), and carbon monoxide (CO); and of triatomic molecules are ozone (O_3), carbon dioxide (CO_2), water (H_2O), and hydrocyanic acid (HCN). See Fig. A. Besides these simplest atomic aggregates there are molecules known to contain many atoms. Along with triatomic molecules, they are called *polyatomic molecules*. It is clear from the diagrams in Fig. A that the atoms of a molecule may be of the same kind or different.

The question as to why some atoms cling together in pairs, and others do not, is a subject involving the structure of the atoms themselves. If the individual atoms of a molecule are brought much closer together than their normal separation, they repel each other and are pushed apart. If they are pulled farther apart, the forces become attractive, pulling them together. In other words, they act as though they were connected by springs as shown in Fig. B. Pushed closer together or pulled

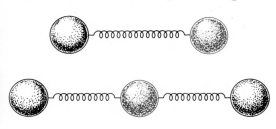

Fig. B. The forces between atoms in a molecule behave like springs.

farther apart, they tend to move back to some equilibrium distance. In terms of energy, they occupy a position of *minimum potential energy*. To push them closer together or to separate them requires work.

At large distances, all atomic forces become very weak so that if, by some means or

other, the atoms of a molecule are pulled far enough apart, they become completely separated as free atoms. A graph of the forces between atoms is shown in Fig. C.

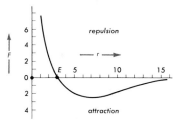

Fig. C. Typical graph of the force between the two atoms of a diatomic molecule.

The horizontal scale, giving the distance r between atoms, will be slightly different for different atoms, but the equilibrium position, E, is approximately 3×10^{-10} meters.

Molecular Weight. The molecular weight of a substance is defined as the sum of the atomic weights of the atoms that make up one molecule of the substance. A carbon dioxide molecule, for example, has two oxygen atoms of weight 16 and one carbon atom of weight 12. The molecular weight of carbon dioxide is therefore $16 + 16 + 12 = 44$. Similarly, the molecular weight of nitrogen is 28, oxygen is 32, and helium is 4. To find the mass of a single molecule in grams, its molecular weight should be multiplied by unit atomic mass 1.66×10^{-24} gm.

Three States of Matter. As already stated, matter may exist in three states: (1) the solid state, (2) the liquid state, and (3) the gaseous state. If a solid is heated sufficiently, it can be made to melt or liquefy, and by continued heating can be boiled or vaporized. As a vapor, it is in the gaseous state. If, on the other hand, a gas is cooled sufficiently, it will condense and become a liquid. The continued cooling of a liquid will cause it to solidify or freeze. In the case of water, nature performs all these changes of state: ice is melted to become water, and water is vaporized to become steam; water vapor or clouds condense to become rain, and rain freezes to become ice or hail. Although it may sometimes require extreme heat or extreme cold, all substances can be transformed from any one state to another, if they do not decompose in the process.

Brownian Motion. Although no one has ever observed directly the random motions of molecules, it is possible to observe in a microscope the resultant recoils of larger particles under their continual bombardment. The effect was first discovered in 1827 by Robert Brown, a British botanist, who observed the irregular but "lifelike"

then another. Such motions are called *Brownian movements*, after the name of their discoverer.

One method of observing Brownian motion in a gas is illustrated in Fig. D. Smoke from the tip of a match, just extinguished, is drawn into a small box by squeezing and releasing the rubber bulb. A strong beam of light from an arc light, entering the box through a glass lens in the side, illuminates the smoke particles, enabling them to be seen from above with a high-power microscope. The tiny smoke particles appear as bright, starlike points, darting first one way then another.

The Solid State. As the temperature of a liquid is lowered, the molecular activity decreases. This permits the atoms to pack a little more closely together and accounts for the slight contraction of a liquid on cool-

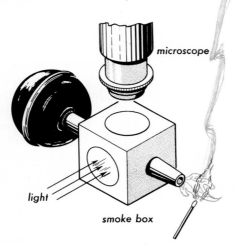

Fig. D. Experimental arrangement for observing the Brownian motion of smoke particles.

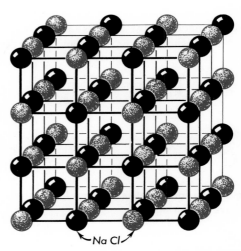

Fig. E. Atomic model for sodium chloride (NaCl is common table salt).

motions of small particles suspended in a liquid. These microscopic particles appear to be continually agitated and make a succession of quick jumps first one way and

ing and, conversely, for its expansion on heating. As they come closer and closer together, the tendency of each atom to wander through the liquid decreases. If the temperature is lowered still further, a point is ultimately reached where the liquid freezes and becomes a solid.

In the solid state, each atom is confined to a definite small space between neighboring atoms. This is illustrated in Fig. E by an atomic model of an ultramicroscopic crystal. The model illustrates a cubic lattice, a simple type of structure in which the atoms take positions at the corners of cubes. Common table salt with its two kinds of atoms, sodium and chlorine, always forms such a cubic lattice, the individual atoms alternating in kind in each of the three directions, Na, Cl, Na, Cl, Na, etc.

Actual photographs of two crystals shown in Fig. F clearly show the tendency

Fig. F. Natural crystals of quartz and calcite.

for substances to take on regular forms upon solidifying. Quartz is composed of silicon and oxygen, while calcite is composed of calcium, carbon, and oxygen.

QUESTIONS

1. (a) What are the three states of matter? (b) How do these states differ from each other? (c) Which, in general, is the most compact? (d) Give three examples of each state.

2. How do you explain the fact that water, contrary to most other substances, expands when it solidifies?

3. (a) Where would ice be formed in a pond if it behaved like most other substances? (b) Would this make any difference to living things in the pond?

4. What general treatment of most solids will change their state to the liquid or gas?

5. (a) How could you make liquid salt? (b) Could you use the same method for making liquid sugar? Explain.

6. (a) How many known elements are there? (b) What constitutes an element?

7. What is meant by (a) atomic number and (b) atomic weight? (c) How is the atomic weight related to weight in grams?

8. Give an example of a (a) monatomic molecule, (b) diatomic molecule, (c) triatomic molecule, and (d) polyatomic molecule.

9. Why are not the newly man-made elements found in nature at present?

10. (a) Can you tell by looking at water that it is a compound and not an element? Why? (b) How would you go about proving that it is a compound?

11. (a) What is Brownian motion? (b) How is it observed?

12. In the Brownian movement experiment, which molecules are proven to be in random motion?

13. What indirect evidence can you think of that indicates that gas molecules are in constant motion?

14. Astronomers assert that plasma, of which stars are composed, is a fourth state of matter. (a) What is plasma? (b) In what way is it different from the other three states?

15. (a) What can you say about the arrangement of atoms in a solid, like iron? (b) In a solid like common table salt?

16. Make a graph similar to Fig. C, but showing the potential energy with respect to the distance r.

17. Use the molecules shown in Fig. A to find an example of a compound and a mixture that contains: (a) carbon and oxygen, (b) hydrogen and oxygen, and (c) only oxygen.

18. (a) How could you set up a model that demonstrates the forces between the atoms of a linear triatomic molecule? (b) If you were to push the outer atoms of a molecule toward each other and suddenly release them, what kind of motion do you think would ensue?

PROBLEMS

1. A chemist uses 8 gm of oxygen to make carbon monoxide. What is the mass of the CO?

2. How many benzene molecules can be made using 8×10^{22} molecules of methane?

3. A chemist finds that an unknown compound has a molecular weight of 18.0160 and contains oxygen. What is it?

4. What is the mass of one molecule of helium?

5. What is the mass of 100 molecules of ordinary table sugar, whose formula is $C_{12}H_{22}O_{11}$?

6. How many molecules of sugar did you bring home from the grocery store when you bought a 1-lb package?

7. A glass of water weighs approximately 200 gm. How many molecules of water do you swallow when you drink such a glass of water?

8. Knowing the answer to Problem 7 and that 200 gm of water occupies 200 cm^3 of volume, calculate the volume of 1 molecule of water.

PROJECTS

1. Make models using Styrofoam or other plastic-foam balls to show a variety of molecules and crystal lattices. Gumdrops of different colors and toothpicks can also be used.

2. Make a report on how man-made elements are produced and how their properties are studied.

PROPERTIES OF MATTER

Lesson 34   *ELASTICITY*

Stretching of a Spring. If a vertically mounted rod, wire, or spring is supported rigidly at its upper end and weights are added to its lower end, the amount by which it is stretched is found to be directly proportional to the weight applied. This is known as *Hooke's Law*. The stretching of a spring is illustrated in Fig. A. Owing to an

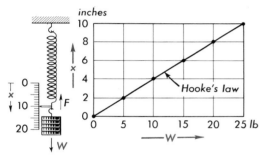

Fig. A. Experiment illustrating Hooke's law.

added weight, W, the spring is stretched a distance x. If a second equal weight is added, the total distance stretched will be twice that for the first one. If a third weight is added, the total distance stretched will be three times that for the first one, etc. This is illustrated by the graph in Fig. A. Each value of x is plotted vertically and the corresponding loads, W, are plotted horizontally.

More specifically, when a 5-lb weight is added, the stretch, or elongation, is 2 in.; with two 5-lb weights, the total elongation is 4 in.; with three 5-lb weights $x = 6$ in., and so forth. A continuation of this shows, as does the graph in Fig. A, that each 5-lb weight produces an added elongation of 2 in. To make an equation of this we write

$$W = kx \qquad (1)$$

where k is a constant and equal, in this experiment, to 2.5 lb/in. Each value of x multiplied by 2.5 gives the corresponding weight, W. When the spring in Fig. A is stretched a distance x, the spring itself exerts an upward force, F, equal but opposite in direction to W. For the spring, then—

$$F = -kx \qquad (2)$$

The minus sign indicates that x and F are in opposite directions. This equation is often referred to as Hooke's law.*

The Stretching of a Wire. Because a wire or rod will not stretch very far before reaching the breaking point, one must, in order to check Hooke's law, resort to some method of measuring extremely small changes in length. This is frequently done by means of a device known as the *optical lever*.

As shown by the experiment illustrated in Fig. B, a beam of light is reflected from a small mirror, M, mounted on a small three-legged stool, two legs of which rest on a stationary platform, as shown, and the third on a small clamp, C, at the lower end of the wire. As the wire stretches under an added weight, W, the mirror tips back and the

* Robert Hooke (1635-1703), English experimental physicist, is known principally for his contributions to the wave theory of light, universal gravitation, and atmospheric pressure. He originated many physical ideas but perfected few of them. Hooke's scientific achievements would undoubtedly have received greater acclaim had his efforts been confined to fewer subjects. He had an irritable temper and made many virulent attacks on Newton and other men of science, claiming that work published by them was due to him.

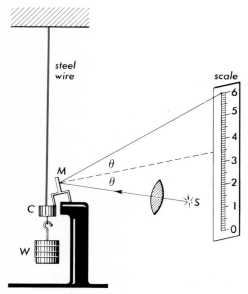

Fig. B. The stretching of a wire under increasing tension can be measured by an optical lever.

light beam is reflected up a measurable amount on the distant scale.

The amount the wire is stretched is directly proportional to the force applied and is illustrated by the straight part of the graph *AE* in Fig. C. If the weights are removed, the wire will return to its original

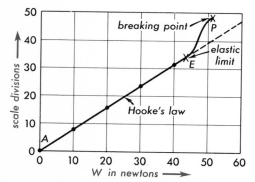

Fig. C. A graph of the stretching of a wire showing Hooke's law, the elastic limit, and the breaking point.

length. If weights are continually added, the forces applied will eventually become too great, and Hooke's law will no longer hold as the elongation will increase too rapidly. This is the region *EP* on the graph. Carried too far in this direction, the wire will break. The point *E*, at which Hooke's law ceases to hold, is called the *elastic limit*. If the wire is stretched beyond this point, it will be permanently stretched and will not return to its original length when the weights are removed.

Stress and Strain. When a force of any magnitude is applied to a solid body, the body becomes distorted. Whether the distortion is large or small, some portion of the body is moved with respect to some neighboring portion. As a result of this displacement, atomic forces of attraction or repulsion set up restoring forces, which resist the alteration and tend to restore the body to its original shape. The greater the applied force, the greater will be the deformation, thereby setting up greater atomic restoring forces, which act to bring about equilibrium.

It is common engineering practice to describe the restoring forces in a distorted body as a *stress* and to give to this term the quantitative definition of *force per unit area*. The actual deformation of the body produced by an applied force involves a change in geometrical form called *strain*. Strain is defined as a quantitative measure of deformation.

Hooke's Law. Hooke's law applies equally well to other types of deformation. In general, Hooke's law states that *stress is proportional to strain*. The stress set up within an elastic body is directly proportional to the strain caused by the applied load:

$$\textbf{stress} \propto \textbf{strain} \qquad (3)$$

To make an equation of this, a proportionality constant K is introduced:

$$\textbf{stress} = K \textbf{ strain}$$

or—

$$K = \frac{\textbf{stress}}{\textbf{strain}} \qquad (4)$$

The constant K has a value characteristic of the material of the elastic body and is called the *modulus of elasticity*.

Young's Modulus. Consider the experiment, diagramed in Fig. B, where a wire or rod is clamped at one end and a load is applied at the other. Let l represent the wire's original length, A its cross-sectional area, and e the elongation produced by the applied load F. See also Fig. D.

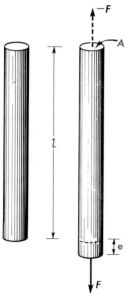

Fig. D. Young's modulus for the stretching of a wire or rod is given by Fl/Ae.

By definition, stress is the force per unit area, and strain is the elongation per unit length:

$$\textbf{stress} = \frac{F}{A} \qquad (5)$$

$$\textbf{strain} = \frac{e}{l} \qquad (6)$$

When these defining equations are substituted in Eq. (4), the modulus of elasticity, K, is called *Young's* modulus*, written as Y, and is given by—

$$Y = \frac{F/A}{e/l}$$

or—

$$Y = \frac{Fl}{Ae} \qquad (7)$$

Young's modulus, Y, is a very practical constant, for if its value is known for any

Table 1. Young's Modulus

Material	newtons/ sq m		lb/ sq in.	
aluminum.........	7	$\times 10^{10}$	10.2	$\times 10^6$
brass.............	9.02	"	13.09	"
copper...........	12.5	"	18.0	"
iron.............	21.0	"	30.0	"
steel (mild).......	19.2	"	27.9	"
tendon (human).....	1.6	"	2.3	"
muscle (human).....	0.009	"	0.013	"
bone (tension)......	22	"	32	"
bone (compression)..	22	"	32	"
nerve............	0.1850	"	0.2680	"
vein.............	0.0085	"	0.0123	"
artery...........	0.0005	"	0.0007	"

given material, the amount of stretch produced in any size of wire or rod of that material can be calculated. Careful labora-

* Thomas Young (1773-1829), English scientist, born of a Quaker family, had read the Bible twice through at the age of four and, at fourteen, could speak seven languages. He studied medicine in London, Edinburgh, Göttingen, and Cambridge and at twenty-eight was appointed professor of physics at the Royal Institution. Young is best known for his experiments proving the wave theory of light, but he also made valuable contributions to mechanics, medicine, and to the mechanism of sight and vision. He was one of the first to decipher successfully Egyptian hieroglyphic inscriptions.

tory experiments have established such values for many common substances. (See Table 1.)

Example. A copper wire, 3 m long and 2 sq mm in cross-sectional area, hangs from the ceiling. What will be its elongation if a 2-Kg mass is suspended from the lower end?

Solution. Rearrange Eq. (7) to solve for e, and substitute known dimensions and Young's modulus for copper from Table 1:

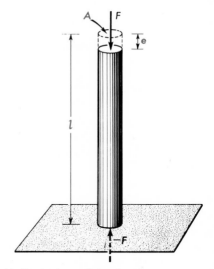

Fig. E. Young's modulus for the compression of a rod is given by Fl/Ae.

$$e = \frac{Fl}{AY} = \frac{2 \text{ Kg} \times 9.8 \text{ m/sec}^2 \times 3 \text{ m}}{2 \times 10^{-6} \text{ m}^2 \times 12.5 \times 10^{10} \text{ n/m}^2}$$

$$= 2.35 \times 10^{-4} \text{ m}$$

Care must be taken, in solving such problems as this, to express the force, F, in the same units as the force in the modulus.

Compression. When a load, F, is applied to the ends of a rod to compress it as shown in Fig. E, the decrease in length is of the same amount as the elongation it would acquire when the same load is applied as a tension. In other words, Hooke's law applies to compression, the values of Young's modulus for stretching are valid, and Eq. (7) can be used for all calculations within the elastic limit.

QUESTIONS

1. (a) What is Hooke's law as applied to a spring? (b) As applied to the stretching of a rod or wire?
2. (a) What is Hooke's law as applied to the compression of a spring? (b) Does it contain a minus sign? Explain.
3. Why does Hooke's law apply equally well to all kinds of deformations of materials, such as stretching, compression, etc.?
4. Some cars use torsion bars instead of springs to suspend the body. Explain how Hooke's law applies in this case.
5. Assume it were possible to measure your actual length very accurately. Would you be longer when you are standing or when you are lying in bed? Explain.
6. (a) Describe another type of deformation that could be applied to a bar and that would obey Hooke's law. (b) Write down Hooke's law, and describe what would be meant by stress and strain in your example.
7. What is the difference between stress and strain?
8. (a) Draw a graph representing the compression of a rod, and indicate the elastic limit. (b) If the rod is compressed beyond the elastic limit, what would the graph look like as the load is gradually removed?

9. (a) How is k in Eq. (2) related to Young's modulus? (b) Why is it Young's modulus that is tabulated instead of k?
10. If the same force is applied to each of two wires, one twice as long as the other, how will elongations compare?
11. If the lengths of two copper wires are the same, but one has twice the diameter of the other, how will their elongations compare under the same force?
12. (a) How would you go about experimentally determining Young's modulus for a brass wire? (b) How could you use a lever to determine the very small elongations under the different loads?

PROBLEMS

1. A steel-coil spring, 12 cm long, is stretched to a total length of 18 cm by a load of 30 Kg. What would be its length if stretched by a 7.5-Kg load?
2. A bronze-coil spring, 25 cm long, is stretched to a length of 28 cm when a weight of 0.75 newton is fastened to the lower end. Find the length of the spring when 0.05 newton more is added to the lower end.
3. A force of 45 lb stretches a coil spring 5 in. What force will compress the same spring 1.5 in.?
4. A brass wire, 2.5 m long and 2 mm in diameter, hangs from the ceiling. If a mass of 2 Kg is suspended from the lower end, what will be the elongation?
5. A copper wire, 6 m long and 0.01 cm² in cross-sectional area, hangs from the ceiling. If a mass of 4.0 Kg hanging from the lower end stretches the wire 0.2 cm, what is the value of Young's modulus?
6. Find the elongation of a tendon 5 cm long and 0.4 cm in diameter if put under a tension of 2000 newtons.
7. Two iron wires, each 3 m long, are joined end to end and are subjected to a tension of 5 Kg. If the wires have cross-sectional areas of 0.01 cm² and 0.02 cm² respectively, what is the elongation?
8. A copper tube, 2 in. on a side, is compressed 0.003 in. What force was applied?

PROJECTS

1. Devise an experiment to determine Young's modulus for a brass or steel wire. You will have to devise a method to determine very small differences in length.
2. Make a wire-testing machine.

PROPERTIES OF MATTER

Lesson 35 *BENDING, TWISTING, AND BOUNCING*

Bending. When a rod or beam is subjected to a force tending to bend it, the amount of bending is directly proportional to the force applied. This is illustrated in Fig. A, where a uniform board is shown

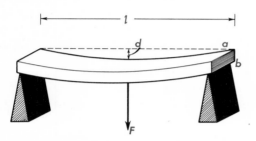

Fig. A. The bending of a beam follows Hooke's law.

supported at both ends and a downward force, F, is shown exerted at the middle.

If we use known weights for the applied force and, for the different loads, we measure the bending displacement, d, we will find that d is directly proportional to F. Such measurements for a piece of pine ¾ in. by 3 in. by 4 ft are easily made and may be plotted to form a graph, as shown in Fig. B. The fact that the resultant is a straight line is a good demonstration that Hooke's law applies to this form of bending, and that—

$$d \propto F$$

From theoretical consideration, the actual relation between d and F is given by the equation—

$$d = \frac{Fl^3}{4Yab^3} \qquad (1)$$

where a is the beam width, b is its thickness, l is its length, and Y is Young's modulus.

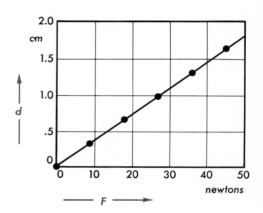

Fig. B. Illustrating Hooke's law for bending.

To see how stretching and compressing enter into the bending of a beam, imagine the beam divided into layers, as shown in Fig. C. In bending, the lower layers are

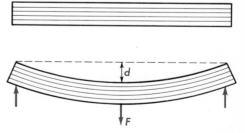

Fig. C. The bending of a beam involves stretching and compressing of different parts.

stretched by varying amounts, while the upper layers are compressed.

The bending of a beam, clamped at one

end, as shown in Fig. D, also follows Hooke's law. The bending displacement, d,

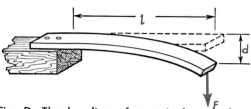

Fig. D. The bending of a springboard obeys Hooke's law.

is directly proportional to the applied bending force, F, and the two are related by the formula—

$$d = \frac{4Fl^3}{Yab^3} \qquad (2)$$

Torsion. A detailed knowledge of torsional stresses and strains has considerable practical application in engineering design. When a rod or bar is clamped at one end and a torque is applied at the other, it is twisted, as illustrated in Fig. E. Within the

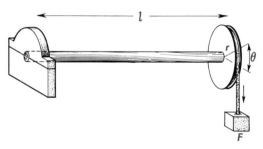

Fig. E. The twisting of a rod obeys Hooke's law.

elastic limit, the angular displacement, θ, is proportional to the applied torque, L, and is given by—

$$\theta = \frac{1}{k} \times \frac{32Ll}{\pi D^4} \qquad (3)$$

where D is the rod diameter. The quantity k is related to the strain in the rod that

is tending to shear it rather than to compress it. This quantity is the *shear modulus* and usually has a value different from Young's modulus.

Again, if one makes measurements on any given rod and plots a graph of θ against L, a straight line is the result.

Eq. (3) agrees with the experimental observation that, if the length, l, of a rod is doubled, the same torque will double the angle θ.

By doubling the rod diameter, D, on the other hand the angle θ is decreased sixteenfold, because $2^4 = 16$.

Fig. F illustrates an application of tor-

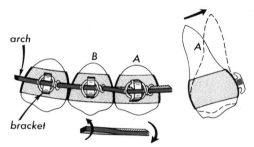

Fig. F. Illustrating an application of torsional stress to the straightening of teeth by the orthodontist.

sional stress in the profession of orthodontics. *Orthodontia*, or *dental orthopedics*, is that branch of dentistry dealing principally with the straightening of teeth. In one technique, it is customary to fit each tooth with a wide metal band containing an arch bracket. Each bracket has a rectangular slot into which a square arch wire is tied.

To produce a rotation of tooth A as indicated at the right, a permanent twist has been put into the square arch wire between that tooth and its neighbor. A torsional stress is thereby produced and, over a period of several weeks, the stress is gradually relieved by the turning of the tooth. The possible movement of the roots of teeth through the mandible, as well as the upper jawbone in any direction, is well known to every dentist.

Impact of Elastic Bodies. When two bodies collide with each other, the law of conservation of momentum states that *the total momentum before impact is equal to*

lead ball or marble, on the other hand, hardly bounces at all.

In this particular experiment, the two bodies in collision are the marble and the anvil. Because of its very great mass, the recoiling velocity of the anvil is negligibly small.

As illustrations of the compression of a solid when in collision with another solid, note the deformation of the two balls in Fig.

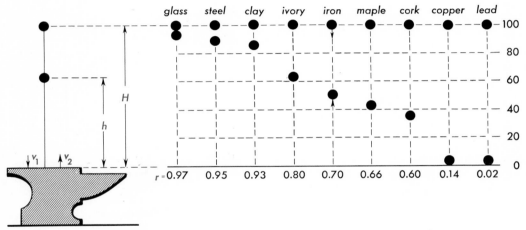

Fig. G. The bouncing marble experiment illustrating the resilience of different substances.

the total momentum after impact. This law is not sufficient, however, to determine what the individual velocities of each of the two bodies will be. Different kinds of material behave differently at impact and will move apart with different velocities. As an illustration, consider the experiment diagramed in Fig. G.

Spheres of different substances are dropped successively, all from the same height, onto the smooth top surface of a large anvil and allowed to bounce to their various heights. Contrary to one's preconceived ideas of elasticity, a glass or steel marble will bounce to a greater height than will a ball made of the best rubber. A

H. These are instantaneous photographs of (a) a golf ball being struck by a golf club and (b) a tennis ball being struck by a tennis racket. They illustrate what is called the *resilience* of matter. *Resilience is defined as the ability of a body to undergo a compression, or rapid deformation, without the development of permanent deformation.* Resilience is the opposite of brittleness.

Coefficient of Restitution. *The coefficient of restitution is defined as a number expressing the ratio of the velocity with which two bodies separate after collision to the velocity of their approach before collision:*

$$r = \frac{\text{velocity of separation}}{\text{velocity of approach}} \qquad (4)$$

or, as a formula—

$$r = \frac{v_2}{v_1} \qquad (5)$$

$\sqrt{2gs}$ for falling bodies, $\sqrt{2gH}$ can be written for v_1 and $\sqrt{2gh}$ for v_2, to give—

$$r = \frac{\sqrt{2gh}}{\sqrt{2gH}}$$

$$r = \sqrt{\frac{h}{H}} \qquad (6)$$

 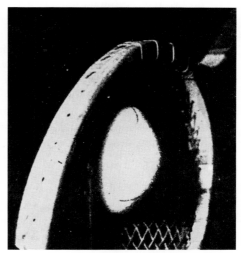

Fig. H. Photographs of (a) the impact between a golf club and ball and (b) the impact between a tennis racket and ball. (After Edgerton)

Values of the constant r for different substances may be obtained from the above experiment by determining the velocity v_1 of a marble just before it strikes the anvil and the velocity v_2 just as it leaves on rebound. Rather than measure these velocities directly, it is more convenient to make use of the laws of falling bodies and to calculate the velocities from the height to which the marbles are carried. Because $v =$

As illustrated in Fig. G, H is the height from which a marble falls and h is the height to which it rebounds. For a very elastic substance, like glass or steel, colliding with steel, r has a value of 0.95 or better, whereas for a very inelastic substance, like lead, colliding with steel, r is extremely small. It is seen from Eq. (4) that the smallest value r can have is zero, whereas the largest value is unity.

QUESTIONS

1. (a) What basic relation is observed in the bending of a beam or rod? (b) What is the law?

2. How does the bending of a beam or rod depend upon (a) the applied force, (b) the length, (c) the width, and (d) the thickness?

3. From a consideration of the formula given for the bending of a beam, explain why floor joists are laid on edge in building a house?

4. (a) What basic relation is observed in the twisting of a uniform rod? (b) What is the law?

5. How does the twisting of a round rod depend upon (a) the applied torque, (b) the length, and (c) the diameter?

6. (a) What is the meaning of the coefficient of restitution? (b) What is resilience?

7. (a) How is restitution most easily demonstrated? (b) How is the coefficient of restitution measured?

8. (a) What are the lowest and highest possible values for the coefficient? (b) Name a substance that, under average impact velocities, has (c) a very small coefficient and (d) a very high coefficient.

9. If you wanted to determine the coefficient of restitution by bouncing a marble on the smooth flat surface of an anvil, how would you determine the two heights, h and H, with high precision?

10. (a) How would you determine how much heat is generated when a marble bounces? (b) Which of the marbles in Fig. G generates the most heat? (c) Which the least?

11. Contrary to the example in Fig. G, a rubber ball will bounce higher than a steel ball if a wooden anvil is used. Explain why.

12. Explain the difference between compressional forces and shearing forces.

13. (a) Does the shear modulus have the same units as Young's modulus? (b) What are the units?

PROBLEMS

1. The two ends of a 12-ft oak plank rest on supports. A man weighing 190 lb, standing at the center, depresses the plank 4 in. If a second man weighing 150 lb joins him there, what is the depression?

2. A certain beam bends 1 cm with a certain load. (a) How much would it bend if the beam were twice as thick? (b) How much would it bend if width were doubled?

3. A boy weighing 80 lb depresses the end of a diving board 3 in. by standing at the very end. How much would the board be bent by a man weighing 250 lb?

4. The free end of a diving board at the edge of a swimming pool is 18 in. above the water. If a man weighing 160 lb, standing on the end of the board, bends it to within 6 in. of the water, how heavy a person will bend it to within 4 in. of the water?

5. An ivory ball is dropped from a height of 72 in. onto the smooth surface of a heavy anvil. To what height will it bounce if the coefficient of restitution is 0.60?

6. A golf ball when dropped from a height of 4 ft and allowed to hit a concrete pavement bounces to a height of 2.5 ft. Calculate the coefficient of restitution.

7. The free end of a springboard at the edge of a swimming pool is 2 ft above the water. How close to the water will the board come if a 200-lb man stands on the end of the board? Assume the board to be 1 ft wide, 2.0 in. thick, and 16 ft long. Young's modulus is 1.4×10^7 lb/in.^{2}

8. The drive shaft in a certain automobile is 1 in. in diameter and 8 ft long. If the shaft is twisted 0.05 rad when a torque of 100 ft-lb is applied by the engine, what is the shear modulus?

9. An 8-Kg lump of putty, moving at 12 m/sec, strikes a second 8-Kg lump of putty. (a) If they stick together, what is their final velocity? (b) What is their coefficient of restitution?

10. An ivory ball with a mass of 200 gm, moving with a speed of 300 cm/sec, collides head-on with another ivory ball of the same mass and size, at rest. If the coefficient of restitution is 0.65, find the velocity of each ball after collision.

PROJECTS

1. Make a delicate scale for weighing small masses using Hooke's law as applied to the twisting of fine fibers.

2. Develop an experiment to measure the coefficient of restitution of a number of common substances. It will be easiest to do if you can arrange to (1) measure the height from which the object is dropped and (2) the height to which it bounces back.

PROPERTIES OF MATTER

Lesson 36 *PRESSURE IN LIQUIDS*

Properties of solids, like bending and twisting, do not exist in liquids. Liquids, however, can be put under compression and, if placed in a thoroughly cleaned vessel or container, can be subjected to very high tensions. Although these properties are of considerable interest, they have not proved to be of much practical importance. There are physical properties of liquids, on the other hand, that are considered to be of general importance. These are pressure, buoyancy, surface tension, and capillarity.

Pressure. It is essential in the following treatment of the properties of liquids to introduce the concept of *pressure* as contrasted with the meaning of *total force*. *Pressure is defined as the force per unit of area*. Written in the form of an equation—

$$\text{pressure} = \frac{\text{total force}}{\text{area}}$$

$$P = \frac{F}{A} \qquad (1)$$

As an illustration of the distinction between pressure and total force, consider the two aluminum blocks in Fig. A. Block

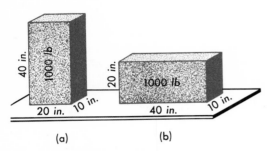

Fig. A. A block standing on end exerts a greater pressure than when it is lying on its side.

(*a*) stands on one end where the area is 200 sq in., while block (*b*) stands on one side where the area is 400 sq in. Weighing 1000 lb, each block separately exerts the same downward force. Standing on end as in (*a*), the downward pressure is given by Eq. (1) as—

$$\text{pressure} = \frac{1000\ \text{lb}}{200\ \text{in.}^2} = 5\ \frac{\text{lb}}{\text{in.}^2}$$

This is read 5 *pounds per square inch*. Standing as in (*b*), on the other hand, the pressure is only one-half as great:

$$\text{pressure} = \frac{1000\ \text{lb}}{400\ \text{in.}^2} = 2.5\ \frac{\text{lb}}{\text{in.}^2}$$

Over each square inch, in the first case, there is a downward force equivalent to 5 lb, while in the second case there is only 2.5 lb. The pressure in (*a*) is, therefore,

twice as great as the pressure in (*b*), but the total downward force is the same.

Solving Eq. (1) for the force on the liquid gives—

$$F = P \times A \qquad (2)$$

Total force equals pressure times area.

Liquid Pressure. It is frequently necessary to determine the pressure at various depths within a liquid as well as the pressure on the bottom and sides of any containing vessel. The rule regarding pressure states that *the magnitude of the pressure at any depth is equal to the weight of a column of liquid of unit cross section reaching from that point to the top of the liquid.*

At a depth of l_1, as illustrated in Fig. B,

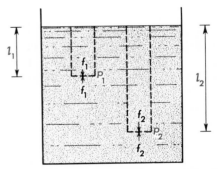

Fig. B. The pressure exerted by a liquid depends upon the depth.

the pressure p_1 is given by the weight of a column of liquid 1 sq cm in cross section and l_1 centimeters in height. At a greater depth of l_2, the pressure p_2 is given by the weight of a column of liquid 1 sq cm in cross section and l_2 centimeters in height.

This can be demonstrated with a glass cylinder and a thin lightweight disk as shown in Fig. C. With water surrounding the empty cylinder the force, f, pushing up, holds the disk tightly against the end. If the cylinder is gradually filled with water, an

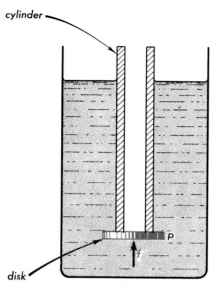

cylinder

disk

Fig. C. Experimental demonstration of pressure within a liquid.

increasing downward force is exerted on the disk. Just as the water inside reaches the level of the water outside, the disk drops from the end of the cylinder, showing that the downward force and upward force at that point and at that instant become equal. We can conclude from this experiment that the pressure at any given point in a liquid is given by the weight of the liquid above it. Moreover, we see that the pressure at one point is equal to the pressure at any other point at the same level. *Pressure in a liquid is defined as the normal force exerted by the liquid per unit area.*

Pressure is usually measured in *pounds per square inch, dynes per square centimeter,* or *newtons per square meter.*

Liquid Density. To find the weight of a column of liquid it is convenient to know the liquid *density* or *weight density.* The density of any given substance or body of matter is given by the *mass per unit volume.* To find the density, one determines the vol-

ume of a given mass of the substance and divides one by the other:

$$\text{density} = \frac{\text{mass}}{\text{volume}}$$

In algebraic symbols—

$$\rho = \frac{M}{V} \qquad (3)$$

where the Greek letter ρ (rho) stands for density.

In the English system of units it is common to find the weight of a given substance, rather than its mass, and to determine its *weight density.* Weight density is defined as the weight per unit volume and is given by—

$$\text{weight density} = \frac{\text{weight}}{\text{volume}}$$

which, in algebraic symbols, can be written—

$$\rho_w = \frac{W}{V} \qquad (4)$$

The densities and weight densities of a few common materials are given in Table 1.

Table 1. Densities and Weight-Densities of a Few Common Liquids

Material	ρ (gm/cm^3)	ρ_w (lb/ft^3)
alcohol	.79	49.3
benzene	.70	43.7
blood	1.04	65.0
gasoline	.69	41.2
mercury	13.6	849
olive oil	.918	57.3
water	1.000	62.4

The mass of any column of liquid is found from Eq. (3):

$$M = \rho V \qquad (5)$$

To find the weight of any mass, M, we multiply by g, the acceleration due to gravity. The weight, then, is the total downward force, F, of a liquid column, and we can write—

$$F = Mg \qquad (6)$$

and then

$$F = \rho V g$$

The volume, V, of a column of liquid (see Fig. A) is given by—

$$V = hA \qquad (7)$$

so that, upon substitution in Eq. (6), we have—

$$F = \rho h A g \qquad (8)$$

By direct substitution of ρhAg for F in Eq. (1), we obtain our final equation:

$$P = \frac{\rho h A g}{A} \qquad (9)$$

or—

$$P = h\rho g \qquad (10)$$

Pressure Acts in All Directions. In a liquid at rest, the force exerted by the liquid upon any surface is perpendicular to the surface. At any given point, the force exerted on an element of surface is independent of the orientation of that surface. This can be illustrated in many ways. For example, in Fig. D a hollow steel ball, B, filled with water, is connected at the top by a metal tube, T. By pushing down on the handle, H, the plunger, P, forces water out of the several metal tubes, J, leading from the sides and the bottom of the ball. Equal force in all directions is indicated by the water jets all coming to the same height as drawn.

Pressure on a Surface. Because of pressure, the force, f, exerted by a liquid at rest is perpendicular to the wall with which the liquid is in contact. As a proof, suppose the force were not perpendicular but at some angle to the surface. Such a force could be

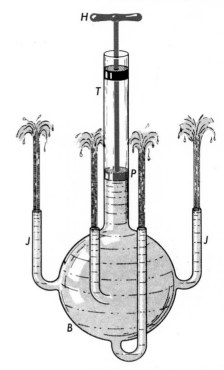

Fig. D. Experimental demonstration of equal pressures in all directions.

resolved into two components, one normal and the other tangent to the surface. But, the tangent component cannot exist, for if it did, the wall would exert an equal and opposite force on the liquid and the liquid would move. Because the liquid is assumed to be at rest, the force, f, must be normal to the surface.

The vessels shown in Fig. E are known as Pascal's* vases. Three glass vessels of different shape but the same height have screw-in metal bases that fit into the same

---

* Blaise Pascal (1623-1662), French religious philosopher, physicist and mathematician is noted principally for his discoveries in pure mathematics, and for his experiments with the barometer. His experiments and his treatise on the equilibrium of fluids entitle him to rank with Galileo and Stevinus as one of the founders of the science of hydrostatics and hydrodynamics.

(a)   (b)   (c)

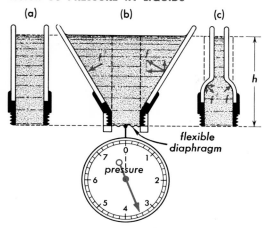

Fig. E. Demonstration with Pascal's vases.

pressure meter shown at the lower center. The three vases are inserted one after the other and filled with water to the same height, h. Even though the amount of water is greatly different in each vase the pressure, as measured by the meter, is the same.

The experimental fact that the small amount of water in vessel (c) can exert the same downward force as the large amount in vessel (b) may be considered as a verification of equal pressure. Let f represent the force of the water on unit area of the wall and f' the equal and opposite force of the wall on the water. The latter is shown resolved into vertical and horizontal components. The vertical component in (b) is upward and supplies the additional force needed to support the extra amount of water, while in (c) the vertical component is downward and supplies the additional force equivalent to the missing column of water above.

Pressure Transmission; Pascal's Principle. *Any change of pressure in an enclosed fluid is transmitted undiminished to all parts of the fluid.* A practical application of this principle is to be found in hydraulic systems, where a force is applied on one part

of the liquid and some load is moved at another. Consider as an illustration the hydraulic press illustrated in Fig. F.

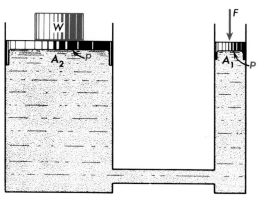

Fig. F. Illustrating the principles of the hydraulic press.

Two pistons, one large and one small, connected by a pipe, are filled with a liquid. When a force, F, is applied to the smaller piston, the increased pressure, P, created immediately underneath the piston of area A_1 is transmitted undiminished to the larger piston of area A_2.

Because pressure is defined as force per unit area, $P = F/A_1$ for the smaller piston, while $P = W/A_2$ for the larger. Since these pressures are equal,

$$\frac{W}{A_2} = \frac{F}{A_1}$$

from which

$$W = \frac{A_2}{A_1} F \qquad (11)$$

Should the larger piston of such a press have ten times the area of the smaller, a load ten times that of the applied force may be lifted. Such a system, therefore, has a mechanical advantage equal to the ratio of the piston areas, A_2/A_1.

Although the mechanical advantage of

this direct-transmission type of hydraulic system is high, it is achieved at the expense of distance. The force distance, like the mechanical advantage, is also equal to the ratio of the piston areas, A_2/A_1. Thus, if the force piston, A_1, has one-tenth the area of the load piston, A_2, the force piston will have to move through ten units of distance in order to move the load through one unit of distance. Such direct-transmission hydraulic systems, therefore, are used only when the required load distance is small, as for automobile brakes. Elevators, such as those used in garages to lift cars to head height, are operated by pumps, rather than by a single-stroke piston.

QUESTIONS

1. How is pressure defined?
2. Explain why a girl wearing spike heels can damage a floor whereas her boy friend, weighing almost twice as much, does not.
3. Why was it necessary to reduce the weight of the tone arm in phonographs, when needles were reduced in size from 3 mils to 1 mil to accommodate the narrower walls of the LP record?
4. (a) How can the pressure at any depth within a liquid be calculated? (b) Is pressure a force? (c) Is pressure a vector quantity?
5. Why do fish that normally live at great depths in the ocean burst when brought up to the surface?
6. If you know the pressure on a flat surface within a liquid, how can you determine the force exerted on a given area of the surface?
7. (a) What do Pascal's vases demonstrate? (b) How can you explain the equal forces exerted on the bottom surface area of each vase?
8. (a) State Pascal's principle. (b) What practical application makes use of the principle?
9. (a) How is it possible that a relatively small force can be applied to the brakes and stop a large car? (b) Why do very large cars have power brakes?
10. Explain why liquids at rest exert a force that is normal to any surface in contact with the liquid.
11. What is the difference between density and weight density?
12. How does the pressure on an immersed object depend upon (a) its depth? (b) its area? (c) the density of the liquid?
13. What is meant by the words *hydrostatics* and *hydrodynamics*?
14. Assume that Pascal's vases shown in Fig. E are resting on a flat surface, rather than being screwed into a base. State in each case whether or not the water will leak out, and give your reasons.

PROBLEMS

1. A concrete block 2 ft wide, 3 ft long, and 1 ft high weighs 1080 lb. Find the pressure it exerts on the ground in (a) lb/ft² and (b) lb/in.²

2. A solid block of sandstone 12 cm wide, 20 cm long, and 10 cm high has a mass of 5 Kg. Find the pressure it exerts on the ground in newtons per square meter.

3. The water pressure on the bottom of a tank is 10 lb/in.² What is the total force on the bottom if the area is 20 ft²?

4. If one cubic inch of mercury weighs 0.50 lb, what will be the pressure at a depth of 2 ft below the surface in a vessel of mercury?

5. If one cubic centimeter of water has a mass of 1 gm, find the pressure at a depth of 5 m in a tank of water.

6. What is the pressure in a barrel of gasoline 88 cm below the surface?

7. Three feet below sea level, the pressure is 192 lb/ft². (a) What is the density of sea water in engineering units? (b) In cgs units?

8. A long vertical glass pipe can be filled with water to a height of 9 ft before the pressure at the base breaks the glass. How high could the pipe be filled with alcohol?

9. The areas of the pistons in a hydraulic press are 1600 in.² and 4 in.², respectively. What force on the smaller piston is required to lift a 2-ton automobile by the larger piston?

10. What minimum diameter could the cylinder of an hydraulic press have if it is to lift a 2-ton car with an applied liquid pressure of 40 lb/in.²?

11. What will be the pressure at the bottom of a dam holding back water that is 300 ft deep?

PROJECTS

1. Make a working model of the hydraulic brake system of an automobile.
2. Make a working model of a hydraulic press.

PROPERTIES OF MATTER

Lesson 37 *ARCHIMEDES' PRINCIPLE*

Archimedes' Principle.* Archimedes' principle states that *a body floating or submerged in a liquid is buoyed up by a force equal to the weight of the liquid displaced.* For example, if a block of wood is floating in water, as shown in Fig. A, the buoyant force, F, holding the block up is equal to

* See footnote on Archimedes in Lesson 21.

the weight of the water displaced (shaded area). When the block is first placed in the water, it sinks until the buoyant force, F, becomes great enough to equalize the downward force, the weight of the block, W.

An experimental demonstration of the truth of Archimedes' principle is shown in

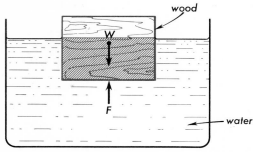

Fig. A. A block of wood lowered into the water sinks until the buoyant force of the water equals the weight of the block.

Fig. B. A small cylindrical cup containing a close fitting solid metal cylinder is accurately balanced by a set of weights on an equal-arm balance. No change in balance occurs when, in diagram (*b*), the cylinder has been removed from the cup and suspended from a hook underneath. In dia-

volume of the cylinder. A slow addition of water to the cup in diagram (*d*) shows that at the very instant the cup becomes filled, exact balance of the beam is restored. The restoring of balance confirms the principle.

Measurement of Density. One of the many ways of measuring the density of solids or liquids is by the use of Archimedes' principle. An experiment in which the density of a solid (aluminum) and of a liquid (kerosene) may be determined is shown in Fig. C. A solid aluminum cylinder is weighed with spring scales (*a*) in air, (*b*) in water, and (*c*) in kerosene.

Diagram (*a*) gives directly the mass of the cylinder as 1400 gm. When submerged in water, the scales indicate a mass of only 880 gm. The difference 1400 − 880 = 520

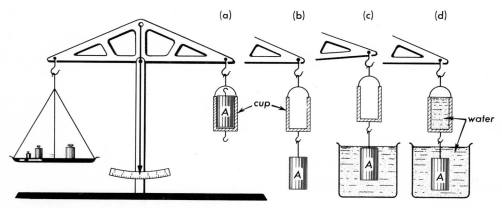

Fig. B. Illustrating the four steps in an experiment demonstrating Archimedes' principle.

gram (*c*), a beaker of water has been raised until the cylinder is completely submerged. Balance is now destroyed because of the upward buoyant force of the water on the cylinder.

If Archimedes' principle is correct, the buoyant force is equal to the weight of a volume of water that is exactly equal to the

gm multiplied by *g* is the buoyant force and, therefore, the weight of the displaced fluid. But because the density of water is equal to 1 gm/cm³, 520 gm of water will have a volume of 520 cm³. Therefore 520 cm³ is the volume of the cylinder.

By definition, we say that the density of any body of matter is given by—

$$\rho = \frac{M}{V} \qquad (1)$$

Having found both M and V for the aluminum cylinder, the density of aluminum is—

$$\rho = \frac{M}{V} = \frac{1400 \text{ gm}}{520 \text{ cm}^3} = 2.7 \frac{\text{gm}}{\text{cm}^3}$$

Submerged in kerosene, the cylinder weighs 1040 gm-wt, indicating a buoyant force $1400 - 1040 = 360$ gm-wt. Because

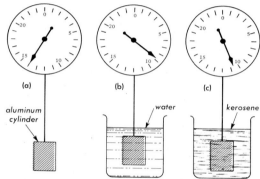

(a)   (b)   (c)

aluminum cylinder   water   kerosene

Fig. C. The buoyant effect of liquids may be used as a means of determining the density of solids or liquids.

the cylinder displaces its volume 520 cm³ of liquid, and this liquid weighs 360 gm-wt, the density of the kerosene is—

$$\rho = \frac{M}{V} = \frac{360 \text{ gm}}{520 \text{ cm}^3} = 0.69 \frac{\text{gm}}{\text{cm}^3}$$

The densities and weight densities of a few common solids are given in Table 1. Liquid densities are tabulated in the previous lesson.

Hydrometers. The densities of liquids are measured by the buoyant force they exert on a floating body called a *hydrometer*. One form of hydrometer is used by service-station attendants to measure the density of the acid in car storage batteries. The acid density in a battery is a direct

Table 1. Densities and Weight-Densities of a Few Solids

Material	ρ (gm/cm^3)	ρ_w (lb/ft^3)
aluminum.........	2.7	169
brass.............	8.5	530
copper...........	8.9	556
diamond..........	3.5	218
gold.............	19.3	1205
ice..............	.917	57.2
iron.............	7.5	468
lead.............	11.4	712
osmium...........	22.5	1405
platinum..........	21.5	1342
silver............	10.5	655
maple wood.......	~0.7	44
glass.............	~2.6	162

measure of the amount of stored electrical energy it contains.

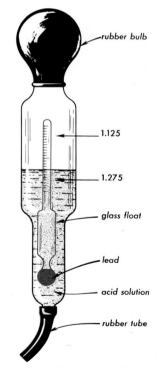

rubber bulb

1.125

1.275

glass float

lead

acid solution

rubber tube

Fig. D. Diagram of a typical hydrometer used for measuring the density of the acid in a storage-battery cell.

The battery hydrometer shown in Fig. D consists of a hollow glass tube with a weight at the bottom and a graduated stem at the top. For convenience, the hydrometer is enclosed in a larger glass tube with a rubber bulb at the top and a short rubber tube at the bottom. The density of the battery liquid is measured by inserting the rubber tube through the vent in the top of the cell and drawing up a small sample of the solution into the main glass tube. Having a constant mass, M, the hydrometer tube sinks until it displaces its own weight in liquid; the more dense the liquid, the higher it floats. A suitable scale on the stem is calibrated directly in gm/cm^3. For a fully charged battery, the hydrometer will float high, the liquid level indicating about 1.275 gm/cm^3. If the battery is completely discharged, the hydrometer will sink to a low level, indicating a density of about 1.125 gm/cm^3.

Hydrometers for measuring very slight differences of density and with a high degree of accuracy have a large float and very thin stem, while those designed for greater ranges of density with less accuracy have a smaller float and thicker stem.

QUESTIONS

1. (a) State Archimedes' principle. (b) Why will a block of wood float on water? (c) Why will a solid block of metal sink?
2. How does the weight of a block of metal in air compare with its apparent weight submerged in water?
3. Why can a ship made entirely of steel float on water, when a solid steel sphere will sink?
4. What is the apparent weight of a block of wood floating on water?
5. (a) How can one find the density of an irregularly shaped body like a stone? (b) How can one find the density of a liquid using Archimedes' principle?
6. (a) What is a hydrometer? (b) Upon what principle is it based? (c) What practical uses do you think it has?
7. (a) What element has the greatest density? (b) Could you lift a solid gold sphere 6 in. in diameter?
8. Give the reasons why the hydrometer would be made to the dimensions stated in the last paragraph in this lesson.
9. How is Archimedes' principle involved in the diving and surfacing operations of a submarine?
10. How would you use Archimedes' principle to measure the density of a gas, if you knew the density of air?
11. How could one find the density of an irregularly shaped body like a log?
12. How can Archimedes' principle be used to tell how much fat a person actually has in his body?
13. (a) Why does a dirigible have to be so large? (b) Why have they been largely ignored as means of transportation?

14. Why do you feel momentarily very heavy after spending a long time in a swimming pool?

15. What would you have to do in order to weigh a material of fairly low density accurately if you were using brass weights on the balances.

16. What would happen to the water line of a ship as it went from a fresh water river into the ocean?

PROBLEMS

1. A stone weighed in air is found to have a mass of 2360 gm. When weighed in water it has an apparent mass of 1720 gm. Find its density.

2. A 15-lb stone has an apparent mass of 12 lb when weighed in water. Find its weight-density. The weight-density of water is 62.4 lb/ft³.

3. An iron casting has a mass of 36 Kg in air. What will be its apparent mass when weighed in water if it has a density of 7.5 gm/cm³.

4. An ivory ball weighed in air has a mass of 280 gm. When weighed in water, its apparent mass is 132 gm; and weighed in oil, its apparent mass is 193 gm. Find (a) the density of ivory and (b) the density of the oil.

5. When weighed in air, a solid metal casting has a mass of 772 gm. When weighed in water its mass is 732 gm. (a) What is the density of the metal and (b) what is the metal? (See Table 1.)

6. A solid brass cylinder weighs 6 lb in air and 5.4 lb when submerged in a liquid. Find the weight density of the liquid.

7. A 22-lb wooden block requires a force of 7 lb to hold it under water. What is its density?

8. A 5-lb cube of cork is 6 in. on a side. (a) What force is needed to hold it under water? (b) How high will it extend above the water if it is floating?

9. A 12-cm³ iron weight is attached to a 12-cm³ gold weight, and the combination is found barely to float in a certain liquid. (a) What is the approximate density of the liquid? (b) What is the liquid?

10. A crown supposedly made of pure gold has a mass of 1.65 Kg when weighed in air and an apparent mass of 1.47 Kg when weighed in water. (a) What is its density? (b) Is it pure gold? (c) Could it be copper plated with gold?

11. You weigh yourself on a scale and find that the scale reads 160 lb. What is your true weight if your volume is approximately 2 cubic feet and air weighs 0.08 lb/ft³?

12. Air has a density of 1.29 g/liter while hydrogen gas has a density of 0.09 g/liter. How many liters of hydrogen would it take to lift 1 metric ton (1000 Kg)?

13. Helium is safer than hydrogen because it does not burn or explode, but it has double the density. How many more liters will it take of helium to lift what hydrogen does in Problem 12?

14. What part, or fraction, of an iceberg is below the surface of the water?

PROJECTS

1. Make a Cartesian diver and demonstrate how it works.
2. Study the methods used to make very deep sea dives.

PROPERTIES OF MATTER

Lesson 38 SURFACE TENSION

Adhesion and Cohesion. All matter is composed of atoms and molecules of one kind or another. As already stated in Lesson 33, these ultramicroscopic particles attract each other with forces that depend upon the kinds of atoms or molecules involved and upon the distance between them. The closer two atoms or molecules are together, the greater is the attractive force between them. *The attractive force between molecules of different substances is called* adhesion, *and the attractive force between two molecules of the same substance is called* cohesion.

Although the force of attraction between two molecules is extremely small, the combined attraction of billions of molecules contained within a very small bit of matter is astonishingly great. A steel cable 1 in. in diameter, for example, will support a maximum load of 25 or more tons without breaking. This is a direct measure of the cohesive forces between hundreds of billions of atoms.

The difference between adhesion and cohesion can be demonstrated by an experiment diagramed in Fig. A. A glass plate, G, is supported by one arm of a beam balance. The plate, after being balanced by weights on the left-hand scale pan, is brought into contact with the surface of water as shown. The water immediately exerts an attractive

force on the plate. Additional weights are next added at W, until the plate breaks free from the water surface. Upon examining the glass, water is found clinging to the under

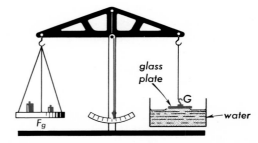

Fig. A. Experiment illustrating the forces of adhesion between glass and water.

surface, showing that the break came between water molecules only. The adhesive forces between glass and water molecules, therefore, exceed the cohesive forces between water molecules. The weight added in the experiment is, therefore, a measure of the cohesive forces between water molecules.

If mercury is substituted for the water in the above experiment and the glass plate pulled away from the mercury surface, the added weights will measure adhesion, the force of attraction between glass and mercury molecules. This is shown by the fact that no mercury clings to the bottom of the glass plate. Thus the cohesion between mercury molecules is greater than the adhesion between mercury and glass.

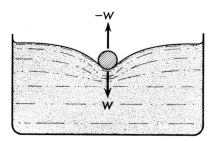

Fig. C. A steel needle can float by itself on water.

Surface Tension. The cohesion of molecules gives rise in liquids to a phenomenon called *surface tension.* According to this aspect of molecular attraction, the surface of a liquid acts at all times as though it has a thin membrane stretched over it and that this membrane is under tension and trying to contract. It is for this reason that fog-drops, raindrops, soap bubbles, etc., assume a spherical shape as they fall through the air. (For any specific volume of matter, the surface is smallest when the substance is in the form of a sphere.)

An experiment designed to illustrate the spherical form of a liquid drop is shown in Fig. B. Alcohol and water are poured care-

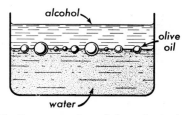

Fig. B. Demonstration of the spherical form.

fully into a glass vessel where they form a separation boundary, the water with its greater density going to the bottom. Olive oil, which is not soluble in either water or alcohol, is then dropped into the liquid. The drops quickly take on a spherical form and, due to their intermediate density, settle slowly to the boundary level where they remain suspended.

A second illustration of surface tension is the floating needle experiment. A common sewing needle lowered horizontally to the surface of water in an open dish will be found to float as shown in Fig. C. (If the

needle is first drawn through the fingers, a thin film of grease is deposited on the surface, making it easier to float. The adhesion between water and grease is very weak.) For the needle to break through the surface, water molecules must be pulled apart. Rather than separating, the surface is depressed until the upward buoyant force, $-W$, is equal in magnitude to W, the weight of the needle. Surface tension keeps the film intact.

An interesting experiment is performed by fastening a bit of soap to the back of a small wooden boat, and then placing the boat in water. As the soap goes into solution, the surface tension is reduced in back of the boat, and the surface tension in front pulls the boat forward. As soon as the soap film covers the entire surface, the boat will stop.

Surface tension in the laboratory is usually measured by an arrangement illustrated in Fig. D. A small wire frame of length l is dipped into water and then pulled slowly out. As a result of both cohesion and adhesion, a thin film of water is formed in the frame. This film pulls down by a force that can be measured by balancing the frame from the arm of a beam balance. The weight added measures directly the cohesive forces of the water film, the surface tension.

The coefficient of surface tension is defined as the force of contraction across a

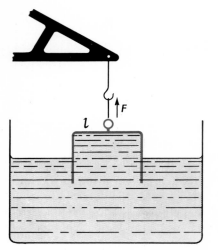

Fig. D. Wire loop for measuring surface tension.

line of unit length, the line and the force being perpendicular to each other, both lying in the plane of the liquid surface: Thus,

$$T = \frac{F}{l} \qquad (1)$$

In the case of the wire loop in Fig. D—

$$T = \frac{F}{2l}$$

The factor 2 enters, because there are two surfaces to a thin film, thus making the effective length of the surface to $2l$.

Table 1. The Coefficient of Surface Tension
of a Few Liquids
(T in dynes/cm)

Liquid	0°C	20°C	50°C
acetone............	26.3	23.7	19.9
alcohol............	24.0	22.3	19.8
benzine...........	31.5	28.9	25.0
mercury...........	508	480	445
water.............	75.6	72.7	67.9

Capillarity. When a long glass tube is placed in a dish of water, as illustrated in

Fig. E, the water rises in the tube until it reaches a certain height and then stops. The finer the bore of the tube the higher the water rises.

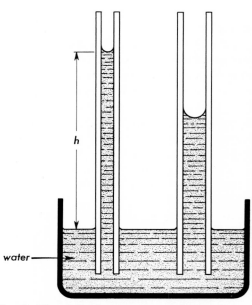

Fig. E. The rise of water in capillary tubes is due to adhesion, cohesion, and surface tension.

Water rises in capillary tubes, because the adhesive forces of glass for water are greater than the cohesive forces of water. When a fine-bore tube is first placed in water, the glass walls immediately above the edge of the water attract molecules to it by adhesion. These molecules in turn attract other nearby molecules, pulling them up by cohesion. This process continues, filling up the space below, as the water rises higher and higher. Surface tension, the result of cohesion, prevents any of the water from dropping back. The water continues to rise until surface tension is equalized by the weight of the liquid in the tube.

The upward force due to surface tension is given by Eq. (2):

$$F = 2\pi r T \qquad (2)$$

The downward force is just the weight of the liquid in the capillary:

$$F = mg$$

$$= \rho g \times \textbf{volume}$$

$$= \pi r^2 h \rho g$$

Because the upward and downward forces must balance for equilibrium, we have—

$$2\pi r T = \pi r^2 h \rho g$$

Therefore, the height, h, to which a liquid will rise in a capillary tube is given by the following formula:

$$h = \frac{2T}{r\rho g} \qquad (3)$$

In the cgs system of units, T is the surface tension measured in dynes per centimeter length, r is the radius of the bore in cm, ρ is the density of the liquid in gm/cm³,

and g is the acceleration due to gravity and equal to 980 cm/sec².

Surface tension is largely responsible for the rise of sap in trees. Carefully performed experiments show that water, by surface tension, can be raised to heights of one hundred feet or more.

Example. One end of a capillary tube is placed in a dish of water. Assuming the surface tension to be 70 dynes/cm and the diameter of the tube to be 1 millimeter, find the height of rise.

Solution. By direct substitution in Eq. (3) we obtain—

$$h = \frac{2 \times 70}{0.05 \times 1 \times 980} = 2.86 \text{ cm}$$

In cases where the cohesive forces of a liquid are greater than the adhesive forces, a liquid column in a capillary tube is depressed. Mercury in a glass capillary is a good example.

QUESTIONS

1. (a) What is the difference between adhesion and cohesion? (b) How do the cohesive forces of mercury molecules compare with their adhesive forces for glass?

2. When you are writing with chalk on a blackboard, what force keeps the chalk on the surface?

3. Can the adhesive force between water and glass be measured by pulling glass from a water surface? Explain.

4. What factors determine whether or not a specific liquid will wet a specific surface?

5. (a) Why does a duck sink if a detergent is added to the water in which it is floating? (b) Would the same thing happen to a man who is also floating in the same water?

6. (a) Why does the surface of water have a meniscus shape? (b) What would you have to do to flatten it out? (c) Would it be possible to give it a surface such as mercury has?

7. (a) What shape should a house have if it were to have the maximum volume for a given amount of house surface? (b) Have any buildings been built this way?

8. (a) Why can a razor blade float on water? (b) What holds the steel body up?

9. (a) Define the coefficient of surface tension. (b) How does surface tension change with temperature? (c) Which has the greater coefficient, mercury or water? (d) What would this difference have to do with the rigidity of water and mercury drops of the same size?

10. (a) What is capillarity? (b) Why does water rise in a glass capillary tube?

11. (a) Upon what does the height of the water column in a capillary tube depend? (b) Does the thickness of the glass walls of the tube affect the height?

12. Where in nature do you think capillarity plays an important role in the functioning of animate and inanimate objects?

13. When a glass tube is placed in mercury the liquid is depressed rather than raised. Why do you think this should be so?

14. An inventor planned to pump water uphill by dipping a capillary tube into water and letting it run out the upper end. Will it work? Explain.

PROBLEMS

1. A U-shaped wire, having a length of 3.5 cm, is lowered into water at 0°C. What force is required to lift the wire slowly from the water as shown in Fig. D?

2. Draw a graph from the values of T given in Table 1 for water and, from it, determine the coefficient of surface tension of water at 15°C and at 30°C.

3. A U-shaped wire 5.4 cm long requires a force of 270 dynes to pull it out of liquid benzene and break the film as shown in Fig. D. (a) What is the coefficient of surface tension? (b) What is the temperature?

4. A glass capillary tube has an internal diameter of 0.15 mm. How high will the water rise in this tube if its lower end is placed in water at 20°C?

5. Water at 50°C is found to rise to a height of 8 cm in a glass capillary tube. What is the diameter of the bore?

6. A circular disk with a 2 cm radius requires 950 dynes to remove it from a liquid. What is the liquid and its temperature?

7. A square loop of wire, 4 cm on a side, is pulled from a dish of acetone at 20°C so that all sides are raised from the surface at once. What is the force required?

8. (a) How could the square in the previous problem be removed with a smaller force? (b) What is the minimum force?

9. Derive Eq. (3) for a square capillary tube.

10. If water at a temperature of 80°C rises to a height of 8 cm in a glass capillary tube, what is the diameter of the bore? (Extrapolate the values from the graph drawn in Problem 2.)

PROJECTS

1. Make a set of capillary tubes from glass tubing to show the relation between the diameter of the tubing and the height of water in them.

2. Develop a sensitive device for measuring the surface tension of water and measure the effects that a variety of impurities have on the surface tension.

PROPERTIES OF MATTER

Lesson 39 **THE ATMOSPHERE**

The Earth's Atmosphere. We, on the earth's surface, although little conscious of the fact, are submerged in a great sea of air called the atmosphere. This air, which to the earth is the most common of all gases, is really a mixture of well-known gases: about 77% nitrogen, 21% oxygen, and 1% argon. The remaining 1% includes small qauntities of such gases as carbon dioxide, hydrogen, neon, krypton, helium, ozone, and xenon.

Being most dense at sea level (see Fig. A), the atmosphere extends upward to a height of from fifty to several hundred

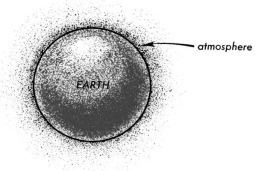

Fig. A. Illustration of the air surrounding the earth. The height is exaggerated to bring out the decrease in density with increase in altitude. (If drawn to scale, the earth's atmosphere would be represented by a line much thinner than the one that represents the earth's surface here.)

miles. The apparent uncertainty as to the exact height of the atmosphere is not real, for the air gets thinner and thinner the higher one goes and finally thins out into interstellar space. Observations show that even interstellar space, which is often referred to as the most perfect vacuum, contains a small but definite amount of matter in the gaseous state: about one molecule per cubic centimeter.

Living, as most of us do, near sea level, we are constantly subjected to an enormous pressure due to the weight of the air above us. Unbelievable as it may seem, the air exerts a pressure of close to 15 lb for every square inch of surface. This, the atmospheric pressure, is given by the weight of a column of air 1 sq in. in cross-section that reaches from sea level to the top of the atmosphere.

Standard Atmospheric Pressure. If a column of mercury stands at exactly 76 cm, we say we have *standard atmospheric pressure,* or a pressure of *one atmosphere.* The pressure at any depth below the surface of a liquid is given by—

$$P = h\rho g \qquad (1)$$

where h is the height of the liquid column, ρ is the liquid density, and g the acceleration due to gravity. Since mercury has a density of 13.6 gm/cm³, standard atmospheric pressure is given by Eq. (1) as—

$$1 \text{ atm} = 76 \text{ cm} \times 13.6 \frac{\text{gm}}{\text{cm}^3} \times 980 \frac{\text{cm}}{\text{sec}^2}$$

from which—

$$1 \text{ atm} = 1{,}013{,}000 \frac{\text{dynes}}{\text{cm}^2} \qquad (2)$$

Because barometric pressure is used so much by the Weather Bureau as an aid in predicting the weather, it has become common practice to define a new pressure unit called the *bar:*

$$1 \text{ bar} = 1{,}000{,}000 \frac{\text{dynes}}{\text{cm}^2} \qquad (3)$$

With this as a definition, we have—

$$1 \text{ atm} = 1.013 \text{ bars} \qquad (4)$$

A smaller unit of pressure, the *millibar,* is one thousand times smaller, so that—

$$1 \text{ atm} = 1013 \text{ millibars} \qquad (5)$$

It is in millibars that the atmospheric pressure is indicated on all U.S. weather maps published daily in Washington, D.C.

In addition to the slight daily variations in barometric pressure at sea level, the barometric pressure decreases rapidly with altitude. At a height of 3.5 mi, the barometer stands at 38 cm, or half an atmosphere. This means that, if we are 3.5 mi above the surface of the earth, half the atmosphere lies below us. At a level 19 mi above sea level, 99% of the air lies beneath us.

The Mercury Barometer. A barometer is a device for measuring the atmospheric pressure. There are in common use today two kinds of barometers—the *mercury barometer* and the *aneroid barometer.* The mercury barometer was invented by the Italian physicist, Evangelista Torricelli, some three hundred years ago. Torricelli's experiment is illustrated in Fig. B. A long glass tube is filled with mercury, and a finger is placed over one end as shown in

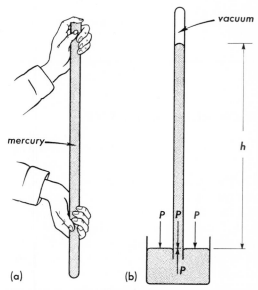

Fig. B. Torricelli's experiment. The making of a mercury barometer.

diagram (*a*). This tube is then inverted and, with the open end in a dish of mercury, the finger is removed, as in diagram (*b*). At the instant the finger is removed the mercury level drops in the tube to a height, *h,* as shown. The mercury drops until the pressure due to its own weight inside the tube (at the level *P*) is equal to the atmospheric pressure outside.

At sea level, the height at which the mercury column stands is about 76 cm or nearly 30 in. This height will be the same regardless of the diameter of the tube or the length of the vacuum space at the top. Torricelli's experiment shows that a column of air 1 sq cm in cross section and reaching to the top of the atmosphere is equal in weight to a column of mercury of the same cross section and 76 cm high.

The height of the mercury in a barometer measures directly the atmospheric pressure. Instead of specifying the pressure in lb/in.² or in dynes/cm², it is customary to

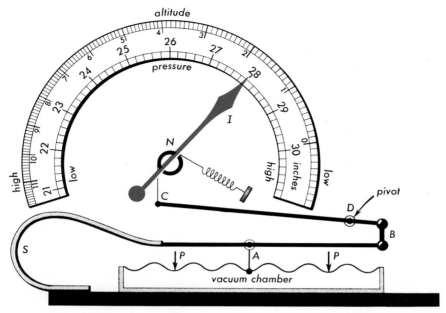

Fig. C. Schematic diagram and cross section of an aneroid barometer.

give the height of the mercury column in inches or centimeters.

If a barometer were made to employ water in place of mercury, the barometer tube would have to be at least 13.6 times as high, or 1034 cm. This is equivalent to about 34 ft. Such an instrument would be too cumbersome to be of much practical value.

The Aneroid Barometer. The desirability of a small, portable pressure-measuring instrument has led to the development of the aneroid barometer. This device is frequently used as an altimeter and barometer combined. A cross-section diagram of such an instrument is shown in Fig. C, and an overall view is shown in Fig. D. A small, flat, metal box, evacuated and with a flexible top, is attached at A to a multiplying system of levers. The end of the lever system is connected to a small cable, C, which is wrapped around a spindle, N, carrying a pointer, I. If the atmospheric pressure, P,

increases, the flexible boxtop is pushed down at A. This lowers the end of the lever system at B and, with a pivot at D, raises

Fig. D. Aneroid barometer used for measuring atmospheric pressure.

the point C. The cable winds up on the spindle, N, turning the pointer, I, to the right to a scale reading of higher pressure. The scale of the aneroid is calibrated by a standard mercury barometer, so the pressure is always given in centimeters or inches of mercury.

Because the atmospheric pressure decreases as one goes to higher altitudes, a barometer is often used to determine elevation. As a matter of fact, aneroid barometers are frequently made with an altitude scale attached. Such instruments, called *altimeters*, are found on the instrument panel of every airplane.

Experiments Illustrating Atmospheric Pressure. Normal atmospheric pressure of 15 lb/in.^{2} does not ordinarily impress a person as being very great. Taken over a considerable area, however, such a pressure gives rise to a tremendous force.

An experiment illustrating atmospheric pressure is diagramed in Fig. E. In diagram

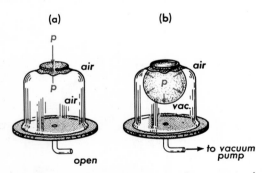

Fig. E. Experiments illustrating the magnitude of atmospheric pressure.

(*a*), a thin sheet of rubber is first tied over the top end of a jar. When this is done, the air pressure inside is the same as that outside. If, now, the inside force, upward on the rubber, is removed by means of a vacuum pump, the outside force pushes the

rubber down inside as shown in diagram (*b*).

The principles of breathing in the human body are demonstrated in Fig. F. Mus-

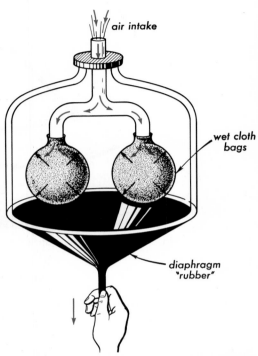

Fig. F. Experimental demonstration of the principles of breathing by the human body.

cular contraction in pulling down on the *diaphragm* creates a low pressure around the lungs and atmospheric pressure pushes air into the lungs. Retraction of the diaphragm raises the pressure and compresses the lungs, forcing air and carbon dioxide out.

Two additional experiments are illustrated in Fig. G. The first diagram represents an inverted cylinder and piston. By pumping out the air from the cylinder chamber, the atmospheric pressure lifts the piston and accompanying heavy weights, W. With a circular piston only 5 in. in di-

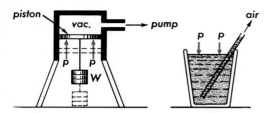

Fig. G. Experiments illustrating the presence of atmospheric pressure and its action in all directions.

ameter, a total weight of 295 lb can be lifted. The second diagram represents the drinking of water from a glass by means of a straw. The water is not drawn up through the straw; it is pushed up from the outside. Suction at the top end of the straw removes the air and, hence, the pressure at that point. The atmospheric pressure at the liquid surface in the glass pushes the water up the straw and into the mouth. This is similar in its action to a siphon.

The Magdeburg Hemispheres. In 1654, Otto von Guericke[*] performed before the Emperor Ferdinand III, at Regensburg, the celebrated experiment of the "Magdeburg hemispheres." Two copper hemispheres, about 22 in. in diameter, were placed together to form a sphere as shown in Fig. H. A ring of leather soaked in oil and wax was set between them to make an airtight joint. When the sphere was evacuated, two teams of eight horses each were unable to pull the hemispheres apart. This it not to be wondered at, for the force required to pull them apart is easily calculated and amounts to nearly three tons.

Measurement of Gas Pressure. There are many kinds of gauges used for measur-

[*] Otto von Guericke (1602-1686), German philosopher, lawyer, physicist, and magistrate was incited by the discoveries of Galileo, Pascal, and Torricelli. He produced the first vacuum and made the first air pump. From researches in astronomy he predicted the periodic return of comets.

ing gas pressure. One of the simplest instruments used in fixed installations is the manometer. As shown in Fig. I, these devices are U-shaped glass tubes containing mercury, alcohol, water, or other liquids.

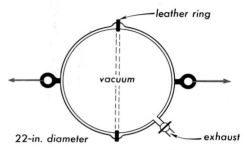

Fig. H. The Magdeburg hemispheres designed by Otto von Guericke.

In the open-tube manometer at the left, atmospheric pressure, P_0, acts downward on the exposed liquid surface at B. The pressure at the level A in the right-hand column is therefore P_0 plus the pressure due to the liquid column of height, h. Because this must be equal to the pressure at the same level, A, in the left-hand column—

$$P = P_0 + h\rho g \qquad (6)$$

This is the pressure, P, exerted by the enclosed gas on the liquid surface and the container walls. If P and P_0 are in dynes/cm^2, then h is in centimeters, ρ is the density of the liquid in the manometer in gm/cm^3, and g is the acceleration due to gravity in cm/sec^2.

If the liquid in the manometer is mercury, it is customary to specify P, P_0, and h in centimeters of mercury:

$$P = P_0 + h \qquad (7)$$

A similar reasoning applied to the open manometer tube of diagram (b) shows that the absolute pressure, P, inside the vessel (indicated by dotted lines) is less

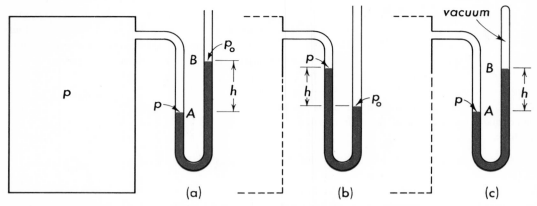

Fig. I. Diagrams of open and closed manometer tubes as used in measuring gas pressure.

than atmospheric pressure by an amount equal to the mercury column, h—

$$P = P_0 - h \qquad (8)$$

The closed-tube manometer, shown at the right, is frequently used where pressures of only a fraction of 1 atm are to be measured. The right-hand side of the U-tube is closed at the top and evacuated. With the atmospheric pressure thus eliminated, the gas pressure to be measured is given by the mercury column, h—

$$P = h \qquad (9)$$

Absolute Pressure. When an automobile tire goes flat from a puncture, the small amount of air remaining in the tire is at atmospheric pressure the same as the air outside. This is roughly 15 lb/in.[2] If the tire is repaired and pumped up to a pressure of 30 lb/in.[2], as read on a standard air pressure gauge, the absolute pressure of the enclosed gas is 30 + 15 or 45 lb/in.[2] In other words, a pressure gauge gives the difference between atmospheric pressure outside and the air pressure inside.

In the manometer tubes of Fig. I, the mercury column, h, is the gauge pressure, and to this is added the atmospheric pressure, P_0, to get the absolute pressure. In the closed-tube diagram (c), h measures directly the absolute pressure. Pressure gauges are usually adjusted to a zero reading when disconnected, so that atmospheric pressure must be added to their reading to obtain the absolute pressure.

QUESTIONS

1. (a) What is an aneroid barometer? (b) Why is it preferred to a mercury barometer?
2. Why is it so difficult to tell the exact height of the earth's atmosphere?
3. (a) Why are astronomers convinced that there is no atmosphere on the moon? (b) How do astronauts expect to live on the moon?
4. Why do cross-country jet planes have pressurized cabins?
5. (a) Because there is a pressure of 15 lb on each square inch of our bodies, why

don't our bodies crush under this enormous force? (b) Estimate the total pressure on your body.

6. What is the significance of a falling barometer?

7. What advantage might a mercury barometer have over an aneroid barometer?

8. A manufacturer makes two aneroid barometers, one to use as an altimeter, and one to measure changes in pressure at sea level. (a) How would these barometers differ? (b) Would a pilot rely on this type of altimeter to avoid hitting a mountain at night? Why?

9. What phenomenon does the Magdeburg-hemisphere experiment illustrate?

10. (a) If a flat plate were placed over the open side of one hemisphere of the kind shown in Fig. H and the air removed from inside, how would you calculate the force required to pull the plate off? (b) How would this force compare with that of pulling the two hemispheres apart?

11. Describe an experiment that would measure the density (a) of air and (b) of helium.

12. (a) State Archimedes' principle as it would apply to an object in air. (b) Name a useful application of Archimedes' principle in the atmosphere.

13. Since there is no such thing as suction, how is it that soda water can be brought up into one's mouth with a straw?

14. How does a syphon work?

PROBLEMS

1. A hollow glass sphere 8 in. in diameter is evacuated. Calculate the total inward force on the outside surface under standard atmospheric pressure of 15 lb/in.^{2} (*Note:* The area of a sphere is $4\pi r^2$.)

2. A circular screen of a TV picture tube is 20 in. in diameter. With the tube thoroughly evacuated and standard atmospheric pressure outside, what is the total inward force on the screen? Assume the screen to be flat.

3. Magdeburg hemispheres, with an internal diameter of 4 in., are put together and thoroughly evacuated. What minimum force will pull them apart under normal atmospheric pressure?

4. How large would a pair of Magdeburg hemispheres have to be to resist a force of 600 lb, assuming that an almost perfect vacuum could be made?

5. One Magdeburg hemisphere, 2 ft in diameter, with a thick glass plate over the opening is evacuated. Calculate the total inward force on the glass plate.

6. If a cylindrical tin can, 8 cm in diameter and 10 cm tall, were thoroughly evacuated, what would be the force on each end?

7. If a barometer contains water in place of mercury, how high will the water column be at sea level?

8. The cylinder and piston in Fig. G have an internal diameter of 6 in. What maximum load can be lifted by the piston as the cylinder is evacuated? Assume atmospheric pressure to be 15 lb/in.^{2}

9. Mt. Popocatepetl in Mexico is 17,887 ft high. What is the approximate pressure at the top (a) in cm of mercury? (b) in atmospheres? (c) in millibars?

PROJECT

Make a model showing how our lungs function.

PROPERTIES OF MATTER

Lesson 40 *FLUIDS IN MOTION*

The term *fluid* applies to any substance capable of flowing and includes gases, as well as liquids. Because all fluids have mass, Newton's Second Law of Motion implies that unbalanced forces are required to set them in motion. As a matter of practical interest, we will consider the various means by which such forces are obtained, how they are applied to fluids, and what factors control the resultant motion. In these discussions, the student would do well to keep in mind the fact that liquids are practically incompressible.

Velocity Through an Orifice. Many city water-supply systems store water in reservoirs on some hilltop or in a nearby water tower and, from these, the water runs through pipes into the houses, stores, and factories in and around the city. Such an arrangement is called a *gravity system.*

When a hole is opened in the side of a vessel containing a liquid, the velocity of flow through the orifice increases with depth. Here, the unbalanced force setting the liquid in motion is gravity acting through the liquid as pressure. We have already seen how the pressure at any given

depth is the same in all directions. At a depth h_1 (see Fig. A), the liquid exerts a pressure, P_1, against the walls and the walls exert an equal and opposite pressure against the liquid.

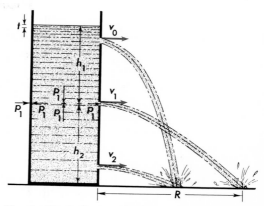

Fig. A. The velocity of efflux through a hole in the side of a vessel of water increases with depth.

The instant an opening is made in the side of the vessel, the wall pressure is destroyed at that point and the liquid pressure inside pushes the liquid directly in front of the hole, giving it an acceleration outward and normal to the plane of the opening. To find the velocity of escape, consider the potential energy of the liquid body in the vessel when the hole is first opened and, then, a short time later, when a small amount of liquid has escaped, dropping the surface level a distance t.

As far as energy is concerned, the change is the same as though the top layer of water had been lowered a distance h and its potential energy, mgh, has converted into

to the velocity acquired by free fall from the same height.

This relation, first discovered by Torricelli, is known as *Torricelli's* Theorem.*

Flow Through a Pipe. One of the factors determining the flow of water, oil, or gas through a pipe, or the flow of blood through the arteries and veins of the body, is the resistance to flow offered by confining walls. Consider the experiment

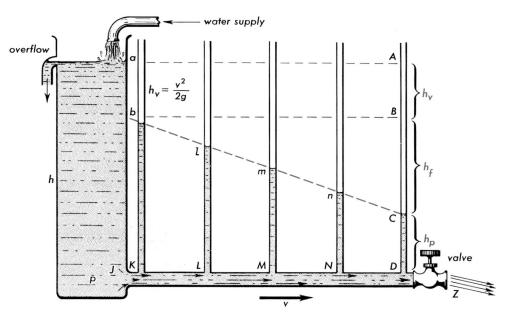

Fig. B. Flow of water through a pipe showing the velocity head h_v, friction head h_f, and the pressure head h_p.

kinetic energy, $\frac{1}{2}mv^2$, in the emergent stream. By the conservation of energy,

$$mgh = \tfrac{1}{2}mv^2 \qquad (1)$$

Because m is the same on both sides, it may be eliminated, giving—

$$v = \sqrt{2gh} \qquad (2)$$

the same as the law of falling bodies. *The velocity of efflux at any depth is equivalent*

shown in Fig. B in which water from a vertical tank at the left is made to flow through a horizontal glass tube at the bottom. The pressure at five equally spaced points along the tube is measured by verti-

* Evangelista Torricelli (1608-1647), Italian physicist and mathematician, was a disciple of Galileo. He is most noted for his scientific articles on fluid motion, on the theory of projectiles, and on geometrical optics.

cal standpipes, and the velocity of flow is controlled by the valve at the right. By means of a water supply and an overflow pipe, the water level in the tank is maintained at a constant level, thus assuring a constant pressure and, hence, a steady flow.

With the valve closed, the water, "seeking its own level," soon brings all standpipes to the same level, aA. Their heights thereby indicate equal pressures at all points along the pipe K to D. When the valve is partially opened and a steady flow is attained, the water in each pipe drops to different levels similar to those shown. The more the valve is opened, the more rapid is the flow and the steeper is the straight line $blmnC$.

At all times, the heights of columns bK, lL, mM, nN, and CD measure the pressures at the points K, L, M, N, and D, respectively. Therefore, the straight line bC indicates a smooth and uniform drop in pressure all along the pipe from K to D. Such a drop in pressure, designated h_f in the figure, is due to *fluid friction* in the pipe and is called the *friction head*. By measuring the friction head for different rates of flow, a comparison of the results will show that h_f is proportional to the square of the velocity. This may be expressed as an equation:

$$h_f = Kv^2 \qquad (3)$$

where K is the proportionality constant.

At extremely low velocities, which are seldom realized, the friction head is proportional to v.

The pronounced drop in level from a in the tank to b in the first standpipe measures the drop in pressure at K, where the water is practically at rest in the tank, and is then speeded up to a velocity v upon entering the pipe. Just as in Torricelli's Theorem, the drop in potential energy from a to b is

converted into kinetic energy in the stream, and by Eq. (2)—

$$h_v = \frac{v^2}{2g} \qquad (4)$$

Here h_v equals ab and is the *velocity head*.

The final pressure at the point D, where the water is being drawn from the pipe, is directly measured by the height of the liquid column, CD, and is called the *pressure head*, h_p.

Viscosity of Liquids. If a thick syrup or heavy oil is subjected to pressure and made to flow through a pipe, the rate of flow will not be so great as when gasoline or water is sent through the same pipe under the same total pressure. This difference in rate of flow is due to an internal fluid resistance called viscosity. In some ways, viscosity resembles the friction between solids and in other respects it is quite different.

Consider the slow, steady flow of water over the sandy bed of a river or stream. See Fig. C. Flow measurements show that the

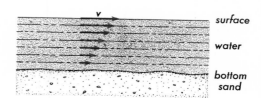

Fig. C. The water in a river flows fastest at the surface.

speed is a maximum at the top surface and decreases with depth, becoming approximately zero at the bottom.

If we imagine the water divided into thin layers as indicated, it will be seen that the motion is such that the layers are sliding over one another. Because of the attractive forces between molecules, the sandy river bed tends to keep the bottom layer from moving at all, the bottom layer in turn tends to hold back the second layer, this second layer tends to hold back the third, etc.

Because the division into layers is an arbitrary one, we see that, all the way up through the liquid, there must be frictional forces tending to resist relative motion. The greater the resistance to motion, the greater is the viscosity.

A simple demonstration of the effect of viscosity on the flow of a liquid around an obstacle is given in Fig. D. Two identical

weights are dropped simultaneously, one into water and one into glycerine. In water, the weight settles quickly, but in glycerine the descent is very slow.

A demonstration of the viscosity of gases is illustrated in Fig. E. A cardboard

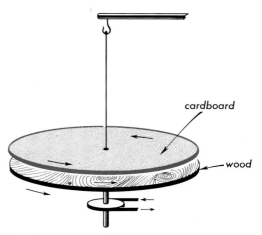

Fig. E. Because of the viscosity of the air, the cardboard disk is carried around by the rotating disk below.

disk, suspended at its center by a thread, is placed close to, but not touching, a wooden disk. When the latter is set into rapid rotation, the cardboard disk begins to rotate in the same direction and gradually picks up speed.

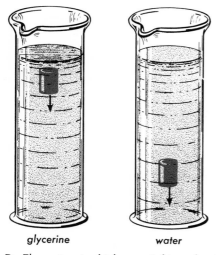

glycerine   water

Fig. D. The rate at which a weight settles in a fluid is a measure of viscosity.

QUESTIONS

1. (a) What is a fluid? (b) What is an orifice? (c) What fluids are readily compressible? (d) What fluids are nearly incompressible?
2. (a) What is meant by the velocity head for water flowing through a pipe? (b) What is the friction head? (c) How does the velocity head vary with the velocity of the liquid? (d) How does the friction head vary?
3. What kind of path is made by water coming out of a hole in the side of a tank? Why?
4. How is it possible to measure the pressure of a liquid flowing in a pipe?
5. (a) What is viscosity? (b) Name two liquids having high viscosity and two liquids with low viscosity.

6. (a) Do gases qualify as fluids? (b) Do gases have viscosity? (c) How could you demonstrate the viscosity of a gas?

7. (a) If a freely suspended pendulum is set swinging, why will it slow and stop? (b) Would it stop more quickly if submerged in oil?

8. It has been said that glass is a fluid. (a) If this is true what must be true of its viscosity? (b) Can you think of an experiment that would prove or disprove that glass is a fluid?

9. Why does water in a river flow fastest at the top?

10. A hole in the side of a vessel is releasing water. (a) If the diameter of the hole is increased, will the velocity of the water increase? (b) Will the distance that the water must go to reach the ground increase?

11. The valve in Fig. B is opened completely so that there is no fluid friction past this point, D. (a) In what way do the friction head, pressure head, and velocity head change? (b) What happens to these values if the valve is closed?

PROBLEMS

1. A farmer's milk can develops a hole in the side, 40 cm below the liquid level inside. Find the escape velocity of the milk.

2. A cylindrical tank, 20 ft high and full of water, develops a hole in its side 16 ft below the top. Find the velocity of the water flowing through the orifice.

3. At what speed will the velocity head of a stream of water be equal to 15 cm of mercury?

4. A cylindrical tank, 8 m high and full of water, has a horizontal pipe connected near the bottom and running into a house. If water flows through the pipe at 2 m/sec, what is the velocity head?

5. A cylindrical tank, 80 ft high and full of water, develops a hole in its side 16 ft below the top. How far from the base of the tank will the emerging water strike the ground? See Fig. A.

6. Show that the distance R in Fig. A is given by $2 \sqrt{h_1 h_2}$.

7. The values of h_v, h_f and h_p in Fig. B are 10 cm, 20 cm, and 10 cm, respectively. If the valve is partially closed so that the water velocity is halved, what are the values of h_v, h_f, and h_p?

8. Water flowing with a velocity of 2 m/sec in a pipe 4 cm² in cross section enters a short section of pipe having a cross section of 1 cm². Calculate (a) the velocity in the smaller pipe. Find the velocity head in (b) the larger pipe and (c) the smaller pipe.

9. Water flowing with a velocity of 1 m/sec in a pipe 3 cm in diameter enters a section having a diameter of only 1 cm. Find (a) the velocity in the second pipe, (b) the velocity head in the larger pipe, and (c) the velocity head in the smaller pipe.

10. A cylindrical tank, 80 ft high and full of water, develops a hole in its side 16 ft below the top. A second hole develops vertically below the first hole,

from which water strikes the ground at the same point as water from the first hole. How far up from the base is the lower hole located?

11. An open-top tank, 3 m deep, is kept level full of water, while a steady stream flows out through an orifice in the side wall at a point $\frac{1}{2}$ m from the bottom of the tank. At the orifice, the stream enters an elbow with the open end pointed upward. Calculate the height above the orifice to which the issuing stream will rise.

12. A main 6 in. in diameter branches into two pipes, each 4 in. in diameter. The piping system is horizontal and full of flowing water. Assume the velocity in the 6-in. main to be 2 ft/sec. Calculate the velocity in the 4-in. pipes.

13. Water flows with a velocity of 2 m/sec in a pipe 4 cm^2 in cross section. Calculate the kinetic energy of the water contained in a 10-m length of the pipe.

14. In Fig. A, at what height must the hole be to give the greatest value to R?

PROJECTS

1. Develop an apparatus that you can use to measure the viscosity of a variety of fluids.

2. Make an apparatus similar to Fig. A. Use it to measure the velocity of water as it emerges from different heights.

PROPERTIES OF MATTER

Lesson 41 *BERNOULLI'S PRINCIPLE*

When a river runs through broad, open country, the water runs slowly; but when it comes to a narrow rocky gorge, its velocity increases many fold. Similarly, when a gas or liquid flowing through a pipe comes to a narrow constricted section, the velocity increases as it enters the constriction and decreases again as it leaves the other end. This is illustrated by an experiment diagramed in Fig. A.

The arrangement is the same as in the preceding lesson, Fig. A, except that the horizontal flow pipe contains a short section, *DE*, having only half the cross-sectional area as of the rest of the pipe. When the valve is opened and a condition of steady flow exists, the water in the standpipes will have dropped from *sr* to new levels like *a*, *b*, *d*, etc., as shown. Note that, as the water enters the constriction at *C*, the velocity of flow increases and the pressure drops from *c* to *l*. Farther along, where it leaves the narrow tube at *F*, the velocity decreases and the pressure rises from *f* to *k*.

This illustrates Bernoulli's principle, which may be stated as follows: *Where the velocity of a fluid is high, the pressure is low and, where the velocity of a fluid is low, the pressure is high.*

The change in pressure due to the moving fluid is given by Bernoulli's equation—

$$\Delta P = \tfrac{1}{2}\rho v^2 \qquad (1)$$

where ρ is the density of the fluid in Kg/m^3, v is the velocity of the fluid in m/sec, and

$\Delta P = \tfrac{1}{2} \times 1.25 \times (.20)^2$
 $= .025$ newton/m^2
$\Delta F = \Delta P \times A$
 $= .025 \times (.10)^2 = 2.5 \times 10^{-4}$ newtons

Experiments Illustrating Bernoulli's Principle. Bernoulli's principle is often referred to as a physical paradox and is the basis of many interesting phenomena. In the first illustration, (*a*), in Fig. B, a blast

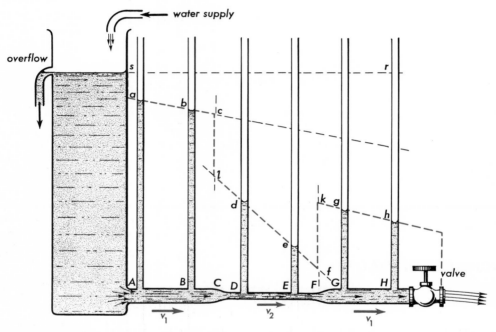

Fig. A. When the velocity of a fluid increases, the pressure drops, and when the velocity of a fluid decreases, the pressure rises.

ΔP is the change in pressure in newtons/ m^2.

Example. A stream of air flows over the top of a square piece of paper, 10 cm on a side, with a velocity of 20 cm/sec. What is the change in pressure? What is the force acting to lift the paper? The density of air is 1.25 Kg/m^3.

Solution. By substituting into Eq. (1), we have—

of air from a nozzle is blown between two sheets of cardboard suspended about 3 in. apart by cords. Instead of being blown apart, as one might expect, they come together. The reason for this action is that, between the two sheets, where the velocity of the air is high, the pressure, P_2, is low. On the two outside surfaces, where the air is not moving, the pressure, P_1, (atmos-

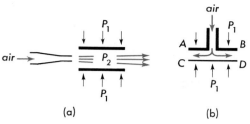

Fig. B. Demonstrations of Bernoulli's principle.

pheric pressure), is high and pushes the two sheets together.

In the second diagram, (b), air is blown through a hole in the center of a disk AB as shown. When a piece of paper, CD, is placed close to the opening, it is not blown away but is drawn toward the disk. Where the velocity of air between the disk and paper is high, the pressure is low; and the higher pressure, P_1, on the underside of the paper pushes it up against the disk.

One often hears it said that, during a certain windstorm, tornado, or hurricane, the roofs of one or more houses were blown off without otherwise damaging the house.

This is not as freakish an accident as one might think, for there is a simple explanation. A high wind blowing over the roof creates a low pressure on top, and the atmospheric pressure inside, where the wind is not blowing, lifts off the roof. An excellent experiment illustrating the phenomenon is shown in Fig. C. A jet of compressed air is blown over the surface of a board on which is located a balsa-wood model of a house roof or an airplane wing, hinged at one edge.

Diagram (a) in Fig. D represents a

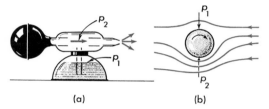

Fig. D. Demonstrations involving Bernoulli's principle.

common form of perfume atomizer. Squeezing the bulb sends a stream of air through the central tube, creating a low pressure, P_2, inside. Atmospheric pressure, P_1, on the liquid surface pushes liquid up the stem to be blown out the right-hand tube with the air stream.

Most of the baseballs thrown by a pitcher are curves, some up or down and others in or out, i.e., to right or left. This is an art, accomplished by throwing the ball so that it spins rapidly about some particular axis. To produce a downward curve, i.e., a *drop ball*, the ball is given a top spin as shown in diagram (b). Here, instead of having the ball moving to the right, we can imagine the ball standing still, but spinning, and the air to be moving from right to left. At the top surface,

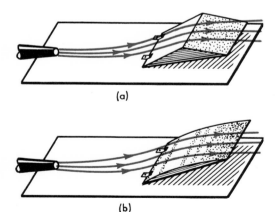

Fig. C. Experiments illustrating the lifting forces on a roof and an airfoil when a fast stream of air is blown over the top surface.

where the wind and ball are moving in opposite directions, the air is slowed down by friction, giving rise to a high-pressure region. On the underside, the surface moving with the wind keeps the velocity high, thus creating a low-pressure region. The resultant downward force thus causes the ball to drop faster than usual.

If a Ping-Pong ball is placed in a vertical stream of air or water, it will rise to a given height above the nozzle and stay at that level, spinning and bobbing around without falling. If the ball goes to one side, as illustrated in Fig. E, the fluid going by

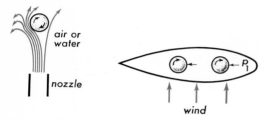

Fig. E. Demonstrations involving Bernoulli's principle.

on the left side causes the ball to spin as shown. The velocity being high on the left means a low pressure. The higher pressure on the right, where the velocity is low, pushes the ball back into the stream.

The same principle has been applied to the historical *Flettner rotor ship* which, instead of using sails, employed two tall, rotating cylinders, motor driven. As shown by the top-view diagram, Fig. E, a wind from broadside the ship produces a forward force. Such a ship, carrying a cargo, crossed the Atlantic twice not many years ago. Although the trips were successful, the uncertainty of a strong wind makes shipping with such ships unreliable.

The Lift of an Airplane Wing. The major part of the lift of an airplane wing is at the top surface. This discovery has been

made in laboratory wind tunnels by setting up sections of airfoils in fast moving currents of air and measuring the pressure at various regions of the surface with pressure gauges. Fig. F shows how this can be done

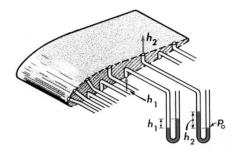

Fig. F. Experimental arrangement of mercury manometers showing how the air pressure can be measured at various points over the surface of an airfoil.

with mercury manometers connected by long tubes to small openings on the top and bottom surfaces.

When the air is still, all manometer tubes show equal heights in their two arms and normal atmospheric pressure, P_0, exists at all points inside the hollow wing as well as outside. When the air stream is set in motion, manometer openings at the top surface show a drop from atmospheric pressure, while those openings at the bottom surface show a rise. Because atmospheric pressure on the outside surfaces was previously counterbalanced at all points by the atmospheric pressure inside the hollow wing, the manometer readings, h_1 and h_2, give directly the resultant pressures on the two wing surfaces.

A graphic representation of the manometer pressures is shown in Fig. G. Note the very large effect of the upper surface as compared with the lower surface, particularly near the leading edge. Note also that the direction of the net force on the lower surface of the wing is opposite to the di-

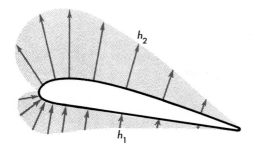

Fig. G. Diagram of an airfoil showing pressure differences over the surfaces.

rection expected from Bernoulli's principle alone. In flight, the wing makes an angle with the direction of the relative wind. As the wind deflects off the wing, it gives an equal but opposite push to the wing. It is this application of Newton's Third Law of Motion that also contributes to the lift of a plane. In upside-down flight, the deflection from the larger "top" surface would of necessity be the only force that could keep the plane from falling.

QUESTIONS

1. Explain how Bernoulli's principle arises from Bernoulli's equation.
. 2. (a) Why does a baseball curve when it is thrown with a spin? (b) What direction must the ball spin in order to curve "out" for a right-handed batter? (c) Make a diagram.
3. (a) Why does a floating ball remain directly in a water stream, falling vertically on it? (b) Make a diagram and explain how Bernoulli's principle is involved.
4. Why does Bernoulli's principle appear, at first glance, to be wrong?
5. How does Bernoulli's principle explain the lift-off of roofs during a windstorm?
6. Make a diagram similar to Fig. A, but with an enlarged section of pipe instead of the constricted section. Show the expected levels in the standpipes, etc.
7. Suppose the apparatus in Fig. A was moved into a pressure chamber and subjected to twice atmospheric pressure. How will the velocity of the water change?
8. Explain the operation of (a) an atomizer, (b) a "curve ball" baseball throw, and (c) the Flettner rotor ship.
9. Why does a Ping-Pong ball stay in a given position above a stream of air?
10. Which of the two surfaces, upper or lower, gives rise to the greatest lifting force on an airplane wing?
11. (a) What other principle, besides Bernoulli's principle, accounts for the lift of an airplane? (b) Under what conditions of flight would it be most important in keeping a plane aloft?

PROBLEMS

1. Air flows over a 10 m² canvas sheet lying on the ground. (a) If the wind velocity is 20 m/sec, what is the pressure on the sheet? (b) What force is acting to lift the sheet?
2. The force trying to lift the roof off a barn during a storm is about 600 lb. What

would the force become if the wind velocity changed from 35 mi/hr to 50 mi/hr?

3. What is the density of water in Kg/m^3?

4. Hydrogen at 0°C and 760 mm pressure has a density of 8.9×10^{-5} g/cm³. What is its density in Kg/m^3?

5. A spacecraft re-entering the earth's atmosphere has a velocity of 0.3 Km/sec. What is the pressure difference across the hull, assuming standard air density on both sides?

6. A jet passenger plane flies at 320 mi/hr. Owing to the shape of the wing, the velocity across the top is 370 mi/hr. What is the lift, if the wing area is 400 m²?

PROJECTS

1. Develop a set of experiments that demonstrates Bernoulli's principle.

2. Make a small wind tunnel to measure the lift on differently shaped airplane wings.

Heat

It is hardly necessary to add, that any thing which any insulated *body, or system of bodies, can continue to furnish* without limitation, *cannot possibly be a* material substance: *and it appears to me to be extremely difficult, if not quite impossible, to form any distinct idea of any thing, capable of being excited, and communicated, in the manner the heat was excited and communicated in these experiments, except it be MOTION.*

Lord Rumford—*An Experimental Inquiry Concerning the Source of the Heat Which Is Excited by Friction*

Heat is nothing but motive power, or rather motion which has changed form. It is a motion of the particles of bodies. Wherever there is destruction of motive power, there is, at the same time, production of heat in an amount precisely proportional to the quantity of motive power which has been destroyed. Reciprocally, wherever there is destruction of heat, there is the production of motive power.

One might then propose as a general thesis, that motive power is a constant quantity in nature, that it is never, properly speaking, produced or destroyed. In truth, it changes form, that is to say it produces now one kind of movement, now another; but it is never annihilated.

Sadi Carnot—from his notebook

◄ **A technician "tunes" the blades of the huge rotor of a steam turbine.**

General Electric Co.

Lesson 42 *TEMPERATURE AND EXPANSION*

Temperature, like time, is difficult to define in terms of the simplest concepts. In Lesson 49, we shall see how it may be defined in terms of molecular motion. The word *temperature* means intensity of heat and may be defined as a number on a scale.

Thermometers. The first authentic record of a thermometer dates back to the time

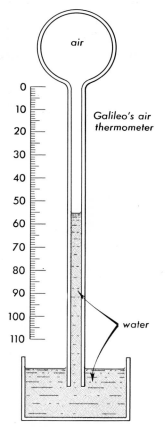

air

0
10
20
30
40
50
60
70
80
90
100
110

Galileo's air thermometer

water

Fig. A. Air, on heating, expands and pushes the water down in the tube. On cooling, the air contracts and the water rises.

of Galileo. Galileo's thermometer, as illustrated in Fig. A, consists of a narrow glass tube with an opening at one end and a bulb at the other. The open end of the tube is filled with colored water and inverted in a dish of water. When the temperature of the surrounding air rises, the air within the bulb expands, forcing the water down the tube. If the bulb is cooled, the air inside contracts, drawing the water up. (To be exact, atmospheric pressure outside pushes the water up.) A scale attached to the narrow tube can be calibrated to any temperature scale, low temperatures at the top and high temperatures at the bottom.

Of the many forms of temperature measuring devices, the mercury thermometer is the most common. See Fig. B. A mercury thermometer consists of a narrow glass tube (a capillary), the bottom end being sealed to a small bulb and the top end being closed. The bulb and part of the capillary are filled with mercury, and the remaining section is evacuated. When the temperature rises, the mercury and the glass bulb both expand. The mercury, however, expands more than the glass, forcing a small part of the mercury up the narrow capillary. A scale on the glass or the mounting makes it possible to read temperature.

Temperature Scales. There are, in general use today, four different temperature scales. These are the Fahrenheit, Rankine, Celsius, and Kelvin.

(Note: For many years the Celsius temperature scale was called centigrade. Recently, however, the International Bureau of Weights and Measures agreed to rename

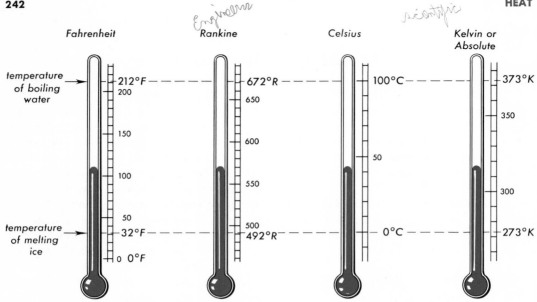

Fig. B. Mercury thermometers illustrating the four common temperature scales.

the scale after its inventor. Fortunately, this change from *centigrade* to *Celsius* still allows the use of the same abbreviation, C.)

Each scale is shown by a diagram in Fig. B. The thermometers are all identically made, but each has a different scale. In the United States, the Fahrenheit scale is commonly used in civil life, and the Rankine scale is used by engineers. The Rankine and Kelvin scales are called, respectively, the *absolute* Fahrenheit and Celsius temperature scales. They are used throughout the world for scientific measurements.

To calibrate a thermometer, the bulb is first cooled in a mixture of ice and water and the height of its mercury column is marked on the stem. It is next placed in steam just above boiling water and again marked. These two fixed points are the bases for whatever scale is to be used.

Between the temperatures of melting ice and boiling water there are 180° on the Fahrenheit and Rankine scales, as compared with 100° on the Celsius and Kelvin scales. The ratio of these numbers is 9:5.

This comparison shows that a temperature rise of 9°F, or 9°R, is equivalent to a rise of only 5°C, or 5°K.

The lowest temperature ever reached is approximately −273.16°C, or −459.60°F. For theoretical reasons, which will be given later, this is the lowest temperature that can ever be attained. It is called *absolute zero*. The Kelvin and Rankine scales are called absolute temperature scales, because they both put 0° at this lowest-possible temperature point. On the basis of the Celsius and Fahrenheit scale divisions, this locates the freezing point of water, to the nearest whole number, at 273°K or 492°R, and the boiling point at 373°K or 672°R.

It is frequently necessary to change temperature readings from one temperature scale to another. Rather than develop formulas for such changes, it is more convenient to consult tables or a temperature conversion scale as shown in Fig. C. For example, 0°C = 32°F, 5°C = 41°F, 10°C = 50°F, 15°C = 59°F, etc.

Many equations require *absolute tem-*

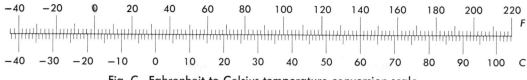

Fig. C. Fahrenheit-to-Celsius temperature-conversion scale.

peratures, which are calculated as follows (*T* designates absolute temperature and *t* refers to relative temperature):

$$T_K = t_C + 273.16°C$$

and

$$T_R = t_F + 459.60°F$$

Electrical Thermometers. If very low or very high temperatures are to be measured, something other than mercury thermometers must be employed.

A diagram of an *electrical thermometer* is shown in Fig. D. A fine piece of platinum

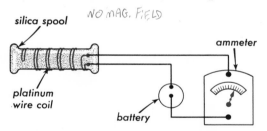

Fig. D. Electrical-resistance thermometer showing connection of the platinum wire coil to the battery and the ammeter.

wire is wound around a small spool made of silica. The ends of this wire are connected to a battery and an ammeter. The purpose of the battery is to supply the electric current, and the ammeter is to determine its exact value. When the temperature of a hot body, like a furnace, is to be measured, the spool of platinum wire is placed inside the furnace and the battery and ammeter outside. A rise in temperature causes the resistance of the platinum wire to increase, and the current, therefore, to decrease.

When the platinum wire reaches the temperature of the furnace, its resistance reaches a constant value and the ammeter pointer indicates a steady current. In many cases, the ammeter scale is calibrated to give the temperature in degrees.

Another form of electrical thermometer, called a *thermocouple*, is illustrated in Fig. E. This temperature-recording device is

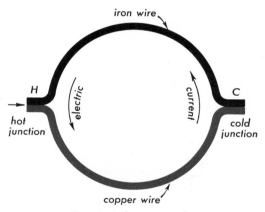

Fig. E. A thermocouple.

based upon a principle, discovered in 1821 by Seebeck, known as the *thermoelectric effect*. Two pieces of wire, one copper and one iron, are joined together at the ends to form a complete loop. When one junction is heated and the other kept cool, an electric current flows around the loop in the direction indicated by the arrows. The greater the difference in temperature between the two junctions the greater is the electric current.

Fig. F represents a thermocouple connected by wires to an ammeter. If the junction of the thermocouple is first placed in melting ice and then in boiling water, the scale of the ammeter can be marked 0°C and 100°C at the appropriate points. This calibrates the instrument, making of it a direct-reading thermometer.

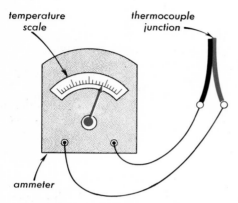

Fig. F. A thermocouple thermometer circuit diagram.

Thermocouples are not always made of copper and iron as shown in Fig. E. Any two different metals when brought into contact will exhibit a thermoelectric effect. Some combinations of two metals, however, produce larger currents than others. For very high-temperature measurements, platinum and platinum-iridium alloys are used, because of their very high melting-point temperatures.

Two recent developments of electrical thermometers have made it possible to make sensitive temperature measurements of remote places from a single position. *Thermistors* are special resistors that have a very high negative-temperature resistance coefficient. If a thermistor is included in an electrical circuit, then changes in the temperature of the thermistor will cause large changes in a meter measuring current in the circuit. *Transistors* are especially temperature sensitive and, in very simple circuits,

can be used both as thermometers or very sensitive thermostats. A more detailed discussion of transistors will be given in the unit on electronics.

Thermal Expansion of Solids. In general, when an object is heated—whether it be a solid liquid, or gas—it expands. There are but a few known exceptions to this. The expansion of a solid with a rise in temperature can be demonstrated by heating a long wire and measuring its over-all elongation. One experimental arrangement for demonstrating this is shown in Fig. G. An iron

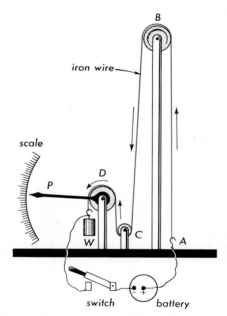

Fig. G. Demonstration of thermal expansion.

wire about 2 m in length is fastened to a hook, A, at one end and to a weight, W, at the other. Between these two points, the wire passes over three pulleys B, C, and D. The wire is heated by connecting it to a battery and sending an electric current through it from end to end.

As the wire is heated and lengthens, the

weight slowly falls, thus turning the pulleys as well as the pointer, P. When the current is turned off by opening the switch, the wire cools and at the same time contracts to its original length.

Not all substances expand by the same amount when heated through the same difference in temperature. It is common practice to describe the expansion of any solid by specifying its linear coefficient of thermal expansion. *The ratio of the change in length per degree Celsius to the original length of a substance is called the linear coefficient of thermal expansion:*

$$\alpha = \frac{\Delta l/l}{\Delta t} \qquad (1)$$

where Δl is the change in length, l is the original length, and Δt is the change in temperature.

A list of a few common metals with their known values of α are given in Table 1. Be-

Table 1. Linear Coefficients of Thermal Expansion

Material	α per °C
aluminum......................	25×10^{-6}
brass.........................	18×10^{-6}
copper........................	17×10^{-6}
glass (soda)..................	17×10^{-6}
glass (pyrex).................	3×10^{-6}
gold..........................	14×10^{-6}
iron..........................	11×10^{-6}
lead..........................	29×10^{-6}
nickel........................	13×10^{-6}
platinum......................	9×10^{-6}
quartz........................	0.4×10^{-6}
silver........................	18×10^{-6}
steel (common)...............	8×10^{-6}

cause the values of α are known for most materials in common use, the expansion Δl is usually the unknown quantity. Solving Eq. (1) for Δl, we find—

$$\Delta l = \alpha l \Delta t \qquad (2)$$

Example. A steel rod is ground and polished to a length of 10 cm when the room temperature is 25°C. What will be its length when its temperature is raised to 300°C?

Solution. In Table 1, we find $\alpha = 8.0 \times 10^{-6}$ per °C. By direct substitution in Eq. (2), we obtain—

$$\Delta l = 8.0 \times 10^{-6} \times 10 \times (300 - 25)$$
$$\Delta l = 22000 \times 10^{-6} = 0.022 \text{ cm}$$

The rod, therefore, lengthens by 0.022 cm to give an over-all length of 10.022 cm.

It should be noted that, if the length of the rod were 10 ft, the elongation would be 0.022 ft. In other words Δl and l are always in the same units.

Differential Expansion. In the previous section, it was stated that all substances do not expand to the same extent. Some metals, like brass and aluminum, expand twice as much as others, like iron and platinum.

This difference in expansion is demonstrated by the heating of a bimetallic strip as shown in Fig. H. Two thin strips of dif-

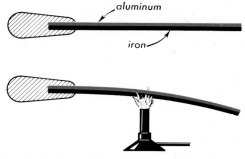

Fig. H. A bimetallic strip bends when heated.

ferent metals are placed side by side and welded together over their entire length. When heated, one metal expands more than the other, causing the strip to bend. The hotter it becomes, the more it bends. When it cools to its original temperature, the strip becomes straight again; and if cooled still further, it bends in the opposite direction.

Differential expansion, as shown by this experiment, finds many practical applications in industry. Bimetallic strips are used, for example, in the making of balance wheels for fine watches, for timers in electric toasters, and in thermostats for refrigerators, hot water heaters, and car radiators. When, on a hot day, the spokes of the balance of a watch expand, they shift the weight of the rim farther from the center, causing the balance wheel to oscillate more slowly. By making the rim of the wheel of two bimetallic strips this can be compensated for as shown in Fig. I. With a rise in temperature, the ends of the spokes, S,

move out and the free ends, R, of the bimetallic strips bend in closer to the axis of

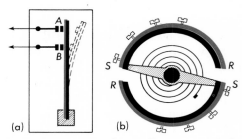

Fig. I. Devices using bimetallic strips: (a) thermostat, and (b) balance wheel of a watch.

rotation. One expansion compensates the other, keeping the watch running at the same rate.

QUESTIONS

1. What feature does the Kelvin and Celsius scale have in common?
2. What feature does the Kelvin and Rankine scale have in common?
3. One of the temperature scales was originally defined such that on a very cold day the temperature is 0° whereas a person running a fever had a temperature of 100°. Which scale is this?
4. How many degrees are there between the freezing and boiling points of water on each of the four temperature scales?
5. Is there such a thing as a negative temperature? Explain.
6. (a) What is an electrical-resistance thermometer? (b) What is it used for? (c) What physical property changes with temperature? (d) Where does the electric current come from?
7. (a) What is a thermocouple? (b) Is a battery used to supply the electric current? (c) What metals are used for very high temperature measurements?
8. If you had a mercury thermometer without a scale, how could you make (a) a Celsius scale for it? (b) a Fahrenheit scale?
9. (a) Which temperature scales are absolute? (b) What does absolute mean? (c) Why aren't the other scales called absolute?
10. (a) In the formula for thermal expansion, does l refer to the length before or after the temperature has changed? (b) Does it make any difference? Explain.
11. (a) If the temperature rises from 10° to 20° Celsius, would you say the temperature has doubled? (b) How many times hotter is a substance at 10°C than it was at 0°C? (c) What is wrong with these two questions?

12. What method do you think might be used to measure the temperature of a hot furnace?

13. The Bay Bridge linking Oakland and San Francisco is 8 mi long. What special precautions did the engineers have to take to prevent the bridge from buckling during a heat spell? Why?

14. (a) What special device is used in many home-heating systems to keep the temperature constant? (b) How does it work?

15. What is the difference between an ordinary mercury thermometer and one used to measure one's body temperature?

16. What determines the accuracy of a mercury thermometer?

PROBLEMS

1. A standard gauge block, made of silver, is exactly 4.000 cm long at 25°C. Calculate its length when the temperature is 60°C.

2. The standard platinum meter bar at the Bureau of Standards is exactly calibrated at 27°C. Find the distance between the end marks when the temperature is 52°C.

3. The iron rails used in building cross-country railroads are 60 ft in length. If the temperature is 40°C at the time they are nailed into place, how large will the gaps between rails be when the temperature drops to −40°C?

4. A 50-cm silver bar becomes 1 mm shorter when it is cooled. How much was it cooled?

5. The iron rim of a wagon wheel has an internal diameter of 1.0 m when the temperature is 150°C. What is its diameter when it cools off to 25°C?

6. A hole is drilled in a block of copper and reamed to a diameter of 3.60 cm when the temperature is 30°C. What is the diameter when it is heated to a temperature of 80°C?

7. A steel tape measure, 100 ft long, is standardized to be used at 72°F. What will be its error in length when used at a temperature of 0°F?

8. At what temperature will a Celsius and a Fahrenheit thermometer read the same numerical temperature?

9. At what temperature will the Kelvin and Rankine scales read the same temperature?

10. An assayer wanted to determine whether or not a brick of yellow metal is gold. When placed in boiling water, it was 20 cm long, whereas in freezing water, it was 19.964 cm long. What is it?

PROJECTS

1. Using a bimetallic strip, make a thermostat that could be used to control the temperature for a chicken incubator.

2. Using a thermistor or transistor sensitive to heat, make a thermometer that could measure the temperature outdoors and be read indoors.

3. Make a simple model of a bridge that would show what would happen to it if the engineers did not allow for its expansion on a hot day.

4. Using two dissimilar metals, make a thermocouple and measure the amount of electricity it produces with different temperatures. How efficient can you make it?

HEAT

Lesson 43 *HEAT CAPACITY*

According to the kinetic theory of matter, the individual atoms of which all substances are made are in a state of rapid motion. As a body is heated to a higher temperature, this atomic motion increases and the body expands. As a body cools, the atomic motions decrease and the body usually shrinks. That heat is a form of energy and is due to the kinetic energy of molecular motion was first proposed by Count Rumford in the latter part of the eighteenth century.[*]

The Calorie. The difference between temperature and quantity of heat is well illustrated by the following experiment. See Fig. A. Five marbles, all of the same size but made of different materials, are heated in boiling water to a temperature of 100°C.

[*] Benjamin Thompson (1753-1814) was born in Rumford, New Hampshire, but he spent most of his adult life in Germany, where, among other things, he managed an artillery factory. From his observations about the heat developed in boring cannon, he was able to show that heat is not a pervading fluid, but a form of internal energy of the atoms or molecules forming the substance. His own expression was that heat was a mode of motion of these particles. For these and other services, the Emperor appointed him to the German nobility, and Thompson chose the name of his birthplace, Rumford, as his title.

At a given instant, they are all placed on a sheet of paraffin about 0.5 cm thick and permitted to melt their way through. The iron

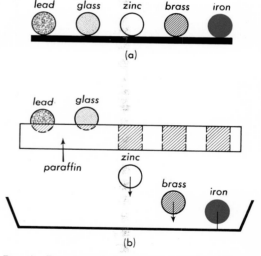

Fig. A. Experiment demonstrating the different heat capacities of different substances of the same size.

and brass marbles are observed to drop through first, but the lead and glass marbles never do. This illustrates the fact that the heat content of the iron and brass, even though raised to the same temperature as the others, is considerably greater than the heat content of the glass and lead.

In order to determine the exact heat capacity of a substance, we must first define the *calorie* and the *British thermal unit.*

The quantity of heat required to raise the temperature of 1 gm of water 1°C is called the calorie.

The quantity of heat required to raise the temperature of 1 lb of water 1°F is called the British thermal unit.

The ratio between these two units is readily computed and found to be—

$$\textbf{1 BTU = 252 cal} \qquad (1)$$

Once the calorie or the BTU is defined, the amount of heat required to raise any amount of water from one temperature to another may be calculated by simply multiplying the mass of water by the temperature rise. For example, to raise 25 gm of water from 10°C to 50°C requires $25 \times 40 = 1000$ cal, or to raise 6 lb of water from 32°F to 60°F requires $6 \times 28 = 168$ BTU.

Because the calorie is a more useful unit than the BTU, it will be stressed from here on.

While 1 cal of heat will raise 1 gm of water 1°C, a different number of calories will be required to raise the temperature of 1 gm of some other substance 1°C. For example, to raise 1 gm of iron 1°C requires only one tenth of a calorie, while to raise 1 gm of lead 1°C requires only one thirtieth of a calorie. In other words, the thermal capacities of equal masses of different materials have different values.

The thermal capacity of a substance is defined as the number of calories required to raise 1 gm of that substance through 1° C in the cgs system (or the amount of heat required to raise 1 lb 1°F in the engineering system).

The ratio between the thermal capacity

of a substance and the thermal capacity of water is called specific heat.

Numerically, *specific heat* has the same value as *thermal capacity;* being a ratio, however, it is like *specific gravity* and has no units.

The specific heats or thermal capacities of some common materials are given in Table 1.

Table 1. Specific Heats

Material	c
aluminum	0.220
brass	0.092
copper	0.093
glass	0.160
gold	0.031
glycerine	0.60
ice	0.50
iron	0.105
lead	0.031
mercury	0.033
silver	0.056
zinc	0.092

To illustrate the use of this table, consider the calculation of the heat content of the marbles used in the foregoing experiment. The measured mass of each marble is given in the second column of Table 2 and the corresponding thermal capacity in the next column. The product of these two

Table 2. Results of Marble Demonstration

Marble	m (gm)	c	H for 1°C	H for 80°C
lead	45	.031	1.39	111
glass	10	.160	1.60	128
zinc	24	.092	2.20	176
brass	30	.092	2.76	221
iron	28	.105	2.94	235

quantities gives the values shown in the fourth column; they represent the amount of heat required to raise that marble 1°C. Because all marbles were raised from room temperature, 20°C, to the boiling point of water, 100°C, the values in the fourth column have been multiplied by the rise in temperature 80°C to obtain the total heat values in the last column.

These numbers clearly indicate that, in this experiment, iron and brass should melt through the paraffin first; they have available within them the largest amounts of stored thermal energy, 235 and 221 calories, respectively.

The definition of thermal capacity and the calculation of total heat content may be summarized by a generally useful formula of the following form:

$$\Delta H = mc\Delta t \qquad (2)$$

where ΔH represents the total amount of heat added or removed, or change in calories (or BTU); m is the mass of the body to which it is added; c is the thermal capacity; and Δt is the change in temperature.

Change of State. The continuous addition of heat to a solid or liquid mass will eventually bring about a change of state. The general behavior of many substances can be illustrated by a detailed description of the changes that occur with the most common of all liquids, water. If a block of ice at a temperature of $-50°C$ is placed in a pan and put on a stove to heat, its temperature will rise slowly until it reaches 0°C.

At 0°C, the temperature stops rising and the ice begins to melt. More and more ice is melted as heat is continually added, and not until the ice has all turned to water does the temperature resume rising. As the water becomes hotter and hotter, it eventually reaches a temperature of 100°C, when vig-

orous boiling sets in. Here again, the temperature stops rising and, as heat is added, more and more water becomes steam. Finally, when all has become steam at 100°C, the temperature begins to rise once more.

All of these changes of temperature and changes of state are shown by a graph in Fig. B. The horizontal sections represent

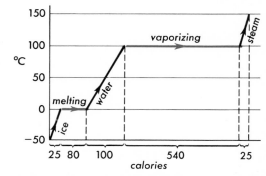

Fig. B. Heat-temperature graph for one gram of ice from $-50°$ to 150°C, illustrating the latent heat of fusion and vaporization.

changes of state without change in temperature, while the slanted sections on either side represent changes in temperature without abrupt changes in state.

Melting Point. *The* melting point *is defined as the temperature at which a substance, under normal atmospheric pressure, changes from the solid to the liquid state, or vice versa.* Every substance has its own melting point, which for water is at 0°C. As shown by a few common substances listed in Table 3, some melt at very low temperatures, while others require extremely high temperatures.

Recent studies of the atomic structure of certain liquids show that, at temperatures approaching the freezing point, the lattice formation assumed by the individual atoms is essentially that of the solid state, whereas others show no such resemblance or similarity right up to the freezing temperature.

Boiling Point. *The* boiling point *is defined as the temperature at which a substance, under normal atmospheric pressure, changes from the liquid to the vapor state,* ature. To melt 1 gm of gold requires 16 cal, 1 gm of silver 21 cal, etc. These values, the *latent heat of fusion,* are tabulated for a number of elements in Table 3.

Table 3. Melting Point, Latent Heat of Fusion, Boiling Point, and Latent Heat of Vaporization of Some Common Substances

Substance	Melting Point °C	Latent Heat of Fusion cal/gm	Boiling Point °C	Latent Heat of Vaporization cal/gm
Air..........................	−212	5.5	−191	51
Aluminum.....................	658	77	1800	. .
Copper.......................	1080	42	2310	. .
Gold.........................	1063	16	2500	. .
Helium.......................	−271	. .	−268	6
Hydrogen.....................	−259	14	−252	108
Iron.........................	1530	6	2450	. .
Lead.........................	327	5.9	1525	. .
Mercury......................	−39	2.8	357	65
Nitrogen.....................	−210	6.1	−195	48
Oxygen.......................	−219	3.3	−184	51
Platinum.....................	1760	27	3910	. .
Silicon......................	1420	. .	3500	. .
Silver.......................	962	21	1955	. .
Sulfur Dioxide...............	73	24	−10	95
Tin..........................	232	14	2270	. .
Tungsten.....................	3400	. .	5830	. .
Water........................	0	80	100	540

or vice versa. These temperatures, too, are listed in Table 3. A knowledge of melting and boiling points is of considerable practical importance. Solid carbon dioxide, liquid air, liquid hydrogen, and liquid helium are used as refrigerants for cooling, whereas metals like tungsten and platinum are used in furnaces designed for the heating of bodies to very high temperatures.

Latent Heat of Fusion. We have seen above that, when ice is melting, heat is continually added, with no resultant rise in temperature. To melt 1 gm of ice, starting at its melting point, requires 80 cal. Similar heat determinations for other solids show that they too require a definite amount of heat to melt them without a rise in temper-

The latent heat of fusion *is defined as the quantity of heat necessary to change 1 gm of solid to 1 gm of liquid with no change in temperature.*

The reverse of fusion is *solidification,* a process in which heat is liberated by the substance. The amount of heat liberated by matter on solidification is equal to the amount of heat taken in on fusion; pure water on freezing gives up 80 cal/gm, gold 16 cal/gm, silver 21 cal/gm, etc. Letting L represent the latent heat of fusion and m the mass of a given substance to be fused or solidified, the quantity of heat required or liberated, as the case may be, is given by—

$$H = mL_f \qquad (3)$$

If m is the mass in grams, then L_f should

be in cal/gm, and H will be in calories. If m is in pounds, then L_f should be in BTU/lb, and H will be in BTU.

Latent Heat of Vaporization. When water is being boiled, heat is continually added without a rise in temperature. This added heat is not retained by the liquid, but is carried off by the vapor through the boiling process. To vaporize 1 gm of boiling water requires 540 cal. This value, the *heat of vaporization*, is tabulated along with others for a number of substances in Table 3. (For metals with very high melting points, the heat of vaporization has never been measured.)

The same Eq. (3), used for calculating heat quantities during fusion, may be used to determine heat quantities during vaporization. If we let L_v be the heat of vaporization and m the mass of substance to be vaporized, the quantity of heat, H, required is given by—

$$H = mL_v \qquad (4)$$

This is also the amount of heat liberated by the same amount of vapor when it condenses to the liquid state.

Because heat is a form of energy, and its addition to a body raises the average kinetic energy of the molecules, the absolute temperature increases proportionately. *During fusion and vaporization, however, heat is added without a temperature change.* During change of state, the heat energy goes into the potential energy of the molecules, exerting forces through collision, which push the molecules farther apart against their attractive forces.

Example. Calculate the amount of heat required to change 50 gm of ice at $-20°C$ to steam at $140°C$.

Solution. To find the heat required to raise the ice from $-20°C$ to the melting point at $0°C$, use Eq. (2) and the thermal capacity of ice from Table 1:

$$H_1 = mc(t_2 - t_1) = 50 \times 0.50 \times 20 = 500 \text{ cal}$$

To find the heat required to melt the ice to water at $0°C$, use Eq. (3) and the heat of fusion from Table 3:

$$H_2 = mL_f = 50 \times 80 = 4000 \text{ cal}$$

To find the heat required to raise the water from $0°C$ to the boiling point at $100°C$, use Eq. (2) and the thermal capacity of water:

$$H_3 = mc(t_2 - t_1) = 50 \times 1 \times 100 = 5000 \text{ cal}$$

To find the heat required to vaporize the water to steam at $100°C$, use Eq. (4) and the heat of vaporization of water:

$$H_4 = 50 \times 540 = 27{,}000 \text{ cal}$$

To find the heat required to raise the steam from $100°C$ to steam at the desired $140°C$, use Eq. (2) and the thermal capacity of steam (0.5):

$$H_5 = mc(t_2 - t_1) = 50 \times 0.5 \times 40 = 1000 \text{ cal}$$

By adding all of these results, we obtain the total required heat:

$$H = 500 + 4000 + 5000 + 27{,}000 + 1000$$
$$= 37{,}500 \text{ cal}$$

QUESTIONS

1. (a) What is the kinetic theory of matter? (b) What happens when a solid is heated and then cooled?
2. (a) What is a calorie? (b) What is a British thermal unit?
3. (a) What is the thermal capacity of a substance? (b) What are the units of thermal capacity in the cgs system?

4. (a) What is the specific heat of a substance? (b) What are the units of specific heat?

5. (a) What is the general formula for finding the total heat content of a substance? (b) In what units should each factor be specified?

6. (a) How does one cause a change of state of matter? (b) Will the addition of heat to a body always raise its temperature?

7. (a) What is meant by the boiling point? (b) What is meant by the melting point?

8. (a) What is the melting point of lead? (b) What is the boiling point of lead? (c) What are the melting and boiling points of oxygen?

9. (a) How could you determine the melting point of tin? (b) Could you use a mercury thermometer? (Glass melts at about 450°C.)

10. The heats of fusion and vaporization are often referred to as "latent." Why is this?

11. When a teakettle is heated on a stove, it always takes a much shorter time for the water to start to boil than for all the water to vaporize. Why is this?

12. How does the kinetic theory of matter explain the expansion of solids when they are heated?

13. Why is a British thermal unit a larger unit than a calorie?

14. At a science exhibit, a demonstrator boiled water in a paper cup over an exposed gas flame. Was he using specially treated paper or could you do the same thing yourself? Explain.

15. What molecular explanation can you give for the large heat of vaporization of water compared to the much smaller heat of melting of ice?

16. What molecular explanation can you give for the large heat of vaporization of water compared to the very small heat of vaporization of mercury?

17. From a heat standpoint, justify the use of the expression "liquid sunshine" when it rains.

18. Why might placing a large tub of water in a cellar prevent other objects in the cellar from freezing?

19. Explain what happens to the latent heat of water vapor in the air when it condenses to form clouds.

20. Looking at Fig. A, how do you account for the fact that, while the specific heats of zinc and brass are identical, the brass comes through the paraffin first?

21. Why is a steam burn more serious than one obtained from spilling hot water?

PROBLEMS

1. How many calories are required to raise the temperature of 5 Kg of water from 25°C to 100°C?

2. How many BTU are required to raise the temperature of 35 lb of water from the freezing point to the boiling point?

3. Find the number of calories required to raise the temperature of 2 Kg of iron from 24°C to 184°C.

4. A copper cup weighing 200 gm contains 600 gm of water, all at 20°C. How many calories are required to raise their temperature to 100°C?

5. A 100-gm gold bar is placed in an aluminum cup of mass 200 gm containing 600 gm of water, all at 30°C. How much heat is required to raise their temperature to 100°C?

6. When 500 gm of an unknown metal was heated by 13,750 cal, its temperature rose from 27°C to 152°C. What is the metal?

7. A block of copper requires 12,000 cal to raise it from 20°C to 330°C. What is its mass?

8. How much heat is required to raise 200 gm of ice at −20°C to water at 70°C?

9. How much heat is required to boil 1.2 Kg of water out of a teakettle starting with water at 22°C?

10. Starting with 12 gm mercury at −39°C, how much heat is required to boil it away?

11. Starting with 80 gm of ice at −20°C, what is the state and temperature achieved by adding: (a) 1600 cal, (b) 7200 cal, (c) 9200 cal?

12. If a certain amount of steam at 100°C is added to an equal weight of ice at −200°C, what is the result?

13. A 2 Kg block of iron at 100°C is dropped into 750 gm of water contained in a 325-gm copper calorimeter cup. If the initial temperature of the water is 12°C, what will be its final temperature?

14. A 5 Kg piece of iron is heated in a flame and then is dropped into a 300-gm aluminum cup containing 400 gm of water at 10°C. The temperature after the iron entered the water rose to 70°C. How hot was the iron before it was dropped in the water?

15. The burning of 6 gm of charcoal raised the temperature of 1200 cm³ of water from 10° to 49°C. What is the heat value of charcoal in cal/gm?

16. 500 gm of aluminum at 400°C is dropped into a large glass jar, which weighs 1000 gm and which contains 500 gm of water and 50 gm of ice. What would be the final temperature of the mixture?

17. Given the thermal capacity of air at constant pressure, .237 cal/liter/C°, how much heat would be required to heat the air in a room 2.5 × 6 × 5 m from 0° to 20°C? The pressure assumed to be constant.

PROJECT

Determine the temperature of a Bunsen-burner flame indirectly by heating a piece of iron in the flame until it is as hot as it will get and then transferring it quickly to a water calorimeter.

HEAT

Lesson 44 **HEAT TRANSFER**

There are numerous methods by which heat may be transmitted from one place to another. Some of these methods are slow and indirect, while others are very fast and direct. A careful study of all known methods has led to the realization that there are but three general types of heat transfer. These are *conduction, convection,* and *radiation.* Conduction is a slow process by which heat is transmitted through a substance by molecular activity. Convection is a more rapid process involving the motion of heated matter itself from one place to another. Radiation of heat from one place to another takes place in the same manner and with the same speed as light, 186,000 mi/sec.

Conduction. Not all bodies are good conductors of heat. Metals like copper and silver are much better for this purpose than are other substances like wood, glass, paper, and water. The ability of a given substance to conduct heat is called its *thermal conductivity.*

The relative conductivities of different substances can be illustrated by an experiment performed as follows: Similar rods of six different metals—copper, aluminum, brass, tin, german silver, and lead—are coated with a special yellow paint and arranged as shown in Fig. A. The rods, mounted in rubber corks, project through holes in a metal tube where their lower ends are heated to 100°C by steam passing through the tube. As the heat travels slowly up each rod the yellow paint turns red.

After 5 or 10 min, the height to which the paint has turned color is approximately as shown in the figure. Of these six metals, copper is observed to be the best conductor and lead the poorest.

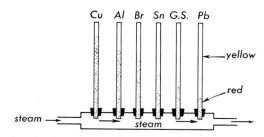

Fig. A. Experiment illustrating the relative heat conductivities of six different metals: copper, aluminum, brass, tin, german silver, and lead.

In order to heat an object, it is customary to bring it into contact with some other body at a higher temperature. A pan of water, for example, is generally heated by placing it over an open flame. The combustion of natural gas first sets the gas molecules into a rapid state of motion. These molecules striking the bottom of the pan set the molecules of the metal into rapid vibration. They in turn strike other metal molecules, thus transferring the motion through to the other side. This is called heat conduction. The metal molecules set the first layer of water molecules moving and they in turn set others moving. Thus molecular motion, called heat, has been given to the body of water.

Laboratory experiments show that the amount of heat flowing through a rod is proportional to the time, the cross-sectional area, and the difference in temperature between the ends, and is inversely proportional to the length.

Using appropriate symbols for each of these factors and inserting a proportionality constant, the following equation is set up:

$$\frac{\Delta H}{\Delta \tau} = k \frac{A}{L} \Delta t \qquad (1)$$

where $\Delta H / \Delta \tau$ is the amount of heat per second flowing through the body of length L and cross section A, k is the thermal conductivity, and Δt is the temperature difference between the hot and the cold ends. It is quite clear to almost everyone that, if the temperature difference, Δt, or the area, A, is increased (see Fig. B), the amount of

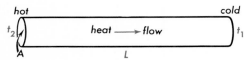

Fig. B. Illustrating the various measurable factors involved in the flow of heat through a body by conduction.

heat passing through is increased. It is not as obvious, however, that an increase in the length, L, causes a decrease in heat flow, or that a decrease in length produces an increase. This latter will be illustrated by two experiments.

Although paper is a poor conductor, the flow of heat through it can be made very great by increasing A, the cross-sectional area, and decreasing L, the distance it has to flow. Diagram (a) in Fig. C illustrates thermal conductivity by the boiling of water in a paper cup. Although the gas flame plays directly against the surface of the paper, the cup will not burn. The reason for this is that the heat from the lower surface of the paper is conducted through to the water fast enough to keep the tempera-

ture of the paper from rising too high. If the paper is thick, the lower surface will burn. Strange as it may seem, the thinner the paper, the less is the chance of burning.

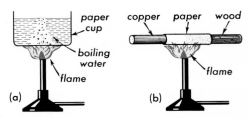

Fig. C. Illustrating the conduction of heat through paper.

In diagram (b) of Fig. C, a thin piece of paper is wrapped once around a rod made half of wood and half of copper. When the flame is brought up as shown, the paper burns only where it is in contact with the wood and not at all where it is in contact with the copper. Copper, being a good conductor, carries the heat into the interior of the metal and away from the metal surface. Because wood is a poor conductor it cannot conduct the heat away from the surface fast enough, and the paper heats up and soon burns.

The thermal conductivities of a few common substances are given in Table 1.

The number k is the quantity of heat in calories that in 1 sec will pass through a 1 cm cube when two opposite faces are maintained at 1°C difference in temperature. Knowing the value of k for a given substance, it is possible to calculate, by means of Eq. (1), the amount of heat flowing through any sized object made of that same substance.

Example. One end of an aluminum rod 40 cm long and 5 cm² in cross section is maintained at a temperature of 100°C and the other end at 20°C. Find the amount of heat that will flow through the rod in 2 min.

Table 1. Thermal Conductivities
(k, in cal cm/sec cm² C°)

Substance	k
silver...........................	0.97
copper..........................	0.92
aluminum........................	0.50
brass............................	0.26
iron.............................	0.16
lead.............................	0.08
german silver....................	0.10
mercury.........................	0.02
tile..............................	0.002
glass............................	0.0025
water...........................	0.0014
wood............................	0.0005
paper...........................	0.0003
felt..............................	0.00004

Solution. Substitution in Eq. (1) gives—

$$\frac{\Delta H}{120} = \frac{.50 \times 5 \times 80}{40}$$

or—

$$\Delta H = 600 \text{ cal}$$

Convection. Why is it that a poor conductor of heat like water can be heated so quickly when it is placed in a pan over a hot fire? It is due to the second method of heat transfer known as *convection*. Water on the bottom of a pan is heated first. Because of a rise in temperature it expands. Being lighter than the cold water above, it then rises to the top, permitting cold water to come to the bottom from the sides. This action sets up a flow of water called a *con-*

vection current. See Fig. D. Convection currents thus keep the water stirred up as it heats.

Convection currents set up by the heating of a vessel of water are illustrated in Fig. E(a). A glass tube, in the shape of a rounded-corner square, is filled with water and then heated at one of the lower corners

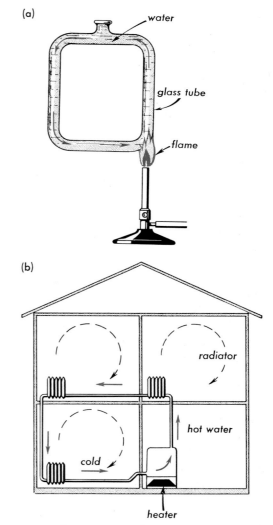

(a)

water

glass tube

flame

(b)

radiator

hot water

cold

heater

Fig. D. Convection currents in a pan of water being heated over a stove burner.

Fig. E. Illustrations of heat convection by the circulation of water in a pipe and air in a room.

as indicated. A drop of ink admitted at the top opening will mix with the water and quickly flow around the tube in a counterclockwise direction. This circulation is the basis of the hot-water heating systems used in some houses. As illustrated in diagram (b), hot water from a supply tank in a lower room or basement rises and flows through several radiators, only to return, somewhat cooled, to the tank, where it is reheated.

Similar to this in its action is the hot-air heating system used in some houses. Air heated in a furnace in the basement rises through an outlet in or near the floor as shown in Fig. F. Rising up one side of the room this air travels across the ceiling, down the other side, and across the floor to return to the furnace by another opening. Convection results from differences in density and pressure, because hot gases and liquids expand on heating.

Convection currents in the atmosphere are quite noticeable and account for the wind. Along the sea coast, cool air from over the ocean comes as a sea breeze due to convection. The sun's rays are absorbed more readily by the land than they are by water, and the warmed air over the land rises, while cooler air from the ocean comes in to take its place.

At night, the land cools quickly by radiation back toward the cold sky, and soon the air over the water is the warmer and, rising, causes a reversal in air movement.

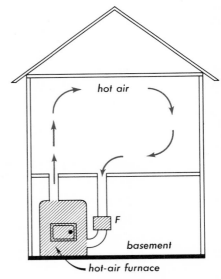

Fig. F. Convection hot-air currents set up by heating.

The wind blows from the land to the sea. These air currents are readily observed by smoke from a fire built on the seashore. During the day the smoke blows inland, and at night it blows seaward.

QUESTIONS

1. (a) What is meant by heat transfer? (b) What are the methods of heat transfer?
2. (a) Name three substances that are good thermal conductors. (b) Name three poor conductors of heat.
3. (a) What is the process by which heat is conducted through a solid? (b) Is this a rapid method of heat transfer?
4. (a) Upon what factors does the amount of heat conducted through a rod depend? (b) Write the formula.
5. (a) What is convection? (b) Is convection a more rapid method of heat transfer than conduction? Why?
6. What causes heated air or water to undergo convection?

7. Although water is a poor conductor of heat, a pan of water is quickly heated on a hot plate or burner. (a) Why? (b) Is conduction involved here? (c) Is convection involved?

8. Where on the earth's surface should one find the air currents rising most rapidly?

9. Explain how a Thermos bottle keeps liquids either hot or cold.

10. Explain how Eskimos can be comfortable in an igloo, which is made of ice.

11. (a) Can heat be transported through a gas or a liquid by conduction? (b) Describe an experiment that would illustrate conductive but not convective heat transfer through a gas.

12. Why is stuffing the walls of a house with glass wool better for keeping heat in or out than just leaving an air space, even though air is a very poor conductor of heat?

13. Why does a piece of metal feel cool while a piece of wood at the same temperature does not?

PROBLEMS

1. One end of a copper rod, 20 cm long having a cross-sectional area of 4 cm², is maintained at 20°C, and the other end at 50°C. What is the rate of heat flow through the rod?

2. A brass rod is 20 cm long and has a cross-sectional area of 2 cm². How much heat will flow through this rod in 4 min if one end is maintained at 25°C and the other end at 100°C?

3. The bottom of an aluminum pan is 2 mm thick and has an area of 500 cm². If the upper surface is maintained at 90°C and lower surface at 91.5°C, how much heat will flow through in 5 min?

4. A large glass window pane 2 m by 3 m is 5 mm thick. If the snow outside maintains the outer surface at 0°C and the heat of the room maintains the inner surface at 15°C, how much heat will be conducted out in 1 hr?

5. The wooden handle of a frying pan is 2.5 cm in diameter and 15 cm long. If the pan temperature is 400°C and the free end of the handle is kept at 40°C, how much heat will flow through in 1 min?

6. A silver rod, with a cross-sectional area of 5 cm², is 25 cm long. If the cold end is maintained at 0°C and 10 cal/sec flow through the rod, what is the temperature of the hot end?

7. The bottom of a copper boiler is 1 mm thick and has a cross-sectional area of 400 cm². If the upper surface is maintained at 80°C and 900,000 calories flow through the rod in 2 min, what is the temperature of the lower surface?

8. A 30 cm by 40 cm plate of glass conducts 10,000 cal/min when there is a temperature difference of 15°C across it. How thick is it?

9. A 2-cm thick aluminum shield forming the front of a re-entrant space vehicle must conduct 1,000,000 cal/sec to the inner surface, which is at 70°C. If the outer surface must not melt (its melting point is 658°C), what must be the area of the shield?

10. An iron automobile radiator has an effective area of 1 m², and a thickness of 0.4 mm. 750,000 cal are conducted to the outside, which was at 85°C. If the inside was heated by boiling water, how long did this take?

PROJECTS

1. What inexpensive device could you devise for demonstrating convection? How could you bring about forced convection?
2. Make a working model of a solar-heated house.
3. Design a house and position it on its lot so as to maximize the comfort of its inhabitants and minimize the expense of heating and cooling.

HEAT

Lesson 45 *RADIANT HEAT*

When the sun comes over the horizon in the early morning, the heat can be felt as soon as the sun becomes visible. This heat, called radiant heat or radiation, travels with the speed of light, 186,000 mi/sec.

Radiant heat is but one of the many forms of energy and is readily detected by means of a radiometer, thermocouple, thermistor, thermometer, etc. A Crooke's radi-

Fig. A. A Crooke's radiometer.

ometer, shown in Fig. A, will often be found in a jewelry store window. In daylight or under a bright light, the little pinwheel made of very thin mica, will be found spinning around as if by perpetual motion.

Each vane of such a radiometer is shiny on one face, and blackened on the other. The black faces absorb more radiant energy than the polished surfaces and heat the adjacent air. The recoiling air molecules, therefore, exert a larger force on the blackened sides, driving it around.

If a radiometer is so highly evacuated that little air remains inside the vessel, light waves, in bouncing off the polished surfaces, will exert twice the force they do in being absorbed on the blackened side and the pinwheel will spin the other way.

Radiant-heat rays, like visible light, are electromagnetic waves and have all the general properties known to visible light. The essential difference between the two is that heat waves, sometimes called *infrared rays*, are not visible to the human eye.

A demonstration of the reflection of infrared rays is shown in Fig. B. A candle and into the fire, thus supplying fresh oxygen to the burning wood or coal.

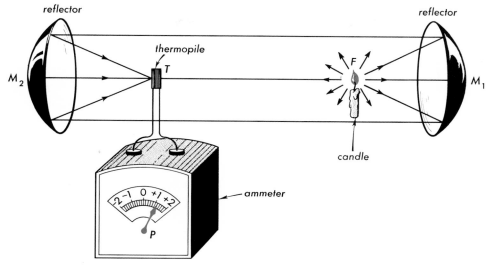

Fig. B. Reflection of heat rays by concave mirrors.

flame acting as a source at F emits light and heat rays in all directions. Of these rays only the ones traveling toward the concave mirror, M_1, are reflected into a parallel beam. Arriving at the second concave mirror, M_2, these rays are again reflected, being brought together to a focus on the exposed junctions of a thermopile, T. As the junctions of the thermopile warm up, an electric current is produced, causing the ammeter pointer, P, to move to the right. When the candle is removed, the pointer returns to zero.

A practical example of heat radiation is a fireplace. Contrary to most beliefs, the heat entering a room from a fireplace is practically all in the form of infrared rays originating in the flames, the coals, and the stone or brick walls. The air that is heated within the fireplace does not enter the room but is carried up the chimney as a convection current. See Fig. C. This rising current of air draws fresh air into the room

A Dewar flask, or *Thermos bottle*, is an example of a practical device in which the

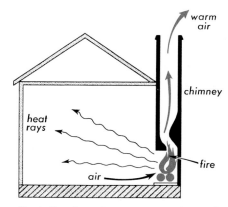

Fig. C. A fireplace heats a room by radiation from the flame, the coals, and the stove walls. Convection currents set up a draft and carry warm air and smoke out the chimney.

conduction, convection, and radiation of heat are reduced as much as possible. As shown by the cross-section diagram in Fig.

D, a Thermos bottle consists of a double-walled glass vessel silvered on the inside. The purpose of the silvering is to reflect all radiant heat attempting to enter or leave the vessel.

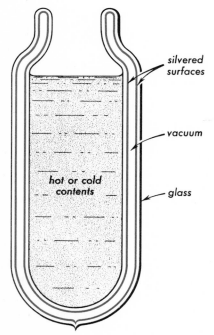

Fig. D. The Dewar flask, or Thermos bottle, minimizes conduction by using glass, convection by evacuating, and radiation by silvering.

the vessel. The space between the walls is highly evacuated to prevent convection, and the glass, being a poor conductor, minimizes conduction through the walls of the neck. With the exception of the vacuum space between walls, a calorimeter of the type commonly used in laboratories is similar to a Dewar flask.

A type of radiant-heating system for public buildings and private dwellings is known to engineers as *panel heating*. In this system, the walls of the rooms are heated by hot air or water pipes that run through them. Even though the windows are open on the coldest days, radiant heat keeps the occupants warm.

Emission and Absorption. The rate at which a body radiates or absorbs heat depends not only upon the absolute temperature but also upon the nature of the exposed surfaces as well.

Objects that are good emitters of heat are also good absorbers of the same kind of radiation. This is known as *Kirchhoff's Law of Radiation.* A body whose surface is blackened is an excellent emitter as well as an excellent absorber. If the same body is chromium plated, it becomes a poor emitter and a poor absorber.

A good demonstration of Kirchhoff's law is shown in Fig. E. Two airtight metal boxes,

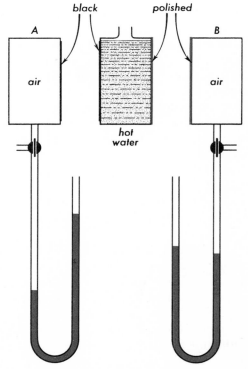

Fig. E. Apparatus for demonstrating Kirchhoff's Law of Radiation.

A and *B*, are connected by small hose connections to two glass, open-ended U-tubes containing mercury. All mercury surfaces are first adjusted to the same level. A third metal box containing boiling water is now inserted between, and equidistant from, the other two as shown. The two adjacent surfaces on the left have been painted with a dull black paint, while the two on the right are chrome plated.

Gradually the mercury levels on the left change more and more in the direction shown, while those on the right change very little. The black surfaces are good radiators and good absorbers. Therefore, heat is seen to be easily transferred, warming the air in box *A* and driving the left-hand mercury level down. The polished surfaces are poor radiators and poor absorbers, and the air in box *B* warms up only slightly.

Black Body Radiation. The relation between the radiant heat, *E*, emitted by a body and its temperature was first made through the extensive laboratory experiments of Josef Stefan. The same law was later derived from theoretical considerations by Ludwig Boltzmann, and is now known as the *Stefan-Boltzmann law:*

$$E = kT^4 \qquad (1)$$

Here *E* represents the energy radiated per second by a body at an absolute temperature *T*, and *k* is a proportionality constant. The law applies only to so-called "black bodies."

A black body is defined as one that absorbs all of the radiant heat that falls upon it. Such a perfect absorber would also be a perfect emitter.

If *E* represents the heat in calories radiated per square centimeter per second of a black body, then $k = 1.36 \times 10^{-12}$. If *E* is measured in ergs/cm² sec, then $k = 5.7 \times 10^{-5}$.

The best laboratory approach to a black body is a hole in a box that is blackened on the inside. Practically all heat entering such a hole would be absorbed inside. Black velvet cloth or a surface painted dull with lampblack will absorb about 97% of the radiant heat falling on it, and may, for many purposes, be considered a black body. Polished metal surfaces, however, are far from being black bodies; they absorb only about 6% of the incident energy and reflect the remainder. Most other substances have absorption ratios between these two extremes.

Prevost's Law of Heat Exchange. Laboratory experiments, as well as the Stefan-Boltzmann law, show that all bodies, whether they are hot or cold, radiate heat. The words "hot" and "cold" are only relative terms, because even ice radiates heat. The greater the absolute temperature of a body, the greater is the rate at which it radiates, and ice at 0°C is 273° above absolute zero.

If a cold block of blackened metal is brought into a warm room, it radiates heat to the walls of the room at the rate—

$$E_1 = kT_1^4$$

the walls of the room radiate heat to the block, which absorbs it at the rate—

$$E_2 = kT_2^4$$

Because the walls are at a higher temperature, they give more heat per second to the block than the block gives up in return. See Fig. F. The difference gives the net rate per square centimeter at which heat is transferred to the block from the walls:

$$\Delta E = k(T_2^4 - T_1^4) \qquad (2)$$

Owing to this unequal exchange of heat, the temperature of the cold block rises until it comes to the same temperature as the room, at which time it radiates and absorbs

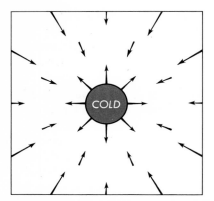

Fig. F. A cold body warms up to room temperature.

at exactly the same rate. This equalization would occur even if the metal and walls were not black, but it would take place at a slower rate.

Prevost's Law of Heat Exchange states that a body at the temperature of its surroundings is radiating and receiving heat at equal rates.

When a person stands near a fireplace, he feels warm because his body receives more heat from the fire than it emits. If he stands next to a cold window, he feels chilly because he radiates more heat than he absorbs. The side of his body facing the window gets noticeably colder than the other.

Newton's Law of Cooling. If the room is warmer than the block of metal by an amount $T_2 - T_1 = \Delta T$, Eq. (2) may be written—

$$\Delta E = k[(T_1 + \Delta T)^4 - T_1^4] \qquad (3)$$

By expanding the quantity in parentheses, we have—

$$\Delta E = 4kT_1^3 \Delta T \left(1 + \frac{3}{2}\frac{\Delta T}{T_1}\right.$$

$$\left. + \left(\frac{\Delta T}{T_1}\right)^2 + \frac{1}{4}\left(\frac{\Delta T}{T_1}\right)^3\right) \qquad (4)$$

Now if the temperature difference is small, the ratio $\Delta T/T_1$ may be neglected, and we find—

$$\Delta E = 4kT_1^3 \Delta T \qquad (5)$$

This shows that the radiative heat transfer from an object to its surroundings depends directly on the temperature difference between them.

The rate at which a hot body cools to the temperature of its surroundings was first determined empirically by Isaac Newton. His law states that the rate at which heat is lost by a body to its surroundings is proportional to the difference in temperature between them. Symbolically—

$$H = c\,\Delta T \qquad (6)$$

where H is the heat lost per second, ΔT the temperature difference between the hot body and the surroundings, and c a proportionality constant. The law holds only approximately for temperature differences that are small compared with the absolute temperature. It also includes losses due to both convection and radiation.

A graph showing the cooling of a beaker of hot water is shown in Fig. G. The data

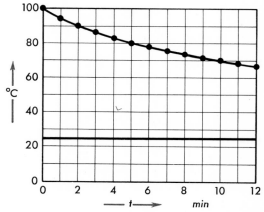

Fig. G. Cooling curve for a beaker of hot water.

were taken by heating a beaker of water to the boiling point and observing its tem- perature with a thermometer at the end of every minute.

QUESTIONS

1. (a) What is radiant heat? (b) How fast does it travel? (c) Can it travel through a vacuum?
2. How are conduction, convection, and radiation involved in the proper operation of a fireplace?
3. How are the three methods of heat transfer reduced in the construction of a Thermos bottle?
4. If the candle in the experiment shown in Fig. B is replaced by an ice cube, the needle of the ammeter will go negative, showing that the themopile is becoming cold. Does this mean that the ice cube is radiating "coldness"? Explain what is happening.
5. (a) What is the Stefan-Boltzmann law? (b) What is a "black body"?
6. Why is the inside of a greenhouse warmer than the air outside?
7. (a) What is Kirchhoff's law? (b) How can the law be demonstrated? (c) What kind of clothes would be the coolest on a hot sunny day?
8. (a) What is Prevost's law of heat exchange? (b) Does ice radiate heat? (c) Why will a hot piece of iron cool off to room temperature but not cool below room temperature?
9. (a) What kind of surface should a stove have if it is to radiate a maximum amount of heat? (b) Why should it not be chromium plated and polished?
10. What do the heat transfer properties of a "black body" have to do with its being black?
11. Why would you feel comfortable on a snow field if the sun is shining, although the air temperature is below the freezing point of water?
12. A waiter in a restaurant serves a patron a cup of hot coffee before he is ready to drink it. Wishing to drink the coffee 8 min later, the patron wants the coffee to be as hot as possible at that time. Should he pour the cream into the coffee immediately and let it stand for 8 min, or should he pour the cream in at the end of 8 min and then drink the coffee? Explain.

PROBLEMS

1. How many calories of heat are radiated from 1 cm^2 of the surface of a dull black stove in 1 min if the temperature is 500°K?
2. How much heat is radiated by a dull black stove in 1 min if the total exposed area is 0.5 m^2 and the surface is 700°K?
3. How many calories of heat are radiated in 1 sec from a black body surface with an area of 5 cm^2 and a temperature of 327°C?
4. A solid copper ball 10 cm in diameter is coated with lampblack and heated

to a temperature of 727°C. How many calories of heat are radiated from this sphere per second? (*Note:* The area of a sphere is $4\pi r^2$.)

5. An iron ball 2 cm in diameter is coated with lampblack and heated to a temperature of 1027°C. How may calories of heat are radiated from this sphere per minute?

6. A blackened iron ball, with a surface area of 10 cm² and temperature of 727°C, is placed in a box whose walls are blackened and that has a temperature of 227°C. Find the net loss of energy in cal/sec from the ball.

7. The exhaust manifold of a racing car radiates heat at the rate of .085 cal/cm²-sec. What is its temperature?

8. The cylinder head of an airplane engine has a surface area of 0.5 m². If it radiates 18,000 cal in one minute, how hot is it?

9. Derive Eq. (4) starting with Eq. (3).

PROJECT

Paint a can a dull black and another as shiny white as possible. Fill both cans with equal amounts of equally hot water. Record the temperature of both cans as they cool off. Plot graphs to show the effect of color on radiation of heat.

HEAT

Lesson 46 CHANGE OF STATE

Expansion and Contraction on Fusion. When molten metal of one kind or another is poured into a mold for casting, the metal may contract or expand on solidifying and then, on cooling to room temperature, contract or expand according to its coefficient of thermal expansion. Cast iron, for example, is a substance that, on solidifying, expands slightly but then, on cooling to room temperature, contracts about 1% of its length. It is, therefore, well suited to casting, because slight expansion on solidifying aids in the reproduction of every detail in the mold.

An experiment illustrating the enormous expansion forces of freezing water is dia-

gramed in Fig. A. A small cast-iron bomb, about 2 in. in diameter and ⅛ in. thick is completely filled with water at a tempera-

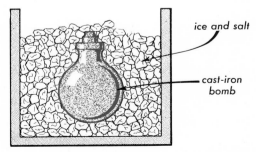

Fig. A. When the water inside the bomb freezes, the expansion bursts the cast-iron walls.

ture close to 0°C. After the threaded iron plug is screwed in tightly, the bomb is packed in a freezing mixture of cracked ice and salt. After some minutes, the water freezes and explodes the bomb with a dull thud.

This experiment shows that, by exerting large pressures on cold water, its necessary expansion on freezing can be held back until a temperature lower than 0°C is reached.

Regelation. If two small blocks of ice are held in opposite hands and two of their relatively flat surfaces pressed tightly together, they will upon release be stuck together. The explanation is that, where contact is made between the blocks, high pressure at localized spots lowers the melting point sufficiently to melt the ice. In order to melt, the ice must acquire heat (80 cal/gm) and this it gets by conduction from the nearby ice. The water then flows to one side and, returning the heat it had taken away from the nearby ice, freezes, sealing the blocks together. This is a process called *regelation*. The same process explains why snow, when squeezed in the hands, sticks together to form well packed snowballs.

Glaciers are well known to seemingly "flow" around hard jutting rocks as they move slowly down a rocky ravine. The ice melts under the pressure it receives from a rock on one side, and the water flowing down and around to the open gap on the other side freezes again to go on as if the rock were never there.

A simple laboratory experiment demonstrating this principle is shown in Fig. B. A small wire with heavy weights attached is hung over a block of ice and allowed to remain for some time. Slowly the wire is observed to melt its way through the ice. On completion of the cut, the block of ice is still in one piece, the gap made by the wire hav-

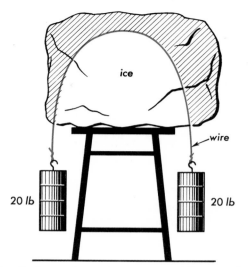

Fig. B. Ice melts under pressure, allowing the wire to work its way through.

ing frozen shut. The high pressure under the wire melts the ice, and the water flows around to the other side where it freezes again.

Cooling by Evaporation. When water is left in an open dish, it slowly evaporates, i.e., it goes spontaneously into the gaseous state. Evaporation, therefore, is a free expansion, and expansion is always accompanied by cooling. This phenomenon of cooling by evaporation, which is so important from the standpoint of its many commercial applications, is explained by the kinetic theory of matter.

Because of the random motions of the molecules of a liquid, some molecules obtain, momentarily, a very high velocity. If a molecule at the surface is given a high velocity in an upward direction, it may escape into the air above. Some of these escaped molecules soon find their way back into the liquid by chance collisions with air molecules from above the surface, but many of them do not. See Fig. C. The sporadic escape of molecules may be speeded up by blowing air across the surface. The air carries the newly escaped molecules away before they have a chance to return to the liquid.

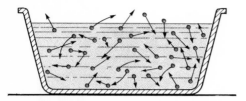

Fig. C. Evaporation of water from an open dish is due to the rapid motion of the water molecules and their occasional escape into the air space above.

By virtue of the high speed of the molecules escaping from a liquid surface, considerably more than the average kinetic energy is carried away with them. A lowering of the average kinetic energy of the remaining liquid molecules means a lowering of the temperature. The more rapid the evaporation, therefore, the faster will be the cooling. This is strikingly demonstrated by pouring a small amount of ether or alcohol on the finger. Either of these liquids, and particularly ether, evaporates very rapidly, cooling the surface of the finger quickly. Ether is often used in this way by surgeons, in place of an anesthetic, to freeze local spots of the body before beginning a minor operation.

Cooling by evaporation can be demonstrated to a large group by pouring a small quantity of ether over the bulb of an air thermometer as shown in Fig. D. Because of the cooling of the glass bulb the air inside contracts, drawing more water up into the stem of the thermometer.

Sublimation. Under certain conditions, many substances will go from the solid to the vapor state without passing through the liquid phase. A good illustration of this is the heating of iodine crystals or the evaporation of "dry ice." Iodine crystals, when placed in a test tube at room temperature and pressure and slowly heated, pass directly into iodine vapor. This is called *sublimation.*

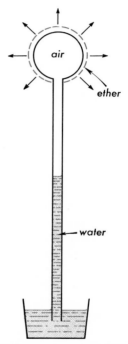

Fig. D. Experiment demonstrating the cooling effect produced by the evaporation of ether.

Dry ice, which chemically is carbon dioxide, CO_2, is normally at a temperature of $-78.5°C$ and, when standing in the open air, evaporates directly without liquefying. The visible fumes rising from it are water vapor from the surrounding air condensed by the cold CO_2 gases that leave.

Ice over the ponds and lakes in cold climates sublimes slowly at the surface. By enclosing the space above ice at below $0°C$, the saturated vapor pressure can be measured just as it is for water.

Humidity. When water molecules escape by evaporation from the free surface of a liquid, they mix with the air molecules above. If the space above the liquid surface is enclosed, as shown in Fig. E, this mixture

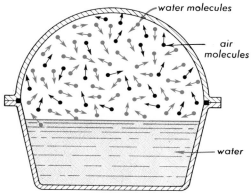

water molecules

air molecules

water

Fig. E. Illustrating the saturation of air with water vapor.

cannot escape. Under these circumstances the water will continue to evaporate until the air above becomes saturated with water vapor, that is, until it can hold no more. When this condition is reached, as many free water molecules will be returning to the liquid every second as there are water molecules escaping.

The maximum amount of water the air can hold in the vapor state depends upon the temperature and very little upon the air pressure. This is illustrated by the values given in Table 1. The temperature of the air is given in one column and the maximum amount of water that can exist in the vapor state in a cubic meter of air is given in the other. It is clearly seen from the table that the hotter the air, the greater is the amount of water it can hold in the vapor state.

The atmosphere, which we might term free air, is not always saturated with water vapor. If it contains very little or no water vapor, we say the air is dry; if it contains a great deal, we say it is damp or humid.

Table 1. Mass of Water Vapor in One Cubic Meter of Saturated Air

Temperature	Water Vapor
0°C or 32°F	4.8 gm
5°C " 41°F	6.8 gm
10°C " 50°F	9.3 gm
15°C " 59°F	12.7 gm
20°C " 68°F	17.1 gm
25°C " 77°F	22.8 gm
30°C " 86°F	30.0 gm
35°C " 95°F	39.2 gm

The quantity of water vapor present in 1 m³ of air is called the absolute humidity. It is, therefore, a measure of the dampness of the air. Absolute humidity is measured by the number of grams of water vapor present in 1 m³ of air. For example, the absolute humidity might be said to be 14 gm/m³.

It is customary, in speaking of the dampness of air, not to specify the absolute humidity but the *relative humidity. The ratio of the quantity of water vapor actually present in any volume of air to the quantity required to saturate the same volume of air at the same temperature is called the relative humidity.*

To illustrate this, suppose the air at the present time contains 5.7 gm/m³ of water vapor and the temperature is 25°C. If the air were saturated at this temperature (see Table 1), it would contain 22.8 gm/m³. Therefore, the—

$$\textbf{relative humidity} = \frac{5.7}{22.8} = 0.25 \quad (1)$$

It is customary to express such answers in percent and to say that the relative humidity in this case is 25%.

If air that is saturated with water vapor is cooled to a lower temperature, some of the water vapor may condense to the liquid state. These are the conditions under which rain and fogdrops are formed. The reason for this condensation is that, at the lower temperature and equilibrium conditions, less water can exist in the vapor state and still saturate the air. If the air cools without the formation of rain or fog, the air takes on an unstable state in which it is *super-saturated.*

The Dew Point. When the temperature of a glass of water is slowly lowered, a temperature is reached at which water condenses on the outside. The temperature at which this occurs is called the *dew point* and signifies that the air has become saturated with water vapor. Any measurement of the dewpoint temperature, therefore, offers a means of determining the relative humidity.

Suppose, for example, the following experiment is performed in a room whose temperature is 35°C. A polished metal cup containing water and a thermometer is slowly cooled by adding cracked ice. The first appearance of moisture on the outside is noted to occur at 20°C. According to Table 1, the saturated density for 20°C is 17.1 gm/m³, and for 35°C is 39.2 gm/m³. The first of these densities gives the actual amount of water vapor present in the room, and the latter gives the amount the air in the room could hold when saturated. The absolute humidity is, therefore, 17.1 gm/m³, and the—

$$\text{relative humidity} = \frac{17.1}{39.2} \times 100 = 43.6\%$$

Meteorologists often determine relative humidity from the dew point by means of a *sling psychrometer.* Such a device, as shown in Fig. F, consists of two identical mercury thermometers mounted on a base with a convenient handle for whirling. One bulb is exposed to the air and is called the *dry bulb,* while the other, with a water-soaked cloth

tied to it, is called the *wet bulb.* When the psychrometer is whirled in the air for several minutes, being stopped occasionally to observe the temperature readings, the wet bulb will be observed to drop to some value and remain there during any subsequent whirling.

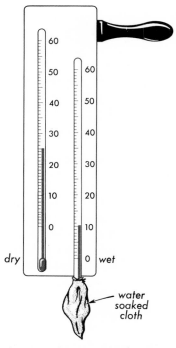

Fig. F. Sling psychrometer with wet- and dry-bulb thermometers for determining the dew point and relative humidity.

Although the lowest obtainable wet-bulb temperature is not the dew point, it is closely related, because whirling causes evaporation and evaporation produces cooling. By applying a correction from well-known tables, the dew point can be determined from the wet- and dry-bulb readings. Relative humidity is then found in Table 1.

QUESTIONS

1. (a) Does water expand or contract on freezing? (b) Does iron expand on freezing? Explain.
2. (a) What is regelation? (b) Where does it occur in nature?
3. (a) What is absolute humidity? (b) How is it measured?
4. (a) What is relative humidity? (b) What does it mean to say that air is saturated? (c) If the air is saturated, what is the relative humidity?
5. (a) What is the dew point? (b) How could you find the dew point for the air in the room?
6. (a) What is a sling psychrometer? (b) Could you easily make one? (c) What is the wet bulb?
7. How would you determine the relative humidity if you knew the absolute humidity and room temperature?
8. (a) Why does evaporation produce cooling? (b) How would you go about demonstrating the effect? (c) Why is ether so effective in producing cooling?
9. What molecular explanation could you give as to why some materials expand on freezing and others contract?
10. (a) Technically, does an ice skater skate on ice or water? (b) Would it be easier to skate on ice that is just below the freezing point of water or on extremely cold ice?
11. Would a sling psychrometer work if you used alcohol instead of water to wet one of the thermometers? Explain.
12. Before going to bed, you learn that the humidity is close to 100%. What kind of weather might you reasonably expect early next morning?
13. (a) Why is alcohol a more suitable rubdown agent than water in relieving the heat of a fever? (b) If ether were even more effective, what other properties might argue against its use?
14. In a room crowded with many people and with little ventilation, what probably happens to the relative humidity and to the temperature of the air?
15. What common substance around the house fortunately changes from a solid to a gas or it would not be suitable for the use for which it was intended?

PROBLEMS

1. If the air contains 16.2 gm of water vapor per cubic meter when the temperature is 77°F, what is (a) the absolute humidity and (b) the relative humidity?
2. One cubic meter of air contains 8.6 gm of water vapor per cubic meter when the temperature is 30°C. What is (a) the absolute humidity and (b) the relative humidity?

3. The air contains 10.4 gm of water vapor per cubic meter when the temperature is 12.5°C. What is (a) the absolute humidity and (b) the relative humidity?

4. One cubic meter of the air contains 15.0 gm of water vapor when the temperature is 30°C. If the temperature is lowered to 10°C, how many grams of water vapor per cubic meter will be condensed?

5. Dew forms on a drinking glass when the air temperature is 68°F. What is the relative humidity if the air temperature rises to 86°F?

6. The relative humidity is 42% when the room temperature is 86°F. To what value must the temperature be changed to saturate the air?

7. The air of a room is saturated when the temperature is 59°F. What will be the relative humidity when the temperature rises to 95°F?

8. Plot a graph with the Celsius temperature horizontally plotted and the water vapor per cubic meter of saturated air vertically plotted. Use the values as listed in Table 1.

9. If, at a temperature of 86°F, the relative humidity is 80%, how much water per cubic meter will be condensed if the temperature goes down to 41°F?

10. The air is saturated at 86°F. If the temperature drops to 77°F, precipitates out the excess moisture, and rises to 95°F, what is the relative humidity now?

11. If the relative humidity is 32% at 15°C, what is it at 30°C?

12. If the relative humidity is 70% at 50°F, what is it at 21°F?

13. How many grams of water are required to fill a room, $3 \times 4 \times 5$ m in size, with saturated water vapor at 20°C?

14. A certain fairly typical schoolroom has the following dimensions: 14 m long, 8 m wide, and 4 m high. A student measures the humidity to be 80% at 72.5°F. What is the total amount of water in the air of this classroom?

PROJECTS

1. Demonstrate the cooling effect of evaporation of methyl chloride placed on the surface of water. It should be possible to remove enough heat to form ice crystals.

2. Make a hygrometer suitable for use in your home or school laboratory. Keep a record of the humidity and your feeling of comfort.

3. Make a human hair hygrometer by treating it first with ether to remove all oily substances and then wrapping it around a slender axis to which a pointer is attached. It is said that blond hair contracts and expands more with the humidity than dark hair. Try it.

HEAT

Lesson 47 *VAPORIZATION*

Boiling. *The boiling of a liquid is but a state of rapid evaporation.* As the temperature of water is raised, the rate of evaporation increases until, at the boiling temperature, it reaches a maximum. Beyond this temperature, water can exist only in the vapor, or gaseous, state.

When water boils at normal atmospheric pressure, evaporation takes place throughout the liquid, as well as at the surface. Evidence of this is seen in the bubbles of saturated vapor that form near the bottom of a vessel and increase in size as they rise to the surface. See Fig. A. The bubbles are able to

point in a liquid unless the vapor pressure is equal to or slightly greater than the pressure within the liquid at that same point.

If the pressure on the liquid surface of boiling water is increased, the bubbles will collapse and boiling will cease. Under this increased pressure, however, boiling can be started again by adding heat and raising the temperature to a higher value. In other words, *the higher the pressure on a liquid, the higher is the boiling temperature.* Conversely, *the lower the pressure within a liquid, the lower is the temperature required to make it boil.*

A graph of the boiling point of water, as it varies with pressure, is shown in Fig. B.

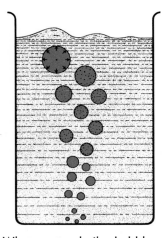

Fig. A. When water boils, bubbles of steam form at the bottom and grow as they rise to the surface.

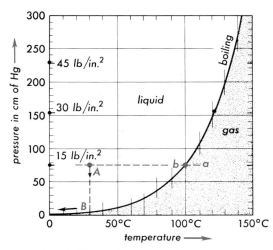

Fig. B. Boiling-point curve for water as it changes with temperature.

expand because the vapor pressure, P, due to the fast-moving water molecules striking the walls of the bubbles, is equal to or greater than the external pressure of the atmosphere, P_0. Boiling cannot occur at any

Note that water boils at 100°C at standard atmospheric pressure of 76 cm of mercury, Hg, which is about 15 lb/in.². At twice this pressure, however, a temperature of 120°C must be reached, etc.

Consider, for example, the boiling of water in a pressure cooker when the safety gauge is set for 15 lb/in.² See Fig. C. As the

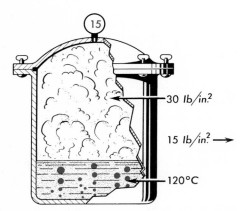

Fig. C. In a pressure cooker set for 15 lb/in.², water boils at 120°C.

water inside gets hotter, some of it vaporizes and the pressure rises. This pressure continues to rise until it becomes 15 lb/in.² greater than the pressure outside. At this point the safety valve opens slightly and prevents the internal pressure from exceeding this value. Under these conditions the pressure outside the vessel is 15 lb/in.², while the pressure inside is 15 lb/in.² greater, or 30 lb/in.² From the graph, it is seen that the confined water must now reach 120°C to boil. At this higher temperature, food cooks more quickly. In an open pan, the water boils at 100°C, and its temperature will not exceed this value.

Geysers. One of the great wonders of the western world is the spontaneous eruption almost hourly of the mammoth geyser "Old Faithful" in Yellowstone National Park. The following explanation of geyser activity was first given by Bunsen in 1847 and is based upon the above explanation of boiling.

Water from a nearby stream seeps into the vertical shaft or hole where, due to volcanic heat below, it is gradually heated to the boiling point. See Fig. D. Because the

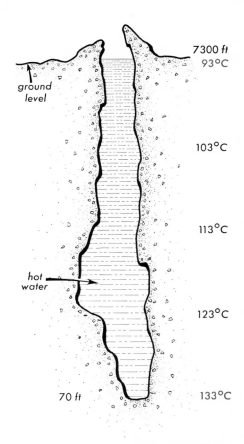

Fig. D. Diagram illustrating the principles of a geyser like "Old Faithful" in Yellowstone National Park.

water is heated from below, and convection currents are shut off by the narrowness of the shaft, a temperature considerably higher than 100°C must be reached before the water at the bottom can boil. Because atmospheric pressure exists at the surface, the water there will boil at 100°C. Far down the shaft, however, the added pressure of nearly 70 ft of water requires a temperature of 130°C to produce boiling. Because the water is heated from below, this high temperature is reached near the bottom, and boiling begins there before it does at the top. When a sufficiently high temperature is reached, the vapor pressure deep down exceeds the pressure due to the air and water column above, and the rise of numerous bubbles, by pushing up the column of hot water above, starts an eruption. Nearing the surface, the vapor pressure of the superheated water is so high that the remaining water is pushed out with great force.

An excellent demonstration of these principles can be performed by an experimental geyser of the form shown in Fig. E.

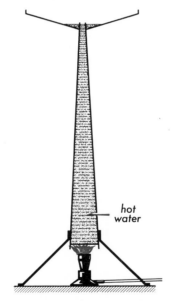

hot
water

Fig. E. Experimental geyser that will erupt periodically.

Such models can be made almost any size from one foot in height to 10 ft or more. The period of their eruption depends upon size as well as the heating rate.

Boiling at Low Temperatures. Just as water can be made to boil at temperatures higher than 100°C by increasing the pressure, so can it be made to boil at temperatures below 100°C by reducing the atmospheric pressure. Because of the practical importance of this basic fact, a detailed explanation should be given. Fig. B is a graph of the saturated vapor pressures of water, and it represents conditions under which water and saturated water vapor can exist together in equilibrium.

Because boiling at the surface of water takes place when the saturated vapor pressure becomes equal to the atmospheric pressure, it follows that, by lowering atmospheric pressure, a lower vapor pressure can bring about the conditions for boiling. The curved line in the graph is, therefore, a *boiling point curve;* all pressures and temperatures to the right of the curve represent the gas or vapor state, all points to the left the liquid state.

Consider, for example, water at the normal boiling point of 100°C and at the standard pressure of 76 cm of Hg. To raise its temperature without raising the pressure, heat must first be added to vaporize the water, and then additional heat will raise the temperature of the resultant steam. To lower its temperature, heat must be given up to liquefy the steam and more heat given up to lower the temperature of all the water. These changes are defined by the line *ab* in Fig. B.

To go one step further, suppose water at 30°C is placed in a vacuum jar, as shown in Fig. F, and the pressure is slowly reduced by means of a vacuum pump. Starting at the point *A* on the graph, the pressure decreases until it reaches *B*, about 3.18 cm of Hg, where bubbles form and the water begins to boil.

To vaporize water requires heat, which is taken from the remaining water, thus

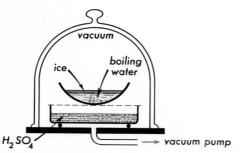

Fig. F. The boiling point of a liquid is lowered by lowering the atmospheric pressure. Water in a vacuum will boil and freeze at the same time.

cooling it to a lower temperature. (This is the principle of the refrigerator-cooling unit.) Continued reduction in pressure causes continued boiling and lowering of temperature until finally the freezing point at approximately 0°C is reached. Continued evaporation cools the surface of the water until ice forms over the surface of the boiling water. Here then is a condition in which water boils and freezes at the same time and at 0°C. (The small dish of sulfuric acid, H_2SO_4, placed in the vacuum chamber absorbs water vapor, thus aiding the pump to keep the pressure sufficiently low.)

Although water under normal atmospheric pressure at sea level boils at 100°C, water at higher altitudes boils at lower temperatures. Evidence of this fact is well known to those who like to camp in the higher mountains. There, at reduced atmospheric pressure, it takes longer than usual to cook all kinds of foods. The boiling points

given in Table 1 show specific values for different elevations.

Table 1. Atmospheric Pressure and Boiling Point of Water at Various Heights Above Sea Level

Atmospheric Pressure		Boiling Point °C	Altitude ft
cm Hg	lb/in.²		
271	52.5	140	—
235	45.5	135	—
203	39.3	130	—
174	33.7	125	—
149	28.8	120	—
127	24.6	115	—
107	20.7	110	—
91	17.6	105	—
76	14.7	100	sea level
70.2	13.6	97.8	2,000
65.6	12.7	96.0	4,000
61.0	11.8	94.0	6,000
56.8	11.0	92.1	8,000
52.2	10.1	89.8	10,000
42.4	8.2	84.4	15,000
35.0	6.7	79.6	20,000
22.5	4.4	69.2	30,000
14.1	2.7	58.8	40,000
8.75	1.7	48.9	50,000
0.82	0.16	9.8	100,000

The boiling point decreases approximately 1°C per 1000 ft elevation above sea level. At high altitudes, the water in water-cooled aircraft engines boils at lower temperatures. At a height of 6 mi, gasoline boils at the normal temperature of −65°C. At a 12-mi elevation, blood boils at the body temperature of 98.6°F (37°C).

QUESTIONS

1. Does the boiling point of a liquid depend upon pressure? If so, how?
2. (a) What are the principles of the pressure cooker? (b) Does the water reach a higher temperature?
3. What are the principles of a geyser like Old Faithful in Yellowstone National Park?
4. (a) Can water be made to boil at a temperature of 90°C? (b) Can water be

made to boil at room temperature of 25°C? (c) Can water be made to boil at its freezing point?

5. (a) Does the boiling point of water vary with altitude? (b) How much is the boiling point of water lowered for each 1000 ft in elevation?

6. (a) Why does food cook more slowly high in the mountains? (b) Would a pressure cooker speed up cooking in the high mountains?

7. What is meant by vapor pressure?

8. What vapor pressure is required for boiling to occur?

9. Frozen orange juice is made by removing most of the water by boiling. How is the taste of the orange juice prevented from changing?

10. In what large city in the United States would you expect the sale of pressure cookers to be especially brisk? Explain.

11. (a) Why does a geyser require a narrow hole? (b) What would happen if the hole were wide?

12. How can you change a gas into a liquid without changing its temperature?

13. Many homes in Arizona have evaporator-type coolers. Would these be effective in a city on the East Coast in the summer (where the humidity is very high)? Explain.

14. It is commonly stated that, in a mercury barometer, the space above the mercury is a vacuum. (a) Is this strictly correct? (b) Would it be equally true at various temperatures? Explain.

15. Suppose that a bucket of water is thrown out the window of a spacecraft in outer space. Describe in detail what would happen to it.

PROBLEMS

1. Plot a graph of the boiling point of water (vertically) against the altitude (horizontally).

2. At what temperature will water boil at the one-mile-high city of Denver, Colorado?

3. At what temperature will water boil at the top of Mt. Everest (29,000 ft)?

4. At what temperature will water boil if the pressure is 30 lb/in.²?

5. At what temperature will water boil if the air pressure above it is 200 cm of Hg?

6. At what temperature would water boil at the bottom of a well where the water is 100 ft deep? Assume normal atmospheric pressure at the water surface.

7. The opening tube in the lid of a pressure cooker is 0.10 cm². What mass must the pressure weight on top of this opening have if the boiling temperature of the water inside is to be 130°C? (See Fig. C.)

8. A geyser in Yellowstone National Park is located at an elevation of 800 ft. What is the boiling temperature (a) at the surface and (b) 34 ft down in the water?

9. A bottle is half filled with water at 80°C. (a) What is the vapor pressure of the water vapor? (b) If the total pressure inside is equal to the atmospheric pressure on the outside, what is the "partial pressure" of the air that is also inside the bottle?

10. Water vapor, initially at 100°C and 50 cm of Hg, has pressure slowly applied until the resulting fluid is at 100 cm Hg, but at the same temperature. Then the temperature is slowly raised to 130°C at constant pressure. Reproduce Fig. B, and show on it the path illustrating what has happened.

11. Describe how you would carry out the previous experiment, and specify the apparatus needed.

12. Apple juice is to be concentrated by boiling it at reduced pressure. Assuming that it behaves sufficiently like water, what pressure must be maintained to have it boil at 50°C?

13. You are camping in a high meadow of unknown elevation. You notice that melted snow boils at a temperature of 91°C. What is your approximate elevation?

PROJECTS

1. Demonstrate that water can be boiled at very low temperatures by filling a round 500 cm³ flask one-third full of water. Boil this water for a few minutes, then cork it after it has been removed from the heat. Place under running water and watch it boil.

2. Make a working model of an evaporator-type cooler, and test its effectiveness by comparing the temperatures inside and outside the model.

3. Build a model geyser that works.

HEAT

Lesson 48 *HEAT ENERGY AND REFRIGERATION*

Thermodynamics. Thermodynamics is the branch of physics that deals with the conversion of mechanical energy into thermal energy, and the reverse process, heat into work. There are numerous ways of carrying out either of these transformations. By rubbing the palms of the hands together, for example, heat is produced; by rubbing two sticks of wood together a fire may be started. If a weight falls freely from some height, heat is developed when the weight strikes the ground. The bearings of a car motor or the wheels of a freight car, if not lubricated, will get hot and either "burn out" or lock together, as in a "hot box." These are all examples of mechanical energy being transformed into heat.

An interesting demonstration is shown in Fig. A. A small hollow brass tube, mounted on the shaft of an electric motor, has a few drops of water in the base and a cork driven into the open end. A wooden clamp, like the one shown at the lower right, is squeezed tightly around the tube as it

Fig. A. Cork gun. Heat of friction boils water, and steam blows cork out.

spins. Because of friction the tube gets hot, boils the water, and steam pressure suddenly blows the cork out as if from a gun.

The First Law of Thermodynamics. The first law of thermodynamics is frequently referred to as the *mechanical equivalent of heat.* It is to the painstaking work of Joule (1843)* that we attribute this fundamental verification of the universal law of conservation of energy. With his apparatus, he was able to show that, when a moving body is brought to rest, the energy that disappears is directly proportional to the amount of heat produced.

In his most famous experiment, he set water into motion in a bucket by means of rotating paddles and then brought the water to rest by stationary paddles. He was able to show that if all of the work used in churning the water goes into producing heat, then the same amount of work will always produce the same amount of heat, regardless of the method used to carry out the transformation. In other words, the calorie, which is a unit of heat energy, is

* James Prescott Joule (1818-1889), English physicist, was born on December 24, 1818, near Manchester. Although he owned a large brewery, he devoted his life to scientific research. At the age of 22 he discovered the law giving the relation between electrical energy and heat. A short time later, the law became known as the first law of thermodynamics.

equivalent to a definite number of joules of mechanical energy.

The mechanical equivalent of heat is defined as the ratio between any given amount of mechanical energy and the amount of heat energy it can produce:

$$\frac{work}{heat} = \text{mech. equiv. of heat}$$

By experiment—

$$1 \text{ cal} = 4.18 \text{ joules} \qquad (1)$$
$$= 4.18 \times 10^7 \text{ ergs}$$
$$1 \text{ BTU} = 778 \text{ ft lb} \qquad (2)$$

As an equation—

$$\frac{\Delta W}{\Delta H} = J \qquad (3)$$

where—

$$J = 4.18 \frac{\text{joules}}{\text{cal}}$$
$$= 4.18 \times 10^7 \frac{\text{ergs}}{\text{cal}}$$
$$J = 778 \frac{\text{ft lb}}{\text{BTU}}$$

Example. A 1-Kg hammer, moving with a velocity of 50 m/sec, strikes a 200-gm iron rod lying on the ground. If half of the energy goes into heating the iron rod, what will be its rise in temperature?

Solution.

K.E. of hammer $= \frac{1}{2}mv^2 = \frac{1}{2} \times 1000$ gm $\times (5000 \text{ cm/sec})^2 = 12.5 \times 10^9$ ergs

From Eq. (3), the heat produced will be—

$$\Delta H = \frac{\Delta W}{J} = \frac{12.5 \times 10^9}{4.18 \times 10^7} = 299 \text{ cal}$$

Because one-half goes to heat 200 gm of iron of specific heat 0.105—

$$149.5 \text{ cal} = 200 \times 0.105 \, \Delta t$$

Solving for the rise in temperature, Δt, gives—

$$\Delta t = \frac{149.5}{200 \times 0.105} = 7.1°C$$

Experiments on Mechanical Equivalent of Heat. There are numerous experimental methods of measuring the mechanical equivalent of heat. If a weight is dropped from any height, heat is developed when it strikes the ground. A 1-lb weight dropped 3.5 ft will, on stopping, produce 1 calorie.

One simple laboratory experiment is to place a measured amount of lead shot (about 200 gm) in a tube 5 cm in diameter and 100 cm long. After finding the temperature of the shot, the tube is turned end for end about 100 times, stopping each time in a vertical position to allow the shot to fall the full 100 cm and strike the bottom. See Fig. B. The temperature of the shot is meas-

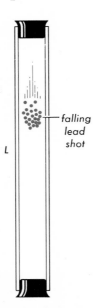

Fig. B. Experiment for determining the mechanical equivalent of heat.

ured again, and from the mass of the shot, its specific heat, and the temperature rise, the total change in heat, H, produced can be calculated. The work done lifting the shot to the top of the tube 100 times makes it possible to calculate W. By putting these

values of ΔW and ΔH in Eq. (3) the value of J can be computed.

Frequent reference has been made to the fact that heat is a form of energy. To add heat to a body is to increase the motion of the molecules. Having mass and velocity, each molecule has kinetic energy, $\frac{1}{2}mv^2$.

The transformation of potential energy into heat usually occurs by first changing it into kinetic energy. In the above experiment, for example, the lead shot acquired a velocity in falling and its kinetic energy, $\frac{1}{2}mv^2$, was changed into heat at the bottom. Because of the impact, the molecules of the colliding bodies were given additional kinetic energy.

When two surfaces are rubbed together, the heat generated by friction is a direct and continuous transformation of the work into kinetic energy of individual atoms. With one surface moving past the other, atomic collisions with greater average velocities occur with the net result of a rise in the total kinetic energy.

Refrigeration. Such devices as refrigerators, freezers, and air conditioners are all forms of the "heat pump." The details of operation differ somewhat from one model to the next, but they all serve to pump heat from one region to another in order to cool the former region to below the ambient, or surrounding, temperature. The operation of nearly all refrigerators is based upon the principle that the rapid evaporation of a liquid or the expansion of a gas produces cooling.

Compression and Expansion. The compression of a gas causes heating, and the expansion of a gas causes cooling. To obtain a clear understanding of how this comes about, consider the action of a piston as it moves down, compressing the gas in a cylinder as shown in Fig. C. Gas molecules striking the walls and bottom of the cylinder will bounce away with the average velocity of those throughout most of the volume.

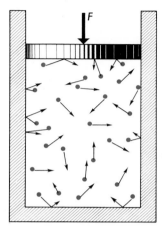

Fig. C. Illustrating the random motions of atoms and molecules in a gas.

Molecules colliding with the downward moving piston, however, will, on the average, bounce away with a higher velocity. The piston action on the molecules is analogous to a bat as it swings and hits a ball.

As the piston rises in the cylinder, the molecules colliding with it rebound with a lower average velocity, much the same as a ball rebounds with little or no velocity when a batter draws his bat backward in a "bunt."

Liquefaction of Air. The present method of liquefying air and other gases is based upon the principle of cooling by expansion. It was by this method that Dewar liquefied oxygen for the first time in 1891, and Linde liquefied air in 1895. Oxygen gas becomes a liquid at the extremely low temperature of −184°C, as does air at −191°C. On the Fahrenheit scale, these correspond to −300°F and −312°F, respectively.

On the Kelvin scale, water boils at 373°K and freezes at 273°K. Air becomes a liquid at 82°K and a solid at 61°K. Hydrogen gas becomes a liquid at 20°K and freezes at 14°K. Helium liquefies at 4°K and remains a liquid down to absolute zero.

A schematic diagram of the two absolute temperature scales in common use is given in Fig. D. The zero point of both these

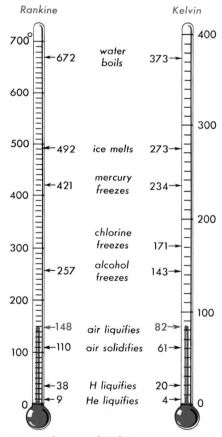

Fig. D. Rankine and Kelvin temperature scales.

scales is called *absolute zero* and represents the temperature at which all molecular motion is believed to cease.

In the liquid-air machine (see Fig. E), air is compressed by a pump to a pressure

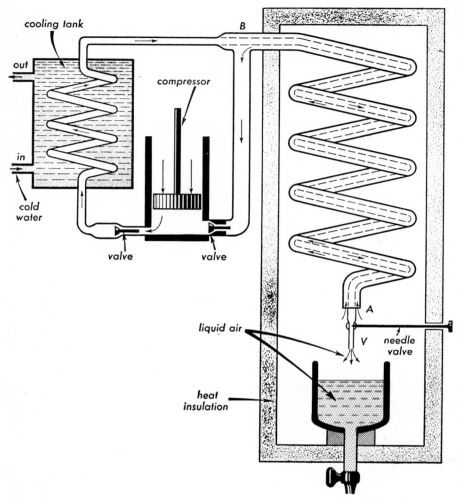

Fig. E. Cross section of a machine used in the liquefaction of air.

of about 3000 lb/in.² Because of compression this air is heated to a fairly high temperature. It must, therefore, be cooled by running it through a cooling tank. This cooled compressed air passes through the inner tube of a double-walled coil, B, and escapes through the very narrow opening of a needle valve, A. The escaping air expands so much that its temperature is lowered considerably below room temperature.

The continual pumping of the com-

pressor draws this cold air up through the outer tube of the coil, thus cooling the compressed air on its way down to the needle valve. This air is compressed again and cooled to go around the circuit again. The cycle continues until the temperature in the region of V is so low that drops of liquid air form in the jet from the needle valve. These drops fall into the Dewar flask and accumulate to be drawn off later as needed.

Liquid Air Experiments. The physical properties of matter at extremely low temperatures differ sharply from their room-temperature properties. This may be illustrated by a number of experiments with a small quantity of liquid air.

First, liquid air has the same general appearance and density as water. When a little is poured out onto the table top or into an open dish, it runs around over the surface in little spherical drops and behaves just like water drops on the flat surface of a hot stove. The drops of liquid air move quickly over the surface, riding on a film of evaporated air, just as the water drops ride around on a steam layer.

Mercury and gasoline will freeze when cooled in liquid air. An interesting demonstration is to make a small cardboard box about 1 in. × 1 in. × 2 in., fill it with mercury, and clamp a small wooden stick into it as shown in Fig. F. Liquid air poured over

Fig. G. Cooled to the temperature of liquid air, a lead bell will ring.

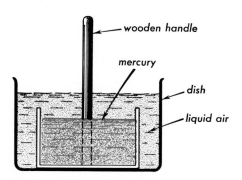

wooden handle

mercury

dish

liquid air

Fig. F. An easily made small mercury hammer.

the box will soon freeze the mercury. When it is well frozen, the cardboard can be peeled off, and the resulting small mercury hammer used to drive nails in a block of wood.

For another experiment, use a hollow rubber ball, which is about 2 in. in diameter, and put it into a vessel containing liquid air for several minutes. When the

bubbling subsides, indicating the rubber's temperature is closely that of liquid air, remove the ball and drop it to the floor. Instead of bouncing it will break into many small pieces as if it were made of glass. A small bunch of grapes, or a flower, cooled in liquid air will behave the same way and break like fine glass.

An interesting demonstration can be performed by hammering or molding a small bell out of lead metal. Such a bell at room temperature will give only a dull thud, but

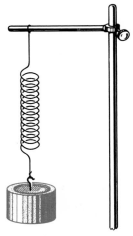

Fig. H. At liquid-air temperature, a coil of lead solder becomes a spring.

after being cooled in liquid air, it will ring quite well. See Fig. G.

A piece of wire solder can be wound into a coil spring and suspended from a clamp stand, as shown in Fig. H. At room temperature it will neither show elastic properties nor support a mass of several hundred grams. Cooled to liquid-air temperature, however, it will exhibit springlike action.

QUESTIONS

1. (a) What is the meaning of the word *thermodynamics?* (b) What is the first law of thermodynamics?
2. (a) What is meant by the mechanical equivalent of heat? (b) When mechanical energy is converted into heat, what is the atomic process? (c) What happens when the palms of your hands are rubbed together? Explain.
3. (a) What are the two temperature scales that start at absolute zero? (b) What is the absolute temperature at which ice melts?
4. (a) At what temperature does mercury freeze? (b) At what temperature will air become a liquid? (c) Can air be made solid? If so, how?
5. (a) At what temperature on the Celsius scale does hydrogen liquefy? (b) on the Fahrenheit scale?
6. (a) What is a liquid-air machine? (b) What are its principal components called? (c) What is the function of each? (d) Make a diagram and label essential parts.
7. What are the physical properties of liquid air?
8. What happens to a thin-rubber ball when it is cooled in liquid air and thrown to the ground?
9. What changes take place in a lead bell by lowering its temperature to that of liquid air?
10. What change takes place in mercury when cooled to the temperature of liquid air?
11. If a flower were cooled to liquid air temperature, would the petals be highly flexible, rigid, or brittle?
12. (a) Grapes are largely composed of water. (b) What physical properties might they have when cooled to 82°K?
13. On a hot day, a housewife opens the refrigerator door in order to cool the room. Does it work? Explain.
14. Explain how the law of conservation of energy applies to the compression of a gas, as shown in Fig. C.
15. How does the liquid-air machine qualify as a heat pump?
16. How could a refrigerator unit be used in the winter time to heat a home?
17. (a) Why must an air conditioner be mounted in a window? (b) What happens to the heat that is removed from the room?
18. Considering the molecular structure of matter, what does the fact the helium liquefies at a lower temperature than hydrogen tell us about the force of attraction between these molecules?

PROBLEMS

1. A heavy box having a mass of 200 Kg is pulled along the floor for 15 m. If the coefficient of sliding friction is 0.40, how much heat is developed?

2. A horizontal force of 35 newtons is required to pull a heavy trunk along the floor. How much heat is developed for each 100 m it slides?

3. The water drops 80 m in a large waterfall. Assuming that the available energy all goes into heat, find the temperature difference between the water at the bottom and the water at the top.

4. A 2-ton truck is moving along the highway with a velocity of 60 mi/hr (88 ft/sec) when the brakes are applied, bringing it to rest. If all of this energy goes into heat in the brake drums and shoes, how many BTU of heat are developed?

5. A sports car with a mass of 1200 Kg is moving along the highway with a velocity of 72 Km/hr when the brakes are applied bringing it to rest. If all of the energy goes into heat in the brake drums and shoes, how many calories are produced?

6. A 50-gm lead bullet at 27°C is fired from a rifle at a velocity of 300 m/sec. (a) What temperature will it have upon impact? (b) Will it melt? (c) Show how you would solve the problem if you didn't know the mass of the bullet.

PROJECTS

1. Obtain a small amount of liquid air in a suitable Dewar flask and try some of the experiments mentioned in the chapter. Observe suitable precautions.

2. Obtain a cylinder of carbon dioxide. Put a cloth loosely around its nozzle and permit the gas to escape slowly. Demonstrate the production of dry ice.

HEAT

Lesson 49 **GAS LAWS AND KINETIC THEORY**

Boyle's* Law. This is a law dealing with the compression and expansion of a gas at

* Robert Boyle (1627-1691), English natural philosopher, was the fourteenth child of Richard Boyle, the great earl of Cork. At fourteen years of age, he was in Italy studying the paradoxes of the famous star gazer, Galileo. Besides enunciating the law now known by his name, he discovered how sound is propagated through the air, in-

constant temperature. A simple laboratory experiment can be used to develop the relationship between the pressure and volume of a gas, as shown in Fig. A.

vestigated the refractive powers of crystals, and proposed the corpuscular theory of chemical compounds and mixtures. He had a profound interest in theology and spent much time and money "for proving the Christian religion against all others."

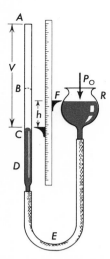

Fig. A. Apparatus for studying Boyle's law for gases.

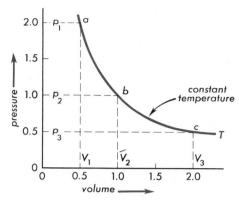

for the gas to return to its original temperature.

The graph shown in Fig. B is a plot of

Fig. B. Isothermal curve for the compression and expansion of gas.

data obtained at a given temperature for three different pressures. It is difficult to tell from the curve what relation exists between the volume and pressure.

If, however, we plot pressure on the y-axis as in the graph and the reciprocal of volume $(1/V)$ on the x-axis we get a straight line as shown by Fig. C. This shows plainly that the pressure of a gas is directly proportional to the reciprocal of its volume, if the temperature is kept the same. In algebraic symbols: $P = \text{const.} \times (1/V)$, or—

$$PV = \text{constant} \qquad (1)$$

The value of this constant depends on the units of the pressure, P, and the volume, V, and also on the amount of gas in the given problem.

Example 1. A student collects 1.5 liters of carbon dioxide gas in a plastic bag when the mercury barometer in the room reads 76.0 cm of mercury. On the following day, assuming the temperature remained the same, the barometer reading dropped to 70.0 cm. What would be the volume of the gas?

A quantity of gas (air) is trapped by a column of mercury in a straight uniform tube, AD. By raising the mercury reservoir, the gas pressure increases and the volume of air decreases. By lowering the reservoir, the pressure falls and the gas expands.

For each set position of the reservoir, R, the volume, V, is read directly from the scale and pointer (shown at C). The pressure of the gas is determined by measuring the difference in mercury level, h. If the level of mercury in the tube and in the reservoir are the same, that is if h is equal to zero, then the gas pressure is equal to the atmospheric pressure. If the level F lies above C, the total gas pressure, P, is equal to the atmospheric pressure measured in cm of mercury, plus the height, h, in cm. If F lies below C, the height, h, is subtracted from the atmospheric pressure. Atmospheric pressure is easily measured by either a mercury or aneroid barometer. The atmospheric pressure must be measured in the same units as the length of the column, h, so that their sum and difference will be the actual pressure in the gas. With each new setting of the bulb, adequate time must be allowed

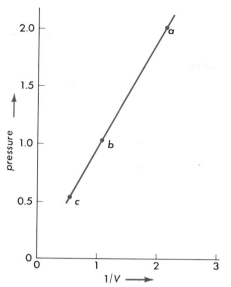

Fig. C. Graph showing relation between pressure and reciprocal of volume of a gas at constant temperature.

Solution. Using the first values of P and V, and substituting in Eq. (1), we obtain—

constant = 76 cm $\times$ 1.5 liters
constant = 114 cm liters

Using the second value of P and the value of the constant just calculated, we again use Eq. (1) to find—

$$V = \frac{114 \text{ cm liters}}{70 \text{ cm}}$$

$$V = 1.63 \text{ liters}$$

While Boyle's law is reasonably accurate, it is not quite correct for large ranges of pressure and volume. At high pressure, when the molecules are close together, an attractive force becomes evident between the molecules, which adds to the external pressure. In addition, when the molecules are close to each other, the volumes of the molecules themselves become an appreciable fraction of the space to which the gas is confined. An ideal gas is one in which

these factors can be ignored. Strictly speaking, however, an ideal gas does not exist, for it would be one in which the molecules were geometrical points having no volume, and their intermolecular forces would be zero.

Charles' Law. Suppose we perform an experiment in which we try to find the relation between the volume of a gas and its temperature at constant pressure. Fig. D

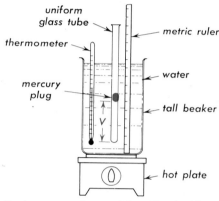

Fig. D. Apparatus for studying Charles' law for gases.

shows a mercury column in a glass tube. The volume of air trapped by the mercury is proportional to the length of the tubing it occupies. This length and the temperature of the gas are measured for different ranges of temperatures as provided by warming the water with the hot plate. Because the gas is free to expand, the pressure on the gas remains constant.

Table 1 is a record of the data from such an experiment. A graph of this data shown in Fig. E is made by plotting volume on the x-axis and temperature on the y-axis. The shape of the graph shows that there is a linear relationship between the volume of the gas and its temperature. However, the

Table 1. Charles' Law Experiment

Temperature	V
20°C	11.0 cm
40°C	11.8 cm
60°C	12.5 cm
80°C	13.3 cm

volume of the gas does not vary directly with the Celsius temperature as can be seen

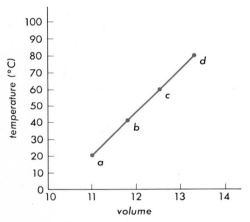

Fig. E. Graph showing relation between volume and temperature at a constant pressure.

from a consideration of the following example.

If the volume, V, were proportional to the temperature, T, then algebraically—

$$V = \text{constant} \times T \qquad (2)$$

According to our experiment, at 20°C we had a volume of gas proportional to a volume reading of 11.0 cm on the ruler. If Eq. (2) is correct, then at 0°C, whatever the value of the constant, the volume of the gas should also be zero. We know this is an absurdity, so what is wrong? Let us replot the same data on a different scale, as shown in Fig. F. If we extrapolate the

straight line until the volume of the gas is zero, the indicated temperature is approximately −273°C. Physically, the gas volume will not reach zero, because the molecules of the gas cannot disappear. In addition, all gases change either to a liquid or a solid

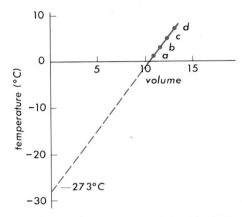

Fig. F. Extrapolation of data of Charles' law experiment showing temperature at which the volume of a gas would be zero.

before this temperature is reached. However, it does indicate that there is some lower limit to temperature. Because the coldest temperature ever reached in the research laboratory has never gone below this value, it would appear that this is the coldest temperature that is possible. Later, it will be seen that it is also the temperature corresponding to zero molecular motion. This temperature is known as the *absolute zero.*

Many experiments have shown that Eq. (2) is valid with a temperature scale that starts with absolute zero. The value of the constant depends on the quantity of gas in the particular problem and the units used to measure the volume.

Example 2. A student collected 150.0 cm³ of oxygen gas by the displacement of water in a flask at a temperature of 20°C. What would the volume of the gas be during the night if the temperature dropped to 5°C?

Solution. Using the first values of volume and temperature and substituting in Eq. (2) we obtain—

$$\text{constant} = 150.0 \text{ cm}^3/(20 + 273)°\text{K}$$
$$\text{constant} = 0.512 \text{ cm}^3/°\text{K}$$

Using the second value of temperature and the value of the constant just calculated, we again use Eq. (2) to find—

$$V = 0.512 \frac{\text{cm}^3}{°\text{K}} \times (5 + 273)°\text{K}$$

$$V = 142 \text{ cm}^3$$

General Gas Law. It is possible to combine Eqs. (1) and (2) into one having the form—

$$PV = \text{constant} \times T \qquad (3)$$

If T is held constant, then we have Boyle's law, because the product of two constants is a constant. If P is maintained constant, then Eq. (3) becomes Charles' law. If V is held constant then another special gas law is evident, namely *Gay-Lussac's law*. According to this law—

$$P = \text{constant} \times T \qquad (4)$$

This law has been verified by many experiments. Note that again the constant depends on the amount of gas used in a given problem and the units used to measure P and V. The constant, therefore, can vary from problem to problem.

Example 3. A balloon in a partially filled condition contains 1000 ft³ of helium gas at ground level where the pressure is 14.7 lb/in.² and the temperature is 27°C. Calculate the gas volume of this balloon when it rises into the stratosphere to a height of 10 mi, where the pressure drops to 1.5 lb/in.² and the temperature is −55°C.

Solution. Using the first values of V, T, and P, and substituting in Eq. (3) we obtain—

$$\text{constant} = \frac{14.7 \text{ lb/in.}^2 \times 1000 \text{ ft}^3}{(27 + 273)°\text{K}}$$

$$\text{constant} = \frac{49 \text{ lb/in.}^2 \text{ ft}^3}{°\text{K}}$$

Using the second values of P and T and the value of the constant just calculated, we again use Eq. (3) to find—

$$V = \frac{\dfrac{49 \text{ lb/in.}^2 \text{ ft}^3}{°\text{K}} \times (-55 + 273)°\text{K}}{1.5 \text{ lb/in.}^2}$$

$$V = 7130 \text{ ft}^3$$

It is possible to measure the constant for the case of one mole of gas and get a universal gas constant, R. A mole of a gas is that quantity of gas whose weight in grams is equal to its molecular weight.

The general gas law for mole of gas is—

$$PV = RT \qquad (5)$$

where the value of R is equal to 0.08206 if the pressure is measured in atmospheres, the volume in liters, and temperature in degrees Kelvin.

Kinetic Theory of Gases. According to the kinetic theory of matter, the pressure exerted by a gas upon the walls of the containing vessel is due to the continual bombardment of the walls by the rapidly moving gas molecules. If the temperature of the gas is raised, the molecules move faster and the pressure rises, whereas if it is lower, they move more slowly and the pressure decreases. The absolute temperature of a gas is proportional to the average kinetic energy of translation of the molecules.

The more gas that is pumped into a vessel of constant volume, the more molecules there are to bombard the walls per second and the greater is the resultant pressure. At any given instant of time some molecules are moving in one direction and some in another; some are traveling fast, some slow, and a few are momentarily at rest.

In any reasonably large volume of gas, there are many molecules (about 10^{24} molecules/ft³ at normal atmospheric pressure and room temperature). According to the mathematical laws of probability, some average speed can be determined, which, if possessed by all the molecules, would correspond to the same temperature and would give rise to the same wall pressure. Denoting this average speed by $\bar{v}$, we will now derive a formula for the pressure.

Consider a cubical vessel whose volume, as shown in Fig. G, is l^3. Because the total

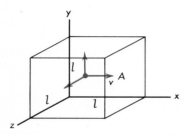

Fig. G. Gas molecules in a closed compartment create pressure by their impact against the walls.

number of molecules present, N, is very large, the calculations are simplified by assuming that one-third are moving in the x-direction, one-third in the y-direction, and one-third in the z-direction.

Select, now, the one-third that are moving in the x-direction. Each molecule, as it approaches the right-hand wall of the vessel, is moving with a velocity $\bar{v}$, and, after collision, it rebounds with a velocity $-\bar{v}$. There has been a change in velocity of $2\bar{v}$. Because the impulse Ft exerted on the wall is given by the change in momentum, we may write—

$$Ft = 2m\bar{v} \qquad (6)$$

Bouncing back and forth between oppo-

site walls of the vessel, each molecule will make many impacts on the same wall in unit time. Now, t is the average time required for the molecule to make the round trip, $2l$, from the right-hand wall to the left-hand wall and back. Therefore—

$$t = 2l/\bar{v}$$

Because the impulse, Ft, is given by the change of momentum, we may write—

$$F \times 2l/\bar{v} = 2m\bar{v} \qquad \text{or} \qquad F = m\bar{v}^2/l$$

For $\frac{1}{3}N$ molecules, then, the force will be $N/3$ times that for one molecule, or—

$$F = \frac{Nm\bar{v}^2}{3l}$$

Because pressure is the force per unit area, and the area of the wall is l^2—

$$P = \frac{F}{l^2} = \frac{Nm\bar{v}^2}{3l^3} \qquad (7)$$

Because the number of molecules N multiplied by the mass of a single molecule gives the total mass of the gas, and l^3 gives its volume, the density ρ is given by—

$$\rho = \frac{Nm}{l^3}$$

By substituting ρ for Nm/l^3 in Eq. (7), we obtain for the pressure—

$$P = \tfrac{1}{3}\rho\bar{v}^2 \qquad (8)$$

Eq. (8) enables one to calculate the speed of gas molecules if their density and pressure are known. This relationship has been shown to be correct by actual measurement of molecular velocities.

Eq. (7) may be written as—

$$P = \frac{M\bar{v}^2}{3V} \qquad (9)$$

where M is the total mass of the gas and V is its volume. Multiplying both sides of Eq. (9) by V gives—

$$PV = \tfrac{1}{3}M\bar{v}^2 \qquad (10)$$

Because, from Eq. (5), $PV = RT$, it is possible to equate these two equations and get—

$$\tfrac{1}{3}M\bar{v}^2 = RT$$

or—

$$M\bar{v}^2 = 3RT \qquad (11)$$

From this equation it can be seen that, if the temperature is absolute zero, either the mass or the velocity of the molecules must be zero. Because the mass cannot disappear, it is presumed that at this temperature molecular velocity is zero.

Kinetic Energy of a Single Molecule. Eq. (11) applies to one mole, or 6.02×10^{23} molecules, of gas. We can divide both sides of Eq. (1) by 2 and by N_0, which is the number of molecules in a gas, and get—

$$\frac{M\bar{v}^2}{2N_0} = \frac{3}{2}\frac{R}{N_0} T$$

or—

$$\tfrac{1}{2}mv^2 = \tfrac{3}{2}kT \qquad (12)$$

where m is the mass of one molecule, and k is known as Boltzmann's constant. The reason for dividing by two is to get the average kinetic energy of a single gas molecule. Boltzmann's constant is given by—

$$k = 1.38 \times 10^{-23} \text{ joule/}^\circ K$$

Example 4. Calculate the average kinetic energy of an oxygen molecule at 0°C. What is its average velocity? The oxygen molecule has a mass of 5.3×10^{-26} Kg.

Solution. Using Eq. (12) and the value of Boltzmann's constant we get—

$$K.E. = \tfrac{1}{2}mv^2$$

$$= \tfrac{3}{2} \times 1.38 \times 10^{-23} \frac{\text{joule}}{^\circ K} \times 273^\circ K$$

$$K.E. = 5.66 \times 10^{-21} \text{ joule}$$

From the equation for kinetic energy,

$$v = \sqrt{\frac{2 \text{ K.E.}}{M}}$$

$$v = \sqrt{\frac{2 \times 5.65 \times 10^{-21}}{5.3 \times 10^{-26}}}$$

$$v = 460 \text{ m/sec}$$

QUESTIONS

1. (a) What is Boyle's law? (b) What is kept constant? (c) What quantities vary? (d) If the volume of a given gas is doubled, how does the pressure change? (e) What is the equation for Boyle's law?
2. (a) What is Charles' law? (b) What is kept constant? (c) If the absolute temperature of a gas is doubled, how do the other factors vary according to Charles' law?
3. (a) What is the kinetic theory of gases? (b) To what is gas pressure due? (c) Why does one pump more air into an automobile tire to raise its pressure?
4. (a) What is the general gas law? (b) What three measurable factors does it involve? (c) What temperature scales must be used?
5. (a) On the basis of the kinetic theory, why do gases exhibit the same coefficient of expansion? (b) Why does this change if the temperature is very low or the pressure high?
6. Why must absolute temperature be used when using Charles' law?
7. (a) What is the actual significance of absolute zero? (b) How does this differ from the zero of the Celsius scale?

8. (a) What basic assumption is made in the derivation of absolute zero in the text? (b) Is this necessarily true?

9. Why does the pressure of air in a tire increase when the car is driven at high speed?

10. Does a gas molecule lose energy when it bounces against the wall of its container? Explain.

PROBLEMS

1. A gas tank contains helium gas at a pressure of 600 lb/in.^{2} when the temperature is 27°C. Calculate the pressure when the temperature goes up to 47°C.

2. A cylinder with a piston contains 6 m^3 of nitrogen gas at a pressure of 76 cm of mercury and a temperature of 27°C. If the gas is compressed to a volume of 2 m^3 and a pressure of 270 cm of Hg, what is the temperature in °C?

3. An automobile tire has a gauge pressure of 28 lb/in.^{2} when the temperature is 59°F. After running at high speed on a hot pavement, the temperature rises to 140°F. Find the gauge pressure, assuming the volume is unchanged (*Note:* 15 lb/in.^{2} must be added to gauge pressure to obtain the correct gas pressure.)

4. One liter (1000 cm^3) of helium gas at normal atmospheric pressure is compressed to a volume of 250 cm^3. What is the resulting pressure if the temperature is kept constant?

5. Five liters (5000 cm^3) of oxygen gas at a temperature of 27°C are heated until the gas occupies a volume of 10 liters. What will be its temperature? Assume constant pressure.

6. The pressure on a gas is doubled while its absolute temperature is tripled. How does its new volume compare with what it was originally?

7. The volume of a gas was 100 cm^3 at 10°C. What will its volume be if the temperature is raised to 20°C?

8. The absolute pressure in a tire is 40 lb/in.^{2} at 0°C. What will its pressure be after a hard drive when its temperature has reached 60°C?

9. Find the average velocity of an oxygen molecule at 20°C and normal atmospheric pressure.

10. What is the average kinetic energy of a hydrogen molecule at 100°C and normal atmospheric pressure?

11. Calculate the average velocity of helium atoms in a gas at 0°C and normal atmospheric pressure.

12. 250 cm^3 of gas at 10°C and a pressure of 70.5 cm of mercury are collected by an experimenter. What will the volume be if the temperature of the gas changes to 20°C and the pressure is 78.4 cm of mercury?

13. A tank holds 200 gm of nitrogen gas at 1000 psig (pounds per square inch gauge pressure) and at 27°C. Additional nitrogen is pumped in, raising the pressure to 2000 psig, and the temperature to 57°C. How much gas was added?

PROJECTS

1. Devise a simple and inexpensive device for demonstrating Charles' law.
2. Devise a simple and inexpensive device for demonstrating Gay-Lussac's law.

HEAT

Lesson 50 *HEAT ENGINES*

In general, heat engines may be classified under one of these three headings: (1) *steam engines*, (2) *internal-combustion engines*, and (3) *jet-propulsion engines*. While the first engines ever made were probably based upon jet propulsion using steam, reciprocating steam engines and turbines were the first to be developed. These were followed by gasoline and diesel engines and, in recent years, by the jet-propulsion engines used principally in airplanes and rockets.

In this lesson, we will not be concerned so much with the detailed mechanical parts of all kinds of engines, but rather with the fundamental principles involved in their transformation of heat into mechanical energy and with their general over-all efficiency in the process. To begin with, however, some of the mechanical details of at least one typical heat engine will be given.

The Gasoline Engine. Because the operation of most heat engines is based upon the same thermodynamic principles, an internal-combustion engine will be explained as a typical example of all. A cross-sectional diagram of one of the six or more cylinders in a gasoline engine with overhead valves is given in Fig. A. As the crankshaft, H, of

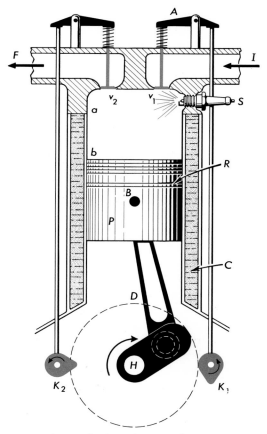

Fig. A. One cylinder of a gasoline engine of the type used in automobiles.

such an engine turns clockwise as shown, each piston moves up and down in its cylinder while the cam shaft, D, turns the small valve cams, K_1 and K_2, at half speed.

When the piston is at the top of its stroke (a) and it starts down, cam K_1 opens the intake valve, V_1, and gasoline vapor mixed with air enters from the carburetor. The falling of the piston reduces the pressure and atmospheric pressure outside forces air and gasoline vapor in. Upon the piston's reaching (b), the cylinder is full of explosive gasoline mixture and the intake valve closes. The rising piston now compresses the gas, raising its temperature.

This time, when the piston reaches the top and starts down, an electric spark at the tip of the spark plug ignites the already hot vapor, and the resulting explosion drives the piston down with great force. At the bottom of the stroke, the cam K_2 opens the exhaust valve, V_2, and the rising piston drives the waste fumes out. At the top of this stroke, the closing of the exhaust valve is followed immediately by the opening of the intake valve and the above process is repeated.

With this type of engine, the piston moves up and down twice for each explosive impulse. The several cylinders of the motor, however, are so connected to the crankshaft that they fire one after the other. In an eight-cylinder engine, for example, two pistons are at the top when two others are on their way down, two are at the bottom and two more on their way up.

The cylinders then fire one-quarter of a turn apart so that in two complete revolutions each cylinder has fired once. With impulses coming at regular intervals one-quarter of a cycle apart, the driving action is so nearly continuous that a smooth development of power from the crankshaft to the wheels results.

For the average automobile in high gear, five turns of the engine produce one turn of the wheels. At 60 mi/hr, when most cars develop their maximum power and the wheels are making about 10 r/sec, an eight-cylinder engine is turning at 50 r/sec and firing 200 times/sec.

The Efficiency of Heat Engines. The thermodynamic principles of heat engines were first explained by Sadi Carnot in 1824. The efficiency of any heat engine is defined as the ratio of the external work done by the engine to the total energy input. Expressing the output work in heat units—

$$\text{efficiency} = \frac{H_2 - H_1}{H_2} \qquad (1)$$

Carnot proved that no heat engine could be more efficient than this formula indicates and that the same result can be expressed in terms of the two absolute temperatures between which the engine works:

$$\text{efficiency} = \frac{T_2 - T_1}{T_2} \qquad (2)$$

In practical cases, the efficiency of heat engines is relatively low and never attains Carnot's efficiency. Nearly all heat engines, steam, gasoline, diesel, etc., have efficiencies in the range 10 to 20%. Some, however, reach as high as 34%. A good steam locomotive averages 10% efficiency, while a steam turbine may go as high as 25%. An automobile engine in the best tuned-up condition will give about 25% efficiency and a diesel engine about 34%. As yet, jet-propelled planes have relatively low efficiencies, about 10%, but they are rapidly being improved. The following figures for a gasoline engine of 21% efficiency will indicate where all of the consumed energy goes; 21% into work done, 36% into cooling water and radiation, 35% out the exhaust, and 8% into friction.

Example. A steam engine takes heat into its cylinders from the steam boilers at a temperature of 200°C and a pressure of 225 lb/in.² and exhausts it at a temperature of 100°C and a pressure of 15 lb/in.². Calculate the maximum efficiency as given by Carnot's formula.

Solution. The specified temperatures correspond to the absolute temperatures of 473°K and 373°K. Substitute these values in Eq. (1):

$$\text{efficiency} = \frac{473 - 373}{473} = 0.21$$

Multiplying by 100 gives 21% efficiency.

A pressure-volume indicator diagram may be, and frequently is, used to study the operating conditions of various kinds of engines in order to determine what experimental factors may improve their running efficiency. Such indicator diagrams as the one shown in Fig. B are made from actual

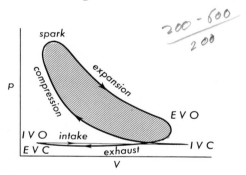

Fig. B. Pressure-volume indicator diagram for a gasoline engine.

measurements on machines while running. The shaded area is proportional to the amount of work done by the gasoline.

The effect produced by premature, or delayed, opening and closing of valves shows up as reduced curve areas. The larger the area of a curve, the greater is its efficiency. The time of the *Opening* and *Closing* of the *Intake* and *Exhaust* valves is indicated in the diagrams by *IVO*, *IVC*, *EVO*, and *EVC*.

Diesel engines greatly resemble gasoline

engines in construction. In operation, they employ a lower grade of fuel and no spark plugs. The fuel vapors reach such high temperatures upon compression in the cylinders that they spontaneously ignite at the proper time.

The Gas Turbine and Turbojet. The gas-turbine engine, used extensively in high-speed aircraft, is shown schematically in Fig. C. Air needed for combustion enters the nose of the *shroud*, where it is compressed by a fanlike centrifugal *compressor*, This air, along with the fuel to be burned, is injected into a *combustion chamber*, and there the mixture is ignited. The rapidly expanding gases drive a fanlike *turbine* wheel and at the same time create a forward thrust on the walls by exhausting through the rear as shown.

While the principal function of the turbine is to drive the compressor and small auxiliary equipment like fuel pumps, generators, etc., some aircraft have propellers to assist *take-off*. At high speeds, such propellers may be stopped and "feathered" by a suitable clutch mechanism, and all forward thrust comes from the exhaust jet.

The Rocket. The rocket of today owes much of its early development to the American experimenter, Robert Goddard. Rockets are classified as engines of very low efficiency but are definitely capable of enormous power and high speeds. While the turbo-jet and the ram-jet engines require large quantities of air for their proper operation, and are thereby confined to aircraft operating within the earth's atmosphere, the rocket carries its own *oxygen* supply as well as *fuel* and is capable of operating beyond the earth's atmosphere.

Because *fuel* and *oxidizer* must both be carried along, rocket ships are, as yet, relatively limited in range.

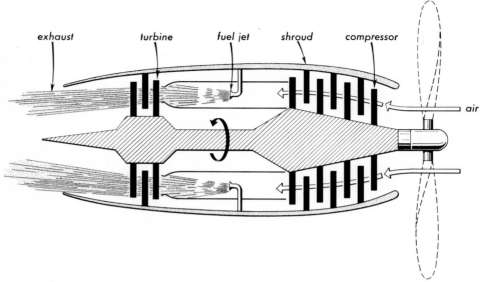

exhaust   turbine   fuel jet   shroud   compressor

air

Fig. C. Cross-section diagram of a turbojet engine, used principally in aircraft (pro-peller optional). Its top speed is probably about 600 mi/hr.

Like that of all heat engines, the efficiency of the turbojet, ramjet, and rocket depends upon the operating temperatures T_1 and T_2 in Eq. (2). The high temperature T_2 is limited in large measure by the melting point of the engine parts, and a great deal of effort has been expended in the search for materials that will maintain the required mechanical strength at higher temperatures.

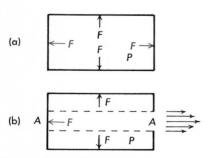

Fig. D. Diagram illustrating the thrust arising from the gas exhausted from a hole in a tank containing gas under pressure.

The thrust of a rocket engine is readily explained in terms of gas pressure and Newton's Third Law of Motion. Consider a hollow vessel having the shape of a cylindrical tin can and containing a mixture of combustible fuels as shown at the top in Fig. D.

When the fuel is ignited, the high pressure developed inside exerts outward forces normal to the walls as shown. The forces, F, on the ends are equal and opposite, as are also the forces on opposite sides. All of these forces are balanced, and the net resultant force is zero.

Imagine that we now remove a circular section of area from the center of the right-hand end as shown in (b). The container now experiences an unbalanced force F to the left given by the product of the pressure P and the exit area A:

$$F = P \times A \qquad (3)$$

At the earth's surface, the atmosphere outside the container exerts inward forces on all the walls and must be taken into account. See Fig. E. The pressure P then be-

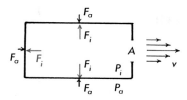

Fig. E. Illustration of internal and external gas pressures on the walls of a gas container and the thrust from an exhaust jet.

comes the difference between the inside pressure P_i and the outside or ambient pressure P_a. The pressure thrust on the rocket becomes, therefore—

$$F = (P_i - P_a)A \qquad (4)$$

The principal elements of a typical liquid-propellant rocket engine are shown by a cross section diagram in Fig. F. Oxidizer and fuel, kept in separate tanks, are pumped into the combustion chamber

area causes the molecules to speed up. Once they are through the narrowest section, the low pressure of free space provides an additional acceleration.

Out in free space, far removed from all external forces, the resultant accelerating force acting upon a rocket is due entirely to the momentum change of the mass of the particles ejected through the exhaust. Applying Newton's Second Law of Motion to these gases, the force on them equals the rate of change of their momentum. The total thrust of the rocket engine is given by the impulse equation (Eq. (3) in Lesson 28):

$$F = \frac{\Delta(mv)}{\Delta t} \qquad (5)$$

Assuming steady burning of the fuel, the exhaust velocity, v, of the waste products is constant, and Eq. (5) may be written—

$$F = -\frac{\Delta m}{\Delta t}\, v \qquad (6)$$

The minus sign indicates that v is oppo-

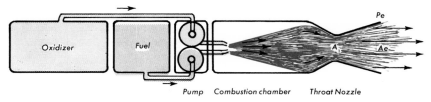

Fig. F. Schematic diagram of a liquid rocket engine.

where they are sprayed out of jets to form an efficiently combustible mixture. Burning at a steady rate, liquid fuel and oxidizer not only expand into a gas, but rise in temperature to a very high value.

The purpose of a well-designed nozzle is to accelerate the gas particles to still higher velocity and at the same time to direct their motion into a smoothly flowing exhaust stream. As the gases approach the throat of the nozzle the decreasing cross-sectional

sitely directed to the force F. The velocity, v, is measured with respect to the rocket, and F is called the *momentum thrust*.

The exit pressure, P_i, of the gas from within the rocket is usually quite different from the ambient pressure, P_a, of the surrounding gas. Although P_i may stay fairly constant as a rocket climbs through the atmosphere, the ambient pressure, P_a, will decrease and become practically zero in free space.

To take these varying conditions into account, it is convenient to write for the total thrust of the rocket engine—

$$F = -\frac{\Delta m}{\Delta t} v_{\text{eff}} \qquad (7)$$

where v_{eff} is called the *effective exhaust velocity*. As the rocket climbs through the atmosphere where the ambient pressure, P_a, decreases and becomes zero, the effective velocity, v_{eff}, increases the approaches v, while the thrust, F, increases and becomes constant in free space.

Specific Impulse. Specific impulse is the term applied to the performance of a rocket engine and is given by the total thrust divided by the weight of the propellant consumed per second:

$$I_s = \frac{F}{\Delta w/\Delta t} \qquad (8)$$

Because F and w are both measured in the same units, newtons or pounds, specific impulse is in seconds. Because total thrust varies with altitude, the value of F given by Eq. (7) may be substituted in Eq. (8):

$$I_s = \frac{\Delta m/\Delta t}{\Delta w/\Delta t} v_{\text{eff}}$$

By Newton's Law, weight = mass × acceleration due to gravity, $\Delta w = \Delta m \times g$. Direct substitution gives—

$$I_s = \frac{\Delta m/\Delta t}{\Delta m/\Delta t} \cdot \frac{v_{\text{eff}}}{g}$$

$$I_s = \frac{v_{\text{eff}}}{g} \qquad (9)$$

The value of g is assumed to be a constant and equal to 9.80 m/sec², or 32 ft/sec², wherever the rocket is located. Specific impulse can be found either by dividing the thrust by the fuel consumption, or by dividing the exhaust velocity by the constant g.

According to Eq. (11) in Lesson 49—

$$Mv^2 = 3RT$$

The higher the temperature reached through combustion and the lower the mass of the propellant molecules, the greater will be the exhaust velocity, v, and the greater will be the specific impulse, I_s.

Typical values of these two quantities for a number of liquid propellants are given in Table 1.

Table 1. Performance of Liquid Propellants Calculated for Expansion from 20 Atm to 1Atm Pressure

Propellant	Exhaust Velocity (Km/sec)	Specific Impulse (sec)
Oxygen and hydrogen	3.30	338
Oxygen and ethyl alcohol	2.34	240
Oxygen and kerosene	2.43	248
Nitric acid and analine	2.00	204
Hydrogen and fluorine	3.80	388
Hydrogen and ozone	3.60	368
Hydrazine and oxygen	2.22	227

These are theoretical values only and are not fully realized in practice. A specific impulse of 240 means that a thrust of 240 lb is obtained per pound of propellant consumed per second, or a thrust of 240 newtons per newton of propellant consumed per second. A mass of 1 Kg has a weight of 9.8 newtons.

QUESTIONS

1. (a) What is an internal-combustion engine? (b) What are its essential parts? (c) Make a diagram and explain how it works.

2. (a) What determines the efficiency of a heat engine? (b) Why is the efficiency of most engines so very low?

3. Why are steam engines and combustion engines not considered much for space travel?

4. Of what significance is the shaded area on the indicator diagram of a running engine?

5. Why are spark plugs not needed in the diesel engine?

6. A flywheel, with a large moment of inertia, is usually built onto the crankshaft of a gasoline engine. Why?

7. (a) In what basic way does a jet-turbine engine differ from a rocket engine? (b) How does this affect the realms into which each can travel?

8. Describe how Newton's Third Law of Motion applies to the jet-turbine engine.

9. What effect, if any, would there be on engine design if a cheap alloy could be found that could resist temperatures 50% better than the ones that are available now?

10. What relation is there between the number of cylinders an engine has and the size of its flywheel? Explain.

11. How do you explain the fact that occasionally an engine will continue to run even after the ignition system has been turned off?

12. Why is the diesel engine more efficient than the average gasoline engine?

13. Why has there been such a long delay in the use of turbine engines in cars?

14. Why is a satellite launched with multistage rockets instead of one large rocket?

PROBLEMS

1. A coal-burning locomotive supplies steam to its cylinders at 320°F and exhausts this steam into the surrounding air at 230°F. Find the theoretical efficiency.

2. An oil-burning steam turbine takes in steam at 350°C and exhausts it into the surrounding air at 188°C. Find its theoretical efficiency.

3. While in flight, the effective high temperature of the flaming gas in a jet-fighter engine reaches 2100°F. If its efficiency is 25%, what is the effective exhaust temperature?

4. Each of the four jet engines in a transport plane operates between a high temperature of 1182°F and an exhaust temperature of 800°F. Find their efficiency.

5. A gasoline engine of modern design, having a compression ratio of 10 to 1, reaches a temperature of 4700°F on ignition and exhausts spent gases at 2950°F. What is its efficiency?

6. A gas turbine operates between the temperatures of 650°C and 350°C. Find its efficiency.

7. A jet-fighter plane making 600 mi/hr exhausts gas from the tail pipe at a speed of 8000 ft/sec with respect to the plane and at the rate of 10 lb/sec. What is the forward thrust on the plane?

8. A rocket ship far out in space exhausts gas from the tail pipe at the speed of

12,000 ft/sec with respect to the ship and at the rate of 0.4 lb/sec. What is the forward thrust on the rocket?

9. A gas turbine, operating at a 30% efficiency, exhausts spent gases at 350°C. What is the initial gas temperature?

10. A spacecraft achieves a thrust of 6000 newtons by exhausting gases at the rate of 2 Kg/sec. What is the exhaust velocity?

11. The combustion chamber of a rocket engine maintains an internal pressure of 300 lb/in.², when at sea level where atmospheric pressure is 15 lb/in.². If the exit area has a diameter of 8 in., find the thrust.

12. A rocket engine using liquid oxygen and liquid hydrogen as propellant develops a specific impulse of 300 sec. If propellant is consumed at the rate of 100 Kg/sec, find (a) the exhaust velocity and (b) the total thrust in newtons.

13. A rocket engine using nitric acid and analine as oxidizer and fuel has a total weight of 5 tons. If propellant is consumed at the rate of 200 lb per second, what is (a) the theoretical exhaust velocity, (b) the specific impulse, (c) the total thrust, and (d) the vertical acceleration as it leaves the ground?

14. A rocket engine using liquid oxygen and hydrogen as a propellant has a total mass of 50,000 Kg. If propellant is used at the rate of 250 Kg/sec, what is (a) the theoretical exhaust velocity, (b) the specific impulse, (c) the total thrust, and (d) the vertical acceleration as it leaves the ground?

PROJECTS

1. Make a model showing the difference between a four- and a two-cycle internal-combustion engine.

2. Make a working model of Hero's jet engine.

Sound

As to sounds, since they arise from tremulous bodies, they can be nothing else but pulses of the air propagated through it; and this is confirmed by the tremors which sounds, if they be loud and deep, excite in the bodies near them, as we experience in the sound of drums; for quick and short tremors are less easily excited. But it is well known that any sounds, falling upon strings in unison with the sonorous bodies, excite tremors in those strings.

Sir Isaac Newton's Mathematical Principles, F. Cajori, ed., Andrew Motte, trans., University of California, Berkeley, 1934, p. 382.

◄ **This device generates and detects sound waves oscillating at 70 billion cycles per second, when immersed in the liquid helium below. The device is a superconductive tunnel diode fixed to a quartz rod, being inserted here into a microwave cavity. Its operation is based on the interactions between electrons and sound waves propagated through solids.**

R.C.A. Electronic Age

Lesson 51 *VIBRATIONS AND WAVES*

Sound is one of the most interesting of all of the subjects studied in physics. This is due in large part to the fact that it is connected with that all-important sensory manifestation we call hearing.

Simple Harmonic Motion. Most solid objects in nature are set into vibration when struck a sudden blow. Any motion, simple or complex, which repeats itself in equal intervals of time is called *periodic motion.* There are many examples in everyday life that give rise to a special kind of periodic motion called *simple harmonic motion.* The swinging of the clock pendulum, the turning of the balance wheel of a watch, or the vibration of a tuning fork are good examples of such motions. The term "simple harmonic motion" applies to these because each can be described in terms of one of the simplest known types of periodic motion, namely, *uniform circular motion.*

Simple harmonic motion is defined as the projection on any diameter of a point moving in a circle with uniform speed. This is illustrated in Fig. A. The point, *p*, moves around the circle of radius, *r*, with uniform speed, *v*. If at every instant a perpendicular is drawn from *p* to the diameter *AB*, the intercept *P* will move with simple harmonic motion. Moving back and forth along the straight line *AB*, the velocity, v_x, is continually changing. At the center point *C* it has its greatest velocity, while at *A* and *B* it is momentarily at rest. Starting from rest at either end of its path, *P* increases velocity until it reaches *C*; from there, *P* slows down again, coming to rest at the opposite end of its path.

The amplitude, r, of any simple harmonic motion is defined as the maximum value of the displacement, x, and the period is defined as the time required to make one complete vibration.

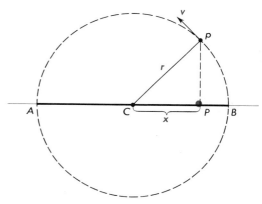

Fig. A. Diagram illustrating simple harmonic motion along a straight line.

If a vibration starts at *A*, it is not completed until the point moves across to *B* and back again to *A*. If it starts from *C* and moves to *B* and back to *C*, only half a vibration has been completed. The amplitude, *r*, is usually measured in centimeters and the period, *T*, in seconds.

The frequency of any harmonic motion is defined as the number of complete vibrations per second. For example, if a particular vibrating object completes one vibration in one-half second (the period $T = \frac{1}{2}$ sec), then it will make two complete vibrations in 1 sec (the frequency $n = 2$ vibrations/ sec). If again a body completes one vibration in one tenth of a second, $T = 1/10$ sec, it will make ten vibrations in 1 sec, $n = 10$

303

vibrations/sec. In other words, n and T are reciprocals of each other:

$$\text{period} = \frac{1}{\text{frequency}} \qquad (1)$$

or—

$$T = \frac{1}{n} \qquad (2)$$

The Spring Pendulum. Two kinds of pendulum are shown in Fig. B. The first

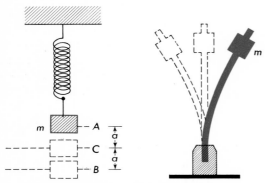

Fig. B. Two types of spring pendulums.

consists of a mass, m, fastened securely to the lower end of a coil spring. If the mass is raised to the point A as shown, and released, the mass will move up and down with simple harmonic motion and with an amplitude a.

The second pendulum consists of a mass, m, attached securely to a leaf spring. Pulled to one side or the other, it, too, will vibrate with a definite frequency and period. The period, T, of both of these spring pendulums is given by the formula—

$$T = 2\pi \sqrt{\frac{m}{k}} \qquad (3)$$

where k is the spring constant given by Hooke's law:

$$F = -kx$$

See Eq. (12) in Lesson 34. The stiffer the

spring, the larger is the spring constant, k, and the shorter is the period, T.

The Simple Pendulum. A simple pendulum consists of a mass, m, called the *bob*, fastened to one end of a lightweight cord, wire, or rod, and free to swing about a pivot point, P, as shown in Fig. C.

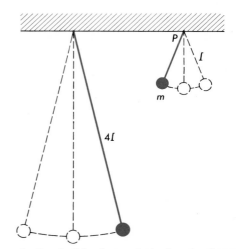

Fig. C. To double the period of a simple pendulum, the length must be increased fourfold.

When such a pendulum is set swinging in an arc that is relatively short, its period, T, is given by the following formula—

$$T = 2\pi \sqrt{\frac{l}{g}} \qquad (4)$$

The length of the pendulum, l, is the distance from the pivot, P, to the center of mass of the bob, and g is the acceleration due to gravity. The fact that the mass of the bob does not appear in Eq. (4) signifies that pendulums of equal length but different mass have the same period. See Fig. D.

The effect of the acceleration of gravity, g, on the period is illustrated in Fig. E. If the pull of gravity could be increased, the period of all pendulums would decrease,

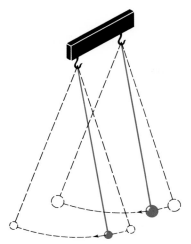

Fig. D. Two simple pendulums of the same length, but of different masses, have the same period of vibration.

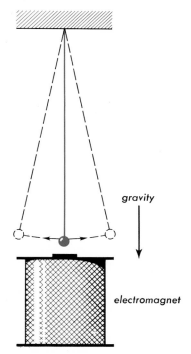

gravity

electromagnet

Fig. E. An increase in gravitational attraction, like the downward pull of the magnet, will shorten the period of a simple pendulum.

that is, they would swing faster. If gravity could be decreased, the periods would be greater, that is, they would swing more slowly. In the diagram, the pull of gravity is imitated by means of an electromagnet. When the magnet is turned on it pulls down on the iron bob and makes it swing more quickly.

Transverse Waves. The motion of any material object may be considered as a source of waves. A board striking the water, the snap of a finger, or a bowed violin string are examples of this.

Transverse waves are those in which each particle vibrates along a line perpendicular to the direction of propagation. Suppose that a rope is somehow supported in a horizontal position as shown in Fig. F,

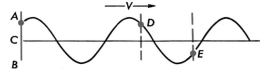

Fig. F. Diagram of a transverse wave along a rope.

and that one end is moved up and down with simple harmonic motion. As a result of this motion, the disturbances travel along the rope in the form of a wave.

If one observes any small section of the rope, like *D* or *E* in the diagram, it will not be found moving along the rope with a velocity, *V*, but moving up and down with simple harmonic motion. Because each part of the rope moves up and down, transverse to the direction in which the waves are traveling, such motions are referred to as transverse waves. Along any one line of travel all particles are vibrating in one plane only.

Wave Length. When a vibrating object sends out waves through a homogeneous

medium, the waves travel with constant velocity. If the source vibrates with simple
harmonic motion and waves are transverse,
they have the general appearance of the
waves shown in Fig. G. *The wave length is*

*The frequency of a train of waves is de-
fined as the number of waves passing any
given point per second.* This is equal to the
frequency of the source and is usually designated by *n*. It is customary to express fre-

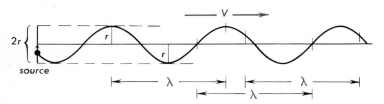

Fig. G. Illustration of the wave length λ as the distance between corresponding points
on two consecutive waves and of the amplitude r as the maximum displacement.

*defined as the distance between two similar
points of any two consecutive waves* and
is represented by the Greek letter lambda,
λ. The distance between two consecutive
wave crests, for example, is equal to one
wave length.

*The amplitude of a wave is defined as
the maximum value of the displacement.*
This is illustrated by *r* in Fig. G, the amplitude of the waves being proportional to the
amplitude of the source.

quency in *vibrations per second* or in *cycles
per second.*

From the definitions of velocity, frequency, and wave length, the following
very simple relation exists among them:

$$V = n\lambda \qquad (5)$$

The length of one wave, λ, times the number of waves per second, *n*, equals the total distance traveled in 1 sec, *V*.

QUESTIONS

1. Concerning the term simple "harmonic motion," (a) what is meant by "simple"?
   (b) What is meant by "harmonic"?
2. Describe a motion that is harmonic, but not simple.
3. Describe a motion that is not harmonic.
4. (a) What is amplitude? (b) What is meant by the frequency of a simple harmonic motion? (c) What is the period of vibration? (d) What is the relation
   between period and frequency?
5. (a) Upon what factors does the vibration frequency of a spring depend? (b)
   Does the frequency change with amplitude?
6. (a) Upon what two factors does the frequency of a simple pendulum depend?
   (b) Does the frequency change with amplitude? (c) How can you double the
   period of a simple pendulum?
7. Why does an electromagnet shorten the period of a pendulum?

8. Would a pendulum made of brass be slowed down by the action of an electro-magnet? Explain.
9. Would a pendulum of the same length go slower or faster on the moon? Would it make a big or small difference?
10. How could you determine whether or not the mass of a pendulum makes no difference to its period?
11. (a) In a grandfather clock, what is the function of the pendulum? (b) What do you have to do if the clock is too fast?
12. (a) What is the period of the moon? (b) of the earth?
13. (a) What kind of a wave is produced when a rock is thrown into a pool of water? (b) How do you know?
14. (a) Give two examples of transverse waves. (b) Can you think of a type of wave that is not transverse?
15. Concerning a traveling transverse wave, what is the relationship among the velocity, frequency, amplitude, and wave length?
16. Explain how a transverse wave can move in a horizontal direction when each point on the wave is moving in a vertical direction.

PROBLEMS

1. A steel spring vibrates with a frequency of 360 vibrations/sec. Find the period.
2. A strip of bronze clamped at one end vibrates with a period of 0.0250 sec. Find its frequency.
3. (a) Find the period of a simple pendulum 15 m long. (b) What is its frequency?
4. Find the length, in meters and inches, of a "seconds pendulum." A seconds pendulum is one for which the period is one second.
5. Find the period and frequency of a pendulum 1 m long.
6. What length pendulum (in meters) will have a frequency of 2 vibrations/sec?
7. A pendulum bob of 1 Kg mass is suspended by a cord 2 m long. When set in motion, it made 22 complete vibrations in 1 min. What would the value of the acceleration due to gravity be according to this experiment?
8. A grandfather clock, which is running accurately, stops and is taken to a watchmaker for repairs. By mistake the watchmaker replaces the original pendulum with one that is 10% shorter than the original one. What effect will this have on the accuracy of the clock?
9. A tuning fork with a frequency of 450 vibrations/sec sends out sound waves having a wave length of 27 in. Find the speed of the waves.
10. Transverse waves, traveling along a stretched cord with a speed of 40 ft/sec, have a wave length of 2.5 in. Calculate the frequency.
11. A tuning fork of frequency 500 vibrations/sec sends out sound waves with a speed of 355 m/sec. Find the wave length.
12. A mass of 25 gm hangs from the lower end of a coil spring. (a) What will be

its period of vibration if the spring constant is 2000 dynes/cm? (b) What is the frequency?

13. A 32-lb weight hangs from the end of a coil spring. (a) What will be its period of vibration if the spring constant is 4 lb/in.? (b) What is the frequency?

14. A mass of 2 Kg hanging from the lower end of a spring stretches it 1 cm. What (a) period and (b) frequency will this system have when set into vibration?

15. A 64-lb weight supported at the end of a coil spring stretches it 6 in. What (a) period and (b) frequency will this system have when it is set into vibration?

16. A mass of 3 Kg is suspended from a spring 6 in. long and allowed to vibrate. A mass of 6 Kg is then substituted for the original mass. In what way will the period of vibration be changed?

PROJECTS

1. Make an exhibit that would demonstrate the fact that the period of a pendulum depends on the square root of its length.

2. Make a project that would demonstrate the effect of an electromagnet on a swinging pendulum.

SOUND

Lesson 52 *SOUND WAVES*

Longitudinal Waves. Suppose that a coil spring is suspended by strings in a horizontal position as shown at the bottom of Fig. A and that one end is moved back and forth with simple harmonic motion. As a result of this motion the disturbance travels along the spring from left to right in the form of bunched sections. Points where the coils are closest together are called *points of condensation,* and where they are farthest apart, they are called *points of rarefaction.*

Any one coil of the spring will be found to move back and forth with simple harmonic motion, the same as the source. Because such motions are along a line parallel to the direction the waves are traveling, they are called *longitudinal waves.*

Sound waves, whether they travel through solids, liquids, or gases, are longi-

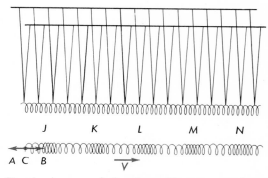

Fig. A. A suspended spring will propagate longitudinal waves when one end is moved back and forth.

tudinal in character. Each air molecule vibrates back and forth about some equilibrium position as the wave train passes by. In Fig. B the prongs of a tuning fork are

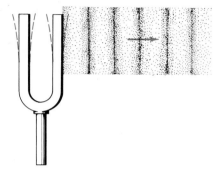

Fig. B. Sound waves are longitudinal waves.

shown vibrating with simple harmonic motion. By collisions with air molecules, each prong sends out longitudinal waves through the atmosphere. The compressional regions in a longitudinal wave are analogous to the troughs in a transverse wave, while the rarefied regions are analogous to the crests in transverse waves.

Sound Transmission. That sound is transmitted by air, or any other gas, may be demonstrated by ringing a small bell in an evacuated jar. This is illustrated in Fig. C. As the air is slowly removed from the jar, the ringing of the bell grows fainter and fainter until, when a good vacuum is obtained, no sound can be heard. As soon as the air is admitted, however, the ringing becomes clearly audible again. The vibrating bell strikes air molecules, knocking them away from the metal surface. These fast-moving molecules strike the adjacent air molecules and they in turn strike others. Upon reaching the side of the jar, the glass walls are periodically bombarded by the molecules and set vibrating. The walls in turn set the outside air vibrating. Arriving at the observer's ear, the disturbance strikes the eardrum, setting it into motion. Without air to transmit the vibrations from the bell to the inside surface of the glass jar, no sound could ever leave the jar.

The transmission of sound by liquids may be illustrated by an experiment shown in Fig. D. A tuning fork with a disk at-

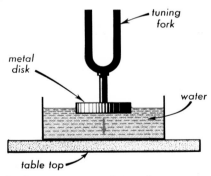

Fig. D. Demonstration of sound waves traveling through water.

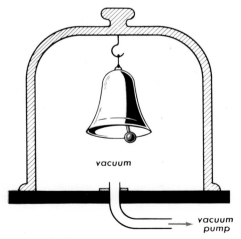

Fig. C. A bell ringing in a vacuum cannot be heard.

tached to its base is set vibrating and then touched to the surface of a dish of water. The vibrations of the fork and disk travel through the water to the bottom of the dish and to the table top. The table top itself is set into vibration with the same frequency as the fork, thus acting like a *sounding board* to make the sound louder.

The transmission of sound by solids is illustrated in Fig. E. A vibrating tuning fork

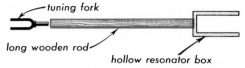

Fig. E. Demonstration of sound waves traveling through wood.

is brought into contact with the end of a long wooden rod. The longitudinal vibrations travel down the length of the rod, setting the hollow wooden box at the other end vibrating. Sound is clearly heard coming from the box.

Speed of Sound. Although light and sound both travel with a finite velocity, the speed of light is so great in comparison that an instantaneous flash may be regarded as taking no time to travel many miles. When we see the light of a distant lightning flash and hear the thunder later, we know that the difference in time is due to the relatively low speed of sound. Knowing that sound requires 5 sec to travel 1 mi, the distance of a passing thunderstorm can be noted by the second hand of a watch. Similarly, when we look for a jet plane in the direction that its sound indicates, we do not see it where we expect to. By the time the sound reaches us, the plane has flown far beyond the point of origin of the waves that reach our ears at a given moment.

The earliest successful attempts to measure the speed of sound in air were made in 1640 by Marin Mersenne, a French physicist, and in 1656 by Giovanni Borelli and Vincenzo Viviani, Italian physicists. Since

that time many experimenters have improved upon these earliest measurements by using various different methods and devices. The most recent and probably the most accurate measurements are those made in 1934 by Miller.[*] With coast defense guns as a source of sound and a set of receivers located at certain distances apart, he made very accurate speed determinations. The results gave a speed of 331 m/sec at a temperature of 0°C. This is equivalent to 1087 ft/sec at 32°F.

As a general rule, sound travels faster in solids and liquids than it does in gases. This is illustrated by the measured speed for a few common substances given in Table 1.

Table 1. Speed of Sound in Different Substances

Substance	$\dfrac{m}{sec}$	$\dfrac{ft}{sec}$
air (at 0°C)........	331	1,087
carbon dioxide......	258	846
helium.............	973	3,195
water.............	1,435	4,708
alcohol............	1,213	3,890
iron...............	5,130	16,820
glass..............	5,000	16,410

It is well known that the temperature has a small, but measurable, effect upon the speed of sound in air. For each degree Celsius rise in temperature, the speed in air increases by 61 cm/sec, or for each degree Fahrenheit rise, 1.1 ft/sec. Written as an equation—

[*] Dayton C. Miller (1866-1940), American physicist, noted for his experiments on the quality of musical sounds and on the ether drift. He collected and had in his possession the largest collection of flutes in the world. These instruments he turned over to the Smithsonian Institution in Washington, D.C., where they are now on exhibit. A member of the National Academy of Sciences, and one-time president of the American Physical Society, he was awarded the Elliott Cresson Medal and the Cleveland Distinguished Service Medal.

$$V = V_0 + 0.61t_C \qquad (1)$$

where V_0 is the speed in meters per second at 0°C, and t_C is the temperature in °C. If the speed V_0 is in ft/sec at 32°F, and t_F is the temperature in °F above 32°, the speed, V, is given by—

$$V = V_0 + 1.1t_F \qquad (2)$$

A speed of 1087 ft/sec is equivalent to 741 mi/hr. High in the stratosphere where the daytime temperature reaches 200°F, the speed of sound increases 185 ft/sec. There a speed of 1272 ft/sec is equivalent to 867 mi/hr.

Pitch. The pitch of a musical note refers to its position on a musical scale and is determined principally by the frequency of the sound impulses sent out by the vibrating source. The dependence of pitch upon frequency can be demonstrated in many ways. Fig. F represents a toothed wheel (called Savart's wheel) rotating at high speed. A small card held against the teeth is set into vibration, giving out a musical note. As the wheel slows down, the vibration frequency of the card decreases and the note lowers in pitch.

Fig. G represents a siren in which a

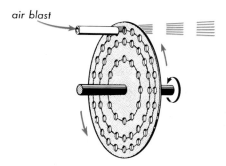

Fig. G. Air through rings of holes in a rotating disk can be made to produce a musical scale.

single blast of air is interrupted by a rotating disk containing several rings of holes. When the air is blown through one ring of holes, the air pulses emerging from the opposite side will produce a note whose frequency depends on the number of *equally spaced holes* in the ring and the speed of the wheel.

Because each ring may contain a different number of holes, a musical scale can be arranged and played by putting the air nozzle in front of the rings in proper succession.

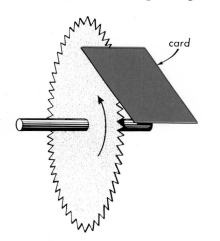

Fig. F. A card held against the teeth of a rotating wheel produces a musical note.

QUESTIONS

1. (a) What is the difference between transverse and longitudinal waves? (b) Give an example of each.
2. What is meant by (a) the amplitude, (b) the wave length, and (c) the period of a longitudinal wave?

3. (a) Will sound waves travel through a vacuum? (b) Will sound travel through gases, liquids, or solids? (c) What experiments bear on this question?
4. In what general kinds of matter do sound waves have their highest speeds?
5. You are waiting for a train at a station that is located along a curved track so that the train is not visible until it is almost at the station. What could you do to be the first one to know when the train is arriving?
6. Approximately how long does it take sound to travel one mile in air?
7. During an electrical storm, how could you estimate the distance at which lightning had discharged?
8. (a) Do all sound waves travel with the same speed? (b) How do you know? (c) What proof do you have for your answer?
9. (a) What determines the pitch of a sound? (b) How is pitch related to the frequency?
10. What is the difference between noise and a musical sound?
11. Why does the sound of wood being cut by a circular saw vary as the wood is pushed through the machine?

PROBLEMS

1. Calculate the speed of sound in air if the temperature is 30°C.
2. If the temperature is 72°F, what is the speed of sound in air?
3. Forty-five seconds after a lightning flash is seen, the thunder is heard. How far away did the lightning strike if the air temperature is 75°F?
4. Lightning strikes the arrestor on the top of a building five miles from an observer. How long after the flash of light is the sound heard if the temperature is 60°F?
5. How long does it take sound to travel 1 mi in the metal of an iron pipe?
6. A heavy blow is delivered at one end of an iron pipe 5 mi long. What is the time interval between the arrival of the sound through the iron and through the air? Assume 0°C.
7. If the disk in Fig. G is rotating at 1800 r/min, (a) what is the frequency of the sound emitted? (b) What is the wave length at 25°C?
8. A police siren has a disk with eight holes in it. What will its frequency be if the wheel is rotating at 10,000 r/min?
9. If an explosion 1 Km away is heard 2.9 sec after it is seen, what is the temperature of the air?
10. A sonar operator in a submarine hears the returning signal from the bottom of the ocean 3 sec later. How far is the submarine above the ocean floor?
11. Sound travels through a 15-m rod in 3 millisec. What is the rod made of?

PROJECTS

1. Make a device as shown in Fig. G. Make the spaces in the several circles in the correct ratios so as to make the first part of a musical scale.
2. Devise an experiment to determine the speed of sound very accurately.

SOUND

Lesson 53 *RESONANCE, BEATS, AND DOPPLER EFFECT*

Resonance. An experimental demonstration of resonance is easily set up, as shown in Fig. A. Two simple pendulums of dif-

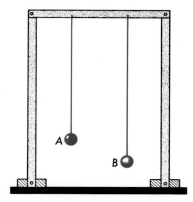

Fig. A. A demonstration of resonance can be performed with two pendulums.

ferent lengths are suspended from a flexible support, such as a thin bar. One, A, has a heavy bob made of metal, and the other, B, a bob made of wood.

The heavy bob, A, is pulled to one side and released to swing freely. The horizontal support responds to the motion and, in swaying back and forth in step with A, acts to set the other pendulum swinging. The response of pendulum B to this forced vibra-

tion depends upon the relative lengths of the two pendulums. If there is considerable difference in their lengths, the response is very slight. The closer they are to the same length the greater is the response.

When A and B have the same length, their natural periods become equal, and B responds to the swaying support and swings with a large amplitude. It responds in sympathy with the driving pendulum A. This is a case of *resonance*, a phenomenon that occurs only if two objects have the same natural frequency of vibration.

If two violin strings are tuned to the same frequency and one is set vibrating, the other stationed some distance away will soon pick up the vibrations and give out the same note. This also is a case of resonance.

Another experimental demonstration of resonance is illustrated in Fig. B. Two tun-

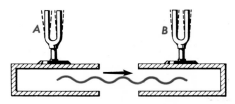

Fig. B. Tuning forks mounted on resonator boxes for demonstrating resonance.

ing forks with exactly the same pitch are mounted on separate hollow boxes as shown. Fork *A* is first set vibrating for a moment and then stopped by touching the prongs with the fingers. Fork *B* will then be found vibrating. Taking into account the hollow boxes, whose purpose it is to act as sounding boards and intensify the sound, the explanation is quite simple. Each sound pulse emerging from the box with each vibration of fork *A* passes into the other box, pushing out the sides at just the right time to make the prongs of fork *B* move in the same direction.

Beat Notes. When two notes of slightly different pitch are sounded together, beats are heard. This phenomenon is used in organ pipes to produce the familiar vibrato effect. Two pipes tuned to slightly different frequencies are used for every note.

The phenomenon of beats may also be demonstrated by two tuning forks mounted as shown in Fig. B. One fork is made slightly out of tune with the other by looping rubber bands *tightly* around the prongs. If the two forks are sounded simultaneously, the loudness, or *intensity,* of the sound rises and falls periodically. This is illustrated by means of vibration graphs as shown in Fig. C. The upper curve represents the amplitude of the sound vibrations arriving at the ear from one fork, and the second curve the

vibrations from the other. Both waves arriving at the ear are first in phase, *i.e.,* in step with each other, then out of phase, then in phase, then out of phase, etc.

The resultant action of these two waves on the eardrum is represented by the third curve. When the waves are in phase, the resultant has a large amplitude equal to the sum of the amplitudes of the two. When they are out of phase, the amplitude becomes zero. The number of beats per second, N, is determined by the difference between n_2 and n_1, the respective frequencies of the two sources producing the sound:

$$N = n_2 - n_1 \qquad (1)$$

When the beat frequency lies between about 1 and 6 vibrations per second, the ear perceives an intertone representing an average of n_1 and n_2, but periodically waxing and waning in intensity. As the beat frequency increases, the smooth rise and fall gives way to a succession of pulses, then to a sensation of roughness. Finally two clearly perceived tones are heard, one of which has a pitch corresponding to the beat frequency.

The Doppler Effect. Everyone has at some time, perhaps without realizing it, observed the *Doppler effect.* The sounding horn of a car passing at high speed on the highway exhibits this phenomenon. The

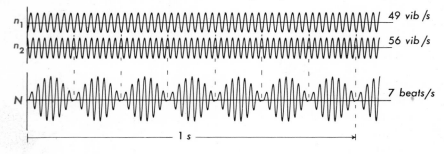

Fig. C. Wave graphs illustrating how beat notes are produced by two different frequencies.

pitch of the horn, as the car goes by, drops as much as two whole notes on the musical scale. A similar observation can be made by listening to the roar of the motor of a racing car as it approaches and recedes from an observer at the race track. The motor seems to slow down as it passes by. Again, the pitch of the whistle on a fast-moving train sounds higher as the train approaches the observer than it does after the train has passed by.

This change in pitch is due to the relative motions of the source of sound and the observer. To see how this produces the effect, consider the following example. In blowing its whistle, a train at rest sends out waves traveling with the same velocity in all directions. To all stationary observers, no matter in which direction they are located, the true pitch of the whistle is heard, because just as many waves arrive at the ear per second as there are waves leaving the whistle. If, on the other hand, the train is moving as shown in Fig. D, the whistle is

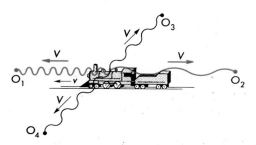

Fig. D. The Doppler effect. The pitch of a whistle on a fast-moving train sounds higher to an observer in front of the train, lower to an observer in back, and normal to observers off at the sides.

moving away from the waves traveling to the rear and toward the waves traveling forward. The result is that the waves behind are considerably drawn out while those in front are crowded together. With

each new wave sent out by the source, the train is farther from the preceding wave sent out to the rear and nearer to the one sent out ahead. Since the velocity of sound is the same in all directions, an observer at O_1, therefore, hears more waves per second and an observer at O_2 hears fewer.

To an observer O_3 or O_4, at right angles and at some little distance from the moving source, the pitch remains unchanged until the source has moved beyond its perpendicular position in respect to the observer. For these side positions, the source is momentarily neither approaching nor receding from the observer, so that approximately the same number of waves are received per second as there are waves leaving the source.

The general relation for the Doppler effect is given by the following single equation:

$$N_o = n_s \frac{V \pm v_o}{V \pm v_s} \qquad (2)$$

where N_o is the frequency heard by the observer, n_s is the frequency of the source, V is the velocity of sound, v_s the velocity of the source, and v_o the velocity of the observer.

To decide whether to use the plus or minus sign in Eq. (2) requires that a decision be made as to whether the observer will hear more vibrations per second as the result of the relative motion between himself and the sound source. To make N_o larger than n_s will require that the fraction $V \pm v_o / V \pm v_s$ be larger than one. To make it smaller, the reverse would have to be true. The numerical value of the fraction can be changed in the right direction by either adding or subtracting v_o and v_s.

Example. A racing car passes the grandstand traveling at a speed of 150 mi/hr. (a) If the sound from the exhaust has a frequency of 540 vibrations/sec, what frequency is heard by the audience as the car approaches the grandstand? (b) What frequency is heard by a car next to the track going 30 mi/hr in the opposite direction toward the racer? Assume the speed of sound to be 1120 ft/sec.

Solution. (a) Because the sound is approaching the observers, they will hear more vibrations per second than the actual sound source. The fraction $\dfrac{V \pm v_o}{V \pm v_s}$ must then be made larger than one in order to make N_o larger. Because the observers are not moving, $v_o = 0$. Therefore, v_s, which is 150 mi/hr or 220 ft/sec, must be subtracted from V to give the correct value to the fraction:

$$N_o = \frac{540(1120 \pm 0)}{1120 - 220}$$

$$N_o = 672 \ \frac{\text{vibrations}}{\text{sec}}$$

(b) In this case, as before, the observer will hear even more vibrations per second and, therefore, v_o must be added:

$$N_o = \frac{540(1120 + 44)}{1120 - 220}$$

$$N_o = \frac{540(1164)}{900}$$

$$N_o = 698 \ \frac{\text{vibrations}}{\text{sec}}$$

Suppose that a sound source is approaching a stationary observer at a velocity $v_s = 2V$. Here, $v_o = 0$ and v_s is $-$. This is an interesting case, because n_o is the negative of n_s. The observer hears the sound backward, as if played backward on a tape recorder, and it is heard after the source has passed him.

QUESTIONS

1. A violin note shattering a glass, and a marching patrol destroying a bridge are both examples of resonance. In each case, describe the conditions that cause the described effects.
2. In Fig. B, are the resonator boxes necessary? Explain.
3. The famous tenor Enrico Caruso could break a glass tumbler with his voice. Explain the physics of this phenomenon.
4. Several large bridges have been destroyed by winds of a certain velocity. What did the engineers who designed these otherwise strong structures overlook?
5. Make a sketch of two waves of slightly different wave lengths, and show how the beats can be graphically constructed.
6. (a) If two notes differ by 2 cycles/sec, what do you hear? (b) If they differ by a large amount, what do you hear?
7. (a) How is the principle of beats used by piano tuners? (b) Is this a very accurate method of tuning?
8. Does it make any difference to the Doppler effect whether the observer or the sound source is in motion? Explain.
9. If an observer is receding from a source of sound, what happens to the apparent pitch?
10. If the source recedes from the observer, what happens to the apparent pitch?
11. What conditions of motion will prevent the observer from hearing the sound from a source?
12. What general principle is used by police to trap speeders, using radar?

PROBLEMS

1. The A and E strings of a violin have frequencies of 440 and 660 vibrations/sec, respectively. Find their beat frequency.
2. When two cello strings are sounded, with 185 and 215 vibrations/sec, respectively, what is heard?
3. Three notes are sounded simultaneously: 264, 355, and 440 vibrations/sec. (a) Taken in pairs, what three beat frequencies are produced? (b) List the notes and beat frequencies in the order of increasing frequency.
4. Radio waves exhibit the same properties as all waves. What sound would you expect to hear if two radio stations of 1020 and 1023 kilocycles/sec were picked up simultaneously on a radio receiver?
5. A train approaching a station at 45 mi/hr (66 ft/sec) blows its whistle of 320 vibrations/sec. What frequency is heard (a) in the station and (b) by a stationary observer behind the train? Assume the speed of sound to be 1100 ft/sec.
6. The horn of a car is blown as the car approaches an intersection at 60 mi/hr. If the horn has a frequency of 220 vibrations/sec, and the velocity of sound is 1100 ft/sec, what frequency is heard by an observer standing at the intersection? (*Note:* 60 mi/hr = 88 ft/sec.)
7. The siren of a ranger station along the highway is sounded with a frequency of 550 vibrations/sec. What frequency is heard by motorists traveling 60 mi/hr along the highway if they are (a) approaching and (b) receding from the station? Assume the speed of sound to be 1120 ft/sec.
8. An airplane flying close to the ground at 320 mi/hr produces an engine roar of 500 vibrations/sec. What frequency is heard by a ground observer when the plane is (a) approaching and (b) receding? Assume sound to travel 1150 ft/sec.
9. Two cars approach each other from the opposite directions on the highway, when one sounds his horn with a frequency of 200 vibrations/sec. If they are both traveling at 60 mi/hr (88 ft/sec), what frequency is heard in the other car when they are (a) approaching and (b) receding? Assume sound to travel 1140 ft/sec.
10. Assume you had a device that could measure the frequency of sound accurately and instantly and that a police car with a siren of 500 vibrations/sec was picked up by you as having a frequency of 550 vibrations/sec. (a) What was the speed of the car if the speed of sound at this time was 1120 ft/sec? (b) Is the car coming toward or away from you?

PROJECTS

1. Develop an experiment that would illustrate resonance.
2. Devise an experiment that will illustrate beats.
3. Devise an experiment that would demonstrate the Doppler principle.
4. Make a stereo tape-recording of actual examples of the Doppler principle.

SOUND

Lesson 54 *SOUND ENERGY AND HEARING*

Intensity of Sound. There are three fundamental characteristics of all sounds: (1) *intensity*, (2) *pitch*, and (3) *tone quality*. The intensity of sound is characterized by its loudness and is measured scientifically by the amount of energy in a given volume of the space through which the sound is traveling. In other words, sound waves constitute a flow of energy through matter. This may be demonstrated by an experiment, arranged as shown in Fig. A. A vibrating

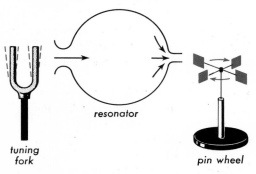

Fig. A. A pin wheel may be set rotating by sound waves from tuning fork, demonstrating that sound waves have energy.

tuning fork is placed near one opening of a Helmholtz* resonator and a very lightly constructed pin wheel is placed near the other. Air pulses from the vibrating prongs of the fork traveling through the resonator

* Hermann Helmholtz (1821-1894), noted German physicist, made outstanding contributions to the subjects of light, sound, and electricity. Probably his greatest contribution was his explanation of tone quality in musical notes. He demonstrated that quality depends upon the number and intensity of the overtones or harmonics present in the musical tone.

come out reinforced at the other opening and strike the vanes of the pin wheel, setting it in motion. When the fork is removed, the pin wheel stops rotating.

Loudness is a subjective measurement of sound power and is, therefore, a sensory magnitude. Intensity, on the other hand, is an objective measurement of the sound power.

One method of specifying the intensity of a sound is to state the amount of energy flowing through unit area per second. Because the rate of flow of energy in most common sounds is extremely small, the ordinary unit of power, the *watt*, is too large to be practical. Consequently, a unit one million times smaller, the *microwatt*, is used. One microwatt equals 10^{-6} watt, which is equivalent to 10^{-6} joules/sec, or 10 ergs/sec.

Sound intensity is defined as the power flowing through a unit area taken normal to the direction of the waves. See Fig. B.

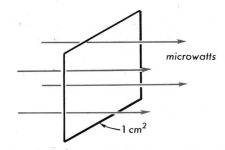

Fig. B. Sound intensity is measured in microwatts of power flowing through 1 cm² of area.

A common method of specifying intensity is to compare the power in a given sound with the power in another. *When the power in one sound is ten times that in another, the ratio of intensity is said to be 1 bel.* The *bel* is named in honor of Alexander Graham Bell, the inventor of the electric telephone. According to this definition, an intensity scale in bels is—

$$E/E_o = 1 \quad 10 \quad 100 \quad 1000 \quad 10,000$$
$$\text{bels} \quad 0 \quad 1 \quad 2 \quad 3 \quad 4$$

where E is the intensity, or power, of one sound and E_o that of another.

According to these figures, a sound with 1000 times the power of another is 3 bels louder.

Because the *bel* represents large differences in intensity, a smaller unit, the *decibel*, or *db*, has been introduced and used by telephone and radio engineers, as well as by physicians (ear specialists). According to this smaller unit, the bel is divided into ten equal ratios in the following way:

Table 1. Relative Power and Relative Intensity

Relative Power E/E_o	Relative Intensity, in Decibels (db)
1.00	0
1.26	1
1.58	2
2.00	3
2.51	4
3.16	5
3.98	6
5.01	7
6.31	8
7.94	9
10.0	10

Each power ratio in the first column is 26% greater than the preceding value. Because such a change is just detectable by the human ear, the decibel is considered a practical unit.

The sounds from several common sources are compared in different units, as follows:

Table 2. Relative Intensities of Sounds

	Sound Level in Decibels	Intensity in Microwatts/cm²
threshold of hearing.	0	10^{-10}
rustling leaves.....	20	10^{-8}
talking (at 3 ft)....	40	10^{-6}
noisy office or store.	60	10^{-4}
subway car.......	100	1
threshold of pain....	120	100

An audiogram for the normal human ear is given in Fig. C. The lower curve gives the faintest sounds that can be heard and the upper curve the loudest that can be heard without pain. It will be noted that the ear is most sensitive to frequencies between 2000 and 4000 cycles and that the sensitivity diminishes rapidly at higher and lower frequencies.

As a practical matter, sound experts have adopted as a zero level of sound intensity, $E_o = 10^{-10}$ microwatts/cm² at a frequency of 1000 cycles. This is the lower limit of audibility of the average human being for a thousand cycle note.

Inverse Square Law. Theory indicates and experiments prove that the intensity of sound is inversely proportional to the square of the distance from the source. As an equation—

$$E = \frac{E_o}{d^2} \tag{1}$$

where E_o is the intensity at unit distance (1 cm, 1 m, or 1 ft) and E is the intensity at any distance, d, in the same units. This is just one of many instances in which the *inverse square law* operates in nature.

If S in Fig. D represents a source of sound, the waves travel outward in straight

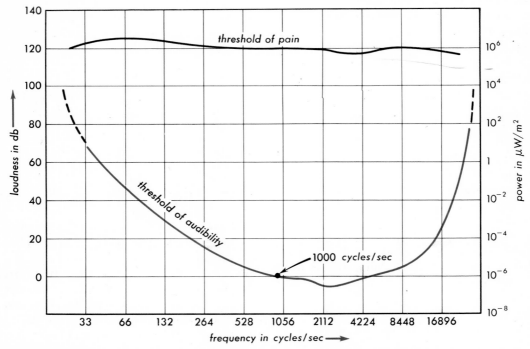

Fig. C. Audiogram of the average human being, showing the threshold of hearing for different frequencies of sound.

lines. Whatever sound energy flows through area A at 1 m, the same energy will flow through area B at 2 m, and area C at 3 m. Because these areas have the ratios 1:4:9, the energy flow per second, through unit area at each distance, will be E_o, $E_o/4$, and $E_o/9$, respectively.

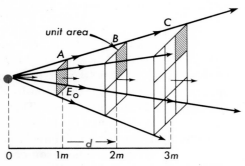

Fig. D. Illustrating the inverse-square law.

The Human Ear. The ear is by far the most important and most universal receiver of sound. It has an enormous range of frequency and sensitivity, and can distinguish between musical tones whose frequencies differ by less than 1%. In addition to this, it can analyze some sounds into their component notes and concentrate on these notes one at a time.

The outer ear, see Fig. E, consists of the pinna, F, used to collect the sound waves from the outside, and the ear canal, M, to carry the waves to the eardrum, D.

The middle ear contains three small bones H, A, and B called the *hammer* (malleus), *anvil* (incus), and *stirrup* (stapes), respectively, and is connected to the nasopharynx and, thus, to the outside air by means of a small canal, the *Eustachian tube*,

E. The function of the three bones is to transmit the vibrations of the eardrum to the *oval window, O,* of the inner ear.

divided lengthwise into three parts by what are called the *spiral lamina* and *Reissner's membrane.* Cross sections of the cochlea are

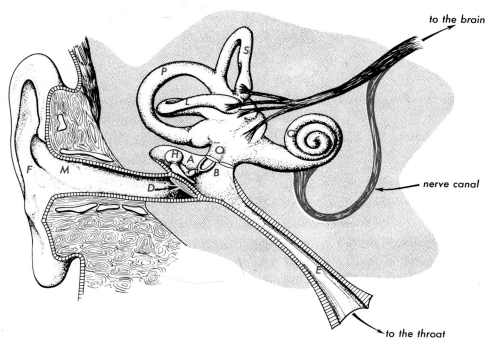

Fig. E. Cross section of the human ear.

The inner ear itself consists of two essential parts: the *cochlea, C,* and the *semicircular canals, P, L,* and *S.* In the cochlea are found the nerve endings which are stimulated by sound vibrations and give rise to the sense of hearing, and in the semicircular canals are the nerve endings that give rise to a sense of balance.

The entire inner ear is contained within the cavity of a solid bony structure, sometimes referred to as the *bony labyrinth.* This labyrinth is entirely filled with a watery liquid through which the sound vibrations from the outside are transmitted to the sensitive membranes of the cochlea. The cochlea consists of two and one-half turns of a spiral cavity shaped like a snail shell and

shown in Fig. F. Diagram (*a*) represents a section directly across one turn of the spiral, and diagram (*b*) a lengthwise cross section as it would appear if the cochlea could be straightened out.

Throughout the total length of the basilar membrane, which is just a little over 3 cm in length, there are about 30,000 nerve endings. This amounts to 1000 nerves per millimeter length, which must pass through the bony spiral lamina and into the cochlear nerve canal leading to the brain. The work of many experimentalists shows that the nerve endings nearest the oval window, where the sound vibrations enter the *scala vestibula,* respond to the notes of highest pitch, whereas those at the farther end re-

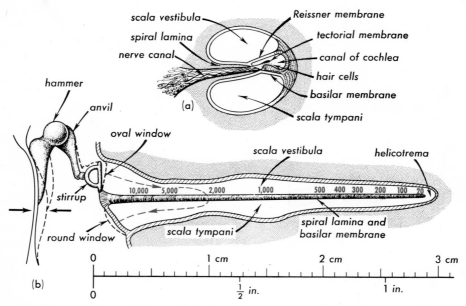

Fig. F. Detail of the cochlea of the human ear: (a) typical cross section and (b) straightened cochlea illustrating the various regions of the spiral lamina sensitive to sounds of various frequencies.

spond to those of lowest pitch. The various regions sympathetic to the entire frequency scale are shown in the diagram.

The eardrum and the bones of the middle ear act as a lever mechanism to decrease the amplitude of the vibrations from the air, a very light medium, to the liquid, a much more dense medium. This reduction in the motion gives rise to a pressure on the stirrup from 30 to 50 times the pressure on the eardrum. As the stirrup tips in and out with a low frequency, the entire liquid column from the oval window down the *scala vestibula* to the *helicotrema,* and back along the *scala tympani* to the *round window,* is set into vibration. Because liquids are practically noncompressible, the round

window moves out when the oval window and stirrup move in, and vice versa.

When a higher frequency, like 2000 vibrations/sec, is sounded, the vibrations in the liquid, set up by the motion of the stirrup at the oval window, travel the path shown by the dotted line in Fig. F, diagram (*b*). As the waves travel through the thin Reissner membrane and across the edge of the spiral lamina, there is a relative motion set up between the *basilar membrane* and the *tectorrial membrane,* causing the local hair cells to stimulate the nerve endings at their base. Somewhere in this stimulation and motion, part of the energy is transformed into electrical impulses, which travel along the cochlear nerve canal to the brain.

QUESTIONS

1. What is the difference between the intensity of a sound and its loudness?
2. Why is sound intensity usually measured (a) in decibels rather than bels? (b) in microwatts/cm^2 rather than watts/cm^2?

3. (a) In what sense is the decibel a relative unit? (b) In what sense is it an absolute unit?

4. In what way does our hearing ability change as the intensity increases from 20 decibels to 40 decibels?

5. What is the purpose of the three small bones in the inner ear?

6. What mechanism in the inner ear transforms sound waves to electrical impulses?

7. (a) What is the purpose of the round window? (b) How does the changing pressure on the outer eardrum compare with that in the cochlea?

8. What is the nature of the impulses that travel through the nerve canal from the cochlea to the brain?

9. A tree falls in a forest miles from any human being. Discuss whether a loud sound has been produced by its fall.

10. Why is it dangerous to attempt to clean out the wax from your ears by doing it yourself?

11. What condition might be causing one to be losing good hearing that could be easily corrected?

12. It is common for older people to lose their hearing, starting with the higher frequencies. From a study of the structure of the ear, can you explain why this happens?

13. Why do many people complain of temporary loss of hearing when making a rapid descent from a mountain?

PROBLEMS

1. If one sound is 8 db louder than another, what are their relative powers?

2. If one sound is 15 db more intense than another, what are their relative powers?

3. If one sound is 50 db more intense than the other, what are their relative powers?

4. What minimum absolute intensity of sound in decibels is required for the average human being to hear at a frequency of 132 cycles/sec? See Fig. C.

5. If the intensity of sound 1 ft from a source is 5 microwatts/cm², what is the intensity at a distance of 40 ft?

6. If the intensity of a sound 2.5 m from a source is 1 microwatt/cm², what is the intensity at a distance of 1000 m?

7. The noise from a racing-car motor is 60 db at a distance of 1 m. How loud is it at a distance of 10 m?

8. Two people are listening to a band playing in the park. One person is 100 ft from the band while the other is 2000 ft away. (a) How many times more sound energy will the closest person receive? (b) Will the music sound louder to the closer person?

9. What is the increase in sound intensity of a noisy office with respect to talking at 3 ft?

10. At a distance of 10 m from a jet plane, the noise level is 60 db. What is the noise level at the ground when the plane flies overhead at 1000 m?

11. Plot a graph of relative power, E/E_0 (vertically), against relative intensity in decibels (horizontally). Plot from 0 to 10 db only.

12. Plot a graph as outlined in Problem 11, but for the vertical scale, use the divisions of the *A* scale on the slide of a slide rule. Use centimeter divisions for the horizontal scale.

PROJECTS

1. Obtain the kit on speech synthesis from the Bell Telephone Co. Try to develop recognizable sounds with it.
2. Develop a simple audiometer to check the hearing of your classmates. You may be able to calibrate your device with the standard machine owned by the school health department.

SOUND

Lesson 55 *STANDING WAVES AND VIBRATING STRINGS*

In this lesson, we will begin the study of musical sounds as they are produced by musical instruments of all kinds. Musical instruments in general can be classified under one of three headings: *strings, winds,* and *percussions.*

In taking up the subject of stringed instruments, we may begin by considering the waves produced on a string or rope as one end is moved up and down with simple harmonic motion.

Reflection of a Traveling Wave. If a rope is given a single shake, a transverse pulse will be generated and will travel along the rope, as shown in Fig. A(*a*). If one end of the rope is firmly anchored, the pulse will, upon reaching that end, generate a reflected pulse with equal but opposite amplitude and velocity. This reflected pulse comes about as a result of the requirement that the amplitude of the rope must always be zero where it is anchored. As seen in Fig. A, the generation of a negative and

oppositely moving pulse will insure that the incident and reflected amplitude will add to zero at the end during the encounter. The dashed-line curves show the continuation of the initial and reflected pulse, and the solid curve shows their sum, which is the actual shape of the rope.

Standing Waves. Standing waves in a string may be produced by two trains of waves of the same frequency and wave length traveling in opposite directions. One of the ways of accomplishing these conditions is shown in Fig. B. The two ends of the string or rope are anchored. A wave train moving to the right and its reflection moving to the left are shown at the top of Fig. B. If there is an integral number of half-wave lengths between the ends, it is seen that the two waves reflect into each other at each end. The rope will sustain such waves as the amplitudes at the fixed points add to zero, as they must. The amplitude at the other points along the rope

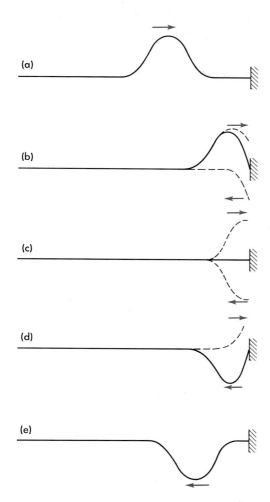

(a)

(b)

(c)

(d)

(e)

Fig. A. Reflection of a traveling pulse in a string with one fixed end.

tude, are called *antinodes.* An entire wave section between two consecutive nodes is called a *loop.* Note carefully that each loop has a length of $\frac{1}{2}\lambda$.

Stringed Instruments. There are two principal reasons why stringed instruments of different kinds do not sound alike as regards *tone quality*—first, the design of the instrument, and second, the method by which the strings are set into vibration. The violin and cello are bowed with long strands of tightly stretched horsehair, the harp and guitar are plucked with the fingers or picks, and the piano is hammered with light felt mallets.

Under very special conditions, a string may be made to vibrate with nodes at either end as shown in Fig. C. In this state of motion the string gives rise to its lowest possible note, and it is said to be vibrating with its *fundamental frequency.*

Every musician knows that a thick heavy string has a lower natural pitch than a thin one, that a short string has a higher pitch than a long one, and that the tighter a string is stretched the higher is its pitch. The G string of a violin, for example, is thicker and heavier than the high-pitched E string, and the *bass* strings of the piano are longer and heavier than the strings of the *treble.*

Harmonics. When a professional violinist plays *in harmonics,* he touches the strings lightly at any one of various points and sets each one vibrating in two or more segments as shown in Fig. D. If a string is touched at the center, a node is formed at that point and the vibration frequency becomes double that of the fundamental. If the string is touched lightly at a point one-third the distance from the end, it will vibrate in three sections and have a frequency three times that of the fundamental.

are also arrived at by simply adding the amplitudes of the two traveling waves, as shown at the bottom of Fig. B.

The general appearance of the resulting standing wave will be that of dividing the rope into stationary sections of equal length as shown. The dark points, where the rope has no up-and-down motion, are called *nodes,* and the points halfway between, where the motion has the greatest ampli-

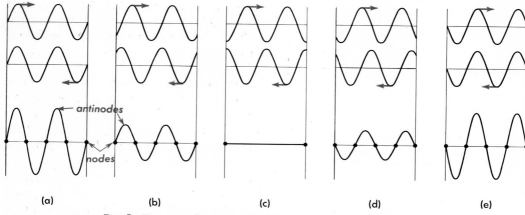

(a)   (b)   (c)   (d)   (e)

Fig. B. Two traveling waves add to produce a standing wave.

It is clear from these diagrams that the vibrating string of any musical instrument is an example of *standing waves* of the *transverse* character.

It is not difficult to set a string vibrating with its fundamental and several of its higher harmonics at the same time. This is accomplished by plucking or bowing the string near its end vigorously. As an illustration, a diagram of an ideal string, vibrat-

ing with two normal harmonics, or modes, at the same time, is shown in Fig. E. As the string vibrates in two loops with a fre-

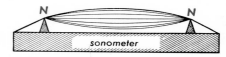

Fig. C. Single string vibrating with its fundamental frequency.

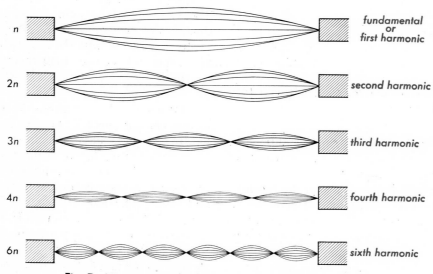

Fig. D. Vibration modes for strings of musical instruments.

Fig. E. String vibrating with its fundamental and second harmonic simultaneously.

quency $2n$, it also moves up and down as a single loop with the fundamental frequency, n.

The sound wave sent out by such a vibrating string is composed of two frequencies, the fundamental or first harmonic of frequency, n, and the second harmonic with the frequency, $2n$.

An interesting experiment with a vibrating string is illustrated in Fig. F. Light from an arc lamp is focused on the central section of a stretched steel string, which, except for a small vertical slot, is masked by a screen. An image of the slot and the string section seen through it is focused by a sec-

ond lens, after reflection from a rotating mirror, on a screen. As the string vibrates up and down, only a blurred image of the short section of string is seen; but when the mirror is rotated, the wire section draws out a clearly visible curve, W.

If the string is plucked gently near the center, a smooth wave form (a) is drawn out on the screen; but if it is plucked hard near the end to produce a harsh sounding note, the wave form is more complex as shown in (b). In the first case, the string is vibrating mainly in its fundamental mode, while in the second case, other harmonics are also present.

The Theory of Vibrating Strings. As a string vibrates with *transverse waves*, it strikes air molecules all around it, sending periodic impulses through the air as *longitudinal waves*. As we have already seen,

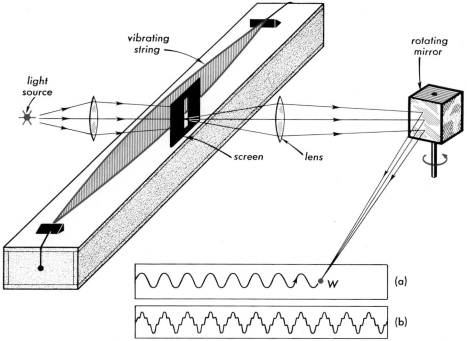

Fig. F. Experiment for observing the detailed vibrations of stretched string.

three measurable quantities are to be associated with such waves. These are *velocity, V, frequency, n,* and *wave length, λ.*

These three factors are related to each other by the equation—

$$V = n\lambda \qquad (1)$$

The length of one wave, λ, multiplied by the number of waves passing by per second, *n*, is equal to the distance a wave travels in one second, V.

Experiments show that the velocity in m/sec of transverse waves along a rope or string under tension is given by—

$$V = \sqrt{F/m} \qquad (2)$$

where *F* is the tension in newtons and *m* is the mass per unit length of string in Kg/m. When standing waves are produced, the distance, *L*, between any two consecutive nodes is just equal to half a wave length, ½λ. Accordingly—

$$\lambda = 2L \qquad (3)$$

To obtain an equation for the fundamental frequency of a vibrating string, the general equation $V = n\lambda$ is used. Solving this equation for *n*, we obtain—

$$n = \frac{V}{\lambda}$$

If we then substitute the above values for V and λ, we obtain—

$$n = \frac{\sqrt{F/m}}{2L} \qquad (4)$$

Accurate measurements with vibrating strings and musical instruments confirm this equation.

QUESTIONS

1. To what classes do the following instruments belong: cello, trumpet, piano?
2. If a vibrating string is touched lightly at a point one-third the distance from the end, it has the frequency three times the fundamental. Could it also have other frequencies? Explain.
3. (a) What kinds of waves are involved with stringed instruments? (b) What different ways are strings made to vibrate?
4. Derive Eq. (4) for a string vibrating in the third harmonic.
5. (a) How many natural vibration frequencies are possible for any one string? (b) What are they called? (c) How are the frequencies related?
6. (a) How are different notes on a musical scale produced by one string? (b) What is a string's lowest frequency?
7. (a) Upon what three factors does the frequency of a string depend? (b) Write the equation.
8. (a)What are the differences between the treble and bass strings of a piano? (b) Why do bass strings look like coiled springs?
9. Where will the amplitude of vibration be greatest in a string that is vibrating at its second harmonic?
10. Will there be a node or antinode at the places where the string is attached in a cello? Explain.

11. Because the strings of a violin are very thin, the number of air molecules it causes to vibrate is relatively small. What method is used to make the transmitted energy more efficient and, therefore, louder?

12. (a) What basic principle of vibrating strings does a violinist use when he plays his instrument? (b) What principle does he use when he tunes up?

13. (a) What is the difference between a traveling wave and a standing wave? (b) Give an example of each.

14. Make a diagram of a standing wave on a string 2λ long. Show at least three different amplitudes. Label the nodes and antinodes, and identify a wave length. Count the number of nodes and antinodes.

15. If a standing wave is at full amplitude at a certain time, what does it look like $\frac{1}{4}$ period later?

PROBLEMS

1. The end of a string is moved up and down with a frequency of 124 vibrations/sec. If the waves produced have a velocity of 42 m/sec, what is their wave length?

2. What frequency applied to a string will produce waves 25 cm long if the wave velocity is 160 m/sec?

3. The frequency of a certain string is 440 vibrations/sec with a certain tension. What will the frequency be if the tension is doubled?

4. The A and E strings of a violin have fundamental frequencies of 440 vibrations/sec and 660 vibrations/sec, respectively. Find the frequencies of their first five harmonics.

5. The lowest-pitched note produced by a B♭ cornet has a frequency of 116.7 vibrations/sec. What would you expect for the frequencies of the first eight harmonics?

6. A 3-m long string has a mass density of .05 gm/cm, and is under a tension of 400 newtons. What is the frequency of the fifth harmonic?

7. Waves travel along a stretched steel wire at 50 m/sec. What is the tension in the wire if its mass is 0.08 gm/cm length?

8. If a long wire of mass 0.05 gm/cm is put under a tension of 500 newtons, with what velocity will transverse waves be propagated?

9. A piano string 20 cm long has a frequency of 1056 vibrations/sec and a mass of 0.008 Kg/m length. Find its tension in newtons.

10. Find the mass per unit length of a violin string 35 cm long if, under a tension of 500 newton, it has a frequency of 440 vibrations/sec.

11. A violin string 35 cm long has a mass of 0.066 gm/cm length. Find the tension in newtons if the frequency is 440 vibrations/sec.

12. Make a series of five sketches, as in Fig. B, showing how two traveling waves on a one-half wave-length string are equivalent to the string vibrating in its fundamental mode.

PROJECTS

1. Use an oscilloscope and filters to show the number and amplitude of harmonics in the sound produced by a number of stringed instruments.
2. Make a small organ using tuned tube or transistor oscillators.
3. Devise an experiment to show that a vibrating string has places where it is not vibrating at all, even though it is vibrating vigorously at other places.

SOUND

Lesson 56 WIND AND PERCUSSION INSTRUMENTS

Longitudinal Standing Waves. When a source of sound waves is located at one end of a hollow pipe that is closed at the other end, as shown in Fig. A, a continuous train

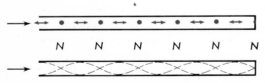

Fig. A. Standing-wave diagrams for a resonating air column.

of longitudinal waves travels down the pipe, reflects from the other end, and travels back toward the source. If the frequency of the source can be continually increased over a considerable range, the pipe will remain quiet most of the time. At certain definite frequencies, however, it will sing out in resonance to the overlapping waves.

Under such resonant conditions as these, longitudinal standing waves exist within the pipe. At certain equidistant points, N, along the pipe, the air molecules remain essentially undisturbed, while at points halfway between they move back and forth with the frequency of the source.

These points, just as with vibrating strings, are called *nodes* and *antinodes,* respectively, and whatever the total number of each may be, a node always forms at the closed end of a pipe and an antinode at the open end.

Because longitudinal standing waves are difficult to represent in diagrams, it is convenient in drawings to indicate nodes and antinodes as if they were standing transverse waves. See the lower diagram, Fig. A.

The existence of standing waves in a resonating air column may be demonstrated by a long hollow tube filled with illuminating gas, as shown in Fig. B. Entering through an adjustable plunger at the left, the gas escapes through tiny holes spaced at regular intervals in a row along the top. Sound waves from an organ pipe enter the gas column by setting into vibration a thin paper sheet stretched over the right-hand end. When resonance is attained by sliding the plunger to the correct position, the small gas flames will appear as shown. Where the nodes occur in the vibrating gas column, the gas molecules are not moving; at these points the pressure is high and the flames are tallest. Halfway between are the antinodes—regions where the molecules vibrate

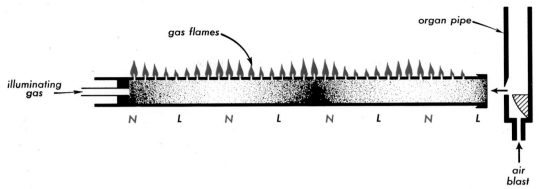

Fig. B. Standing waves in a long tube containing illuminating gas.

back and forth with large amplitudes, and the flames are low. Bernoulli's principle is the chief explanation of the pressure differences, for where the velocity of the molecules is high, the pressure is low, and where the velocity is low, the pressure is high.

Vibrating Air Columns. When a compression reaches a closed end of a pipe, it cannot continue, and must reflect back down the tube. This reflection corresponds to a node, because the air is in contact with the pipe's end, which is fixed.

When a compression reaches an open end of a pipe, it is not reflected as a compression as in the closed pipe. Instead, it spreads out rapidly into the surrounding air, thereby starting a rarefaction back through the pipe. This means that a compression is reflected from the open end as a rarefaction, rather than as a compression. This reflection corresponds to an antinode, rather than a node.

In all vibrating air columns, an antinode always forms at an open end and a node at a closed end.

The various modes in which air columns may vibrate in open or closed pipes are shown in Fig. C. Starting at the top, a pipe open at both ends may vibrate with (1) a single node at the middle and an antinode

at both ends, (2) two nodes and three antinodes, or (3) with three nodes and four antinodes, etc. On the other hand, a pipe closed at one end and open at the other may

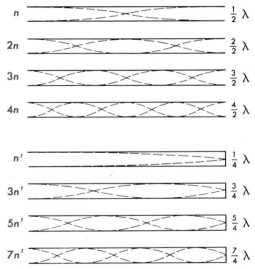

Fig. C. Resonating air columns, showing nodes and loops.

vibrate with (1) one node and one antinode, (2) two nodes and two antinodes, or (3) three nodes and three antinodes, etc.

Natural Frequencies. The various possible frequencies to which a pipe may resonate are definite and fixed in value and depend only upon the length of the pipe and the velocity of sound in air. If, for example, the pipes in Fig. C are all 2 ft long and the velocity of sound in air is 1120 ft/sec, the equation $V = n\lambda$ (Eq. 5, Lesson 51) shows that they will vibrate with the following respective frequencies:

n	$2n$	$3n$	$4n$
280	560	840	1120

n'	$3n'$	$5n'$	$7n'$
140	420	700	980

With an open pipe, the lowest possible vibration frequency is called the *fundamental*, and the others, $2n$, $3n$, $4n$, etc., which are whole-numbered multiples of the fundamental frequency, are called *harmonics*. With closed pipes, the lowest frequency is again the fundamental and the others with odd integral multiples, $3n'$, $5n'$, $7n'$, etc., are harmonics. All these vibration modes are referred to as natural modes and their corresponding frequencies as *natural frequencies. The fundamental is also called the first harmonic.*

Wind Instruments. Musical instruments often classified as *wind instruments* are usually divided into two subclasses: *woodwinds* and *brasses*. Under the heading of woodwinds, we find such instruments as the flute, piccolo, clarinet, bass clarinet, saxophone, bassoon, and contra bassoon, and under the brasses such instruments as the French horn, cornet, trumpet, tenor trombone, bass trombone, and tuba.

The various notes produced by most wind instruments are brought about by varying the length of the vibrating air column. This is illustrated by the organ pipes in Fig. D. The longer the pipe, the lower the fundamental frequency or pitch of the note. In a regular concert organ, the pipes vary in length from about 6 in. for highest note to almost 16 ft for the low For the middle octave of the musical sc the open-ended pipes vary from 2 ft

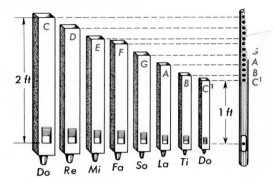

Fig. D. Organ pipes arranged in a musical scale. The longer the pipe, the lower is its fundamental frequency and pitch. The vibrating air column of the flute is terminated at various points by openings along the tube.

middle C to 1 ft for C^1 (high C), one octave higher. In the woodwinds, like the flute, the length of the column is varied by openings in the side of the instrument, and in many of the brasses, like the trumpet, by means of valves. A valve is a piston that, on being pressed down, throws in an additional length of tube.

The basic equation for sound waves through a gas was first derived by Newton and later modified by Laplace:

$$V = \sqrt{K\frac{P}{\rho}} \qquad (1)$$

where V is the wave velocity in cm/sec, P is the gas pressure in dynes/cm², ρ the density in gm/cm³, and K is a proportionality constant. For diatomic gases like air $K = 1.40$, for monatomic gases $K = 1.67$, and for triatomic gases $K = 1.33$.

For standing waves, the distance, L, between any two consecutive nodes, i.e., the length of one loop, is just equal to half a wave length, λ/2. Accordingly—

$$\lambda = 2L$$

Having the speed of the waves, V, and the wave length, λ, one can use the equation—

$$V = n\lambda$$

for all wind instruments.

Example. The longest organ pipe in a cathedral organ is 32 ft long. Find the frequency of the 5th harmonic if the speed of sound is 1140 ft/sec.

Solution. An organ pipe, like all wind instruments, resonates as a pipe open at both ends. Because the fifth harmonic has 5 nodes, the length (see Fig. C) is given by—

$$L = 5 \times \tfrac{1}{2}\lambda$$

Therefore—

$$\lambda = \tfrac{2}{5}L$$

The frequency is then given by—

$$f = \frac{V}{\lambda} = \frac{V}{\tfrac{2}{5}L}$$

$$= \frac{1140 \text{ ft/sec}}{.4 \times 32 \text{ ft}} = 89 \text{ vibrations/sec}$$

Edge Tones. The pitch of the note sounded by any wind instrument is determined by the vibration of an air column according to principles of resonance, but the method by which the air is set into vibration varies widely among instruments. In instruments like the saxophone, clarinet, oboe, and bassoon, air is blown against a thin strip of wood called a reed, setting it into vibration. In most of the brasses, the musician's lips are made to vibrate with certain required frequencies, while in certain woodwinds, like the flute and piccolo, and in organs and whistles, air is blown across the sharp edge of an opening near one end of the instrument, setting the air into vibration. A brief discussion of these

source vibrations is, therefore, important here.

When wind or a blast of air encounters a small obstacle, little whirlwinds are formed in the air stream behind the obstacle. This is illustrated by the cross section of a flue organ pipe in Fig. E. Whether

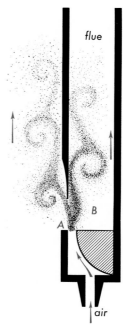

Fig. E. A steady stream of air blown across the lip of an organ pipe sets up whirlwinds along both sides of the partition.

the obstacle is long or small and round, the whirlwinds are formed alternately on the two sides as shown. The air stream at B waves back and forth, sending a pulse of air first up one side and then the other. Although the wind blows through the opening A as a continuous stream, the separate whirlwinds going up each side of the obstacle become periodic shocks to the surrounding air. Coming at perfectly regular intervals, these pulses give rise to a musical note often described as an *edge tone*.

The number of whirlwinds formed per second, and therefore the pitch of the edge tone, increases with the wind velocity. When the wind howls through the trees, the pitch of the note rises and falls, its frequency at any time denoting the speed of the wind. For a given wind speed, smaller objects give rise to higher pitched notes than large objects. A finely stretched wire or rubber band, when placed in an open window or in the wind, will be set into vibration and give out a musical note. Each whirlwind shock to the air reacts on the obstacle (the wire or rubber band), pushing it first to one side and then the other. These are the pushes that cause the rope of a flagpole to flap periodically in the breeze, while the waving of the flag at the top of a pole shows the whirlwinds that follow each other along each side.

Percussion Instruments. If a number of small sticks are dropped upon the floor, the sound that is heard is described as a noise. If one stick alone is dropped, one would also describe the sound as a noise, unless, of course, a set of sticks of varying length are arranged in order of length and each one dropped in its order. If this is done, one notices that each stick gives rise to a rather definite musical note and that the set of sticks could be cut to the proper lengths to form a musical scale. The use of vibrating rods in a musical instrument is found in the *xylophone*, the *marimba*, and the *triangle*. Standing waves in a rod, like those in a stretched string, may be any one of three different kinds: *transverse, longitudinal,* and *torsional.* Only the first two of these modes of vibration will be treated here.

Transverse waves in a rod are usually set up by supporting the rod at points near each end and striking it a blow at or near the center. As illustrated in Fig. F, the center and ends of the rod move up and down,

forming nodes at the two supports. Like a stretched string of a musical instrument, the shorter the rod, the higher its pitch, and the longer and heavier the rod, the lower its frequency of vibration and pitch.

Fig. F. Transverse vibrations of a uniform rod or bar.

The xylophone and the marimba are musical instruments based upon the *transverse vibrations* of wooden rods of different lengths. Mounted as shown in Fig. G, the

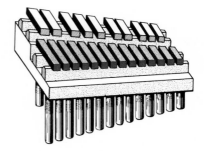

Fig. G. Diagram of the bars and pipes of a marimba.

longer rods produce the low notes and the shorter ones the high notes. The marimba differs from the xylophone in that it has a long straight hollow tube suspended vertically under each rod. Each tube is cut to such a length that the enclosed air column will resonate to the sound waves sent out by the rod directly above. Each resonator tube, being open at both ends, forms a node at its center.

An interesting demonstration of longitudinal waves in a solid is shown in Fig. H. A metal rod, about 4 mm in diameter and 1

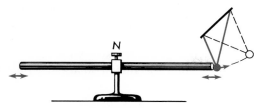

Fig. H. A long rod can be set to vibrate with standing longitudinal waves.

m long, is clamped tightly at the center in a rigid support. With a little alcohol or rosin on a cloth, the rod is stroked from the center toward the free end. After a few strokes the rod will sing out with a high-

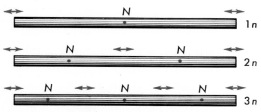

Fig. I. Longitudinal standing-wave modes of vibration for a uniform rod.

pitched note indicating it is vibrating. That the vibrations are longitudinal is shown by the bouncing of a small ball suspended by two cords at the far end.

Vibration modes giving rise to the first three harmonics of such a rod are shown in Fig. I. The top mode gives the lowest frequency note the rod can produce and corresponds to the *first harmonic*, or *fundamental*. The others correspond to the *second* and *third harmonics*, respectively.

Vibrating Plates. Although the drum or the cymbals should hardly be called musical instruments, they are used in nearly all large orchestras and bands. The noise given out by a vibrating drumhead or cymbal plate is in general due to the high intensity of certain characteristic harmonics. These harmonics in turn are due to the very complicated modes of vibration of the source.

Cymbals consist of two thin metal disks with handles at the centers. Upon being struck together, their edges are set into vibration with a clang. A drumhead, on the other hand, is a stretched membrane of

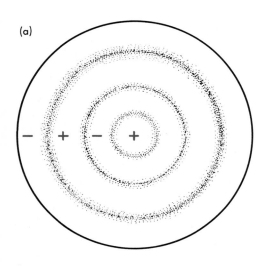

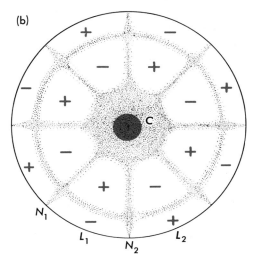

Fig. J. Chladni's sand figures showing the nodes and loops of (a) a vibrating drumhead (clamped at the edge) and (b) a vibrating cymbal plate (clamped at the center).

leather held tight at the periphery, and is set into vibration by being struck a blow at or near the center.

To illustrate the complexity of the vibrations of a circular plate, two typical sand patterns are shown in Fig. J. The sand pattern method of studying the motions of plates was invented in the eighteenth century by Chladni, a German physicist. A thin, circular, metal plate is clamped at the center, C, and sand is sprinkled over the top surface. Then, while touching the rim of the plate with the fingers at two points, N_1 and N_2, a cello bow is drawn down over the edge at a point L. Nodes are formed at the stationary points, N_1 and N_2, and antinodes

in the regions of L_1 and L_2. The grains of sand bounce away from the loops and into the nodes, the regions of no motion. At one instant, the regions marked with a $+$ all move up, while the regions marked with a $-$ all move down. Half a vibration later the $+$ regions are moving down and the $-$ regions up. Such diagrams are called *Chladni's sand figures*.

With cymbal plates held tightly at the center by means of handles, a node is always formed there, and antinodes are always formed at the periphery. With a drumhead, on the other hand, the periphery is always a node and the center is sometimes but not always an antinode.

QUESTIONS

1. (a) What kinds of waves are involved in wind instruments? (b) What different ways are they set into motion?
2. (a) How many natural vibration frequencies are possible with a single air column? (b) What are these frequencies called? (c) How are these frequencies related?
3. (a) What is the difference between a longitudinal standing wave and a longitudinal traveling wave? (b) Give an example of each.
4. How do the pipe ends affect the possible harmonic frequencies?
5. Why is there always a node at the closed end of an air column?
6. Make a series of sketches, similar to Fig. C, showing the amplitudes of the first four harmonics in a resonating air column that is closed at both ends.
7. How are the notes of a musical scale produced in most wind instruments?
8. (a) Upon what factors does the velocity of sound waves in a gas depend? (b) Which of these factors are the same in all wind instruments? (c) Which ones, if any, are different?
9. (a) How is wave length related to loop length in a vibrating air column? (b) How can one calculate the fundamental frequency of an air column of known length?
10. (a) What are edge tones? (b) What natural sounds are produced by edge tones?
11. (a) Can you name four percussion instruments commonly used in symphony orchestras? (b) How are such instruments made to vibrate?
12. (a) Are standing waves involved in the vibration modes of percussion instruments? (b) Are nodes and antinodes formed?
13. Assume that you had a tuning fork of known frequency and a pipe with a movable piston in it. Describe how you could measure the velocity of sound.

14. The sound that is picked up by a microphone and recorded on a phonograph appears as a very wavy curve. If you could unravel the groove and plot it on graph paper, what would this actually represent?

15. Could you tell the difference between a trumpet and a violin if you could only hear the fundamental sounds they produce? Explain.

PROBLEMS

1. Find the frequency of (a) the fundamental and (b) the third harmonic of a 16-ft organ pipe, closed at one end and open at the other. Assume the speed of sound to be 1100 ft/sec.

2. An air column 24 in. long is open at one end. What is its lowest natural frequency if the speed of sound is 1120 ft/sec?

3. The lowest frequency of an air column open at both ends is 264 vibrations/sec. What is its length if the speed of sound is 1120 ft/sec?

4. The third harmonic of a resonating air column 3.24 ft long and open at both ends is 528 vibrations/sec. Find the speed of sound.

5. What is the shortest length of pipe, closed at both ends, that will resonate to a frequency of 440 vibrations/sec? Assume the speed of sound to be 1100 ft/sec.

6. Calculate the speed of sound in nitrogen at normal atmospheric pressure. The density of nitrogen is 1.25×10^{-3} gm/cm³.

7. Calculate the speed of sound in helium at normal atmospheric pressure. The density of helium is 1.78×10^{-4} gm/cm³.

8. Find the speed of sound in carbon dioxide at 0°C and 76 cm of mercury pressure. The density is 1.98×10^{-3} gm/cm³.

9. An air column, 1.6 m long and open at both ends, is filled with helium. What would be its natural fundamental frequency? Assume the speed of sound to be 980 m/sec.

10. The pressure of air in a tank is doubled. What effect would this have on the speed of the sound in that tank?

11. Draw a graph of a fundamental sound wave of 100 cycles/sec. On the same graph, show a second harmonic with ⅓ the amplitude. What is the shape of the sound wave you would hear?

PROJECTS

1. Using pieces of hardwood, make a small xylophone. Try to develop a formula to help determine the correct length necessary to produce a given tone.

2. Using an oscilloscope and an audio oscillator, measure the velocity of sound as accurately as you can.

SOUND

Lesson 57 *THE QUALITY OF SOUND*

From the scientific point of view, the musical scale is based upon the relative frequencies of different sound waves. The frequencies of the various notes are so chosen that they produce the greatest amount of *harmony*. Two or more notes are said to be *harmonious* or *concordant* if they are pleasing to the ear. If they are not pleasant to hear, they are *discordant*.

Quality of Musical Notes. Although two musical notes have the same pitch and intensity, they may differ widely in tone quality. Tone quality is determined by the number and intensity of the harmonics present. This is illustrated by a detailed examination of either the vibrating source or of the sound waves emerging from the source. There are numerous experimental methods by which this is accomplished.

A relatively convenient and simple demonstration is given in Fig. F in Lesson 55, where the vibrating source of sound is a stretched piano string. If the string is made to vibrate with its fundamental alone, its own motion or that of the emitted sound waves has the form shown in diagram (*a*) of Fig. A. If it vibrates in two segments or

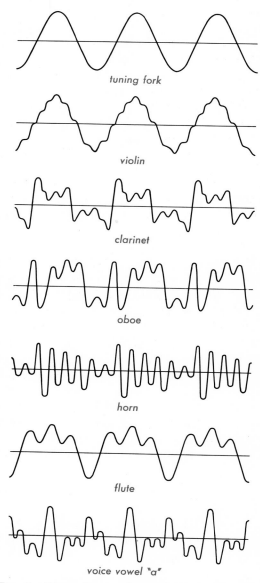

Fig. B. Wave forms of sounds from different musical instruments singing the same note.

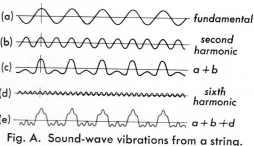

Fig. A. Sound-wave vibrations from a string.

six segments (see Fig. D in Lesson 55), the wave forms will be like those in diagrams (b) and (d) of Fig. A, respectively. Should the string be set vibrating with its fundamental and second harmonic simultaneously, as in Fig. F in Lesson 55, the wave form will appear something like diagram (c) of Fig. A. If, in addition to the fundamental, a string vibrates with the second and sixth harmonics, the wave will look like diagram (e). This is like diagram (c) with the sixth harmonic added to it.

It is difficult to make a string vibrate with its fundamental alone. As a rule, there are many harmonics present. Some of these harmonics harmonize with the fundamental and some do not. Those that do harmonize are called *concordant harmonics*, and those that do not are called *discordant harmonics*. If middle C (264 vibrations/sec) is sounded with its next seven harmonics, they will have 2, 3, 4, 5, 6, 7, and 8 times 264 vibrations/sec. These will correspond to notes C^1, G^1, C^2, E^2, G^2, X and C^3. All of these except X, the seventh harmonic, belong to a harmonic triad. This particular harmonic is discordant and should be suppressed. In a piano, this is accomplished by striking the string one-seventh of its length from one end, thus preventing a node at that point.

The seven different wave forms in Fig. B represent the sound vibrations coming from different musical instruments all sounding the note A (440 vibrations/sec). Observe that each wave form is repeated four times in the same time interval but that the harmonics, the small "wiggles" in the curves, are different in every case.

When complicated sound vibrations enter the ear, they are analyzed into their component frequencies. One set of nerve endings responds to the fundamental frequency, while other sets respond to the other harmonics. The fundamental frequency generally has most of the energy and, therefore, the greatest amplitude, whereas the harmonics with their higher frequencies have relatively small amplitudes.

An excellent experiment for demonstrating the wave forms of musical sounds is diagramed in Fig. C. A microphone is placed a short distance from an audio loudspeaker. The voice coil vibrates, moving the paper cone, C, back and forth to pro-

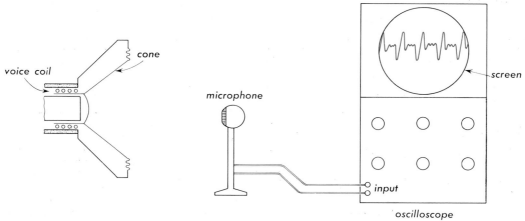

Fig. C. Oscilloscope arranged to display sound waves produced by a radio loudspeaker.

duce sound. The vibrating air sets up vibrations in the cone of the microphone. This in turn, as we shall learn later when we study electromagnetism, sets up an alternating electrical voltage that corresponds exactly to variations in sound produced from the speaker. This voltage is transmitted to the input terminals of an oscilloscope. This instrument is very similar to a television set. By proper adjustment of the controls of the oscilloscope, it is possible to display the shape of the sound wave. The operation of an oscilloscope will be described in detail later in the text.

The Ranges of Musical Instruments. A chart showing the ranges of various musical instruments and singing voices is given in

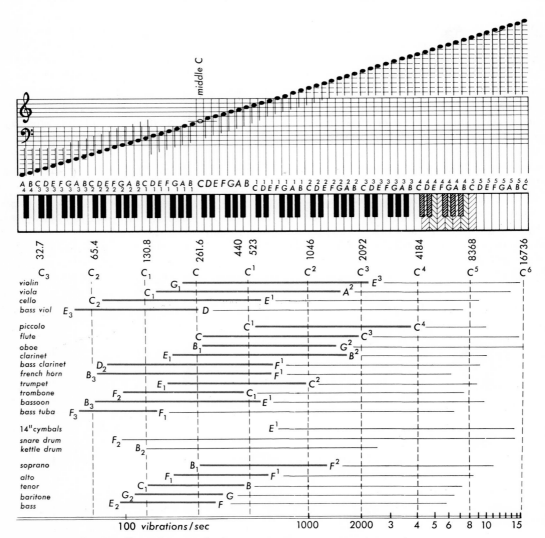

Fig. D. Chart showing the frequency range of various musical instruments.

Fig. D. The male speaking voice has an average fundamental frequency of about 150 vibrations/sec, with a singing range of about six notes up and six down, whereas the average female voice has a frequency of about 230 vibrations/sec, with approximately the same singing range. The *quality*, or *timbre*, depends almost entirely on two sets of harmonics. Good quality singing voices emphasize two sets of resonant harmonics, one around 500 cycles and the other around 2400 to 3200 cycles. The lower frequency seems to be the natural, or resonant, frequency of the *pharynx* (see B in Fig. E) and the higher frequencies resonate in the throat, mouth, and nasal cavities.

The effect of the density of a gas on the pitch of a note may be demonstrated by a very interesting experiment with the human voice. Voice sounds originate in the vibrations of the vocal cords in the larynx (see Fig. E). This source of vibration, which determines the fundamental pitch of the speaking or singing voice, is controlled by muscular tension on the vocal cords. The quality of the voice is determined by the size and shape of the throat, mouth, and nasal cavities.

If a gas lighter than air is breathed into the lungs, Eq. (1) in Lesson 56 shows that the voice quality should change. The demonstration can be performed by exhaling

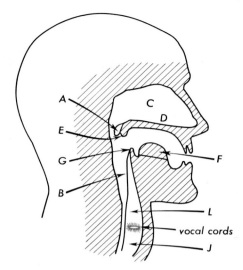

Fig. E. Cross-section diagram showing the mouth, throat, and nasal cavities of the human head.

completely and then filling the lungs with helium gas (hydrogen is unsafe). Upon speaking, the experimenter will be observed to have a very peculiar, high-pitched voice, which must be heard to be appreciated. The peculiarities arise from the fact that the fundamental pitch, due to the vocal-cord frequency, remains practically normal, while the harmonics from the resonating mouth, throat, and nasal cavities are raised by about two and one-half octaves.

QUESTIONS

1. A violinist and a harpist each play an A note. Do these differ (a) in pitch? (b) in quality? Explain.
2. Answer the preceding question in the event that they each play a middle C.
3. (a) What is special about the seventh harmonic? (b) Why do musicians try to suppress it?
4. Is the eighth harmonic concordant? Explain.
5. (a) Are the frequencies of the notes from musical instruments in any way associated with the size of the instrument? (b) In what way are they related? Explain.

6. (a) What is the range of your own voice? What is the range of the voice (b) of the average soprano? (c) of an average baritone?

7. (a) What instrument in the violin family produces the lowest-pitched note? (b) Which produces the highest?

8. Why are the harmonics of the human voice raised when a gas lighter than air is breathed?

PROBLEMS

1. Make a frequency list of the first six harmonics of the fundamental frequency of the musical note C^1. To what notes of the musical scale do these belong?

2. Make a list of the first ten harmonics of the fundamental frequency of the musical note E^2.

3. Make a list of the first fifteen harmonics of the musical note C^3.

PROJECT

Use an oscilloscope to see the waves produced by people talking and to study other sound sources. Make photographs of the screen to have permanent records of different sounds.

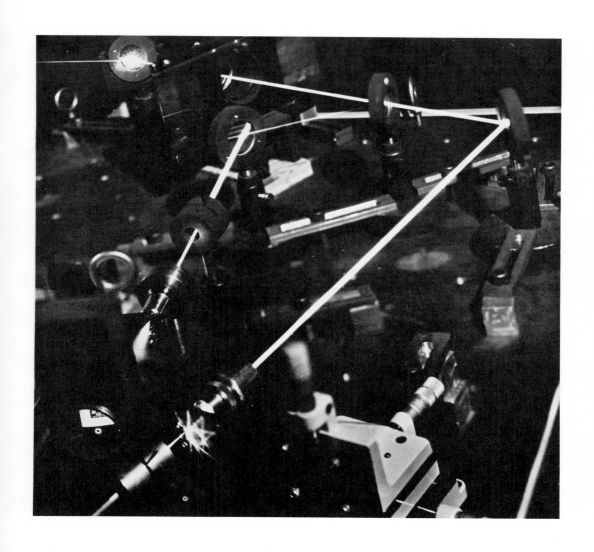

Light

It is inconceivable to doubt that light consists in the motion of some sort of matter. For whether one considers its production, one sees that here upon the earth it is chiefly engendered by fire and flame which contain without doubt bodies that are in rapid motion, since they dissolve and melt many other bodies, even the most solid; or whether one considers its effects, one sees that when light is collected, as by concave mirrors, it has the property of burning as a fire does, that is to say, it disunites the particles of bodies. This is assuredly the mark of motion, at least in the true philosophy, in which one conceives the causes of all natural effects in terms of mechanical motions. This, in my opinion, we must necessarily do, or else renounce all hopes of ever comprehending anything in physics.

And as, according to this philosophy, one holds as certain that the sensation of sight is excited only by the impression of some movement of a kind of matter which acts on the nerves at the back of our eyes, there is here yet one reason more for believing that light consists in a movement of the matter which exists between us and the luminous body.

Christian Huygens, *Treatise on Light,* trans. by Sylvanus P. Thompson, Macmillan, London, 1912, pp. 3-4.

The propagation of light in the ether is produced in a manner similar to that of sound in the air; and just as the vibrations occasioned in the particles of air constitute sound, in like manner the vibration of the particles of ether constitutes light or luminous rays; so that light is nothing else but an agitation or concussion of the particles of ether, *which is everywhere to be found on account of its extreme subtilty, in virtue of which it penetrates all bodies.*

Leonhard Euler, *Of the Propagation of Light*

◄ An optical device for producing holographic images, which are three dimensional and in original colors. An argon laser beam enters from the top left and is split by a half-silvered mirror. The two beams then follow separate paths—the left one to the object to be holographed (a film slide) and the other (the reference beam) to a point where the beams converge and the hologram is formed on a photographic plate (lower left).

R.C.A. Electronic Age

Lesson 58 *LIGHT AND ILLUMINATION*

All of the various known properties of light are conveniently described in terms of the experiments by which they were discovered and the many and varied experiments by which they are now commonly demonstrated. Numerous as they are, these experiments may be grouped together and classified under one of the three following heads: *geometrical optics, physical optics,* and *quantum optics.* Each of these may be subdivided as follows:

Geometrical Optics

> Rectilinear Propagation
> Reflection
> Refraction

Physical Optics

> Diffraction
> Interference
> Polarization

Quantum Optics

> Photoelectric Effect
> Compton Effect
> Atomic Excitation

The first group, geometrical optics, treated in this and the following nine lessons, deals with those optical phenomena that are most easily described (based upon wave behavior) with straight lines and plane geometry. The second group, physical optics, dealing directly with the wave nature of light, is treated in Lessons 67 through 69. The third group, dealing with the quantum aspects of light, is treated in the lessons on Atomic and Nuclear Physics, Lessons 99 through 121.

The Rectilinear Propagation of Light. The rectilinear propagation of light is another way of saying that *light travels in straight lines.* The fact that objects may be made to cast fairly sharp shadows is an experimental demonstration of this principle.

Another illustration is the image formation of an object produced by light passing through a small opening, as diagramed in Fig. A. In this figure, the object is an ordinary incandescent light bulb. In order to see how an image is formed, consider the rays of light emanating from a single point, *a*, near the top of the bulb. Of the many rays of light radiating in all directions, the ray that travels in the direction of the hole passes through to the point *a'* near the bottom of the image screen. Similarly, a ray leaving *b* near the bottom of the bulb and passing through the hole will arrive at *b'* near the top of the image screen. Thus, it may be seen that an inverted image is formed.

If the image screen is moved closer to the pinhole screen, the image will be proportionately smaller; whereas if it is moved farther away, the image will be proportionately larger. The same thing happens when either the object or the pinhole is moved. Excellent photographs can be made with this arrangement by making a pinhole in one end of a small box and placing a photographic film or plate at the other. Such an arrangement is called a "pinhole" camera. For good sharp photographs, the hole must be very small, as its size determines the amount of blurring produced. The photograph shown in Fig. B was taken

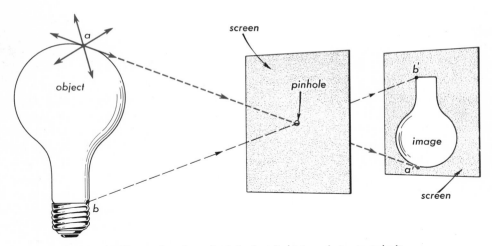

Fig. A. Illustrating the principle that light travels in straight lines.

with such a camera. Note the undistorted perspective lines of the building.

Candela (Candle power). For many years, the luminous intensity of all light sources was expressed in *standard candles,* or *candle power.* The standard candle was defined as the quantity of light given out by the flame of a certain make of candle, the constituents of which were specified by international agreement. The specification

Fig. B. Photograph taken with a pinhole camera.

for a 50-candle power tungsten filament lamp, for example, was one that gave out an amount of light equivalent to 50 standard candle flames. Not many years ago, the candle was considered to be unsatisfactory and, as the result of an extensive research program, was replaced by an incandescent platinum-metal surface. Platinum metal at its freezing temperature of $2033°K$ is "white hot" and each square centimeter of its surface emits an amount of light equal to approximately 60 standard candles.

Today, the unit of luminous intensity is called the *candela,* or *cd.* The name "candela" was adopted in 1946 by the International Committee on Weights and Measures as the unit of luminous intensity of $\frac{1}{60}$ cm^2 of a black body at the freezing temperature of platinum. The name and definition were adopted in the United States by an Act of Congress in 1963.

Ordinary tungsten-filament light bulbs used in general house lighting give a little more than one candela per watt of electrical power used. A 50-watt lamp, for example, has a luminous intensity, I, of about 55 cd and a 100-watt lamp a luminous intensity of about 125 cd, etc. See Table 1.

Luminescent tubes, on the other hand, have a considerably higher efficiency and yield about 4 cd/watt.

Table 1. Efficiency of Tungsten-Filament Light Bulbs

Input (watts)	Output (candelas)
25	20.7
50	55.0
100	125
200	290
500	800
1000	1640

The Inverse-square Law. Light sources are of many kinds, sizes, and shapes. It is convenient when specifying the illumination they provide on a screen, or surface, to distinguish between a *point source* and an *extended source*. A point source of light is one of which the dimensions are negligibly small (for practical purposes less than 10%) when compared with the distance between the source and the receptor. A tungsten-filament lamp, in a 3-in.-diameter frosted glass bulb, for example, would be considered a point source for a receiver of light 30 in. or more away.

The *illuminance* of a surface is defined as the amount of light falling on a unit area. If a screen is placed 1 m from a 1-cd point source, the illuminance on the screen is said to be 1 lux. At 1 m from a point source of 25 candelas, the illuminance will be 25 lux, etc. The *lux*, or *lx*, is the unit of illuminance in the mks system.

If a screen is placed 1 ft from a point source of 1 candela, the illuminance on the screen is said to be 1 foot-candle. One foot from a source of 50 candelas, the illuminance will be 50 foot-candles.

When the top surface of a table is illuminated by a single point source of light directly above it, and then the light is raised to twice the height, the illuminance on the surface will then be only ¼ as great. If it is raised to three times the first height the illuminance will only be ⅑ as great, etc. In other words, *illumination is proportional to the luminous intensity of the light source and is inversely proportional to the square of the distance.* This, another instance of the operation of the inverse square law, is illustrated in Fig. C by the

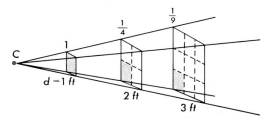

Fig. C. Illustration of the inverse square law.

three shaded patches of equal area. If I represents the luminous intensity of a light source and d the distance to the illuminated surface, the illuminance E is given by—

$$E = \frac{I}{d^2} \qquad (1)$$

If I is in candelas and d is in meters, E is in lux:

$$1 \frac{\mathbf{cd}}{\mathbf{m}^2} = 1 \ \mathbf{lx}$$

If I is in candelas and d is in feet, E is in foot-candles, or *ft-c*:

$$1 \frac{\mathbf{cd}}{\mathbf{ft}^2} = 1 \ \mathbf{ft\text{-}c}$$

To illustrate the use of Eq. (1), consider the following example.

Example. A street lamp with a luminous intensity of 300 cd is located 5 m above the pavement. Find the value of the illuminance on the pavement.

Solution. By direct substitution in Eq. (1) we obtain—

$$E = \frac{300 \text{ cd}}{(5 \text{ m})^2} = 12 \frac{\text{cd}}{\text{m}^2}$$

$$E = 12 \text{ lx}$$

Photometry. The word photometry is applied to the experimental process by which the intensities of two light sources are compared and measured.

One of the earliest methods for accomplishing this was devised by Count Rumford and is known as the *shadow photometer*. His experimental arrangement consists simply of casting two shadows of the same rod as shown in Fig. D. The dis-

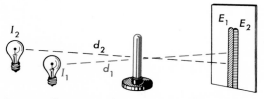

Fig. D. Illustrating the principle of the shadow photometer.

tances between screen and lamps are varied until the illuminance of the two shadows appears equal.

A plan diagram of such an arrangement will show that the shadow cast by lamp I_1 is illuminated only by lamp I_2, while the shadow cast by I_2, is illuminated only by lamp I_1. By the inverse square law, Eq. (1),

$$E_1 = \frac{I_1}{d_1^2} \qquad E_2 = \frac{I_2}{d_2^2}$$

When the illuminated shadow areas are equally bright, E_1 is equal to E_2, and the two equations above become equal to each other. Equating the right sides—

$$\frac{I_1}{d_1^2} = \frac{I_2}{d_2^2}$$

or—

$$\frac{I_1}{I_2} = \frac{d_1^2}{d_2^2} \qquad\qquad (2)$$

In words, the relative intensities of the two lamps are directly proportional to the square of their relative distances from the screen.

If the luminous intensity of one of the lamps is known, its value, along with the measured distances d_1 and d_2, may be substituted in Eq. (2) and the luminous intensity of the unknown lamp calculated.

Recommended Illumination. One important factor involved in the maintenance of good health is good seeing conditions brought about by proper illumination. Experiments show that the speed with which people see things gains rapidly at first, with increasing illuminance, and then begins leveling off with an illuminance of about 25 ft-c. This is borne out by numerous checks on the output of factory pieceworkers of all kinds.

Carefully conducted research in schools, hospitals, office buildings, etc., have also been made to determine proper lighting needed for the most efficient execution of various duties. The results of statistical studies by illuminating engineers, physicians, dentists, etc., under controlled conditions have led to the following values:

	foot-candles
hospital operating rooms..	1000
dental clinic..............	250
fine needlework...........	50–100
bookkeeping, auditing, drafting................	20–50
offices, classrooms, laboratories............	10–30
library reading rooms.....	10–25
factories.................	10–50

These are minimum values only, and higher

levels of illuminance are often desirable and recommended.

Luminance, or Brightness. Whether a body is self-luminous or just a reflector of the light that falls upon it, luminance refers to the light the surface gives off in the direction of an observer. Suppose as an experiment that a number of different kinds of surfaces like rough and polished metal, cotton fabric, black, grey and white paint, wood, etc., are equally illuminated from above as shown in Fig. E.

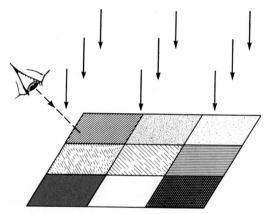

Fig. E. Although equally illuminated, the brightness of different surfaces may be widely different.

Because of different amounts of reflection and absorption, some of these surfaces will appear to be brighter than others. Furthermore, as the angle of observation is altered, the brightness of some will change markedly, while others will remain practically constant.

Brightness is a subjective measurement of the visible light coming from a surface and is therefore a sensory magnitude.

Luminance is an objective measurement of the luminous power coming from a surface. An increase in the luminance results in an increase in brightness.

Luminance is measured in candelas per unit of area: cd/cm^2 or cd/m^2. Examples of luminance, as measured in the metric system, are given in the following table for a number of common surfaces and fields of view.

Table 2. Luminance from Various Sources

Source	Luminance
clear blue sky.............	1 cd/cm^2
desert sand..............	1.5 cd/cm^2
fluorescent lamp...........	2 cd/cm^2
frosted lamp	5 cd/cm^2
full moon................	3 cd/cm^2
snow in sunlight...........	3 cd/cm^2
sun.....................	50,000 cd/cm^2
tungsten filament.........	2,500 cd/cm^2

Luminance and Illuminance. These two terms, commonly used by illumination engineers, sound so nearly alike they are often confusing. *Luminance* refers to the light given off by a source or surface, while *illuminance* refers to light falling on a body or surface. Each are commonly measured in the following units:

luminance
  candelas per square foot (cd/ft²)
  candelas per square meter (cd/m²)
illuminance
  foot-candles (ft-c)
  lux (lx)

QUESTIONS

1. (a) What are the three branches of optics? (b) What does the term "geometrical optics" suggest?

2. (a) What is meant by the rectilinear propagation of light? (b) What is a pinhole camera? (c) How does it work?

3. What is the inverse square law as applied to illumination?

4. Does the inverse square law apply to the light coming from a searchlight? Explain.

5. (a) How is the light output of a lamp measured? (b) What is a candela? (c) What is the standard light source used today?

6. (a) What is photometry? (b) What law is made use of in the method?

7. (a) What is luminance? (b) How is it measured? (c) What is brightness? (d) What is illuminance? (e) How is it measured?

8. (a) What illumination is recommended for classroom or office work? (b) Why should surgery require high levels of illumination?

9. Indirect lighting was once heralded as the best means of lighting a room. Explain why it has not been universally adopted.

10. Give the quantity measured and its units for the following cases: (a) Light from a frosted window. (b) Light shining on a metal surface in the sunlight. (c) Total light emitted by a light source.

11. Light shining out a window of a building on a dark night illuminates the center of the wall of the adjacent building. If a windowshade is pulled halfway down, what can be said concerning the illuminance of the wall?

PROBLEMS

1. A 120-cd lamp is located 3 ft above a table top. What is the illuminance in ft-c?

2. A 1000-cd lamp is located 20 ft above the street. What is the illuminance in ft-c?

3. A 100-watt lamp, located 3 ft above a table top, has an efficiency of 1.27 cd per watt. Find (a) the luminous intensity in cd and (b) the illuminance in ft-c.

4. A 60-watt lamp, located 2 ft above a table top, has an efficiency of 1.1 cd per watt. Find (a) the luminous intensity in cd and (b) the illuminance in ft-c.

5. A fluorescent lamp tube is 3 cm in diameter and 100 cm long. Calculate its intensity if it has a luminance of 2 cd/cm².

6. A point source of 10 cd is in the center of a sphere of 2-ft radius. What is the illumination produced by this light on the spherical surface?

7. A 40-cd lamp is located 120 cm from a lamp of unknown intensity. If both sides of a photometer screen placed between the lamps are equally illuminated when the screen is 40 cm from the unknown lamp, what is its intensity?

8. A 75-cd lamp is located 8 ft from a lamp of unknown intensity. If both sides of a photometer screen placed between the lamps are equally illuminated when the screen is placed 3 ft from the unknown lamp, what is its intensity?

9. Two lamps $I_1 = 60$ cd and $I_2 = 240$ cd, respectively, are located 3 m apart. At what position along a straight line through the lamps will equal illumination be produced? (*Note:* If you find two answers, both may be correct.)

10. A shadow photometer is set up with two lamps of 60 cd and 120 cd. What

would their relative distance from the screen have to be if the shadows produced are to be equal?

PROJECTS

1. Make a pinhole camera using a cardboard box painted black on the inside. Experiment with the size of the pinhole used until you get the sharpest picture. Construction details may be obtained from Eastman Kodak Company.
2. Make a photometer using the new cadmium sulfide cells. Electronic shops have the materials and data. Use your device to measure the range of lighting in your school.
3. Measure the relative efficiencies of incandescent and fluorescent lamps of equal power consumption.

LIGHT

Lesson 59 *THE NATURE OF LIGHT*

Sources of Light. Other than the sun itself, the most common source of light today is the *tungsten-filament lamp* used in house lighting. The light is produced by sending an electric current through a very fine tungsten wire placed at the center of a glass bulb as shown in Fig. A. The purpose of the current is to heat the wire to a very high temperature. The light comes from the hot solid tungsten wire and not from the electric current.

The tungsten filament of most light bulbs, if examined with a magnifying glass, will be found to be made of very fine wire wound in a spiral-like coil or helix. Being closely wound with about two hundred turns to the inch, this helix appears to the naked eye as a larger but straight solid wire.

Tungsten-filament lamps ranging from about 0.15 candela (0.17 watt) up to more than 100,000 candelas (50,000 watts) have

been made. Their efficiencies range from about 0.2 up to nearly 2 candelas per watt.

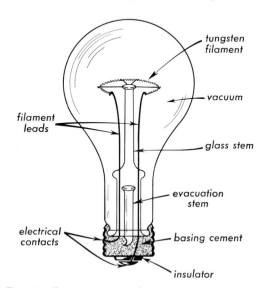

Fig. A. Cross section of a common tungsten-filament lamp used in house lighting.

Perhaps next in importance to the tungsten-filament lamp as a source of light is the *carbon arc*. This very bright source was at one time used for street lighting. Today, the carbon arc is used in moving-picture projectors, in searchlights, lighthouses, and wherever a very bright and concentrated source is required.

An ordinary laboratory arc consists of two carbon rods connected to the positive and negative sides of a battery or generator supplying anywhere from 50 to 250 volts. As shown in Fig. B, a resistor is connected *in*

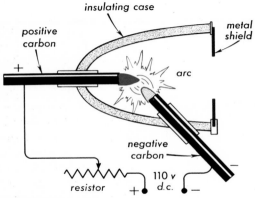

Fig. B. Cross section of a carbon arc showing connections to a resistor and a direct-current line source of 110 volts.

series to keep the current down to about 10 amperes for normal operation. The arc is started by first bringing the ends of the rods together and then pulling them apart. This striking of the arc produces a flame of burning carbon. It is through this flame that the electric current passes from one carbon tip to the other.

The tip of the positive carbon reaches a temperature of about 4000°K, whereas the negative carbon reaches about 3500°K. Most of the visible light comes from the positive carbon and relatively little from the vapor in the arc flame.

The carbon arcs used in searchlights require a current of about 150 amp, and the positive carbon tip reaches a temperature of 4500 to 5000°K.

The neon signs so commonly used for advertising purposes consist of long narrow tubes partially filled with neon, argon, or krypton gases. The tubes, after being bent into the required shape, are thoroughly evacuated and a small amount of gas is admitted to bring up the gas pressure inside to about one-fortieth of an atmosphere. By means of a high-voltage transformer and small wires sealed into both ends of each tube, an electric current is sent through the rarefied gas. The electrical connections are shown in Fig. C. The passage of the elec-

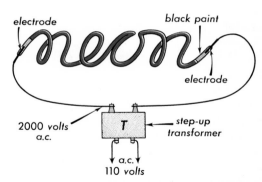

Fig. C. Diagram of a neon sign showing the electrodes in each end of the glass discharge tube and the transformer connections.

tric current through neon gas produces the characteristic red light with which everyone is familiar. Argon and krypton produce a white light. The action of the electric current in producing the light is called an *electric discharge*.

In recent years, fluorescent materials have been used for general illumination purposes. Long glass tubes, containing argon and nitrogen gas and a small drop of mercury, are painted on the inside with luminescent paint.

A diagram of all essential parts and electrical connections of a standard fluorescent lamp is shown in Fig. D. When the switch

Galileo's Experiment on the Velocity of Light. History tells us that Galileo once tried to measure the velocity of light but

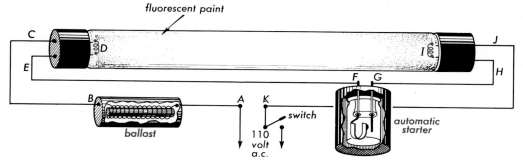

Fig. D. Section diagram of a fluorescent light and accessories.

is closed, applying 110 volts from the house lighting circuit, the voltage at the *automatic starter* terminals, *F* and *G*, is sufficient to produce a glow discharge between the U-shaped *bimetal strip* and the straight contact. The heat generated by the glowing argon gas inside causes the bimetallic strip to bend over, bringing the contacts together. Contact stops the glow and at the same time completes the entire lamp circuit, allowing full current to flow through the lamp-heater filaments, *D* and *I*, and *ballast coil.*

The function of the heaters is to vaporize the mercury in the fluorescent tube. Because the starter glow is shorted out, the contacts soon open the circuit and the sudden decreasing magnetic field of the ballast gives a high-voltage "kick" that starts the glow in the fluorescent tube. The voltage at the starter is insufficient thereafter to cause the switch to operate, so the starter consumes no energy during lamp operation.

Fluorescent lamps have a relatively high efficiency of 3 to 5 cd per watt. This is largely because of the conversion of an invisible ultraviolet light emitted by the mercury-gas atoms into visible light by the fluorescent coating.

without success. Galileo stationed himself on one hilltop with one lamp and an assistant on another hilltop with a similar lamp. Galileo would first uncover his lamp for an instant, sending a short flash of light to the assistant. As soon as the assistant saw this light he uncovered his own lamp, sending a flash back to Galileo, who noted the total time elapsed.

After numerous repetitions of this experiment at greater and greater distances between observers Galileo came to the conclusion that they could not uncover their lamps fast enough and that light probably travels with an infinite speed. Knowing as we do now that light travels with the amazing speed of over 186,000 mi/sec in a vacuum, it is easy to see why Galileo's experiment failed.

Fizeau's Experiment. The first terrestrial method of measuring the velocity of light was devised by Fizeau in 1849. His experimental arrangement is shown in Fig. E. Light from an intense source, *S*, was reflected from a semitransparent mirror, *G*, and then brought to a focus at the point *0* by means of lens L_1. After being made into a parallel beam by a second lens, L_2, the

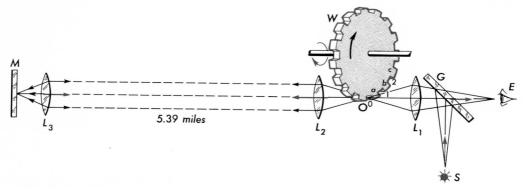

Fig. E. Experimental arrangement used by Fizeau in determining the velocity of light.

light traveled a distance of 5.39 mi to a hill-top, where a mirror, M, and lens L_3 reflected the light back again. Returning by the same path, some of the light passed through the mirror, G, and entered the eye of the observer at E.

The purpose of the rotating toothed wheel was to chop the light beam into short flashes and to measure the time it takes each of these signals to travel over to the far mirror and back. With the wheel at rest and in such a position that the light passes through an opening between 2 teeth at 0, the observer at E will see an image of the light source, S.

If the wheel is now set rotating with slowly increasing speed, a condition will soon be reached in which the light passing through 0 will return just in time to be stopped by a, the light passing through opening 1 will return just in time to be stopped by b, etc. Under these conditions, the image will be completely eclipsed from the observer.

By further increasing the speed, the light will reappear, increasing in intensity until a maximum is reached. This will occur when the flashes sent out through the openings 0, 1, 2, 3, etc., return just in time to get through the openings 1, 2, 3, 4, etc., respectively. With a wheel containing 720

teeth, Fizeau observed this maximum at a speed of 25 r/sec. The time required for the light to travel over and back can therefore be calculated as 1/25 times 1/720, or 1/18,-000th of a second. This, from the measured distance over and back of 10.78 mi, gives a velocity of 194,000 mi/sec, or 313,000 Km/sec.

Michelson's Measurements of the Velocity of Light. In the years that followed these earliest experiments, several investigators improved upon Fizeau's apparatus and methods of observation and obtained more accurate values for the velocity of light. Of these, Michelson's[*] contributions and improvements stand out above the rest. Replacing the toothed wheel by a small eight-sided mirror and increasing the light path to some 44 mi, Michelson in 1926 obtained a value of 299,796 Km/sec.

[*] Albert A. Michelson (1852-1931) was a distinguished American physicist, celebrated for the invention and development of the Michelson interferometer, which is an optical instrument now named in his honor. It was used in establishing the length of the standard meter in terms of the wave length of light, in the ether-drift experiments, in determining the rigidity of the earth, in the measurement of the distances and diameters of giant stars, and for the measurement of the velocity of light. He was the first American scientist to be awarded the Nobel Prize (1907).

An extensive and critical study of the values of the velocity of light measured by all observers has been made by Cohen and DuMond. They conclude that the most probable value at the present time is as follows:

$$c = 299{,}792.5 \text{ Km/sec}$$

or—

$$c = 186{,}282.4 \text{ mi/sec}$$

Because the velocity of light in the metric system is within one-tenth of one percent of being 300,000 Km/sec, it is common practice to use this value in calculations

$$c \approx 300{,}000 \text{ Km/sec}$$

In other metric units, this is equivalent to—

$$c = 3 \times 10^8 \text{ m/sec}$$

or—

$$c = 3 \times 10^{10} \text{ cm/sec}$$

The Velocity of Light in Stationary Matter. In 1850, Foucault completed and published the results of an experiment in which he had measured the velocity of light in water. This was a crucial experiment, for it settled a long-existing controversy concerning the nature of light. According to Newton and his followers, light was believed to be made up of small particles or corpuscles emanating from a source. Huygens, on the other hand, regarded light as being composed of waves, similar in nature, perhaps, to water waves or sound waves. Newton's corpuscular theory required light to travel faster in a dense medium like water than it did in a less dense medium like air, whereas Huygens' wave theory required

it to travel slower. By sending light back and forth through a long tube of water, Foucault found its velocity to be less than that in air. This was a strong confirmation of Huygens' wave theory.

Years later, Michelson also measured the velocity of light in water and found a value of 225,000 Km/sec. This is just three-quarters the velocity in a vacuum. In common glass, the velocity is still lower, being about two-thirds the velocity *in vacuo*, or 200,000 Km/sec. In air, the velocity is very little less than the velocity in a vacuum, differing only by about 70 Km/sec at sea level and less at higher altitudes where the air is less dense. For most practical cases, this difference can be neglected, and the velocity in air said to be the same as in a vacuum.

The Refractive Index. The ratio between the velocity of light in a vacuum and the velocity in a medium is called the *refractive index*, or the *index of refraction* of the medium:

$$\text{refractive index} = \frac{\text{vel. of light in vac.}}{\text{vel. of light in med.}}$$

Symbolically—

$$\mu = \frac{c}{v} \qquad (1)$$

The Greek letter, μ (mu), is frequently used to represent this ratio. Substituting the velocities given in the preceding section, the following refractive indices may be calculated:

for water, $\mu = 1.33$

for glass, $\mu = 1.5$

for air, $\mu = 1.00$

QUESTIONS

1. (a) What is our most important light source? (b) What are the most important manufactured sources?

2. (a) What is the source of light in the tungsten-filament lamp? (b) What is the efficiency in candelas per watt?

3. Because the efficiency of tungsten lamps is so low, what happens to the electrical energy that they consume?

4. (a) How could one increase the light output of a tungsten lamp? (b) What effect does this have on its life?

5. (a) How are photoflood lamps used by photographers able to give such brilliant light? (b) Why are these lamps used in projectors?

6. (a) What are the principles of the fluorescent lamp? (b) To what is its high efficiency attributed?

7. Why are fluorescent lamps more expensive to install?

8. (a) How many things can go wrong with an incandescent lamp? (b) How many in a fluorescent lamp and fixture?

9. (a) What is a carbon arc? (b) Where in the arc does most of the light originate? (c) What is it principally used for? Why? (d) What disadvantages do you think it might have?

10. What is the source of light in a neon sign?

11. (a) Who made the first terrestrial determination of the speed of light? (b) How was it done? (c) What is the most probable value of the velocity of light in (d) the metric system and (e) the English system?

12. (a) Who was first to measure the speed of light in stationary matter? (b) Of what significance were the results of this experiment?

13. Why is the method used by Michelson a more accurate method for measuring the speed of light than that used by Fizeau?

14. What source of light do you suppose Michelson used in measuring the speed of light? Why?

15. (a) What is meant by the refractive index? (b) What is meant by the index of refraction? (c) What is the refractive index for (d) water, (e) glass, and (f) air?

PROBLEMS

1. How long will it take light to travel from the moon to the earth if the distance is 239,000 mi?

2. How long will it take light to reach the earth from the sun, a distance of 93 million miles?

3. How long would it take light to travel a distance equal to the circumference of the world?

4. How fast would the toothed wheel of 720 teeth in Fizeau's experiment have to rotate if the distant mirror were 50 Km away? Assume that the returning light produces a maximum intensity.

5. How many teeth would a Fizeau wheel require in order to produce the first maximum intensity from the light pulses returning from a mirror 30 Km away, if the angular speed was 10 r/sec?

6. Find the speed of light in plastic if the refractive index is 1.425. Assume that $c = 186,282$ mi/sec.

7. Find the speed of light in carbon bisulfide if the refractive index is 1.670. Assume that $c = 186,282$ mi/sec.

8. A Fizeau wheel with 100 teeth is rotating at 1800 r/min. The light reflected from a mirror on a distant mountain produces a maximum intensity. How far away is the mountain?

9. An experimenter has carefully measured the correct distance from the Fizeau wheel to the mirror and determined the correct angular speed of the wheel to obtain a maximum intensity. He then calculates the velocity of light to be 552,882 mi/sec. (a) What mistake has he made? (b) What value of the velocity of light should he deduce from this measurement?

10. Radar is another wave that travels with the same velocity as light. How long will it be, after a beam is sent to the moon, before it returns to earth?

11. In 1926, Michelson used an eight-sided mirror and a light path of 44 miles. His value was approximately 186,000 mi/sec. How fast did the mirror rotate when he made these measurements?

12. If the mirror in the Michelson method were 32-sided, instead of 8-sided, what difference would that make in the experiment?

PROJECTS

1. Make a working model of an electric arc light using the carbon rods that are in small flashlight cells.

2. Make a model of the apparatus used for measuring the speed of light.

LIGHT

Lesson 60 REFLECTION

Wave Theory. The behavior of light was explained in the time of Newton by assuming that light is composed of small particles, or corpuscles, obeying the ordinary laws of motion. This theory also explained quite easily the formation of images in mirrors and lenses. It predicted, however, that the speed of light in water or glass should be greater than in air. Actual measurements of the speed of light in the air and in denser mediums showed this to be incorrect and, therefore, a need was created for a more adequate theory of light.

The wave theory assumes that light is made up of many waves of extremely short wave lengths. This theory was first proposed by the English physicist, Robert Hooke, in 1665, and improved twenty years later by

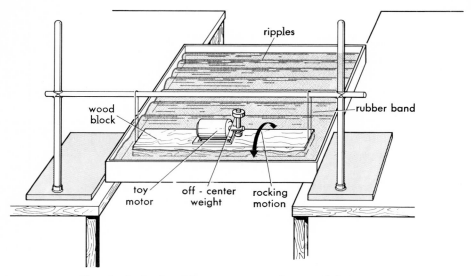

Fig. A. A ripple tank set up to produce straight waves.

the Dutch scientist and mathematician, Christian Huygens. By adopting the wave hypothesis, a complete and adequate account of reflection, refraction, diffraction, interference, and polarization phenomena on a mathematical basis was finally formulated by Augustin Fresnel, a French physicist, at the beginning of the 19th century.

Ripple Tank. Everyone has, at some time or other, dropped a stone in a still pond of water and watched the waves spread slowly outward in ever-widening concentric circles. The behavior of water waves and their similarity to the behavior of light can be studied in detail by the use of a shallow tank of water, arranged as shown in Fig. A, called a *ripple tank*.

Straight waves of constant frequency can be generated by having a straight stick moved up and down in the water by a small electric motor whose shaft is unbalanced. The photograph in Fig. B shows the appearance of the straight waves produced. Wire screening covered with cheese-

cloth acts as an absorber for the water waves.

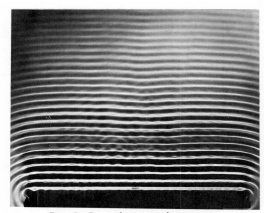

Fig. B. Periodic straight waves.

To study the reflection of the waves from a plane surface, a straight barrier is placed a short distance from the wave generator. The angle this barrier makes with the incident waves can be varied and the angle the reflected waves make with the

barrier can also be measured. A photograph
of this is shown in Fig. C.

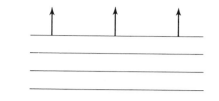

(a)

Fig. C. Periodic straight waves are reflected to
left by barrier.

(b)

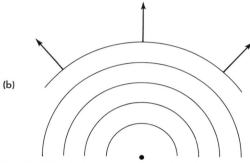

Fig. D. The light ray defines the direction of
the light wave—perpendicular to the wave
crest.

Light Rays. The motion of a light wave
is in a direction perpendicular to the wave
crest. This direction is designated by a
vector called a *ray*. See Fig. D. As we shall
see, it is often easier to describe the motion
of light waves by discussing the behavior
of rays.

The Law of Reflection. Experiment
shows that, whenever a ray of light is reflected from a plane surface, the nature of
the reflected light can be described in terms
of a number of simple and well-defined
laws. The simplest of these is the one known
as *the law of reflection*, which was illustrated in the ripple-tank demonstration.
According to this law, *the angle at which a*

*ray of light strikes the reflecting surface is
exactly equal to the angle that the reflected
ray makes with the same surface.*

Instead of measuring the *angle of incidence* and the *angle of reflection* from the
mirror surface, however, it is customary to
measure both from a line perpendicular to
the plane of the mirror. This line, as shown
in Fig. E, is called the *normal*. As the angle
i increases, the angle i' increases by exactly
the same amount, so that, for all angles of
incidence—

$$\text{angle } i = \text{angle } i' \qquad (1)$$

A second part of this law stipulates that
the reflected ray lies in the plane of incidence, the plane of incidence being defined
as the plane containing the incident ray
and the normal. In other words, *the incident ray, the normal, and the reflected ray
all lie in the same plane.*

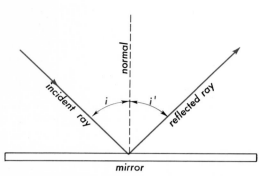

Fig. E. Illustrating the law of reflection from a plane surface.

In speaking of a mirror surface, one does not necessarily mean a silvered plate of glass; a mirror is any surface smooth enough to produce regular reflection as it has just been described.

Image in a Plane Mirror. The image of one's self seen in a mirror is formed by rays

of light traveling in straight lines that are reflected according to the law of reflection. All objects seen in a plane mirror are images formed by reflection. This can be demonstrated by the experiment shown in Fig. F(a). A lighted candle, O, is placed on the table near a glass plate, MN. With the candle itself hidden in the box, H, the observer at E sees only the reflected image at I. If a glass of water is placed at B, this image appears as a real candle burning under water.

As shown in the top view, (b), all rays of light leaving the source, O, are reflected according to the law of reflection. To an observer anywhere between L and R on the right side of the mirror, all light appears to come from the same point, I. This image point is just as far behind the mirror as the object, O, is in front of it; the two lie on the same perpendicular to the mirror.

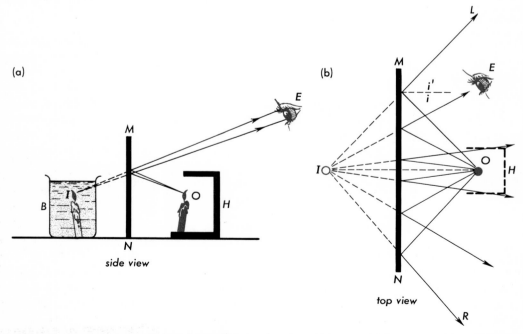

Fig. F. An experiment illustrating reflection from a mirror or glass plate. Light from the candle flame at O appears to come from I.

The image one sees in a plane mirror is not a real image but a virtual image. A virtual image is one from which rays seem to radiate but actually do not. In the figure, the rays do not come from *I*; they come from *O* and by reflection reach the observer.

This experiment illustrates a trick used by many "mediums" to make ghostlike figures appear to move about a room or stage. Light from real persons or objects, located below or above the stage, is reflected from a large sheet of plate glass at the front of the stage. With proper drapes and a dark-ened room, the illusion is very effective.

The image of any object seen in a plane mirror is the same size as the object and appears to be just as far behind the mirror as the object is in front of it.

Multiple Reflections. When light is reflected from two plane mirrors, a number of virtual images may be seen. If the two mirrors are parallel to each other, as illustrated by *M* and *N* in Fig. G, the images all lie on

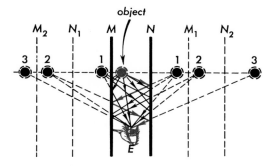

Fig. G. Multiple images as seen in two parallel mirrors all lie in a straight line.

a straight line, a line that passes through the object perpendicular to both mirrors. The images M_1, M_2, N_1, N_2, etc., of both mirrors are all equally spaced and the images *1, 2, 3,* of the object are symmetrically located on each side of them.

The solid lines representing real rays

show that images numbered *2* appear after two reflections, once from each mirror, and that images numbered *3* appear after three reflections, once from one mirror and twice from the other. The number of images visi-ble is limited by the intensity of the light and the reflecting power of the mirrors.

When two mirrors are placed at an angle with each other, the object and all of its images lie on a circle whose center is at the intersection of the two mirrors and whose plane is perpendicular to both mir-rors. In Fig. H, the two mirrors are shown

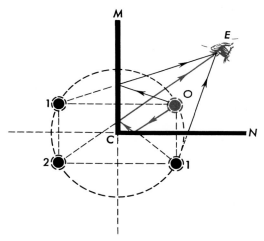

Fig. H. Multiple images seen in two mirrors at an angle all lie in a circle.

at 90° to each other. The two images num-bered *1* appear after one reflection and are the same distances behind their respective mirrors as the object is in front. Image *2* appears after two reflections. If the mirrors are placed at an angle of 60°, five virtual images may be seen, in addition to the ob-ject, making six in all. If the angle is 45°, seven virtual images may be seen, in ad-dition to the object, making eight in all. Drawings of these are left as exercises for the student.

If one looks at his own face in a plane

mirror, the image observed is technically described as *perverted*. The image is the same as though the face were reproduced as a rubber mask and the mask turned inside out and viewed from the new front. The right ear of the subject becomes the left ear of the image and vice versa.

To see one's face as others see it requires that two front-silvered mirrors be placed 90° apart and touching each other along one edge, as shown in Fig. I. The observer's right ear will then be seen, because of two reflections, as the right ear of his image, etc. This experiment must be performed to be appreciated since many people's faces are, unknowingly, slightly unsymmetrical. Seen in 90° mirrors, all such irregularities

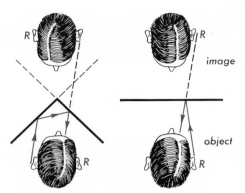

Fig. I. One's own image seen in 90° mirrors is normal; that seen in a plane mirror is perverted.

are reversed and, therefore, appear double in magnitude and are very noticeable.

QUESTIONS

1. (a) What is the law of reflection? (b) From what line are the angles measured?
2. How does the image distance from the mirror compare with the object distance?
3. How does the image size compare with the object size?
4. (a) Is the image seen in a plane mirror a real image? (b) What is it?
5. (a) What is a virtual image? (b) What is a perverted image?
6. When you look at your face in a plane mirror and put your hand to your right ear, which ear of the image does it appear to be?
7. Why is it difficult at first to shave oneself?
8. How can a person see his or her own face as others see it?
9. A man looking into a wall mirror sees his reflection from his waist to his forehead. Could he see more of himself reflected if he stood closer, or further from the mirror? Use a drawing to explain your answer.
10. What general formula can you deduce that relates the angle between two mirrors to the maximum number of images (including the object)?
11. If the angle between two mirrors is 30°, how many virtual images are formed?
12. What kind of shadow would you expect light to produce if it were corpuscular in nature?

PROBLEMS

1. Make a diagram showing two mirrors with their edges together and forming an angle of 45° with each other. Place an object between them and locate all images.

2. A room with six equal reflecting walls, each 4 ft long, has the shape of a hexagon. A lamp is located in one corner 1 ft from each of two walls. Make a diagram and show the positions of all images formed by one reflection only.

3. A box 2 ft wide and 3 ft long has mirrors on the inside walls. A lamp is located in one corner 6 in. from each of the two walls. Make a diagram and show the positions of all images formed by single and double reflections only.

4. Find the distance from the object to the farthest image owing to only one re-

5. What must be the minimum length of a mirror in order for a man to see a full flection for the box in Problem 3.
view of himself in it?

6. Two mirrors make an angle of 60° with each other. Make a drawing showing an object point closer to one mirror than the other and (a) locate all the images. (b) Show the path of light reaching the eye from the farthest image. (Locate the eye closer to the other mirror.)

7. Two mirrors make an angle of 90° with each other. Make a drawing showing an object, in the form of an arrow, close to but making an angle of about 30° with one mirror. Locate the images.

8. Make a drawing showing two plane parallel mirrors some distance apart. Show an object, in the form of an arrow, close to but making an angle of about 30° with one mirror. Locate the first three images as seen in each direction.

9. You are standing, with a camera, 12 ft from a mirror. You wish to take a clear picture of the image of your friend who is 18 ft from the same mirror. To what distance should you set the camera?

10. Through how many degrees does an image move if the mirror is rotated 12°?

PROJECTS

1. Set up a piece of glass to show the illusion of a candle burning under water.
2. With the help of your chemistry teacher make a semitransparent mirror, and demonstrate its usefulness.
3. Make a cat's-eye mirror by properly combining three mirrors and demonstrate its use.

LIGHT

Lesson 61 *REFLECTION FROM CURVED SURFACES*

With the aid of the ripple tank, we can study the behavior of water waves when they are incident on a curved surface. As shown in Fig. A, straight waves striking a rubber tube in the shape of a parabola reflect back to a focus. If a pencil is moved

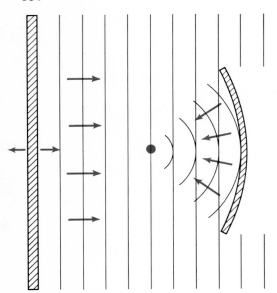

Fig. A. Straight waves brought to a focus by a circular barrier.

is illustrated in Fig. B. A concave mirror is able to bring light rays to a focus in a similar way.

Concave Mirrors. A spherical mirror has the form of a circular section of a hollow sphere, as shown in Fig. C. The center

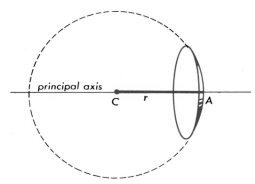

Fig. C. A spherical mirror is a circular section of a sphere.

up and down at the focal point, then the circular waves thus created will be reflected back by the tubing as straight waves. This

point, A, of the section is called the *vertex*, and a line from the center of the sphere through the vertex is called the *principal axis*. The radius of the sphere, r, is called the *radius of the mirror*.

Because spherical mirrors are symmetrical about their axes, cross-section diagrams are usually drawn to show their optical properties. If the mirror is silvered on the inner surface, it is called a *concave mirror,* while if silvered on the outer surface, it is *convex mirror.*

A cross-sectional diagram showing how a beam of parallel light is reflected by a concave mirror is shown in Fig. D. Each ray striking the mirror obeys the law of reflection, namely, that the angle of incidence, i, equals the angle of reflection, i'.

The point F where the rays cross the principal axis is called the *principal focus*, and the distance A to F is called the *focal length, f*.

If the mirror is silvered on the outer sur-

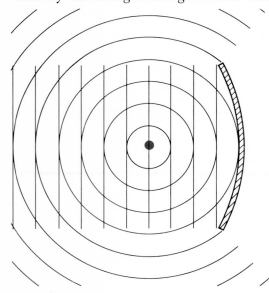

Fig. B. Reflection of a circular pulse in a ripple tank from a circular barrier.

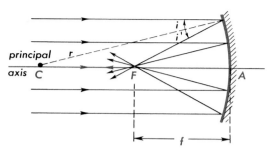

Fig. D. Illustrating the focal point *F* and focal length *f* of a concave mirror.

face as in Fig. E, it becomes a convex mirror and parallel incident light rays are reflected as if they came from a point *F* on the axis. The different rays, each obeying the law of reflection, diverge after reflection and never come to a focus.

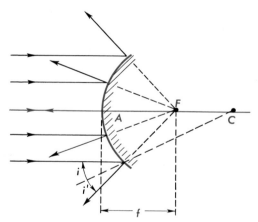

Fig. E. Illustrating the focal point *F* and focal length *f* of a convex mirror.

Nevertheless, the distance *A* to *F* is called the *focal length* of the convex mirror and it is assigned a minus sign in all optical formulas.

The geometry of the incident and reflected rays shown in Figs. D and E can be used to show mathematically that the focal point, *F*, is halfway between *C* and *A*. In other words—

$$AF = \tfrac{1}{2}AC$$

or—

$$f = \tfrac{1}{2}r \qquad (1)$$

Image Formation. If an illuminated object, *O*, is located in front of a concave mirror as shown in Fig. F, a real image, *I*, can

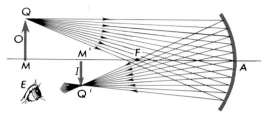

Fig. F. A concave mirror forms a real image.

be formed nearby. All rays emitted by the object point, *Q*, and reflected by the mirror come to a focus at *Q'*. All rays emitted by the object point, *M*, would upon reflection come to a focus at *M'*. For every object point in *QM* emitting rays, there will be a corresponding image point in *Q'M'* where focus is produced.

If the eye is located at *E*, the illuminated object will appear at *Q'M'*, but inverted. If a screen is located at *Q'M'*, a sharply defined image will be observed there. Because the image can be formed on a screen, it is called a *real image*. Such mirrors are often used in optical instruments in place of lenses.

Object Image Formula. Let d_o represent the distance from the object point, *M*, to the mirror vertex, *A*, and d_i the distance from the image point *M'* to *A*; then one finds that—

$$\frac{1}{d_o} + \frac{1}{d_i} = \frac{1}{f} \qquad (2)$$

where d_o is called the *object distance*, d_i the *image distance*, and *f* the *focal length*.

As an illustration, consider the case, shown in Fig. G, of an object, *O*, located

30 cm from a concave mirror of 20-cm radius. By Eq. (1), the focal length $f = \frac{1}{2}r$, or $f = +10$ cm. A light ray from O parallel to the principal axis is reflected, by defini-

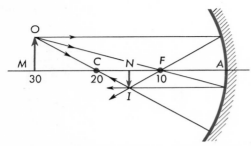

Fig. G. Showing graphical construction for locating the image formed by a concave mirror.

tion of the focal point, through F. By the reversibility of light rays, another ray from O passing through F is reflected parallel to the principal axis. Where these two rays cross at I, the image is formed. A third ray from O through the center of curvature, C, strikes the mirror normally and is reflected back on itself where it passes through I. Any two of these three rays are sufficient to locate the image. The third ray is then a check upon the other two. This graphical construction for image formation is called the *parallel ray method*.

It must be remembered that the actual image is formed by many rays, but we use only those whose path is easy to follow.

To solve this mirror arrangement as a problem, Eq. (2) can be applied directly. Given are the quantities $d_o = 30$ cm and $f = +10$ cm. By substitution in Eq. (2), we obtain—

$$\frac{1}{30} + \frac{1}{d_i} = \frac{1}{10}$$

$$\frac{1}{d_i} = \frac{1}{10} - \frac{1}{30}$$

Using the common denominator of 30—

$$\frac{1}{d_i} = \frac{3}{30} - \frac{1}{30}$$

$$\frac{1}{d_i} = \frac{2}{30}$$

or

$$d_i = +15 \text{ cm}$$

An interesting experiment can be performed with a large concave mirror under the conditions illustrated in Fig. H. A flower

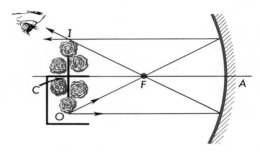

Fig. H. Diagram for the phantom bouquet.

hanging upside down in a box and placed just below the center of curvature will form a real and erect image at O directly above. An observer to the left cannot see the flower directly but can see the real image. So real is this image that it cannot be distinguished from a real object; the rays of light, as shown in the diagram, diverge from I the same as they would if the object were located there.

In Fig. I, an object is placed inside the focal point of a concave mirror and the rays,

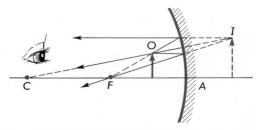

Fig. I. Diagram showing the formation of a virtual image.

after reflection, diverge as if they had come from the point I. To the eye of an observer at E, a magnified and erect (not inverted) virtual image is seen at I. As a problem, let the object distance $d_o = 10$ cm, the focal length $f = +20$ cm. Substitution of these in Eq. (2) gives

$$\frac{1}{10} + \frac{1}{d_i} = \frac{1}{20}$$

$$\frac{1}{d_i} = \frac{1}{20} - \frac{1}{10}$$

$$\frac{1}{d_i} = -\frac{1}{20}$$

$$d_i = -20 \text{ cm}$$

The image is located 20 cm from the mirror, the minus sign indicating that it is virtual and on the opposite side of the mirror from the object.

No matter where a real object is located in front of a convex mirror, the image is *virtual* and cannot be formed on a screen. When, in using Eq. (2), the focal length of a convex mirror is known, its value is substituted with a minus sign.

Aberration. The sharpness of focus in the previous discussion applies only if the diameter of the mirror is small with respect to the focal length. A large-diameter spheri-cal mirror deviates the outer rays to a shorter focus than those near the center. See Fig. J. This focusing defect is called

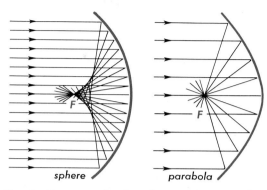

Fig. J. Diagrams showing the caustic curve obtained with a spherical mirror and the point focus with a paraboloidal mirror.

spherical aberration. The paraboloid mirror, on the other hand, brings all rays to focus at one point. A small source of light located at the focal point of a paraboloidal reflector becomes a parallel beam after reflection, a principle used in astronomical telescopes, spotlights, searchlights, and automobile headlights.

Spherical aberration for a spherical mirror is reduced by reducing the diameter or, specifically, by keeping the focal length large compared with the reflector diameter.

QUESTIONS

1. (a) What is a concave mirror? (b) What is a convex mirror?
2. What is the principal axis of a spherical mirror?
3. (a) What is the focal point of a concave mirror? (b) of a convex mirror?
4. What is the focal length of a spherical mirror?
5. How is the focal length related to the radius of curvature?
6. (a) Can images be formed with curved mirrors? (b) Are such images ever real?
7. (a) What kind of mirror is used when one wants an enlarged view of one's face? (b) Where must you put your face to get the enlarged image?
8. (a) What kind of mirror would you use to make people appear fatter than they actually are? (b) Where are these used sometimes?

9. (a) Where are the largest concave mirrors used? (b) What is their principal function?

10. Can real images be formed with a convex mirror?

11. (a) What is spherical aberration? (b) How can it be eliminated? (c) Does a convex mirror have spherical aberration?

12. What are parabolic mirrors used for?

13. How is a paraboloid related to a parabola?

PROBLEMS

1. An object 2 cm high is located 15 cm in front of a concave mirror of 12-cm radius. Find the image distance (a) graphically and (b) by formula. (c) Find the image height.

2. An object 1 cm high is located 10 cm in front of a concave mirror of 12-cm radius. Find the image position (a) graphically and (b) by formula. (c) Find the image height.

3. An object 1.5 cm high is located 4 cm in front of a concave mirror having a 20-cm radius. Find the image position (a) graphically and (b) by formula. (c) Find the image height.

4. An object 2 cm high is located 5 cm in front of a concave mirror having a 30-cm focal length. Find the image position (a) graphically and (b) by formula. (c) Find the image height.

5. An object 2 in. high is located 12 in. in front of a convex mirror of 16-in. radius. Find (a) the image position and (b) the image size. (c) Find the image graphically.

6. An object 3 cm high is located 5 cm in front of a convex mirror of 10-cm focal length. (a) Where is the image formed? (b) Is the image real or virtual? (c) Find the image graphically.

7. An object 1.5 cm high is located 6 cm in front of a convex mirror of 24-cm radius. (a) Find the image distance. Graphically find (b) the image distance and (c) the image height.

8. An object 2 cm high is located 6 cm in front of a convex mirror of 6-cm focal length. (a) Find the image distance. (b) Find the image distance graphically.

9. A concave mirror has a focal length of 10 in. Where should an object be placed if the image distance is to be three times the object distance?

10. A concave mirror has a focal length of 12 cm. Where should an object be placed to form a virtual image twice as far from the mirror?

11. (a) Where would the image be if the object were at the center of curvature of a concave mirror? (b) Is it erect or inverted?

12. Where would the image be if an object were at the focal point of a concave mirror?

13. A 3-cm arrow placed 22 cm from a mirror forms a real, inverted image 10 cm from the mirror. (a) Is the mirror concave or convex? (b) What is its radius of curvature?

14. A pencil 20 cm from a mirror forms an enlarged virtual image 40 cm from a mirror. (a) Is the mirror concave or convex? (b) What is its radius of curvature?

15. A rod 15 cm from a spherical mirror forms a virtual image 25 cm from the mirror. (a) Is the mirror concave or convex? (b) What is its radius of curvature?

PROJECT

Obtain a shaving mirror and measure its focal length. Try to make a reflecting telescope using this crude mirror. You can, of course, improve the image by using only the central part of the mirror.

LIGHT

Lesson 62 *REFRACTION*

Refraction. When light falls upon the smooth surface of a transparent substance, like water or glass, part of it is reflected according to the law of reflection and the remainder continues into the medium and is refracted (see Fig. A). This bending is

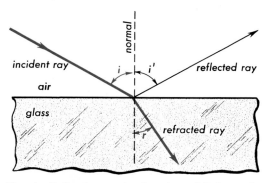

Fig. A. Reflection and refraction of light at the boundary of a glass surface.

caused by the change in the velocity of the light upon entering the second medium.

Refraction can best be understood by first studying the behavior of water waves in a ripple tank. The motor is set to a very slow speed so as to produce relatively long straight waves. By placing a barrier in front of the waves, it is possible to produce standing waves. Standing waves appear stationary because reflected waves come back in phase with those moving forward so that crests and troughs remain in the same position. The distance between adjacent crests or troughs, which is the wave length, is easily measured. If there are different water depths in the same tank, there will be, as in Fig. B, changes in the wave length as the waves pass from deep to shallow water. Because the product of the wave length and frequency is equal to the velocity of the waves, it is seen that the speed of water waves is less in shallow water.

When straight water waves strike the shallow water normal to the boundary, no change in the direction of the waves is noted, although the waves are shorter in the new depth. When the angle of incidence

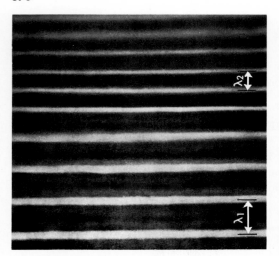

Fig. B. Passage of waves from deep to shallow water. The deep water is at the bottom and the shallow water at the top of the picture. Note that the wave length is shorter in the shallow water.

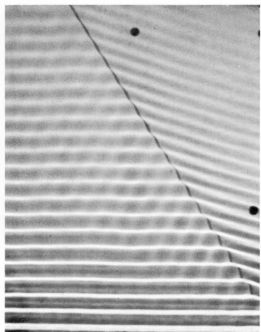

Fig. C. Refraction of periodic straight waves in a ripple tank.

is less than 90°, the waves are bent or refracted, as shown in Fig. C. Careful measurements of the angles of incidence and reflection will show that they follow the same laws as light waves.

The angle of refraction, r, is found by experiment to depend upon two factors: (1) *the angle of incidence, i,* and (2) *the index of refraction, μ.* The direction of the refracted ray, like the incident and reflected rays, is always measured by the angle it makes with the normal.

The index of refraction is the ratio of the speed of light in a vacuum to the speed of light in the medium. To determine the angle of refraction from these two factors, we perform the following graphical construction (see Fig. D).

Assume that the refracting surface is of glass, with air above, and that $μ = 1.5$. First, a ray of light, QA, is selected, incident on

the surface at angle i. Using a ruler, a line segment is measured back from A to a

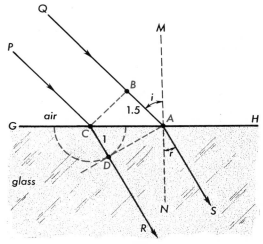

Fig. D. Illustrating the graphical method of determining the angle of refraction.

point B such that AB equals the refractive index. The unit of length to be chosen here is arbitrary and may be 1 cm, or 1 in., or any other. From B, a line is next drawn perpendicular to QA, intersecting the surface GH at C. Line CP is now drawn parallel to QA to represent the other boundary of the incident beam of width CB.

Now, with a compass of radius 1.0 unit centered at C, a circular arc is drawn as shown. Through the point A a tangent is drawn, and from the point of contact, D, the refracted ray CDR is drawn. The other ray, AS, is finally drawn parallel to CR to represent the other edge of the refracted beam of width DA.

The law of refraction may now be stated in terms of the line segments BA and CD as follows:

$$\frac{BA}{CD} = \mu \qquad (1)$$

It was the Dutch astronomer and mathematician, Willebrord Snell,* who first discovered, from experiments, that the ratio of these two lines is the same for all angles of incidence for a given substance. In other words, μ is a constant. The relation as given by Eq. (1) is, therefore, called Snell's law. The reason for the constancy of this ratio is that, while the light travels from B to A in air, it travels the correspondingly lesser distance, CD, in glass.

Snell's Law of Refraction. It is customary, in treating the refraction of light, to express Snell's law in trigonometric terms. Referring to Fig. D, triangles ABC and ADC are right triangles. Because line PC is

*Willebrord Snell (1591-1626) was born at Leyden in 1591. At the age of twenty-two, he succeeded his father as professor of mathematics at the University of Leyden. In 1617, he determined the size of the earth from measurements of its curvature between Alkmaar and Bergen-op-Zoom. In 1621, he discovered the law of refraction, which now carries his name.

$\perp$ to CB, and line MA is $\perp$ to AC, angle i = angle BCA. By similar relations, angle r = angle CAD. From triangles ABC and ACD—

$$BA = AC \sin i$$

$$CD = AC \sin r$$

Substituting these values on the right for BA and CD in Eq. (1) gives—

$$\frac{BA}{CD} = \frac{AC \sin i}{AC \sin r} = \frac{\sin i}{\sin r} = \mu$$

or—

$$\mu = \frac{\sin i}{\sin r} \qquad (2)$$

A more general form is

$$\mu_1 \sin i = \mu_2 \sin r \qquad (3)$$

where μ_1 is the index of refraction in the medium in which the ray is incident, and μ_2 where the ray is refracted. Where one of the media is air or vacuum, one of the indices is equal to 1, and the formula becomes the same as Eq. (2).

Example. Light, in air, is incident at an angle of 45° on the surface of a glass plate for which the refractive index is 1.52. Through what angle is the light deviated upon refraction at the top surface?

Solution. First, find the angle of refraction, r, by use of Eq. (2). By substituting the given quantities, we obtain—

$$\sin r = \frac{\sin i}{\mu} = \frac{\sin 45°}{1.52} = \frac{0.707}{1.52} = 0.465$$

If we look up 0.465 in a table of sines, we find that angle $r = 27.7°$. Because the deviation of the light is the difference between angle i and angle r (45° − 27.7°)—

$$\text{deviation} = 17.3°$$

Displacement in a Parallel Plate. One very useful principle concerning the behavior of light is *reversibility of light rays*. If, in any of the experiments or illustrations already described, the light rays could be reversed in direction, they would be found to retrace their paths exactly.

If a beam of light, on being refracted into a denser medium like glass, is bent toward the normal, light passing through and out of this denser medium into the air should be bent away from the normal. This can be demonstrated by sending light is very thin, as in the case of an ordinary windowpane, the displacement is quite small and for most practical purposes can be neglected.

Refraction by a Prism. When light passes through a prism, it is refracted at two surfaces, once on the way in and once on the way out. If the two sides involved are

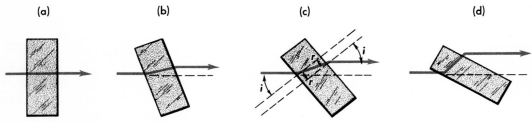

Fig. E. Illustrating the lateral displacement of a beam of light passing through a parallel plate of glass.

through a plane-parallel plate of glass as illustrated in Fig. E. In (c) the light is incident on the first surface at an angle i and is refracted at an angle r. This internal ray is now incident on the second surface at the same angle r and is refracted into the air at the same angle i. The light thus emerges in a direction parallel to the original beam but displaced from it laterally.

This lateral displacement is zero for normal incidence as in (a) and increases with the angle i as shown in figures (b), (c), and (d), respectively. If the parallel plate parallel, as they are in Fig. F, diagram (a), the emergent ray is always parallel to the incident ray. If the sides are not parallel, as in diagrams (b), (c), and (d), the emergent ray has a different direction. The larger the angle, A, between the two refracting surfaces, the larger is the angle of deviation, D. Upon entering the prism at the first surface, see diagram (d), the light is bent toward the normal. Emerging into the air from the second surface, the light is bent away from the normal. Note in Fig. F that neither the apex nor the base of the prism

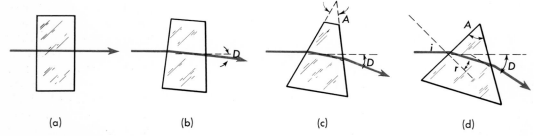

Fig. F. Illustrating the bending of a beam of light by prisms made of the same glass.

has any effect on the deviation of the light.

In verifying these results by experiment, light of only one color should be used, because white light will spread out into a spectrum of colors. Light of one color only is readily obtained by inserting a piece of red or green colored glass into a beam of white light.

The Critical Angle. When light passes from a medium, such as air, into a more dense medium, like glass or water, the angle of refraction is always less than the angle of incidence. As a result of this decrease in angle, there exists a range of angles for which no refracted light is possible. To see what this range of angles is, consider the diagram in Fig. G where, for several angles of

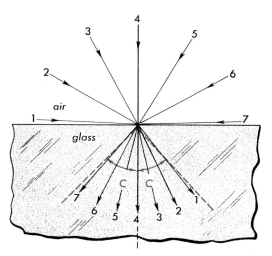

Fig. G. Illustrating the critical angle.

incidence, the corresponding angles of refraction are shown. Note that, in the limiting case where the incident rays approach the angle of 90°, i.e., where they graze along the surface, the refracted rays approach a certain angle, c, beyond which no refracted light is possible. In any medium, this limiting angle, called *the critical angle*, depends

for its value upon the index of refraction.

To calculate the critical angle of refraction, note that the angle of incidence $i = 90°$ and angle $r =$ angle c. Because sin $90° = 1$, Snell's law becomes—

$$\mu = \frac{1}{\sin c}$$

or—

$$\sin c = \frac{1}{\mu} \qquad (4)$$

For the most common of crown glass, $\mu = 1.515$, so that substitution in this formula gives $c = 41.3°$. For water of index $\mu = 1.33$, substitution gives $c = 49°$. It should be noted in particular that the critical angle is measured from the normal and not from the refracting surface.

Total Reflection. Another experiment illustrating the reversibility of light rays is shown in Fig. H. A beam of light is re-

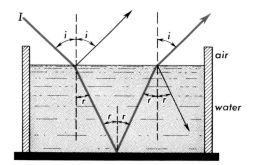

Fig. H. Illustration of reflection and refraction.

fracted at an angle, r, into a tank of water. From there it is reflected from a silvered mirror at the bottom of the tank, illustrating the law of reflection in a medium other than air. The reflected ray arriving at the upper surface at the same angle, r, is refracted into the air at the incident angle, i. At each refraction at the air-water boundary, a small amount of the incident light is reflected as indicated by the black arrows.

When a beam of light within a medium, like water or glass, approaches the surface at an angle greater than the critical angle, all of the light is reflected back into the medium. In other words, a water-to-air or glass-to-air surface acts under these conditions like a perfect reflector. This phenomenon is called *total reflection*. Because no light can be refracted into the water at such an angle (see Fig. G), none inside the water and at large angles of incidence can be refracted out. The experiment is illustrated with a tank of water as shown in Fig. I. If

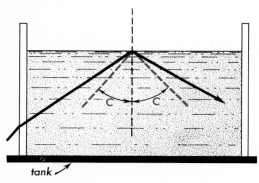

Fig. I. Illustration of total reflection and the critical angle c.

light is sent into the water through a glass plate in one end, the light approaches the upper surface at an angle greater than c, there to be totally reflected back into the water as shown.

The critical angle is the minimum angle of incidence at which light is totally reflected at a boundary.

An interesting demonstration can be performed with a clear glass or plastic rod bent into almost any form as shown in Fig. J. Light, on entering one end, reflects from wall to wall by total reflection, causing it to follow the rod to the end and emerge as a divergent beam. Various instruments used by physicians and surgeons employ this principle for internal body observations.

Total reflection is also employed in such optical instruments as telescopes, microscopes, prism binoculars, and spectroscopes. The optical parts employing this principle

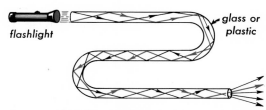

Fig. J. Light follows a bent rod by total reflection.

are known as *total reflection prisms*. Such prisms are usually made of common glass with one angle a right angle and the other two 45° angles. As illustrated in Fig. K,

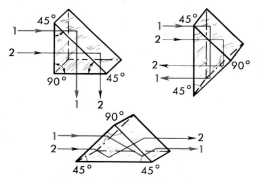

Fig. K. Total reflection prisms.

there are three ways in which these prisms may be used. Incident normally upon the first surface, as in (*a*), the light enters the prism without deviation. Arriving at the second surface at an angle of 45°, just 3° greater than the critical angle, the light is totally reflected according to the law of reflection. Having thus been deviated through 90°, the light passes normally through the third surface without further deviation. The prism has, therefore, acted like a plane mirror.

QUESTIONS

1. (a) What is refraction? (b) Where exactly does it take place?
2. (a) What is Snell's law? (b) What is the refractive index? (c) Does Snell's law hold for all angles?
3. What is meant by the sine of an angle?
4. (a) What is the principle of reversibility of light? (b) Does it hold for both reflection and refraction?
5. (a) How does the principle of reversibility apply to refraction by a parallel plate of glass? (b) When is light not shifted laterally by a thick glass plate?
6. (a) Upon what factors does the deviation of light by a prism depend? (b) Does the angle of deviation depend on the refractive index?
7. How could you trace a ray of light through a prism, using pencil, paper, and a ruler?
8. Why does a properly cut diamond sparkle more than an identically cut piece of glass?
9. Assuming that you were going fishing by using a spear, how would you aim your shot to catch the fish? Explain.
10. Why do objects in water appear to be higher than they actually are?
11. Why are astronomers positive that the moon has no atmosphere?
12. (a) What is the critical angle? (b) How is it determined from the refractive index?
13. (a) What is total reflection? (b) How can it be demonstrated?
14. (a) What is a total-reflecting prism? (b) How is it used?

PROBLEMS

1. Light is incident at 50° on the surface of a clear crystal whose refractive index is 1.25. Construct a refraction diagram similar to Fig. D and determine the angle of refraction. Check your result by calculation, using Snell's law.
2. Light is incident at 60° on the surface of glass whose refractive index is 1.65. Calculate the angle of (a) refraction and (b) deviation.
3. Light is incident at an angle of 70° on the surface of a diamond whose refractive index is 2.42. Calculate the angle of (a) refraction and (b) deviation.
4. Light is incident at an angle of 55° on one face of a 60° prism. Graphically, find the total deviation of the light if the refractive index is 1.50.
5. A rectangular glass-sided aquarium filled with water is 1 ft thick. Find the lateral displacement of a beam of light incident on one of the sides at 30°. Neglect the glass thickness. (Refractive index for water, $\mu = 1.33$.)
6. Light is incident at an angle of 60° on one face of a 5-cm glass cube whose refractive index is 1.50. Calculate lateral displacement of the light that emerges from the opposite side.

7. A ray of light incident on a glass surface at an angle of 45° is deviated through an angle of 18°. Find the refractive index.
8. Light is incident at an angle of 45° on one face of a 60° glass prism. Calculate the total deviation of the light if the refractive index is 1.65.
9. Calculate the deviation of a beam of light incident on a glass surface of index 1.50 at the following angles; (a) 0°, (b) 15°, (c) 30°, (d) 45°, (e) 60°, (f) 75° and (g) 90°.
10. Plot the results of Problem 9 as a graph, with the angle of incidence horizontal and the deviation angle vertical.
11. Calculate the critical angle for yellow light and crown glass. (See Table 1 in Lesson 65.)
12. Calculate the critical angle for violet light and diamond.
13. Calculate the critical angle for green light and ice.
14. If the critical angle of a piece of glass is 40°, what is its refractive index?
15. If the critical angle of a transparent material is 54°, what is its refractive index?

PROJECTS

1. Develop a disk-type demonstration that will show refraction and total reflection by differently shaped prisms.
2. Assemble a collection of variously shaped plastic or glass rods to show how total internal reflection is used by doctors and dentists.
3. Make a working model of the new glass-fiber technique for transmitting pictures, which makes use of the principle of total internal reflection.

LIGHT

Lesson 63 *LENSES*

Lenses. The primary function of a lens is to form images of real objects. Although most lenses are made of common glass, a few special lenses are made of other transparent materials like *quartz* and *fluorite*. To understand how lenses function, imagine a set of several matched prisms and blocks of glass arranged in the order shown in Fig. A.

In the first arrangement, the prisms are made so as to refract the incoming parallel light rays and to converge them to a focus at *F*. In the second arrangement, the parallel rays are made to diverge as if they had come from a common point, *F'*. In each system, the greatest deviation occurs at the outermost prisms, for they have the greatest angle between the two refracting surfaces. No deviation occurs for the central rays, for at that point the glass faces are parallel to each other.

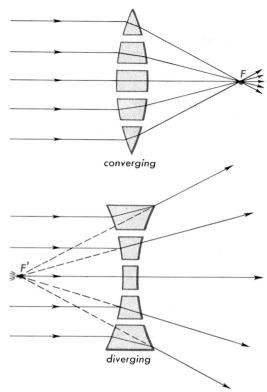

Fig. A. Matched sets of prisms illustrating lens-like action.

A real lens is not made of prisms but of a solid piece of glass with surfaces ground to the form of a spherical surface. Cross sections of several standard forms are shown in Fig. B. The first three lenses, which are

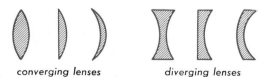

converging lenses   diverging lenses

Fig. B. Cross sections of standard forms of common lenses.

thicker in the center, are called *converging* or *positive lenses,* while the last three, which are thinner in the center, are called

diverging or *negative lenses.* Special names attached to each of the six lens types shown are (1) *double convex,* (2) *plano-convex,* (3) *convex miniscus,* (4) *double concave,* (5) *plano-concave,* and (6) *concave miniscus.*

Diagrams showing the refraction of light by converging and diverging lenses are given in Fig. C. The principal axis in each

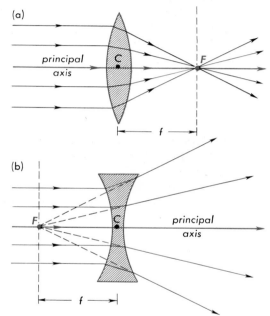

Fig. C. Converging and diverging lenses.

case is a straight line passing through the center of a lens, perpendicular to the two faces at the points of intersection. The principal focus, F, lies on the principal axis and is defined, for a converging lens, as the point where parallel light rays are brought together and, for a negative lens, as a point from which parallel light rays appear to originate.

By symmetry, every lens has two principal foci, one on each side of the lens, each at the same distance from the center of the lens. The distance from the focal point to the lens is called the *focal length:*

$$CF = \textbf{focal length} = f$$

A plane perpendicular to the principal axis, which passes through either principal focus, is called the *focal plane.* Parallel light rays entering the lens from any other direction than shown in the diagrams will come to a focus at some point on the focal plane. This point is readily located by remembering that a ray through the lens center does not change direction.

point, as in diagram (*a*), the expanding waves pass through the lens and come out as plane waves, i.e., as parallel light. In diagram (*b*), incident plane waves are shown emerging from the lens as converging waves, which come to a focus at *F.* The change brought about by the lens can be explained by the fact that light travels faster in air than it does in glass.

It is important to note that the time taken for light rays leaving the point source and arriving at the point image is the same for all paths.

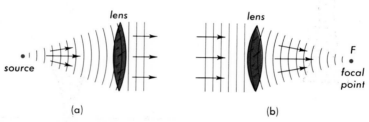

Fig. D. The behavior of light waves as they pass through a converging lens.

The greater the curvature of the two surfaces of a lens, the shorter is its focal length. The reason for this, as can be seen from the diagrams, is that the greater the curvature, the greater is the deviation of the light rays passing through near the edges of the lens.

One important principle concerning lenses is the reversibility of light rays. If a point source of light is placed at *F* in Fig. C(*a*), the rays of light that strike the lens will be refracted into a parallel beam of light moving to the left. Similarly in Fig. C(*b*), if light rays are converging toward the focal point, *F*, they will be refracted by the lens into a parallel beam.

The action of the wave fronts in a converging lens is illustrated in Fig. D. If a point source of light is placed at the focal

Image Formation. When an object is placed on one side of a converging lens beyond the principal focus, a real image will be formed on the opposite side of the lens. This is illustrated in Fig. E. If the object is moved closer to the focal point, the image will be formed farther away from the lens and will be bigger, that is, magnified. As the object is moved farther away from the lens, the image is formed closer to the focal point and is smaller in size.

In general, there are two ways of accurately determining the position of an image: one is by graphical construction and the other is by use of the lens formula:

$$\frac{1}{d_o} + \frac{1}{d_i} = \frac{1}{f} \qquad (1)$$

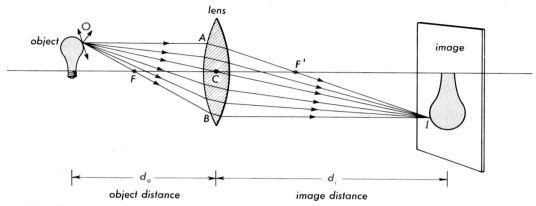

Fig. E. Ray diagram illustrating the formation of a real image by means of a single converging lens.

where d_o is the object distance, d_i the image distance, and f the focal length.

The graphical method is illustrated in Fig. F. Consider the light emitted by some one particular point like O in the object. Of

note that the ray OF, which passes from O through the focal point, F, by the principle of the reversibility of light rays, will be refracted parallel to the principal axis, crossing the other ray at I, as shown.

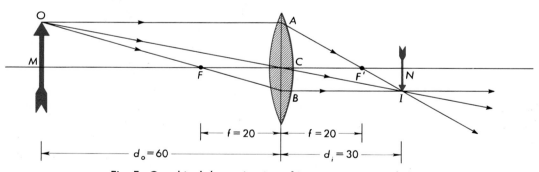

Fig. F. Graphical determination of image position and size.

the rays going out from this point in all directions, the ray, OA, traveling parallel to the principal axis will be refracted to pass through the focal point F'. See Fig. C(a). The ray, OC, arriving at the center of the lens where the faces are parallel will pass straight through, meeting the other ray at some point I. These two rays locate the tip of the image at I. All other rays from the point O that strike the lens will be brought to a focus at this same point. To check this,

The use of the lens formula can be illustrated by the following example. Let an object be placed 60 cm in front of a lens of focal length 20 cm. If we solve Eq. (1) for d_i, we obtain the expression—

$$d_i = \frac{d_o \times f}{d_o - f} \qquad (2)$$

Then, substituting the known quantities, we obtain—

$$d_i = \frac{60 \times 20}{60 - 20} = 30 \text{ cm}$$

The image is formed 30 cm from the lens or 10 cm from F.

Magnification. The size of an image can be calculated from the following simple relation:

$$\frac{\text{size of image}}{\text{size of object}} = \frac{\text{image distance}}{\text{object distance}}$$

This is the image formula:

$$\frac{I}{O} = \frac{d_i}{d_o} \qquad (3)$$

in which the ratio I/O is called the *magnification*. If we substitute known values of O, d_i, and d_o from the lens-formula problem in the preceding section, we obtain—

$$m = \frac{I}{O} = \frac{30}{60} \qquad I = \tfrac{1}{2}O$$

The answer shows that the image is half the size of the object and that the magnification is ½.

If a centimeter rule is used to construct this problem graphically, the resultant diagram will be similar to Fig. F. Each line is drawn in its proper position and size and, when the image is located by rays (1), (2), and (3), its position and size are measured by the same scale. Drawn carefully, the graphical results will agree in every detail with those calculated according to the above formula.

Virtual Images. The images formed by the lenses in Figs. E and F are *real*. *Real images* are defined as those that can be formed on a screen and are characterized by the fact that rays of light are actually brought together to a focus there. *Virtual images* are not real, they cannot be formed on a screen, and the rays from different points on the object do not pass through corresponding points in the image. Virtual images may be observed with a converging lens by placing an object close to the lens and inside the focal point, or by a diverging lens with the object at any point. These two examples are illustrated in Fig. G.

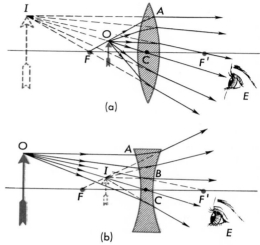

Fig. G. Illustration of the formation of virtual images.

In the first case, the lens is used as a magnifier, or reading glass. Rays of light radiating from the point of the object at O are refracted in the proper direction but are not sufficiently deviated to come to a focus. To the observer's eye at E, these rays appear to be coming from a point, I, back of the lens. This is a *virtual image, right side up and magnified.*

To find this image graphically, we observe that the ray FOA must be refracted parallel to the principal axis. The ray OC through the center of the lens goes on undeviated. These two refracted rays, when extended backward, intersect at I. If the lens formula, Eq. (2), is used to find the image in such a case, the image distance, d_i, will come out as a negative quantity, showing that the image is virtual and on the same side of the lens as the object.

In the case of a negative lens, the image is always virtual, closer to the lens, and smaller in size than the object. As shown in Fig. G(*b*), light rays diverging from the object point, *O*, are made more divergent by the lens. To the observer's eye at *E*, these rays appear to be coming from the point *I* back of, but close to, the lens. To find this image we observe that the ray *OA*, parallel to the principal axis, must be refracted in such a direction that it appears to come from *F*. The ray *OC* through the center goes on undeviated. Because these two directions intersect at *I*, the image is formed there.

In applying the lens formula to a diverging lens, the focal length, *f*, is always *negative* in sign. To illustrate this, consider the following example.

Example. An object is placed 30 cm in front of a diverging lens of focal length of 15 cm. Locate the image position.

Solution. Direct substitution in Eq. (2) gives—

$$d_i = \frac{30 \times (-15)}{30 - (-15)} \quad \text{or} \quad d_i = \frac{-450}{45}$$

From which—

$$d_i = -10 \text{ cm}$$

The image is found at 10 cm from the lens, the negative sign indicating that it is virtual and, therefore, on the same side of the lens as the object.

A convenient sign convention for all lens problems solved with Eqs. (1) or (2) is the following:

(*1*) *Numerical values of real-object distances are always positive.*

(*2*) *Numerical values of real-image distances are positive; numerical values of virtual-image distances are negative.*

(*3*) *Numerical values of focal lengths of convergent lenses are positive; those of divergent lenses are negative.*

QUESTIONS

1. (a) What is a converging lens? (b) What is a diverging lens? (c) How can you tell a converging from a diverging lens by feel?
2. (a) How does one find the focal points of a lens? (b) What is the focal length?
3. (a) If you know the focal length of a lens, how can you produce a parallel beam of light? (b) Can a diverging lens be used for this purpose? Explain.
4. (a) If the object distance and focal length are known, how can you find the image formed by a single lens? (b) Write the formula.
5. (a) Where does the object have to be placed to form a virtual image with a converging lens? (b) Where should it be to insure that a real image will be formed?
6. Can an object be located at any point near a concave lens so that (a) a real image is formed or (b) a virtual image cannot be formed?
7. If object and image are interchanged, will the image be the same in both cases? (Try this with a lens.)
8. What kind of image would be formed by a converging lens if it is viewing an object at infinity?
9. (a) Why is it possible to start a fire with certain kinds of lenses? (b) What kind of lens would it have to be?

10. Why might it be possible for a bottle of soft drink to start a fire? Explain.

11. What kind of image would you see if you held an object at a distance equal to the focal length of the lens? Explain.

12. (a) What can be said about a lens if an object produces a real image? (b) Is the image erect or inverted?

13. (a) What can be said about a lens if an object produces a virtual image? (b) Is the image erect or inverted?

14. Under what conditions does a converging lens produce a real image?

15. Is a concave meniscus lens converging or diverging? Explain.

PROBLEMS

1. An object 5 cm high is located 12 cm in front of a converging lens of focal length equal to +8 cm. Find (a) the position and (b) the size of the image by the lens formula and by the graphical method.

2. An object 3 in. high is located 20 in. in front of a lens of focal length equal to +12 in. Find (a) the position and (b) the size of the image by the lens formula and by the graphical method.

3. A lens has a focal length of +6 cm. Find (a) the position and (b) the size of the image if an object 4 cm high is located 15 cm in front of the lens.

4. An object 3 cm high is located 8 cm in front of a converging lens of focal length 12 cm. Find the position of the image.

5. An object 3 cm high is located 10 cm in front of a converging lens of 5-cm focal length. Find (a) the image distance by calculation and (b) the image size by graphical construction.

6. An object 2 cm high is located 5 cm in front of a converging lens of 10-cm focal length. Find (a) the image distance by calculation and (b) the image size by graphical construction.

7. An object is located 15 cm in front of a diverging lens with a 5-cm focal length. Find (a) the image distance by calculation and (b) the image size by graphical construction.

8. An object is located in the focal plane of a diverging lens. (a) Where is the image formed? (b) How large is the image? (c) Is it real or virtual? (d) Is it inverted or erect?

9. An object 1 cm high is located 4 cm in front of a converging lens of 5-cm focal length. (a) Where is the image formed? (b) Make a diagram and find the height of the image. (c) How much larger is the image than the object.

10. A real image is to be formed three times as far from a converging lens as the object. Find (a) the object distance and (b) the image distance.

11. A converging lens produces an image whose size is equal to the object size. (a) How is the image distance related to the object distance? (b) How is the image distance related to the focal length of the lens?

12. An object 10 cm from a lens produces an image 5 cm from the lens. (a) What

is the focal length if the lens is double concave? (b) What is the focal length if the lens is double convex?

13. A 6-in. pencil close to an 8-in. focal-length lens produces a real image 24 in. long. How far is the pencil from the lens?

PROJECTS

1. Make a simple slide projector using a single converging lens. Try lenses of different focal lengths to measure the effect on the size of image produced at a given projector-to-screen distance.
2. Make a small searchlight, and try to make the beam as parallel as possible.

LIGHT

Lesson 64 *THE EYE AND OPTICAL INSTRUMENTS*

The Camera. Because the photographic camera often employs but a single lens unit, it may be considered as one of the simplest of all optical instruments. As illustrated by the bellows camera in Fig. A, a converging

Fig. A. Diagram of image formation by a camera.

lens forms a *real* and *inverted image* on the film. If the object is far away, the light rays approaching the lens are nearly parallel and the image is formed at the focal plane. If the object is close up, the image will be formed beyond the focal plane as shown in the diagram. To permit distant landscapes

or "close ups" to be photographed with this camera, a bellows is used, allowing the lens distance to be varied at will. Moving the lens to the proper image distance is called *focusing.*

Only a simple converging lens is used in the cheapest of cameras, which means that the common defects of images are present to produce a slightly blurred or diffuse image. In more expensive cameras, however, the most objectionable defects are fairly well corrected by a compound lens made of several individual lenses.

The Eye. When light from a distant object passes through the lens system of the eye, it is refracted and brought to a focus on the *retina*. There, a real but inverted image of the object is formed. It is a most amazing fact that, while all retinal images are inverted as shown in Fig. B, they are interpreted by the brain as being erect.

Accommodation is the ability to focus the eyes on near and far objects. In a

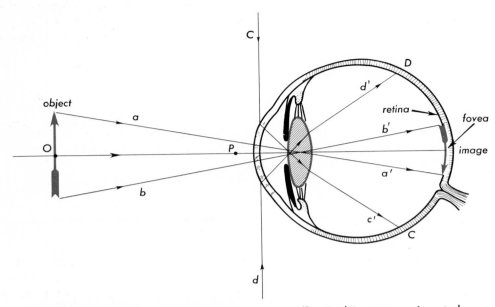

Fig. B. The human eye is similar to a camera. All retinal images are inverted.

camera, the focusing of a picture on the photographic film or plate is usually accomplished by moving the lens toward or away from the film. In the human eye, however, *focusing is brought about by changing the shape of the crystalline lens.* This is accomplished by a rather complicated system of ligaments and muscles. Because of a tension that exists in the *lens capsule*, the crystalline lens, if completely free, would tend to become spherical in shape. The edge of the lens is surrounded by the *ciliary muscle*, which, by contracting, causes the lens to bulge out. This reduces the focal length of the lens, bringing nearby objects to focus on the retina. When the ciliary muscle relaxes, the *suspensory ligaments*, being under tension, pull at the edges of the lens, thus tending to flatten it. Under these conditions the focal length increases, bringing distant objects to focus on the retina. This is the accommodation process.

The normal eye is most relaxed when it is focused for **parallel light, i.e., for objects** far away. To study the detail of an object, however, the object should be brought close to the eye. The reason for this is that the closer the object is to the eye, the larger is the image formed on the retina. A distance of about 25 cm is found to be the distance of most distinct vision. Prolonged observation at distances of 25 cm or less will result in a considerable amount of fatigue and eyestrain.

Eye Correction with Spectacle Lenses. As the average person grows older, the crystalline lens of the eye tends to harden and the muscles that control it to grow weaker, thus making accommodation more and more difficult. The existence of these conditions is referred to as *presbyopia*. The speed of the hardening varies with the individual.

If the length of the eyeball is such that parallel incident rays converge to a point in front of the retina as in Fig. C(*a*), the person is nearsighted and is said to have *myopia*. If parallel incident rays converge to a point back of the retina, as in diagram (b), the person is farsighted and is said to have *hypermetropia*.

rays before they meet the eye lens and thus enable distant objects to be seen in good focus. To see close at hand, this same eye

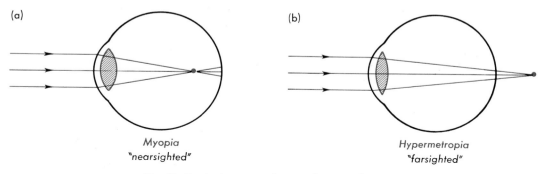

Fig. C. Typical eye conditions of certain humans.

To correct these defects, a diverging lens of the proper focal length is placed in front of the myopic eye and a converging lens of the proper focal length in front of the hypermetropic eye. The function of such

requires the use of a converging lens of still greater power. In other words, this person should wear bifocals, lenses whose upper and lower parts have different focal lengths.

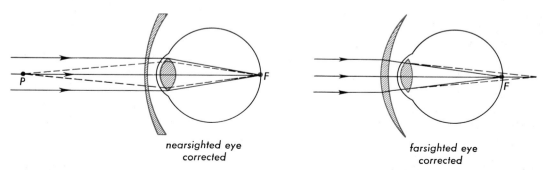

Fig. D. Nearsighted and farsighted eyes can be corrected by the proper selection of spectacle lenses.

lenses is shown in Fig. D. For the nearsighted eye, rays from a nearby object at some point, *P*, will, in the absence of spectacles, come to focus on the *fovea*, *F*. Insertion of the proper diverging lens will now diverge parallel rays as if they came from *P* and thus bring a distant object to focus at, *F*. For the farsighted eye, a converging lens adds some convergence to the incoming

The Telescope. History informs us that the first telescope was probably constructed in Holland in 1608 by an obscure spectacle-lens grinder, Hans Lippershey. A few months later Galileo, upon hearing that objects at a distance may be made to appear close at hand by means of two lenses, designed and made with his own hands the first authentic telescope. The elements of this telescope are still in existence and may be seen on exhibit in Florence, Italy.

Astronomical telescopes today are practically the same in principle as they were in

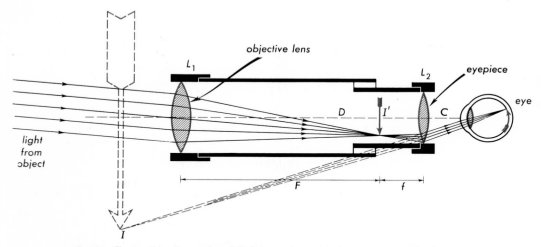

Fig. E. Illustrating the paths of light rays in a simple astronomical telescope.

the earliest days of their development. A diagram of a small telescope is shown in Fig. E. Light rays from a single point of a far distant object are shown entering the *objective lens* as a parallel beam. These rays are brought to a focus and form a point image at I'. In a similar manner, parallel sets of rays from other points of the same object (not shown) will form point images in the focal plane of the objective. Assuming that the distant object is an arrow pointing upward, the image, as shown in the diagram by a black arrow, is *real* and *inverted*.

The function of the second lens in a telescope is to magnify the image formed by the objective. For this purpose a converging lens of short focus, called the *eyepiece*, is usually used.

The magnifying power of a telescope is defined as the ratio between the angle subtended at the eye by the final image, I, and the angle subtended at the eye by the object itself. In other words, it is the number

of times larger an object appears to be when viewed with the telescope. When plane geometry is applied to a simple light-ray diagram of a telescope, it is found that the magnifying power is equal to the ratio of the focal lengths of the two lenses:

$$\textbf{magnifying power} = \frac{F}{f} \qquad (1)$$

where F is the focal length of the objective, and f is the focal length of the eyepiece.

The Reflection Telescope. Nearly all of the very large astronomical telescopes in the world today employ concave mirrors instead of lenses. There are several advantages to this: first, a concave mirror does not exhibit chromatic aberration, thereby requiring but one piece of glass and one surface to be ground; and second, greater stability of the telescope is attained by having the large and heaviest optical part at the bottom of the instrument.

Telescopes are made as large as economically feasible to increase their light-gathering capability as well as to make it possible for them to separate objects that are close together. An 8-in. telescope, which an amateur can make without elaborate tools, but with much patience, will focus approximately one thousand times as much light as the unaided eye on the human retina.

A diagram of the great 100-in. reflecting telescope of the Mt. Wilson Observatory is shown in Fig. F. Parallel light rays enter-

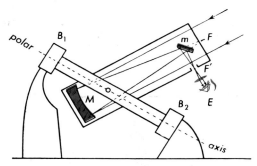

Fig. F. Diagram of the 100-in. reflecting telescope of the Mt. Wilson Observatory.

ing the telescope tube are brought to a focus at F. Instead of viewing or photographing images at this point, a small mirror, m, reflects the convergent rays to a focus at F'. Here, out of the path of the incoming light, the star images can be observed and photographed. The small mirror, m, casts a shadow on the objective mirror, M, but the shadow is relatively so small that only an insignificant percent of the light is lost.

The 200-in. telescope now in operation on Palomar Mountain in Southern California is of the same optical design. The objective mirror is nearly 17 ft in diameter and has a hole 40 in. in diameter through its center. This hole cuts out only 4% of the mirror's total area. For various kinds of observations, photographic instruments are located in an observing booth, 60 in. in diameter, at the focal plane, F, in Fig. F. On other occasions, a 40-in. convex mirror is

placed at m, and the light is reflected back down the telescope tube through the hole in the big objective, where it is brought to a focus below the telescope.

Prism Binoculars. Prism binoculars are in reality a pair of twin telescopes mounted side by side, one for each of the two eyes. The objective lenses in front and the eyepieces at the rear are converging lenses as in the astronomical telescope, but each pair of total reflecting prisms (see Fig. G) in-

Fig. G. Cutaway of a prism binocular showing the lenses and reflecting prisms. (Courtesy of Bausch & Lomb Optical Company)

verts the rays to give erect images. The doubling back of the light rays permits the use of long-focus objective lenses in short tubes, thus giving high magnification in a handier form than that of the telescope. In addition to good achromatic lenses and accurately ground prisms, there are three features that go to make up good binoculars: these are (1) *magnification*, (2) *field of view*, and (3) *light-gathering power*.

For hand-held use, binoculars with a 6-, 7-, or 8-power magnification are most generally useful. Glasses with powers above 8 are desirable but require a tripod mount to hold them steady. For powers less than 4, lens aberrations usually offset the advantage of magnification and the average person can usually see better with the unaided eyes.

The Microscope. The simplest of microscopes is just a single converging lens of short focus used as a magnifier, as shown in Fig. I. Since the shortest focal-length lenses produce the greatest magnification, it is not surprising that small glass beads in the form of perfect spheres were the first really successful microscopes. Lenses of this description were used by the famous Dutch microscopist, Anton van Leeuwen-

where f is the focal length of the lens, and M is the magnification.

The compound microscope, which exceeds by far the magnifying power of a simple microscope, was invented by Galileo in 1610. Like a telescope, this instrument consists of an optical train of two lenses, one called the *objective* and the other the *eyepiece*. The objective of the microscope differs from the telescope, however, in that, instead of having a long focus, it has a short focus and it is placed close to the object, as shown in Fig. H. This lens

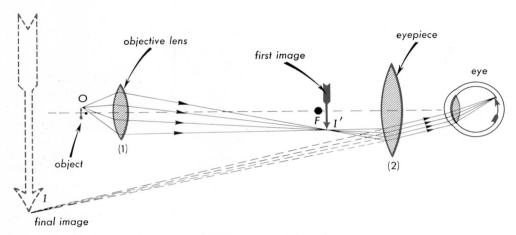

Fig. H. Lens and ray diagram of a compound microscope.

hoek, when in 1674 he discovered and gave an accurate account of the red corpuscles in blood.

With the unaided eye, most people can focus clearly on objects approximately 25 cm away. The closer an object is to the eye, the larger it appears to be. A short focal-length lens can be placed very close to the object and it, in turn, forms a virtual image at about 25 cm from the eye. The approximate magnification is given by the equation—

$$M = \frac{25}{f} \qquad (2)$$

forms a real and magnified image at a point, I', just in front of the eyepiece. Because the eyepiece is another short-focus lens, it is used as a simple microscope, or magnifying glass, to produce a magnified virtual image at I. In other words, the real image, I', of the first lens becomes the object for the second lens.

It is convenient to divide the study of the microscope into two parts. The first part concerns the magnification produced by the objective lens. A diagram of a short focus lens with its focal points, F, as well as object and image, is shown in Fig. I.

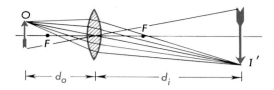

Fig. I. Showing the function of the objective lens of a microscope.

Note how the object, O, lying just outside the focal point at a distance d_o from the lens, forms a large image, I', at a distance d_i. As we have seen, the magnification of such a lens is given by the relation—

$$M_O = \frac{d_i}{d_o} \qquad (3)$$

The second part, as shown in Fig. J, is

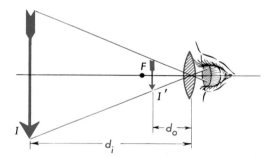

Fig. J. Showing the function of the eyepiece of a microscope.

the eyepiece, with its object I' at a distance d_o from the lens and its image I as a virtual but magnified image. The magnification of such a lens is given by—

$$M_E = \frac{d_i}{d_o} \qquad (4)$$

When the two are combined, as shown in Fig. H, the over-all magnification is just the ratio of the final image size, I, to the original object size:

$$M = \frac{I}{O} \qquad (5)$$

and this is just the product of one magnification by the other:

$$M = M_O \times M_E \qquad (6)$$

For example, if the first lens made a 1-mm object appear 3 mm long, and the second lens made this 3-mm image look 12 mm long, $M_O = 3\times$, $M_E = 4\times$, and $M = 12\times$. The $\times$ is read as *times*.

Early forms of the compound microscope displayed so much chromatic aberration that only low magnifying powers were attained. High-powered microscopes of to-day overcome this and other defects by using an objective containing as many as eight or ten lenses and an eyepiece containing two or more. Under suitable illumination, magnifying powers of a little more than 2000 diameters are commonly attained. Although this is not an upper limit to the magnification for optical microscopes of the future, we know from the wave nature of light that the ultimate limit is not many times that which has already been attained. This is not a pessimistic attitude but a scientific truth based upon our present knowledge of the atomic structure of matter itself.

The electron microscope, capable of magnifications 50 to 100 times that of the best optical microscope, is discussed in Lesson 92.

QUESTIONS

1. (a) What are the principal elements of a camera? (b) What kind of image does it form? (c) How is focus accomplished?
2. (a) What are the principal elements of the human eye? (b) What kind of image

is formed on the retina? (c) How is focus accomplished? (d) What is this process called?

3. (a) What is myopia? (b) What causes it? (c) How can it be corrected optically?

4. (a) What is hypermetropia? (b) What causes it? (c) How can it be corrected or improved?

5. How many lenses are required to make a telescope? (b) What are they called?

6. (a) What is the function of the objective lens? (b) Why should it have a long focal length?

7. (a) What is the function of the eyepiece? (b) Why should it have a short focal length?

8. (a) What determines the magnifying power of a telescope? (b) Where is the final image formed?

9. (a) In what ways do prism binoculars differ from an astronomical telescope? (b) What do the prisms accomplish? (c) How many prisms are required?

10. Why do most people eventually wear glasses as they grow older?

11. What are the main reasons for making telescopes with very large-diameter lenses or mirrors?

12. Why is it easier for an amateur to make an excellent reflecting telescope but not a refractor.

13. To get the maximum magnification in microscope, what focal-length objective should be used? Explain.

14. (a) When you look into a microscope do you see a real or virtual image? (b) Is it possible to photograph what you see? Explain.

15. Why is it possible for an 8-mm movie camera to have universal focusing while a large camera requires bellows—or an adjustable lens?

16. What can be done to a camera that focuses only to 4 ft, in order to take clear pictures at shorter distance?

17. A bellows camera is set for a distant object. If the object moves closer, should the bellows be extended or collapsed? Explain.

18. Suppose a human eye could not accommodate and would focus images on the retina only for objects 25 ft away. (a) What kind of spectacle lens should be used when viewing distant objects? (b) When viewing close objects?

PROBLEMS

1. A farsighted person sees distant objects clearly but cannot accommodate for objects close by. What focal length should his spectacles have if he is to read a book held 16 in. away?

2. A nearsighted person sees objects clearly at a distance of 12 in. (a) What kind of spectacle lenses should he use to see distant objects? (b) What should be the focal length?

3. A person with myopia sees clearly objects 6 in. from his eyes. What focal length lenses should this person use to see things clearly (a) far away and (b) at 18 in.?

4. The objective lens of an astronomical telescope has a focal length of $+8$ ft, while the eyepiece has a focal length of $+2$ in. What is its magnifying power?

5. The eyepiece of a 12-power astronomical telescope has a focal length of $+0.75$ in. What is the focal length of the objective?

6. An astronomical telescope objective has a focal length of $+60$ cm. An eyepiece of what focal length will give it a magnification of 15?

7. To an observer on the earth, the moon subtends an angle of approximately 0.5 degrees. If a telescope objective lens with a focal length of $+20$ ft is used to photograph the moon, what will be the diameter of the image formed at the focal plane of the lens?

8. A pair of prism binoculars (marked 8×50) have a magnification of 8. The objective lenses have a diameter of 50 mm and a focal length of 2.7 cm. Find (a) the focal length of the eyepieces and (b) the diameter of the image of the objective lenses formed by the eyepieces.

9. A microscope is made using a 2-cm focal-length objective and a 3-cm focal-length eyepiece. If these lenses are 24.5 cm apart and the object is 2.2 cm in front of the objective, find (a) the distance of the first image from the objective, (b) the distance of the first image from the eyepiece, (c) the distance of the final image from the eyepiece, and (d) the magnification of the microscope.

10. How much more light would a 200-in. telescope gather than (a) a 100-in., (b) a 40 in.?

11. A camera has a 2-in. focal-length lens. It is focused on an object 30 ft away. (a) Where must the film be located? (b) How much would the lens have to be moved to take a clear picture of an object 5 ft away?

12. A small telescope is made by using a lens of 100-cm focal length as the objective lens and a 20-cm eyepiece. Assuming that the person using this device has a minimum clear vision of 23 cm, what is the distance between the two lenses?

PROJECTS

1. Make a model of an eye in which the various defects of the eye can be demonstrated and also the corrections that are possible.

2. Using a kit, grind your own 6- or 8-in. telescope mirror for a homemade telescope. If time is not available, you can make a 4-in. telescope inexpensively by buying a 4-in. mirror already manufactured and finishing the rest yourself.

3. Examine a cheap toy microscope. Measure its actual performance and compare that with the advertisement that describes it.

LIGHT

Lesson 65 *DISPERSION*

It was known to the ancients that sunlight, on passing through transparent crystals and jewels of various kinds, would produce brilliant colors of light. The early philosophers, attempting to explain the phenomenon, attributed the origin of the colors to the crystal itself. It was Newton who first demonstrated with prisms that the colors were already present in the white sunlight and that the function of the prism was to separate the colors by refracting them in different directions.

We have already seen how light of one color is refracted at the boundary of a medium like glass or water and how it is deviated by a prism. It may be seen in Fig. A

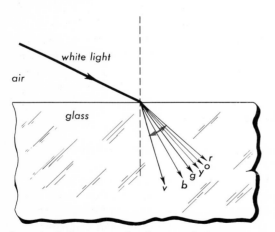

Fig. A. Refraction of white sunlight into its spectrum colors.

how, *with white light, each color is refracted a different amount* to produce its own angle of deviation. *Red light is re-*

fracted least, and violet light is refracted most.

The angular spread of all the colors produced by sending white light through a prism is called *dispersion* and the band of color so produced is called a *spectrum*. See Fig. B.

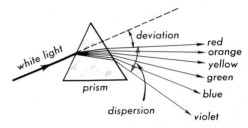

Fig. B. Refraction at both surfaces of a prism produces higher dispersion.

If white light is sent through a group of similar prisms made of different substances, each prism will be found to have a different dispersion. This can be demonstrated for solids by *flint-* and *crown-glass prisms,* and for liquids by *kerosene, carbon dioxide,* and *water.* It will be noted that the two glass prisms in Fig. C, one of flint glass and the other of crown glass, produce quite different dispersions. The liquid prisms, produced by filling thin-walled glass troughs with liquid, also disperse light by different amounts.

Because different colors are refracted by different amounts, the index of refraction is different for each color. In a vacuum, all colors travel with the same speed, about 186,300 mi/sec, but in a transparent me-

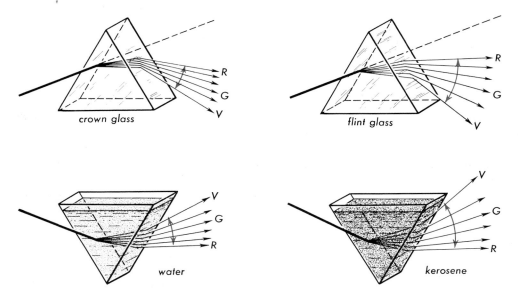

Fig. C. Illustrating the relative dispersion of solid as well as liquid prisms.

dium, like glass or water, they travel considerably slower and at different speeds. Among the spectrum colors, red travels the fastest and violet the slowest, with the speeds of all other colors somewhere in between. In air, there is very little dispersion, and in a vacuum there is absolutely none. This latter statement is proved by the fact that when the dark star of an eclipsing binary (a two-star system) passes in front of its brighter companion, all colors disappear and reappear simultaneously. If one color were to travel slightly faster than another,

the dip in stellar intensity for that color would have plenty of time to get ahead in its many years of travel to the earth.

The refractive indices for a number of transparent solids are given in Table 1. It will be noted that although the values for any one substance do not vary greatly between colors, the values for blue and violet are the largest, and those for orange and red are the smallest. Note the relatively high values for diamond and the relatively low values for ice.

Example. White light is incident at 85° on

Table 1. Refractive Index for Several Transparent Solids

Substance	Violet 4100	Blue 4700	Green 5300	Yellow 5900	Orange 6100	Red 6700
crown glass...............	1.5380	1.5310	1.5260	1.5225	1.5216	1.5200
light flint..................	1.6040	1.5960	1.5910	1.5875	1.5867	1.5850
dense flint.................	1.6980	1.6836	1.6738	1.6670	1.6650	1.6620
quartz.....................	1.5570	1.5510	1.5468	1.5438	1.5432	1.5420
diamond...................	2.4580	2.4439	2.4260	2.4172	2.4150	2.4100
ice........................	1.3170	1.3136	1.3110	1.3087	1.3080	1.3060

one face of a diamond. Calculate the dispersion produced by one surface, that is, the angle between the red and violet rays.

Solution.

$$\sin \theta_r = \sin 85°/\mu_r = .996/2.4100$$
$$= .4132$$
$$\theta_r = 24.4°$$
$$\sin \theta_v = \sin 85°/\mu_v = .996/2.4580$$
$$= .4052$$
$$\theta_v = 23.9°$$

Therefore—

$$\theta_r - \theta_v = 0.5°$$

The Rainbow. The rainbow is nature's most spectacular display of the spectrum of white light. The required conditions for the appearance of the phenomenon are that the sun be shining in one part of the sky and the rain be falling in the opposite part of the sky. With one's back to the sun, one may see the bright *primary bow,* and sometimes the fainter *secondary bow* with colors reversed. Both bows are seen as the arcs of circles. From a high vantage point or from an airplane, these bows may form complete circles whose common center lies in the direction of the observer's shadow.

The general characteristics of the primary and secondary bows are satisfactorily accounted for by considering only the reflection and refraction of light by spherical raindrops. To understand how the phenomenon arises, we first confine our attention to an individual raindrop, as shown in Fig. D. A ray of sunlight is shown entering at a point A near the top. Here, some of the light is reflected (not shown) and the remainder is refracted into the liquid sphere. At this first refraction, the light is dispersed into its spectrum colors, violet being deviated the most and red the least.

Arriving at the opposite side of the drop, each color is partly refracted out into the air (not shown) and partly reflected back into

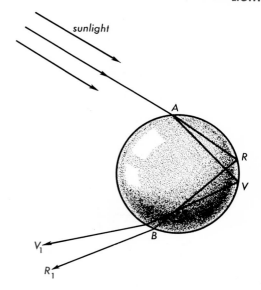

Fig. D. Dispersion of sunlight by a single raindrop. (Primary rainbow)

the liquid. Reaching the surface at the lower boundary, each color is again reflected (not shown) and refracted. This second refraction is quite similiar to that of a prism, as in Fig. B, where refraction at the second surface increases the dispersion already produced at the first. This is the path of the light in thousands of drops giving rise to the bright primary rainbow.

In Fig. E, a ray of sunlight, coming from the same direction as in Fig. A, is shown entering a single raindrop at a point C near

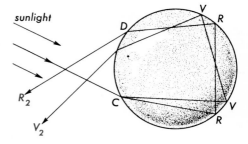

Fig. E. Dispersion of sunlight by a single raindrop. (Secondary rainbow)

the bottom. After one refraction and two internal reflections, the light is again refracted and dispersed, this time in a direction not greatly different from that in Fig. D. This is the path of the light in thousands of drops giving rise to the fainter secondary rainbow.

As shown in Fig. F, the primary bow ap-

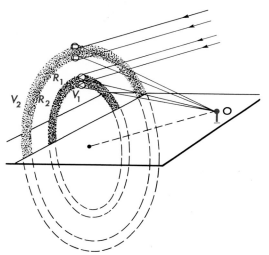

Fig. F. The primary and secondary rainbows as seen by an observer at O.

pears inside the secondary bow and arises from sunlight entering the tops of drops properly located. Those in a region R_1 refract red light toward the observer's eye at O, and the violet and other colors over his head. Drops in the region of V_1 refract violet light to the observer's eye at O, and the red and other colors toward his feet. In other words, the light seen from any one drop is but one color, all drops giving this color lying on the arc of a circle.

Halos. Halos are commonly observed as faint rainbowlike rings around the sun or moon and are due to tiny ice crystals floating in the upper atmosphere. Such crystals are hexagonal in shape and, acting like prisms, refract and disperse white light into

a spectrum. Two halos are frequently observed, the brighter one making an angle of 22° with the luminary and the fainter one an angle of 46°. Both exhibit confused spectrum colors with a decided red tint on the inside.

Crystals, like prisms, refract each color of light at a different angle, as shown in Fig. G. Because they are oriented at random

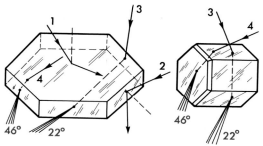

Fig. G. Typical forms of ice crystals showing reflected and refracted rays of sunlight giving rise to halos and "mock suns."

in space, millions of them appear to each observer to concentrate the light in a circle with the luminary at the center.

A demonstration of such color effects can be produced, as shown in Fig. H, by means of a hexagonal or octagonal glass prism rotated rapidly about its axis in a strong beam of white light. Dispersed light, refracted by alternate faces, sweeps in from either side of the screen, slows down, and stops at minimum deviation, and then retreats again. The blurred patches of light on the screen are brightest at the minimum deviation angles, R.

Scattering and the Blue Sky. The blue of the sky and the red of the sunset are owing to a phenomenon called scattering. When sunlight passes through the earth's atmosphere, much of the light is "picked" up by the air molecules and given out again

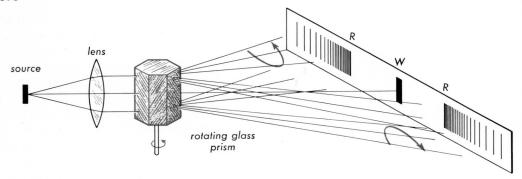

Fig. H. Experiment demonstrating colors produced at minimum deviation by a single rotating prism.

in some other direction. The effect is quite similar to the action of water waves on floating objects. If, for example, the ripples from a stone dropped in a still pond of water encounter a small cork floating on the surface, the cork is set bobbing up and down with the frequency of the passing waves.

Light is pictured as acting in the same way on air molecules and fine dust particles. Once set into vibration by a light wave, a molecule or particle can send out the absorbed light again, sometimes in the same direction but generally in almost any other direction. This is illustrated schematically

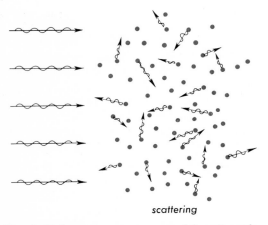

scattering

Fig. I. Light waves are scattered by air molecules.

in Fig. I, where waves of light are shown being scattered at random in all directions.

Experiments show, in agreement with the theory of scattering, that the shortest waves are scattered more readily than longer waves. To be more specific: *scattering is inversely proportional to the fourth power of the wave length:*

$$\text{scattering} \propto \frac{1}{\lambda^4} \qquad (1)$$

According to this law, the short waves of violet light are scattered ten times as readily as the longer waves of red light. The other colors are scattered by intermediate amounts. Thus, when sunlight enters the earth's atmosphere, *violet* and *blue light* are scattered the most, followed by *green, yellow, orange,* and *red,* in the order named. For every ten violet waves scattered from a beam, there is only one red wave:

red orange yellow green blue violet
1   2   3   5   7   10

At noon on a clear day, when the sun is nearly directly overhead, the whole sky appears as *light blue.* This is the composite color of the mixture of colors scattered most effectively by the air molecules. As illustrated by the spectral colors in the lower right spectrum in Lesson 66, Fig. E, light

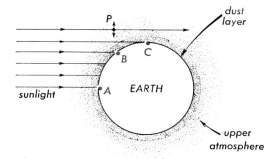

Fig. J. The scattering of light by a layer of dust near the earth's surface causes the sun to turn yellow, then orange, and finally red at sunset.

blue, like cyan, is obtained by adding *violet*, *blue*, *green*, and *yellow* light to the mixture.

The Red Sunset. The occasional orange-red sunset is attributed to the *scattering of light* by fine dust and smoke particles near the earth's surface. This is illustrated in Fig. J. To an observer at *A*, it is noonday and the direct sunlight from overhead, seen only by looking directly at the sun itself, travels through a relatively short dust path. As a result, very little violet and blue are scattered away and the sun appears white.

As sunset approaches, however, the direct sunlight has to travel through an ever-increasing dust path. The result is that an hour or so before sundown, when the observer is at *B*, practically all of the blue and violet have been scattered out, and owing to the remaining colors—red, orange, yellow, and a little green—the sun appears

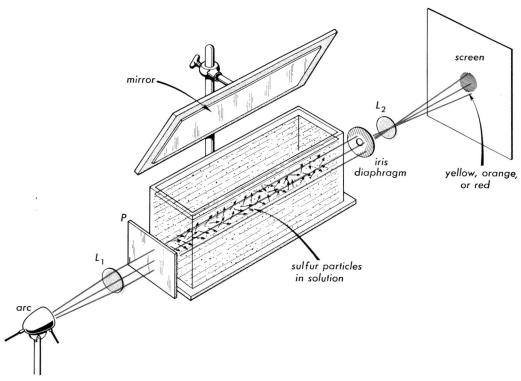

Fig. K. The sunset experiment. Demonstration of the scattering and polarization of light by small particles.

yellow. At sunset, when the observer is at C, the direct rays must travel through so many miles of dust particles that all but red are completely scattered out and the sun appears red. At this same time the sky overhead is still light blue. If the dust blanket is too dense, even the red will be scattered appreciably from the direct sunlight, and the deepening red sun will become lost from view before it reaches the horizon.

An excellent demonstration of scattering by fine particles is illustrated in Fig. K. A parallel beam of white light from a carbon arc and lens L_1 is sent through a water trough with glass sides. After passing through an iris diaphragm at the other end,

a second lens, L_2, forms an image of the circular opening on the screen.*

Tiny sulfur particles develop slowly over a period of from 5 to 10 min. During this time, the beam through the tank turns a sky blue, while the circular disk of light on the screen, representing the sun, turns from white to yellow to orange to red.

---

* To produce the fine particles for scattering, first dissolve about 40 gm of photographic fixing powder (hyposulfite of soda) in about 2 gallons of water. Next, add about 1 to 2 cm³ of concentrated sulfuric acid and mix the two thoroughly in the trough. The correct amount of acid to produce the best results is determined by trial. The first visible precipitate should appear after 2 or 3 min.

QUESTIONS

1. (a) What is dispersion? (b) What kind of light is composed of all colors? (c) Where do the colors come from? (d) Name the colors in their proper order, starting with red.

2. (a) What spectrum color is deviated the most? (b) What color is deviated the least?

3. If 45° prisms were made of the six materials shown in Table 1, which one do you think would produce the largest dispersion?

4. (a) For which color is the refractive index the greatest for a given optical material? (b) For which color is it the least?

5. (a) Under what conditions is a rainbow observed? (b) What is the order of the colors in the primary rainbow? (b) In the secondary rainbow?

6. (a) Could the complete rainbow circle be observed? (b) What are the conditions?

7. (a) What is a halo? (b) What are the conditions for observing halos? (c) How is the color produced?

8. (a) What is scattering? (b) How does it vary with the wave length of light? (c) How does scattering vary with color?

9. (a) Why is the sky blue? (b) If violet light is scattered more than blue, why is the sky light blue in color rather than violet?

10. Under what conditions will the setting sun turn from white to yellow, to orange, and to red? Explain.

11. After a big volcanic eruption, the sky may appear red for many days. In fact, following the eruption of the volcano Agung in 1964, the sunsets viewed all over the world were much redder than usual for over a year afterward. Explain.

12. Make a diagram showing the refraction and dispersion of white light by a single raindrop. Do the same for an ice crystal.

PROBLEMS

1. Light is incident at an angle of 60° on a crown-glass surface. Find (a) the angles of refraction for red and violet light and (b) the dispersion angle between the two colors.

2. Light is incident on dense flint glass at an angle of 60°. Find (a) the angles of refraction for red and violet light and (b) the dispersion angle between the two colors?

3. A ray of white light is incident on one facet of a diamond at an angle of 60°. Find the dispersion angle between red and violet.

4. A 60° prism is made of dense flint glass. A ray of white light is incident on the first surface at an angle of 45°. Find (a) the total deviation for the red and violet light, and (b) the dispersion angle of the spectrum produced.

5. What is the ratio of the scattering of light waves between red light of wave length 7×10^{-5} cm and violet light of wave length 4×10^{-5} cm.

6. For every 200 waves of red light scattered by the air, how many waves of orange light will be scattered? Assume the wave lengths to be 7×10^{-5} cm and 6×10^{-5} cm, respectively.

7. Calculate the ratio of the numbers of light rays scattered by the air for violet light ($\lambda = 4 \times 10^{-5}$ cm) and green light ($\lambda = 5 \times 10^{-5}$ cm).

8. Find the ratio of light waves scattered by fine particles between blue light ($\lambda = 4.3 \times 10^{-5}$) and red light ($\lambda = 7.0 \times 10^{-5}$ cm).

PROJECTS

1. Make a device to show why sunsets are red. A slide projector makes a readily available source of light for this experiment and eliminates need for additional lenses.

2. Make a simple device that could duplicate conditions in nature for the production of a rainbow.

LIGHT

Lesson 66 *COLOR*

Color vision is perhaps the most valued gift of nature. While color is for the most part a physiological phenomenon, its origin is considered by some to belong to the realm of physics. The science of color mixing has been made possible through the discovery that all colors can be completely analyzed by spreading them out into a prismatic spectrum.

Effect of Illumination on Color. For a body to be seen in its true color, that body must be illuminated by light of the same color. If a red rose, as an illustration, is placed in the different colors of a prismatic spectrum, it will appear a brilliant red in red light and grey or black in all the others.

Another experiment is illustrated in Fig. A, where yellow light from a sodium-arc

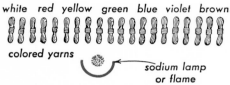

Fig. A. Experiment with colored skeins of yarn showing that, for an object to be seen in its true surface color, it must be illuminated by the proper light.

lamp is shown illuminating a row of colored skeins of yarn. When the lamp is turned on, only the yellow yarn appears with its true color; the white yarn is yellow and the others are black or grey. If the same set of colored yarns is illuminated with red light, only the red yarn will appear in its true color; the white yarn will now be red, and the others will be grey or black. In other words, unless the source emits the proper colors, the body cannot be seen in its true color. Sunlight will show each yarn in its true color, for sunlight contains all colors of the spectrum.

Surface Color. The above discussion explains what is called *surface color.* When sunlight falls on a red rose, red yarn, red paint, or red glass, all of the colors except red are absorbed and do not get through

or out again. The red, as it passes through is reflected and refracted by the fine grains of pigment and comes out in all directions, as shown in Fig. B.

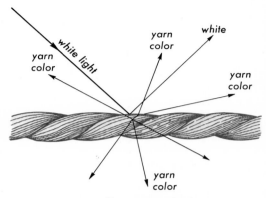

Fig. B. Illustration of color.

Not all of the other colors are completely absorbed, for a small amount of each color is reflected from the first surface the white light strikes. This may be illustrated by a polished sheet of red glass. Although the glass appears red from both sides, a small amount of white light is reflected from the top surface, obeying the law of reflection The red, on the other hand, is reflected and refracted in the usual way at each surface.

The three aspects of surface color are *hue, brightness,* and *saturation.* Hue refers to the *name* of a color, brightness to the relative *magnitude* of the sensory response, and saturation to the color *strength.* Hue is qualitative and is the most distinctive aspect of color, for without hue there is no color. Hue cannot be defined but only exemplified: red, yellow, green, blue, violet, purple, and various intermediaries between these are hues. *Brightness* is a subjective intensity and may exist alone, as in white light. White is devoid of hue and, hence, is devoid of color. Hue cannot exist alone, for if we have hue, it has a certain brightness

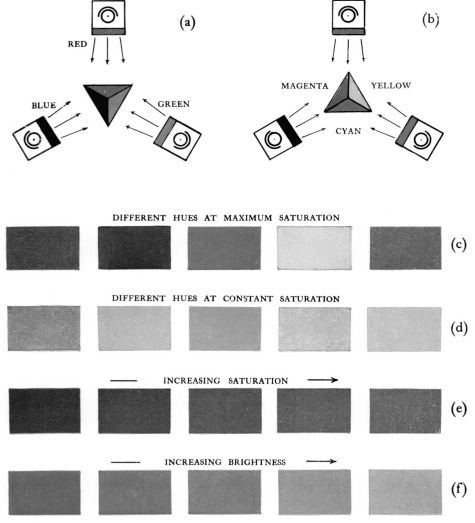

Fig. 66C. (a) Additive primaries. (b) Equal mixing of primary pairs. (c) Different hues at their maximum saturation values. (d) Different hues at constant saturation and equal brightness. (e) The same hue at constant brightness but increasing saturation. (f) The same hue at constant saturation but increasing brightness.

and saturation. Illustrations of these three concepts are shown in Fig. C.

Colors that do not contain any trace of white light are said to be *saturated*. The more white they contain, the less saturated

detailed and complicated. As a result, their principles can be explained here only by simplification of their concepts.

As a starting point, consider the experiment shown in Fig. D in which a narrow

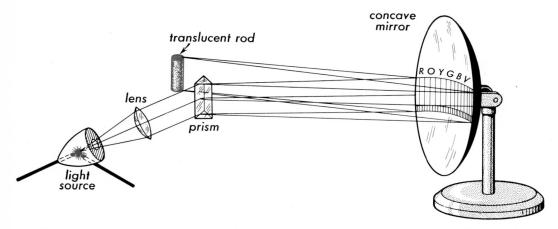

Fig. D. Experimental arrangement for mixing pure spectrum colors to form all primary colors.

they become. Pink is not a saturated color, because it is a mixture of red and white. This may be demonstrated by mixing a small amount of red pigment with white paint, or, what is still more striking, by pulverizing a piece of red glass. As the glass is ground finer and finer the amount of white light reflected is increased by the increasing surface area, until the powder becomes almost white. Although the red light is still present, the white light by comparison is much stronger. A similar effect is produced by transparent substances like crystals and window glass: when powdered, they become white. *The smaller the amount of white light mixed in with a color, the greater is the saturation.*

Mixing Spectrum Colors. Over a period of many years, different color charts and color theories have been proposed. Most successful theories have, of necessity, been

beam of white light from a carbon arc and lens falls on a glass prism and is spread out into a complete spectrum. With the prism located near the center of curvature of a large concave mirror, all colors after reflection are brought to a focus on a translucent glass rod where, combined again, they produce white light. Next, a large white card is held in front of the mirror to act as a screen controlling the colors that are permitted to mix at the rod. By screening off violet, blue, and green, for example, the remaining colors—red, orange, and yellow—come together and the rod appears orange.

Working with the screen and the equipment set up in Fig. D, we now proceed to divide the spectrum into the three equal parts illustrated in the left-hand charts of Fig. E. We call these parts the *additive primaries*. When red and orange light are allowed to mix, the rod appears a bright red; when yellow and green light are mixed, the rod appears bright green; and when blue and violet light are mixed, it appears blue-violet. As colors, these additive primaries—red, green, and blue—appear like the three left-hand circles in Fig. E.

The next step is to mix two additive primaries at a time, observing their resultant color mixture. When primary red and primary green light mix at the glass rod, they produce yellow; red and blue light produce magenta; and green and blue light produce cyan, a light blue-green. These latter colors, the so-called *subtractive primaries*, are shown by the three right-hand circles in Fig. E and by the overlapping areas in the left-hand circles. The pure spectrum colors that go to make up each subtractive primary are illustrated by the right-hand charts.

Complementary Colors. *Two colors are said to be complementary if, when added together, they produce white.* Magenta and green are complementary, for when added together, as can be seen from their spectral distributions in Fig. E, they contain all of the spectrum colors of white light. Similarly, red and cyan, as well as yellow and blue, are complementary.

Additive Method of Color Mixing. The mixing of colored lights described in the two preceding sections is called the additive method of color mixing and differs greatly from the subtractive method to be described in the following section. An interesting experiment for demonstrating the additive method is shown in Fig. C. Three boxes containing white lights are arranged to illuminate separately the three sides of a white pyramid. A matched set of glass filters, one for each of the additive primary hues—red, green, and blue, respectively—

are placed in front of each box opening, thereby illuminating the pyramid faces as shown in the left-hand diagram.

When the pyramid is rotated slowly, a point is reached, as shown at (*b*), where pairs of lights mix in equal amounts on each of the three faces. These mixtures are the subtractive primaries, magenta, yellow, and cyan. As the pyramid turns from position (*a*) to position (*b*), all variations of two colors are seen on the pyramid faces. Television in full color is produced by the additive method of color mixing.

Subtractive Method of Color Mixing. This is the method most familiar to everyone, the method used in the mixing of pigments to produce various colored paints. For this purpose, the subtractive primaries, *magenta, yellow,* and *cyan,* often referred to by artists as *red, yellow,* and *blue,* are the most useful. Mixing equal amounts of any two subtractive primaries will produce the additive primary lying between them on the color triangle. When cyan and yellow paints are mixed, the result is green.

At first, it seems strange that yellow and cyan, neither one of which has the appearance of an additive primary, should produce green when mixed together. A spectrum analysis of these two colors, as shown at the lower right in Fig. E, shows that green and yellow are spectrum colors common to both.

Mixing by the subtractive method is demonstrated with prisms and filters in Fig. F. To see what happens to each spectral hue in each filter, the white light is first spread out into its complete spectrum. To illustrate, the yellow filter alone in diagram (*h*) absorbs blue and violet, and the cyan filter alone in (*f*) absorbs red and orange. When both are inserted as in diagram (*d*), only green and yellow are transmitted. To the eye, this mixture appears bright green.

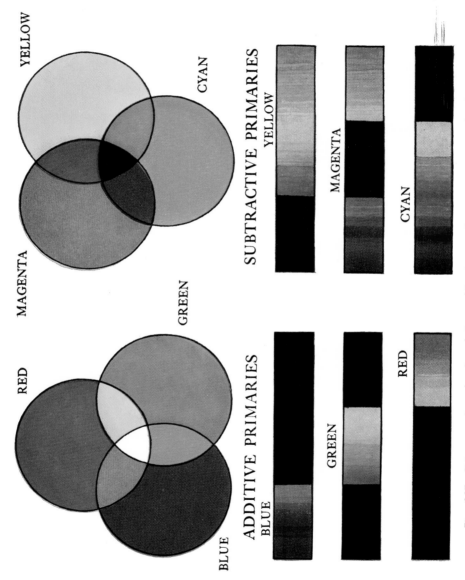

ADDITIVE PRIMARIES

SUBTRACTIVE PRIMARIES

Fig. 66E. Primary colors showing their combinations and component spectral colors.

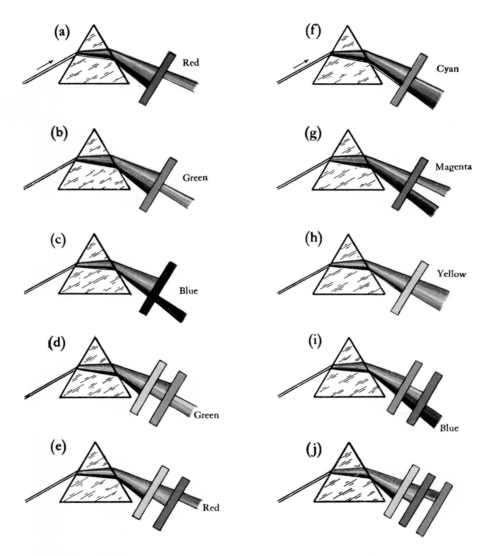

Fig. 66F. Diagram illustrating the absorption of spectral colors by colored filters and the subtractive method of color mixing.

The other two pairs of filters in diagrams (*e*) and (*i*) give the other two primaries red and blue.

To carry these experimental demonstrations to the mixing of paint, each little grain of pigment is like a piece of colored glass, as shown in Fig. G. If the oil in which

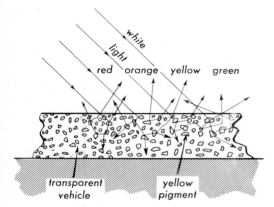

Fig. G. Illustration of the absorption of blue and violet light by yellow paint and the emission of red, orange, yellow, and green.

the yellow pigment is imbedded is transparent, white light entering the paint is reflected and refracted as shown. Wherever blue or violet rays pass through the yellow pigment grains, they are absorbed. After many reflections and refractions, the red, orange, yellow, and green can still escape. Together, these four colors appear as yellow. See Fig. F.

When yellow and cyan pigments are mixed together, as illustrated by the detailed

diagram in Fig. H, only green and yellow hues are transmitted by both pigments.

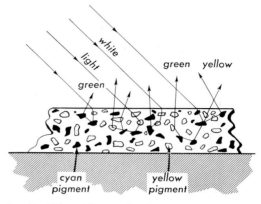

Fig. H. When blue and yellow paints are mixed together, green and yellow are the only pure spectral colors transmitted by both pigments.

The essential difference between the additive method and subtractive method of color mixing is just that suggested by the name: in the additive method the resultant color is just the *sum* of the two constituents used to produce it, and in the subtractive method it is just the *difference* between the two. Addition always produces a brighter color and subtraction produces a darker color. Just as the additive mixing of red, green, and blue produces white, so the subtractive mixing of magenta, yellow, and cyan produces black. Similarly, two complementary colors, when mixed additively, produce white, and when mixed subtractively, produce black.

QUESTIONS

1. (a) How are the six spectrum colors divided to give the additive primaries?
   (b) What spectrum colors produce the subtractive primaries?
2. (a) What are complementary colors? (b) When two complementary colors are added together, what spectrum colors would be present? (c) If they are mixed subtractively, what spectrum colors would be present?

3. Which of the two methods of color mixing produces brighter colors as the result of mixing?

4. Which of the following colors is the brightest: red, yellow, or blue?

5. The following pairs of colors are mixed as pigments: (a) magenta and cyan, (b) yellow and cyan, (c) magenta and yellow, (d) red and cyan, and (e) magenta and green. What is the resultant color in each case?

6. What color crayon would result if you melted and mixed all of the crayons in a box except the black and white ones?

7. What color added to red will give (a) white, (b) magenta, and (c) yellow?

8. What color mixed subtractively with yellow will produce (a) green, (b) red, and (c) black?

9. (a) Make a diagram and briefly explain how yellow and cyan pigments when mixed as paints can produce green. (b) Do the pigment particles themselves become green?

10. (a) When we speak of mixing the "colors" red and green to produce yellow, what is it that is being mixed? (b) Is this additive or subtractive color mixing?

11. Describe an experiment that would demonstrate (a) additive color mixing and (b) subtractive color mixing.

12. Under what conditions would a banana appear (a) red, (b) green, (c) yellow? (d) Why do we say that a banana is yellow?

PROJECTS

1. Make a light-tight box with three primary lights that can be projected on frosted glass or plastic. Arrange it so that different amounts of light can be mixed. Eastman Kodak Tri-color Filters may be used to get the three primary lights and will give fairly good results at minimum expense.

2. Collect colored yarns of all gradations of the spectrum. Use them to demonstrate the appearance of various colors under different kinds of light.

3. Make a color analyzer with a photoelectric cell. The use of a solid-state cell will simplify the project. You can use this to match materials accurately.

LIGHT

Lesson 67 *DIFFRACTION AND INTERFERENCE*

When light passes close to the edge of any object, it is bent in its path and travels in a new direction. This bending of light is called *diffraction*.

Light rays are assumed to always travel in straight lines, because we know from observation that light cannot be seen around corners. Furthermore, according to the rectilinear propagation of light theory, it is customary to assume that an object will cast a sharp and well-defined shadow. A close examination of every shadow, however, shows that the edges are not sharp, but blurred and diffused.

If one is careful to choose a small source of light, such as the light emanating from a pinhole in a screen, the shadow of an object cast on a distant screen is bounded at the edges by narrow bands or fringes of light. To observe these effects the following simple experiment may be performed in a darkened room. A box containing a light bulb and a pinhole is placed on one side of the room and a ground glass observing screen or photographic film is placed on the other. The objects whose shadows are to be observed are then placed about halfway between the source and the screen, as shown in Fig. A. This is the arrangement

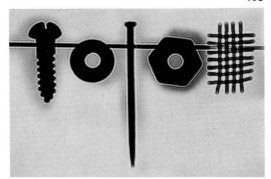

Fig. B. Photographs of the shadows cast by objects. The narrow bands are due to the diffraction of light.

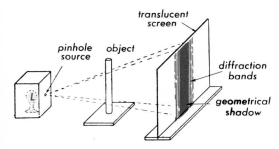

Fig. A. The shadow cast by the light from a small source is not sharp at the edges, but exhibits a banded structure.

used in obtaining the original photographs reproduced in Fig. B. This is a photograph of light diffracted by a pin, a small hexagonal nut, and a piece of wire screen.

Huygens' Principle. The wave theory of light was first proposed by the English physicist, Robert Hooke, in 1665, and improved twenty years later by the Dutch

scientist and mathematician, Christian Huygens.*

According to Huygens' principle, every point on any wave front may be regarded as a new point source of waves. See Fig. C. Regarding each of any number of points, such as *a*, *b*, *c*, etc., as point sources like *S*, secondary wavelets spread out simultaneously as shown. The envelope of these an instant later is the new wave front *A*, *B*, *C*, etc., and still later the wave front *L*, *M*, *N*, etc. Although Huygens' principle at first hand might seem to be a useless play with circles, it has quite general application to many optical phenomena.

Diffraction at a Single Opening. A direct experimental demonstration of Huy-

* Christian Huygens (1629-1695), famous Dutch physicist, was a contemporay of Isaac Newton. Born at The Hague in 1629, young Christian got his first ideas about waves and their propagation by watching the ripples on the canals about his home. Although his chief title-deed to immortality is his development of the wave theory of light, he made many and valuable contributions to mathematics and astronomy. He improved upon the method of grinding telescope lenses and discovered the Orion nebula, part of which is now known by his name. He was elected to the Royal Society of London in 1663 and delivered before that august body the first clear statement of the laws governing the collision of elastic bodies. He died a confirmed bachelor at The Hague in 1695.

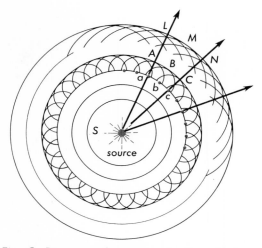

Fig. C. Diagram of waves spreading out from a point source. The secondary wavelets and new wave fronts illustrate Huygens' principle.

gens' principle is illustrated in Fig. D, which is a photograph of a ripple tank arranged to permit straight waves through a small opening in a barrier. In (a), we can see waves spreading out in all directions as if the opening were a point source of new waves. There is a slight tendency for the amplitude to be highest in the forward direction.

Suppose the wave length is decreased, or the width increased, so that the opening width were somewhat longer than the wave length. Then, the waves would be straighter near the center and the amplitude would be even more peaked in the forward direction as seen in (b).

If the width of the opening were much larger than the wave length, the waves

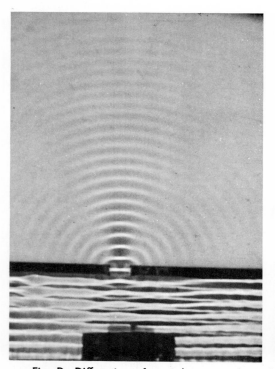

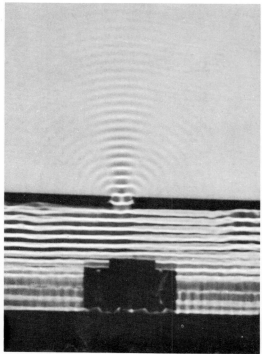

Fig. D. Diffraction of straight waves through a single slit. At left, the slit is about twice the wave length and the diffracted waves are almost circular. At right, the wave length is less and the diffracted waves near the slit are not so curved in their center section.

would travel straight forward through the opening, with little diffraction at the corners. We can conclude, then, that diffraction effects are most pronounced when the dimensions are on the same scale as the wave length.

Interference. Everyone has at one time or another dropped a stone in a still pond of water and watched the waves spread outward in ever-widening circles.

If two stones are dropped simultaneously into the water, two sets of waves will spread outward as shown in Fig. E.

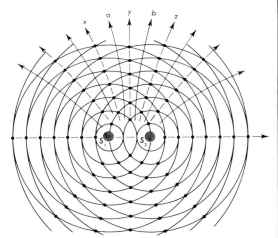

Fig. E. Concentric waves traveling outward from a double source, producing what is called an interference pattern.

For each set of waves, the crests and troughs are represented by concentric circles.

As these waves cross each other, they act one upon the other, producing what is called an *interference pattern*. Where the crests of two waves come together at the dotted intersections, they are *in step*, or *in phase*, and the amplitude of the water surface is increased. Where the crest of one wave and the trough of another come together, they are out of step, or out of phase,

and the amplitude of the water surface is reduced. The *in-phase* regions of the waves move outward along the dotted lines, such as x, y, and z, and we have what is called *constructive interference*. The *out-of-phase* regions move outward along the solid lines, such as a and b, and we have what is called *destructive interference*.

An instantaneous ripple-tank photograph of such a wave pattern is shown in Fig. F.

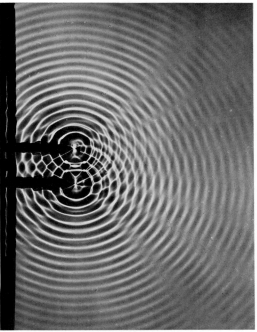

Fig. F. Ripple-tank photograph of the interference of water waves from two sources. (Courtesy, Physical Sciences Study Committee Project)

Note how clearly the interference regions of the waves stand out.

Young's Double-Slit Experiment. The crucial test between Newton's corpuscular theory of light and Huygens' wave theory came in 1801 when Thomas Young performed his now famous interference experiment. This is represented schematically in Fig. G. Sunlight from a pinhole, S, was

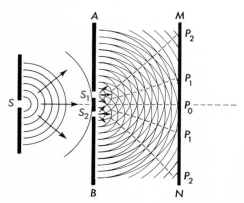

Fig. G. Diagram of Young's double-slit experiment illustrating the interference of light waves.

allowed to fall on a distant screen containing two pinholes, S_1 and S_2. The two sets of spherical waves emerging from the two holes interfered with each other in such a way as to form a symmetrical pattern of bands on another screen, MN. This experiment is now regarded as the first definite proof that light is a wave motion.

For convenience, it is now customary to repeat Young's experiment with narrow slits rather than pinholes. If S, S_1, and S_2 in Fig. G represent the cross sections of three narrow slits, the light falling on the farther screen, MN, has the appearance of equidistant bands or fringes, as shown by the

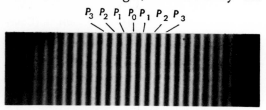

Fig. H. Interference fringes produced by a double-slit, as in Young's experiment.

photograph in Fig. H. The bright fringes correspond to the points P_0, P_1, P_2, etc.,

and the dark fringes to the points halfway between.

As the light waves, like the water waves in Fig. F, travel outward from each slit, S_1 and S_2, they cross each other only at points that lie along the dotted lines shown in the diagram. These represent the points where the crests of two waves come together and produce a maximum brightness. About halfway between these dotted lines lie other points where the crest of one wave and the trough of another cancel each other and produce darkness. This is called *interference*. Where the bright fringes are formed there is *constructive interference*, and where the dark fringes appear there is *destructive interference*.

Measuring the Wave Length of Light.
A formula for the wave length of light can be derived from the geometry of Young's double-slit experiment, as shown in Fig. I.

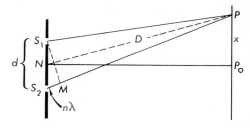

Fig. I. Geometrical relations for the double-slit interference experiment.

Let P be the position of any bright fringe on the screen and x its distance from the central fringe at P_0. P_0 is located on the perpendicular bisector of the double slit S_1 and S_2. A straight line from each slit to the point P is drawn, and with a compass of radius S_1P, the arc of a circle, S_1M, is scribed. By this construction, line MP is made equal to S_1P and the short line, S_2M, becomes the extra distance light must travel from the lower slit. To produce a bright fringe at P, the interval S_2M must be equal to one whole wave length, two whole wave lengths, three whole wave lengths, etc., for only then will the waves from S_1 and S_2 arrive at P in phase. Therefore, S_2M must be equal to $n\lambda$, where n is a whole number, $n = 0$, 1, 2, 3, 4, etc., and λ is the wave length of the light.

Because the distance, d, between slit centers is extremely small compared with the distance, D, to the screen, line S_1M may be considered straight and at right angles to all three lines S_1P, NP, and S_2P. With corresponding sides mutually perpendicular to each other, triangles S_1S_2M and NPP_0 are similar to each other. From the well-known theorem that corresponding sides of similar triangles are proportional—

$$\frac{n\lambda}{d} = \frac{x}{D}$$

or—

$$\lambda = \frac{xd}{nD} \qquad (1)$$

If we let x_1 be the distance from the central fringe to the first one on either side, then $n = 1$, and the equation becomes

$$\lambda = d\frac{x_1}{D} \qquad (2)$$

or because

$$\sin \theta = \frac{x_1}{D} \qquad (3)$$

another more familiar equation is

$$\lambda = d \sin \theta \qquad (4)$$

Because the fringes are evenly spaced, x_1 represents the spacing all along the pattern. By measuring the three distances d, x, and D, the wave length of light can be calculated. Repeated experiments, carefully performed, give the following results:

red	$\lambda = 0.000066$ cm
orange	$\lambda = 0.000061$ cm
yellow	$\lambda = 0.000058$ cm
green	$\lambda = 0.000054$ cm
blue	$\lambda = 0.000046$ cm
violet	$\lambda = 0.000042$ cm

As illustrated by waves in Fig. J, red light has the longest waves.

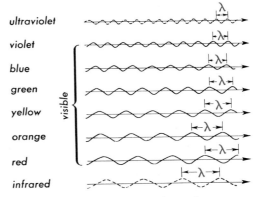

Fig. J. Diagram showing the relative wave lengths of light.

QUESTIONS

1. (a) What is diffraction? (b) How does it modify the edges of otherwise sharp shadows?
2. (a) What is Huygens' principle? (b) How does it apply to light passing through a single, but narrow, opening?
3. (a) What was Young's original double-slit experiment? (b) Was diffraction involved? (c) Where?
4. (a) Is interference involved in Young's double-slit experiment? (b) Where?

5. (a) What is observed on the screen in Young's experiment? (b) What quantities are measured for calculating the wave length of light?
6. (a) What are the wave-length limits for visible light? (b) What color of light has the longest wave length? (c) The shortest wave length?
7. Would it be possible to apply the same formula for the interference of the waves in a ripple tank as for light waves? Explain.
8. Why don't you see an interference pattern when two identical electric lights are placed side by side?
9. (a) Would two loudspeakers close together and connected to the same audio source be expected to interfere with each other? (b) What would you expect to hear as a result?
10. Why is the Young double-slit experiment considered so important?

PROBLEMS

1. Red light of wave length 6×10^{-5} cm is used in observing the interference fringes produced by a double slit. If the centers of the two slit-openings are 0.5 mm apart and the distance to the observing screen is 2 m, what is the fringe spacing?
2. Green light of wave length 5×10^{-5} cm falls on a double slit, and 2 m away on a white screen interference fringes are formed 5 mm apart. Calculate the double-slit separation.
3. Monochromatic light falls upon a double slit. The distance between the slit centers is 1.1 mm, and the distance between consecutive fringes on a screen 5 m away is 0.3 cm. What is the wave length and the color of the light?
4. Light falling on a double slit with a spacing of 1 mm forms fringes with a 2.1-mm spacing on a screen 5 m away. (a) Calculate the wave length of the light. (b) What is its color?
5. Light of wave length 0.000054 cm falls on a double slit with a spacing of 0.5 mm. How far away should a screen be located from the double slit if the fringes are to be 2 mm apart?
6. Light of wave length 0.000061 cm falls on a double slit and produces 8 fringes per centimeter on a screen located 2.5 m away. What is double-slit spacing?
7. Two small speakers 30 cm apart are reproducing 10,000 cycles/second. If you are 3 m away from the speakers and walked slowly parallel to the speakers, how far apart would the distances be where little or no sound was heard?
8. Red light of 6500×10^{-8} cm wave length from a narrow slit falls on a double slit of 0.025-cm separation. If the interference pattern is formed on a screen 100 cm away, what will be the linear separation between fringes on the screen?

PROJECTS

1. Make an adjustable double slit so that you can measure the effect of different slit widths on the pattern obtained.

2. With a pair of stereo speakers driven by the same amplifier, try to introduce signals of various audio frequencies, and study the interference patterns.

LIGHT

Lesson 68 **THE DIFFRACTION GRATING**

The diffraction grating is an optical device widely used instead of a prism for studying the spectrum and measuring the wave lengths of light. Gratings are made by ruling fine grooves with a diamond point either on a glass plate to produce a transmission grating or on a polished metal mirror to produce a reflecting grating. As illustrated in Fig. A, the rulings are all parallel and equally spaced. The best gratings are several inches in width and contain from 5000 to 30,000 lines/in.

The transmission grating and its effect on light is shown in the cross-section diagrams in Fig. B. The heavy colored lines represent the parts that permit no light to get through. The open intervals between them represent the undisturbed parts of the glass that transmit the light and act like the parallel slits in Young's double-slit experiment.

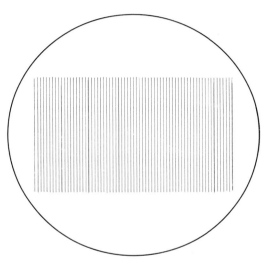

Fig. A. Schematic diagram of the grooves or rulings on a diffraction grating.

In diagram (*a*), parallel light is shown arriving at the grating surface as a suc-

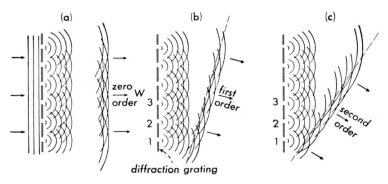

Fig. B. Diagrams showing the formation of wave fronts forming the various orders of interference observed with a diffraction grating.

cession of plane waves. The light passes through the opening and spreads out as Huygens' wavelets, forming new wave fronts parallel to the grating face. These wave fronts, parallel to the original waves, constitute a beam of light, W, traveling in the same direction as the original beam.

Orders of Interference. These are not the only wave fronts, however, for other beams of parallel light are to be found

off at greater angles. By symmetry, all of the orders found on one side of the zero order are also found at the same angle on the other side.

Experimentally, there are two methods of observing the various orders of inter-ference from a small diffraction grating: one is to place the grating directly in front of the eye, and the other is to place it in the parallel beam of light between two lenses as shown in Fig. C. In the latter case,

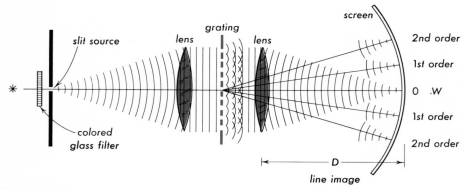

Fig. C. Diagram showing how the wave fronts of the various orders of interference are brought to a focus by the same lens.

traveling away from the grating in other directions. Two other such wave fronts are illustrated in diagrams (*b*) and (*c*). In (*b*), a dotted line is drawn tangent to the seventh wave from opening *1*, the eighth wave from opening *2*, the ninth wave from opening *3*, etc., to form what is called a wave front of the *first order of interference*. In (*c*), a line is drawn tangent to the fourth wave from opening *1*, the sixth wave from opening *2*, the eighth wave from opening *3*, etc., to form what is called a wave front of the *second order of interference*.

Similarly, by taking every third wave or every fourth wave from consecutive slits, other parallel wave fronts corresponding to the third or fourth orders are found moving

the second lens is shown converging the various wave fronts of the different orders to a focus on a distant screen. If the source is a slit, as shown at the left, and a colored-glass filter is used to let through any one color of light, like violet, the light falling on the screen will appear as shown in the top band in Fig. D. Each vertical line is an image of the slit source and is violet in color.

If the three diagrams in Fig. B are re-drawn for light of a longer wave length, *i.e.*, a greater distance between waves, the cen-tral beam of light, W, would travel on in the same direction as before, but the various orders of interference would be diffracted out at greater angles. Should green light of

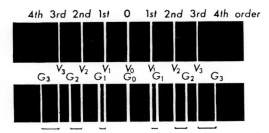

4th 3rd 2nd 1st   O   1st 2nd 3rd 4th order

V_3 V_2 V_1 V_0 V_1 V_2 V_3
G_3 G_2 G_1 G_0 G_1 G_2 G_3

Fig. D. The different orders of interference of violet and green light obtained with a diffraction grating, as shown in Fig. C.

one wave length be used in Fig. C, the slit images formed on the screen would be farther apart than for violet light, as illustrated by the images marked G in Fig. D(b). This lower band is from a photograph taken with both violet and green light from a mercury arc passing through the grating. These line images are called *spectrum lines.*

It will be noted that the separation of the spectrum lines V and G in the *third order* is three times as great as in the *first order*. In other words, any two spectrum lines are separated by an amount that is proportional to the order of interference.

If white light is sent through a grating, all of the different wave lengths, corresponding to the different colors, form their own characteristic wave fronts and produce a complete and continuous spectrum in each order of interference. This is illustrated by a diagram in Fig. E. Because the zero order for all colors comes to the same point,

the central image is white. Because the width of each spectrum is proportional to the order, the higher orders overlap one another more and more. The violet of the third order, V_3, for example, falls on the red of second order, R_2. It is for this reason that only the first and second orders of the spectrum from any grating are the ones generally used in practice.

The general appearance of a spectrum produced by a diffraction-grating spectrograph can be seen in Fig. A, Lesson 102.

Mathematical Analysis of the Diffraction Grating. The theory of the diffraction grating is similar to that of the double slit and is shown in its simplest form in Fig. F. These diagrams derive their construction from Fig. B. The wave fronts for the first order emerge at such an angle, θ, that the difference in path between the rays from any two consecutive rulings, like A and B, is just one wave length. Because any tangent drawn to any circle is always perpendicular to the radius drawn through the point of contact, triangle ABD is a right triangle, and

$$\sin \theta = \lambda/d$$

or—

$$\lambda = d \sin \theta \qquad (1)$$

where λ is the wave length of the light, d is the grating spacing, and θ is the angle that the emergent light of the first order makes with the grating normal.

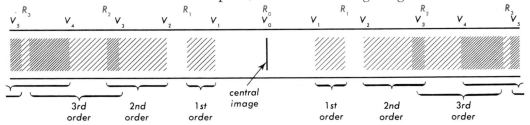

Fig. E. Diagram of the first several orders of continuous spectrum as displayed by a diffraction grating.

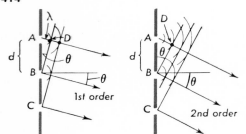

Fig. F. Geometry for the wave theory of the diffraction grating.

By similar reasoning, and by the use of diagrams like the one shown for the second order, it will be seen that spectra of the second, third, fourth, etc., order are formed at such angles, θ, that the difference in path between consecutive slits is 2λ, 3λ, 4λ, etc. In general, the side AD of the right triangle ABD must be equal to $n\lambda$, where $n = 1, 2, 3, 4$, etc., and

$$\sin \theta = n\lambda/d$$

or—

$$n\lambda = d \sin \theta \qquad (2)$$

In this general grating formula, n is the spectrum order.

Example. Red light of one particular wave length falls normally on a grating having 4000 lines/cm. If the second-order spectrum makes an angle of $36°$ with the grating normal, what is the wave length of the light?

Solution. Since the grating has 4000 lines/cm, the spacing between the lines is 1/4000, or $d = 0.00025$ cm. The other given quantities are $\theta = 36°$ and $n = 2$. Substituting in Eq. (2), and solving for λ, we get—

$$\lambda = \frac{0.00025 \times \sin 36°}{2} = \frac{0.00025 \times 0.588}{2}$$

$$= 0.0000735 \text{ cm}$$

The grating formula is identical to the double-slit formula, Eq. (4) in Lesson 67. The reason for using a diffraction grating consisting of thousands of slits, rather than a double slit, is that the grating produces sharp lines, whereas the double slit does not.

QUESTIONS

1. (a) What is a diffraction grating? (b) How does it work?
2. How does the pattern of a diffraction grating differ from that of a double slit if a single wave length of light is present?
3. Why is a diffraction grating better than the Young's double-slit for measuring the wave length of light?
4. Why must the rulings on a diffraction grating be so evenly spaced and parallel?
5. (a) Why is the central image of a diffraction pattern white if white light is used? (b) What would its color be if green light were used?
6. Why do the higher-order spectra overlap?
7. What is wrong with using a picket fence as a diffraction grating for light waves?

PROBLEMS

1. Red light of 6500×10^{-8} cm wave length is incident normally on a grating of 10,000 lines/cm. If the spectrum is observed on a screen 100 cm away, what angle will red light of this wave length make with the normal in the first-order spectrum?

2. Green light of 5500×10^{-8} cm wave length is incident normally on a diffraction grating. How many lines/cm does the grating have if the angle between the normal and this light in the second-order spectrum is 20°?

3. Violet light of 4.3×10^{-5} cm wave length falls as a parallel beam on a diffraction grating containing 800 lines/cm. At what angle will the second-order spectrum be located?

4. A beam of parallel light, $\lambda = 6 \times 10^{-5}$ cm, falls normally on a grating, and the third order is diffracted at an angle of 40° with the grating normal. How many lines/cm are on the grating?

5. Parallel yellow light of 5.8×10^{-5} cm wave length falls normally on one side of a diffraction grating having 6000 lines/cm. Calculate the angle between the first-order spectrum on opposite sides of the grating normal.

6. Yellow light of 6000×10^{-8} cm wave length falls on a grating of 9000 lines/cm. One of the spectral rays makes an angle of about 32° in the forward direction. What is the order?

7. Light falling on a 5000-lines/cm grating produces a second-order ray at 25°. What color is it?

PROJECT

Obtain a diffraction grating replica, which is extremely inexpensive, and make a simple spectroscope.

LIGHT

Lesson 69 *POLARIZATION OF LIGHT*

The experiments described in the preceding lesson, illustrating the *diffraction* and *interference* of light, are generally regarded as proof that *light is characterized by wave motion*. Although such experiments enable the physicist to measure accurately the wave lengths of light, they give no information of the kinds of waves involved. The reason for this is that all types of waves, under the proper conditions, will exhibit diffraction and interference. The desired information in the case of light waves is found in another group of phenomena known as *polarized light*. Some of the phenomena, which will be described in this lesson, are considered to be a proof that *light is a transverse wave motion*, in contrast with the longitudinal wave motion of sound.

Plane-Polarized Light. A better understanding of the experiments to be described can best be attained by first studying the graphical methods of representing transverse waves. We assume at the outset that each light wave is a transverse wave whose vibrations are along straight lines at right angles to the direction of propagation. See Fig. F in Lesson 51. Furthermore, we assume that a beam of ordinary light consists of millions of such waves, each with its own plane of vibration, and that there are waves vibrating in all planes with equal probability. If we could look at such a beam end-on, as in Fig. A, we would see

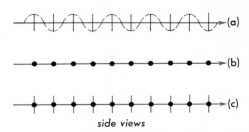

Fig. B. Diagrams illustrating plane-polarized rays of light.

line indicating waves in diagram (a) is usually omitted.

It can be shown that a beam of ordinary unpolarized light, vibrating in all planes, may be regarded as being made up of two kinds of vibrations only, half of the waves vibrating in a vertical plane as in diagram (a) and the other half vibrating perpendicular to it as in diagram (b). Diagram (c), therefore, represents ordinary unpolarized light.

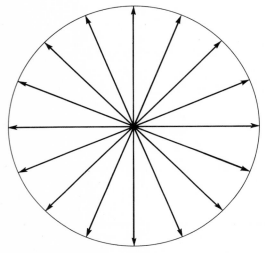

Fig. A. End-on view of a beam of unpolarized light illustrating schematically the equal probability of all planes of vibration.

just as many waves vibrating in one plane as there are vibrating in any other. This, then, can be referred to as perfect symmetry.

If, by some means or other, all the waves in a beam of light are made to vibrate in planes parallel to each other, the light is said to be plane-polarized. Diagrams illustrating such light are shown in Fig. B. Diagram (a) represents plane-polarized light waves traveling to the right and vibrating in a vertical plane, while diagram (b) represents a ray of plane-polarized light vibrating in a horizontal plane. The dotted

Polarization by Reflection. When ordinary, unpolarized light is incident at an angle of about 57° on the polished surface of a plate of glass, the reflected light is plane-polarized. This fact was first discovered by Etienne Malus, a French physicist, in 1808. The experiment usually performed to demonstrate his discovery is illustrated in Fig. C.

A beam of unpolarized light, AB, is incident at an angle of 57° on the first glass surface at B. This light is again reflected at the same angle by a second glass plate, C, placed parallel to the first, as in diagram (a). If the lower plate is now rotated about the line BC by slowly turning the pedestal on which it is mounted, the intensity of the reflected beam, CD, is found to decrease slowly and vanish completely at an angle of 90°. With further rotation, the reflected beam, CD, appears again, reaching maximum intensity at an angle of 180°,

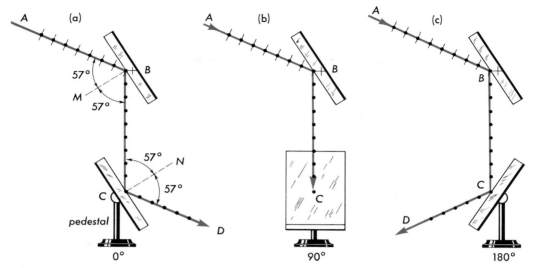

Fig. C. Common experiment performed to demonstrate the polarization of light by reflection from a smooth glass surface.

as shown in diagram (c). Continued rotation causes the intensity to decrease to zero again at 270° and to reappear and reach a maximum at 360°, the starting point as in diagram (a). During this one complete rotation, the angle of incidence on the lower plate, as well as the upper, has remained at 57°.

The explanation of the above experiment is made clearer by a detailed study of what happens to ordinary light reflected at the polarizing angle of 57° from glass. As illustrated in Fig. D, 8% of the light is reflected as plane-polarized light, vibrating in the plane at right angles to the plane of incidence, and the other 92% is refracted as partially plane-polarized light, 42% vibrating perpendicular to the plane of incidence and 50% vibrating parallel to the plane of incidence. The plane of incidence is defined as the plane passing through the incident ray and the ray normal, NN. In nearly all diagrams, the plane of the page is the plane of incidence.

If in Fig. D the angle of incidence is changed to some other value than 57°, the reflected beam will not be plane-polarized but will contain a certain amount of light vibrating parallel to the plane of incidence. In general, the light reflected from a transparent medium, like glass or water, is only partially plane-polarized, and only at a cer-

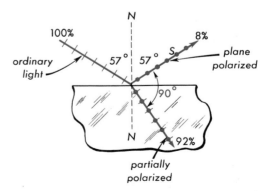

Fig. D. Light reflected from glass at an angle of 57° is plane-polarized, while the refracted light is only partially plane-polarized.

tain angle, called the *polarizing angle*, is it plane-polarized. It was Sir David Brewster, a Scottish physicist, who first discovered that *at the polarizing angle, the reflected and refracted rays are 90° apart.* This is now known as *Brewster's law.*

The polarizing angle ϕ for any optical substance of refractive index μ is given by—

$$\tan \phi = \mu \qquad (1)$$

Double Refraction. The double refraction of light by Iceland spar (calcite) was first observed by a Swedish physician, Erasmus Bartholinus, in 1669, and later studied in detail by Huygens and Newton. Nearly all crystalline substances are now known to exhibit the phenomenon. A few samples of crystals that show the effect are *calcite, quartz, mica, sugar, topaz, selenite, aragonite,* and *ice.* Calcite and quartz are of particular importance, because they are used extensively in the manufacture of special optical instruments.

Calcite, as found in nature, always has the characteristic shape shown in Fig. E(*a*).

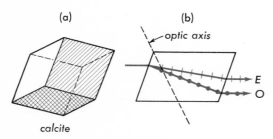

Fig. E. Diagrams of calcite and its behavior with light.

Not only is light doubly refracted by calcite, but both rays are found to be plane-polarized. One ray, called the *ordinary ray,* is polarized with its vibrations in one plane, and the other ray, called the *extraordinary ray,* is polarized with its vibrations in a plane at right angles to the first. This polar-

ization is illustrated by *dots* and *lines,* and can be proved by rotating a glass plate, as plate *C* in Fig. C, or with some other analyzing device such as a *polarizing film.* These devices will be described in the next two sections.

Because the two opposite faces of a calcite crystal are always parallel to each other, the two refracted rays always emerge parallel to the incident light and are, therefore, parallel to each other. If the incident light falls perpendicularly upon the surface of the crystal, as in Fig. F, the extraordinary ray,

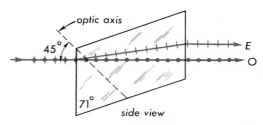

Fig. F. Only one ray obeys Snell's law in double refraction.

E, will be refracted away from the normal and come out parallel to, but displaced from, the incident beam, and the ordinary ray, *O*, will pass straight through without deviation.

The *O* ray travels with the same velocity, regardless of its direction through the crystal, whereas the velocity of the *E* ray is different in different directions. As a result, the *O* ray obeys the ordinary laws of refraction, that is, it obeys Snell's law. In this way, the crystal acts like glass or water. The *E* ray obeys no such simple law, behaving quite abnormally. This behavior is the origin of the designations *ordinary* and *extraordinary.*

The optic axis represents a special direction through the crystal. Along the optic axis, all vibrations travel with the same speed and there is no double refraction.

Polarization by Selective Absorption. When ordinary light enters a crystal of tourmaline, double refraction takes place in much the same way that it does in calcite, but with this difference: one ray, the so-called *O* ray, is entirely absorbed by the crystal, while the other ray, the *E* ray, passes on through. This phenomenon is called *selective absorption,* because the crystal absorbs light waves vibrating in one plane and not those vibrating in the other.

Tourmaline crystals take in ordinary light, dispose of the *O* vibrations, and transmit plane-polarized light, as illustrated in Fig. G(*a*). When two such crystals are

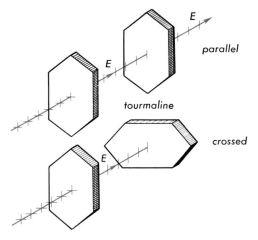

Fig. G. Tourmaline crystals polarize light.

lined up parallel, with one behind the other, the plane-polarized light from the first crystal passes through the second with little loss in intensity. If either crystal is turned at 90° to the other, i.e., in the *crossed position,* the light is completely absorbed and none passes through.

The behavior of tourmaline and similar optical substances is due to the molecular structure of the crystal. To draw an analogy, the regularly spaced molecules of a single crystal are like the regularly spaced trees in an orchard or grove. If one tries to run between the rows of trees carrying a very long pole held at right angles to the direction of motion, the pole must be held in a vertical position. If it is held in the horizontal plane, the runner will be stopped.

A more satisfactory substance for this purpose, which will transmit white light, is a manufactured material known as *Polaroid.* This material is made in the form of very thin films that have the general appearance of a plastic and is made from small needle-shaped crystals of an organic compound *iodosulphate of quinine.* Lined up parallel to each other and embedded in a *nitrocellulose mastic,* these crystals act like tourmaline by absorbing one component of polarization and transmitting the other.

Two such films, mounted separately in rings between thin glass plates, are shown schematically in Fig. H. In the crossed po-

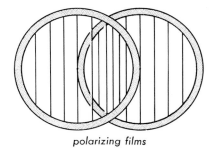

polarizing films

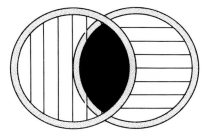

Fig. H. Polarizing films in the parallel and crossed positions.

sition, no light can pass through both films, whereas in the parallel position, white light vibrating in the plane indicated by the parallel lines is transmitted. Polarizing films of this kind are finding many practical applications, particularly wherever glaring light is not desired. The glaring light reflected at an angle from a table top, a book, a window pane, the water, or the road ahead of a car may be highly polarized and can be greatly reduced by polarizing films.

Polarization by Scattering. If the blue of the sky is observed through a piece of Polaroid in a direction at right angles to the sun's rays, the light is found to be partially plane-polarized. This polarization can also be seen in the scattering experiment described in Fig. K, Lesson 65. Observed through a Polaroid film, the beam in the tank appears bright at one orientation of the Polaroid and disappears with a 90° rotation.

QUESTIONS

1. (a) What are transverse waves? (b) What is meant by unpolarized light?
2. (a) What is plane-polarized light? (b) How is unpolarized light broken down into two plane-polarized components?
3. (a) What are three methods of polarizing light? (b) Can sound waves be polarized?
4. (a) What is Brewster's law? (b) What is meant by the polarizing angle? (c) Is refracted light ever plane-polarized?
5. (a) What is double refraction? (b) What is the nature of the light in the refracted rays?
6. (a) Do the O and E rays obey Snell's law? (b) Is it possible to obtain only one refracted ray in a crystal like calcite?
7. (a) What is selective absorption? (b) What is Polaroid? (c) Where is Polaroid used? (d) What is tourmaline?
8. How could Polaroid material be used in cars to eliminate glare at night from oncoming headlights?
9. How is Polaroid material used to make three-dimensional movies?
10. How do Polaroid sunglasses help to reduce glare?

PROBLEMS

1. What is the polarizing angle for a dense flint glass having a refractive index of 1.720?
2. What is the polarizing angle for water, with its refractive index of 1.33?
3. Find the polarizing angle for diamond, with its refractive index of 2.41.
4. If the polarizing angle of a transparent plastic is found to be 55°, what is the refractive index?
5. What is the refractive index of flint glass if the polarizing angle is 59°?
6. If the refractive index for a plastic is 1.45, what is the angle of refraction for a ray of light incident at the polarizing angle?

7. Light is incident at the polarizing angle on the surface of a block of glass of index 1.65. Find the angle of deviation for the refracted ray.

8. The refractive index for the ordinary ray in calcite is 1.658. Find the angle of deviation if the angle of incidence is 30°.

PROJECTS

1. A three-dimensional effect may be shown by taking two photographs of the same scene in two slightly different positions and viewing each photograph by one eye only. Make a three-dimensional slide projector using Polaroid materials to give the three-dimensional effect.

2. Make a polarimeter to measure strengths of sugar solutions.

3. Make a device using Polaroid materials to show the stress in glass before annealing.

Electricity

In experimental philosophy we can, by the phaenomena presented, recognize various kinds of lines of force; thus there are the lines of gravitating force, those of electro-static induction, those of magnetic action, and others partaking of a dynamic character might be perhaps included. The lines of electric and magnetic action are by many considered as exerted through space like the lines of gravitating force. For my own part, I incline to believe that when there are intervening particles of matter (being themselves only centres of force), they take part in carrying on the force through the line, but that when there are none, the line proceeds through space. Whatever the view adopted respecting them may be, we can, at all events, affect these lines of force in a manner which may be conceived as partaking of the nature of a shake or lateral vibration.

Michael Faraday, *Philosophical Magazine,* vol. 28, London, 1846, pp. 347-348.

◄ The huge, spiral duct, shown here during construction at Cherokee Dam, funnels the water to the fins of the turbogenerator. The main body of the generator, built later on a floor above, is connected to the fins by an armature.

Tennessee Valley Authority

Lesson 70 *ELECTRICITY AT REST*

It is impossible to determine when electricity was first discovered. Records show that as early as 600 B.C. the attractive properties of amber were known. Thales of Miletus (640-546 B.C.), one of the "seven wise men" of ancient Greece, is credited with having observed the attraction of amber, when previously rubbed, for small fibrous materials and bits of straw. Amber was used by these people, even as it is now, for ornamental purposes. Just as the precious metals had their names of gold and silver, so amber had its name, *electron*.

It is now a well-established fact that all bodies when rubbed together become electrified, and that amber is just one of a number of substances that show electrification most strongly.

Electrostatic Attraction. The word *electrostatic* means electricity at rest, and the word *attraction* refers to the force exerted by one body upon another at a distance. To demonstrate electrostatic attraction, one often uses a rubber or amber rod and rubs it with a piece of flannel or fur. This electrifies the rod so that, when it is held close above small bits of paper, they jump up to the rod and hold fast.

The attraction of an electrified rubber rod for wood is illustrated in Fig. A. A small arrow cut from a piece of dry wood is mounted so that it is free to turn as shown. When the electrified rubber rod is brought near the pointed end of the arrow, it attracts the wood, turning the arrow until it points toward the rod. Brought near the opposite end, the wood is again attracted, turning the arrow to point away from the rubber rod.

An ordinary hard-rubber comb, when drawn through the hair, becomes charged with electricity and will attract light objects in the same way. So great are the electrical

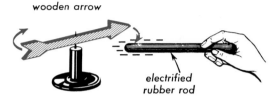

wooden arrow

electrified rubber rod

Fig. A. An electrified rod attracts a wooden arrow.

charges sometimes produced on a comb that tiny sparks can be seen to jump between the comb and hair. This is particularly noticeable in a darkened room. These sparks are the cause for the crackling noise so often heard when hair is being combed.

A spectacular effect is produced by bringing a charged rubber rod close to one side of a smoothly running stream of water from a faucet. As shown above in Fig. B, the stream is diverted to one side and even into the horizontal before it falls again.

An ordinary sheet of writing paper placed on the panel of a door or other similar flat surface and rubbed will hold fast and remain there for some time before falling.

Electricity: + and −. When two different substances are rubbed together and then separated, both are found to be electrified, one with one kind of electricity and the other with another. To illustrate this, one end of a rubber rod is charged by rubbing

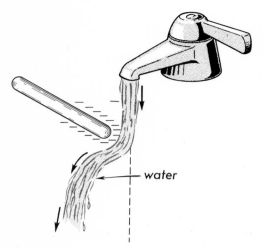

Fig. B. A stream of water is easily deflected by a charged rod.

with fur and then suspended in a small wire stirrup as shown in Fig. C. When the elec-

tracted and turns toward the fur. When a glass rod, previously rubbed with Saran wrap, or similar plastic sheet, is brought close, as in diagram (b), there is attraction, and when the plastic is brought up, there is repulsion.

Because the fur, as well as the glass, attracts the electrified rubber rod, they each have the same kind of electrification: they are said to be *positively charged*. By similar notation, the rubber and silk by their actions are said to be *negatively charged*. Positive charges are designated by a plus (+) sign and negative charges by a minus (−) sign.

Not only do the above experiments indicate the existence of two kinds of electrification, but they also demonstrate a rule concerning the action of one kind on another. Diagram (a) of Fig. C, illustrating a nega-

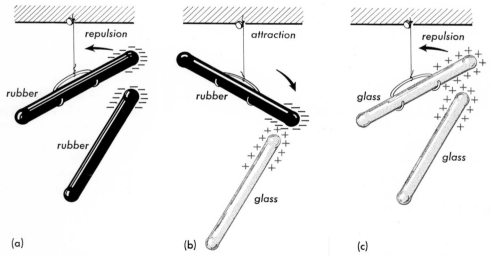

Fig. C. Like charges of electricity repel each other and unlike charges attract.

trified end of a similarly charged rod is brought close, as shown in diagram (a), the suspended rod turns away, showing repulsion. If the fur, instead of the rubber, is brought close, the suspended rod is at-

tively charged rubber rod repelling a similar rod, shows that two negative charges repel each other. Diagram (b) shows that positive and negative charges attract each other, and diagram (c) that two positive charges repel each other. The general law can, therefore, be stated that *like charges repel and unlike charges attract.*

Theory of Electrification. The modern theory of electrification by friction is based upon the principle that all substances are made of atoms and molecules. Each atom contains a nucleus having a known amount of positive charge. See Fig. D. This positive

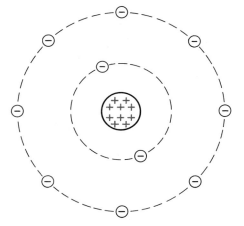

Fig. D. Schematic diagram of a neon atom showing its nucleus at the center with ten positive charges (protons) surrounded on the outside by ten negative charges (electrons).

charge is due to the presence in the nucleus of a certain number of *protons.* All protons are alike and have the same mass and positive charge. Around every atomic nucleus there is a number of negatively charged particles called *electrons.*

Normally, each atom of a substance is electrically neutral; in other words, it has equal amounts of negative and positive charge. Because each electron has the same amount of charge as every other electron, and the same amount as every proton but of opposite sign, there are just as many protons in every nucleus as there are electrons around the outside. While protons are much

smaller than electrons in size, they contain the bulk of the mass of every atom. One proton, for example, weighs nearly two thousand times as much as an electron. The electrons, therefore, are light particles or objects around a small, but relatively heavy, nucleus.

Individual atoms or large groups of atoms and molecules have an *affinity,* an *attraction,* for additional electrons over and above the exact number that will just neutralize the positive charges of the nuclei. This attraction of the atoms for more than a sufficient number of electrons varies considerably from atom to atom and substance to substance. When, therefore, two different substances are brought into contact, the substance with greater electron affinity seizes nearby electrons from the other and, thus, acquires a net negative charge. Such is the case, for example, with rubber and amber when rubbed with fur. Having a strong affinity for electrons, both of these solids become strongly negative, whereas the fur becomes deficient of electrons and, thereby, positively charged.

Coulomb's Law of Electrostatic Force. It has already been demonstrated that like charges repel and unlike charges attract. Nothing thus far, however, has indicated just how strong the repulsion or attraction might be or how it depends on the magnitude of the charges and the distance between them.

The first quantitative measurements of the force between two charged bodies was made in 1780 by Charles Augustin de Coulomb, a French scientist and engineer. He proved experimentally that *the force acting between two charges is directly proportional to the product of the two charges and inversely proportional to the square of the distance between them.* This law is usually written as an algebraic equation:

$$F = k \frac{QQ'}{d^2} \quad (1)$$

where F is the force, Q and Q' are the charges, and d is the distance between them. See Fig. E. The constant of propor-

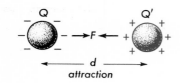

attraction

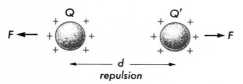

repulsion

Fig. E. Two like charges repel each other and two unlike charges attract each other.

tionality, k, has a value that depends upon the units of charge chosen.

In the mks system, force is given in *newtons*, distance in *meters*, charge in *coulombs*, and $k = 9 \times 10^9$. It is customary to define the coulomb in terms of electric currents.

One coulomb is that quantity of electric charge that, flowing past any point in a wire in one second, produces a current of one ampere. The definition of the ampere will be deferred until later.

Experiments described in later lessons show that electrons are all alike and that each carries a charge—

$$e = 1.6019 \times 10^{-19} \text{ coulomb} \quad (2)$$

This means that a body with a unit negative charge of one coulomb has an excess of 6.24×10^{18} electrons and that a body charged positively with one coulomb has a deficiency of 6.24×10^{18} electrons:

$$1 \text{ coulomb} = 6.24 \times 10^{18} \text{ electrons} \quad (3)$$

Because the unit of charge in the mks system is measured in terms of electric currents, the numerical value of k in Eq. (1) must be determined experimentally. The best value found to date is $k = 8.9878 \times 10^9$. For most practical problems, the approximation $k = 9 \times 10^9$ will be used:

$$k = 9 \times 10^9 \frac{\text{newton-m}^2}{\text{coulomb}^2} \quad (4)$$

Example. A charge of $+25 \times 10^{-9}$ coulomb is located 6 cm from a charge of -72×10^{-9} coulomb. Calculate the force between them.

Solution. The given quantities are $Q = 25 \times 10^{-9}$ coulomb $Q' = -72 \times 10^{-9}$ coulomb, and $d = 0.06$ m. Substitution in Eq. (1) gives—

$$F = 9 \times 10^9 \frac{\text{newton-m}^2}{\text{coulomb}^2}$$

$$\times \frac{(25 \times 10^{-9})(-72 \times 10^{-9}) \text{ coulomb}^2}{(0.06)^2 \text{ m}^2}$$

$$F = -4.50 \times 10^{-3} \text{ newton}$$

The minus sign indicates attraction.

Attraction of Neutral Bodies. An interesting demonstration of electrostatic attraction is shown in Fig. F. A tiny ball cut from the pithy core of a corn cob is coated with tin foil or metallic paint and suspended by a

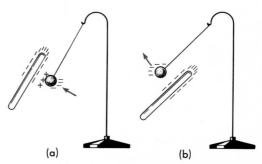

(a)   (b)

Fig. F. (a) A metallic-coated pith ball is attracted by a charged rod. (b) After contact, the pith ball is repelled.

silk thread. When a charged rod is brought near, as in (*a*), the pith ball is attracted to the rod and, upon contact, bounces away. As the rod is now moved toward the ball, the ball avoids the rod and keeps as far away as possible.

To explain this result, assume the rod to be negatively charged in the position shown in (*a*). Free electrons on the sphere are repelled to the opposite side, leaving an equal number of positives on the near side unneutralized. Attraction now takes place, because the positive charges are closest and the attractive force acting on them is greater than the repelling force on the negatives. When contact is made, negatives on the rod neutralize all the positives and the ball moves away with its negative charges by mutual repulsion.

Charging by Induction. To charge a body by induction is to give it a charge without touching it. One method of inducing a charge is illustrated in Fig. G. Two metal spheres, *A* and *B*, insulated by glass standards, are touching each other when a charged rubber rod is brought close to one

of them. If sphere *B* is now moved away and then the rod removed from the vicinity, both spheres are found to be charged, sphere *A* positively and sphere *B* negatively.

Fig. G. Experiment showing how bodies may be charged by induction.

The explanation is similar to that of the pith ball in the preceding section: the close proximity of the charged rod repels free electrons from sphere *A* to the far side of sphere *B*, leaving unneutralized positives behind. Separated under these conditions, both spheres are left with their respective charges. This is called *charging by induction.*

QUESTIONS

1. (a) How many kinds of electrical charges are there? (b) What are they called? What is meant by "electrostatic"?
2. (a) What is the rule regarding repulsion and attraction? (b) How can the rule be demonstrated?
3. (a) What is the structure of the atom? (b) How much negative charge does a neutral atom have?
4. (a) What is the present-day explanation of electrification? (b) Why are things rubbed together to charge them? (c) What kinds of charges do not move in electrification?
5. (a) Do you think that the flow of a liquid through a pipe might produce electrical charges? (b) Do you know of any examples of where this occurs?
6. (a) While combing your hair, you sometimes hear crackling noises. Why? (b) How can you show that your comb becomes electrically charged?

7. Plastic seat covers in automobiles sometimes cause the driver to be electrically shocked. Why?

8. (a) Which substance has a greater affinity for electrons, fur or hard rubber? (b) How could you prove your answer?

9. (a) What is Coulomb's law? (b) Explain its similarity to the law of gravity.

10. The text uses the mks system of units for Coulomb's law. (a) Could some other system be used? (b) Would the value of k be the same?

11. Why will a charged body attract an uncharged body? Make a diagram and explain.

12. Will a charged body attract an uncharged conductor?

13. How can a body be charged positively by induction?

PROBLEMS

1. A positive charge of 5×10^{-8} coulomb is located 5 cm from a negative charge of 10×10^{-8} coulomb. Calculate the force in newtons exerted by either charge upon the other.

2. A charge of -5×10^{-7} coulomb is located 20 cm from another charge of -5×10^{-7} coulomb. Calculate the force in newtons exerted by one charge upon the other.

3. Two charges of -9×10^{-7} coulomb each are located 6 cm apart. What is the repelling force on each in newtons?

4. Two unlike charges of 20×10^{-8} coulomb each are located 30 cm apart. What is the attracting force on each in dynes?

5. Two equal charges are located 12 cm apart and repel each other with a force of 0.36 newton. Find the magnitude of each charge in coulombs.

6. Two small metal spheres 24 cm apart, and having equal negative charges, repel each other with a force of 1×10^{-3} newton. Find the total charge on the two bodies in coulombs.

7. What charge, Q, placed 4 cm from a charge of 8×10^{-8} coulomb, will produce a force of 0.015 newton?

8. How many electrons are there in 0.1 coulomb?

9. An electrical heater in your home uses 10 amp. How many electrons flow through the heater in one hour of use?

10. An electron has a mass of 9.1×10^{-31} Kg and a charge cf 1.6×10^{-19} coulomb. (a) What would be the force of repulsion between them if they are 1 cm apart? (b) What would be the gravitational force between them?

11. Four equal charges of $+5 \times 10^{-8}$ coulomb each are located at the corners of a square, 5 cm on each side. Calculate the resultant force on each charge and show its direction on a diagram drawn to scale.

12. Two positive charges, $+5 \times 10^{-7}$ coulomb each, are located diagonally opposite each other on a square 5 cm on a side. Two negative charges, -5×10^{-7} coulomb each are located at the other corners, respectively. Calculate the resultant force on each charge and show this resultant on a diagram drawn to scale.

PROJECTS

1. Make a sensitive vacuum-tube detector of static charges using a 6C6 or 6D6 vacuum tube, either of which has a connection to its control grid on top of its envelope.
2. Develop an experiment that would prove the inverse-square law of the force between static charges.

ELECTRICITY

Lesson 71 **ELECTRIC POTENTIAL**

The Electroscope. An electroscope is an instrument for measuring the electrical potential of a charged body. A thin strip of gold leaf is fastened to the side of a long, narrow rod of metal, called the "stem," and mounted in a metal and glass box, as in Fig. A. The stem is insulated with amber from the box. When the metal knob, *N*, is touched by a charged rubber rod, some of the charge flows onto, and distributes

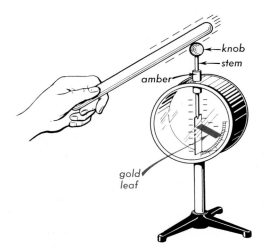

Fig. A. A gold-leaf electroscope is charged by a rod.

itself over, the gold leaf and its support. Because like charges repel each other, the gold leaf is pushed away from the stem, as shown in the diagram. When the source of charge is taken away, the electroscope retains its acquired charge, which, distributing itself more or less uniformly over the stem, causes the leaf to stand out at a somewhat smaller angle. The more charge given the electroscope, the higher the gold leaf is repelled.

If an electroscope is first charged negatively and then a negatively charged body is brought close to, but not touching, the knob, as shown in Fig. B, the gold leaf will rise as indicated. The reason is that the electrons are repelled away from the knob to the far end of the stem, causing the gold leaf to rise still higher. As long as the two bodies do not touch each other and allow more negatives to go to the electroscope, the gold leaf will fall back to its original angle when the negatively charged rod is taken away.

If a positively charged body is brought up, as shown in Fig. C, negatives from the stem and gold leaf are attracted to the knob, causing the gold leaf to fall. *Thus,*

knob, stem, amber, gold leaf

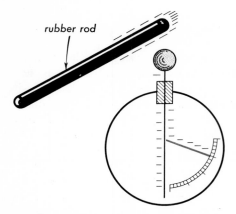

Fig. B. The negatively charged gold leaf rises when a negatively charged body is brought close to the knob.

with a negatively charged electroscope, a positive charge, brought nearby, causes the gold leaf to drop and a negative charge causes it to rise. If the electroscope is positively charged, the action will be reversed —a positive charge causes it to rise and a negative causes it to fall.

Conductors and Insulators. Not all substances are good conductors of electricity.

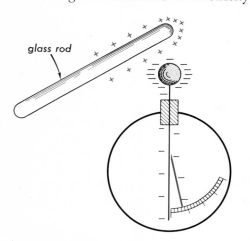

Fig. C. The negatively charged gold leaf falls when a positively charged body is brought close to the knob.

As a general rule, metals are good conductors, whereas nonmetals are poor conductors. The poorest of conductors are commonly called *insulators*, or *nonconductors*. Several examples of conductors and nonconductors are the following

Conductors	Nonconductors
nickel	glass
platinum	amber
iron	rubber
mercury	mica
silver	sulfur
aluminum	porcelain
copper	paper
gold	plastic

The property of electrical conduction is illustrated by an experiment in Fig. D. One

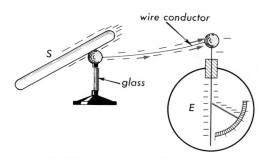

Fig. D. Illustration of an electron current.

end of a long, thin copper wire is connected to an electroscope and the other end to a small brass knob mounted on a glass pedestal. When a charged rubber rod is touched to the knob as shown, the gold leaf of the distant electroscope rises immediately. Electrons have been conducted along the wire. If a positively charged rod contacts the knob, electrons flow away from the electroscope, leaving the gold leaf with a positive charge.

If the copper wire in the above experiment is replaced by a nonconductor, such as a silk thread, the electroscope cannot be charged by the rod contacting the distant knob. Poor conductors, such as glass and amber, are used to support metal parts of electrical apparatus for the purpose of insulating them from unnecessary losses of electricity. An electroscope, for example, will retain its electric charge well if the gold leaf and stem are insulated from the electroscope case with amber, as shown in Fig. A.

The difference between a conductor and an insulator, or dielectric, is that, in a conductor, there are free electrons, whereas in an insulator all the electrons are tightly bound to their respective atoms.

In an uncharged body, the numbers of positive and negative charges are equal. In metals, a few of the electrons are free to move from atom to atom, so that, when a negatively charged rod is brought to the end of a conductor, it repels nearby free electrons in the conductor, causing them to move. They in turn repel free electrons in front of them, thus giving rise to a flow of electrons all along the conductor. Hence, in Fig. D, it is not necessarily the electrons from the charged rubber rod that actually reach the electroscope leaf. Rather, the leaf is affected by the electrons from the end of the wire where it touches the electroscope knob.

Semiconductors.

Numerous solids are neither good conductors of electricity nor good insulators. These substances are called *semiconductors.* Of the large number of semiconductors known to science, certain ones are of considerable importance. Typical examples are the crystalline forms of the elements listed in the fourth column of the periodic table. The ones that are most important today are silicon and germanium. The electrons in these two elements are bound fairly tightly at ordinary temperatures and are, therefore, relatively poor

conductors of electricity. Their important use in transistors will be explained later.

Electrical Potential. When a body has an excess of electrons (and is not close to other charged bodies), it has a *negative potential*. When it has a deficiency of electrons, it is said to have a *positive potential*. There are numerous exceptions to this, however, and it is customary to define positive potential and negative potential in a more general way. This is usually done as follows. If the connection of a body to the ground by an electrical conductor would cause electrons to flow onto the body from the ground, the body is at a *positive potential* as shown in diagram (*a*), Fig. E. Con-

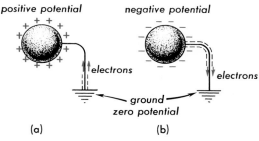

Fig. E. Showing the direction of the flow of electrons when a positively or negatively charged body is connected to the ground by a wire conductor.

versely, if the connection of a body to the ground would cause electrons to flow off the body into the ground, the body is at a negative potential, as in diagram (*b*).

In these definitions of positive and negative potential, *it is assumed that the earth is at zero potential.* The bodies, therefore, had positive and negative potentials, respectively, before they were grounded, but after they were grounded, the flow of electrons *to* or *from* the ground brought them to *zero potential.* Electrical potential is analogous to the potential energy of a body in mechanics.

In mechanics, if a body is raised to a certain height, h, above sea level, its potential energy is positive, i.e., it can, in returning to the ground, perform an amount of work equal to mgh. See Fig. F. Con-

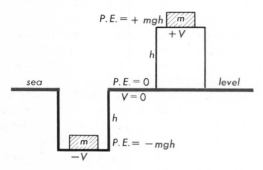

Fig. F. Electrical potential in electricity is analogous to potential energy in mechanics.

versely, a body at a distance h below sea level has a negative potential energy, mgh, for in lowering it to that point energy is given up. To raise it again requires the expenditure of energy. Just as sea level is sometimes taken as the zero level of potential energy in mechanics, so the earth's potential is taken as the zero point of potential in electricity.

A quantitative definition of electrical potential is usually given in terms of work or energy. *The electric potential, V, of a body is equal to the amount of work per unit positive charge done in carrying any charge, Q, from the ground up to the charged body*

$$V = \frac{W}{Q} \tag{1}$$

where W represents the work done and, in the mks system, is measured in *joules*. If the work done is large, the potential of the body is highly positive. If the work done is negative, i.e., if work is given up, the potential is negative. As a rule, potential is expressed in *volts*, and we speak of a po-

tential of a body as being $+110$ volts, -2500 volts, etc.

It is also proper to speak of the potential of a point located anywhere in the free space near one or more charged bodies.

The electric potential at any point in space is equal to the work per unit positive charge done in carrying any charge from the ground up to that point.

To give specific units to this definition, if the unit of charge is one coulomb and the work done is one joule, the potential is one volt:

$$1 \text{ volt} = 1 \frac{\text{joule}}{\text{coulomb}}$$

One one-thousandth of a volt is called a *millivolt* (mv), one-millionth of a volt a *microvolt* (μv), one thousand volts a *kilovolt* (Kv), and one million volts a *megavolt* (Mv).

The work per unit positive charge done in carrying a charge from the ground up to a point near a small body of charge, Q, is given by—

$$V = k \frac{Q}{d} \tag{2}$$

where d, as shown in Fig. G, is the straight-

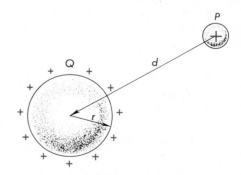

Fig. G. Potential near a charged spherical conductor.

line distance from the center of the charged body to the unit test charge, and k is given by Eq. (4), in Lesson 70.

If the charge is located on a small spherical conductor of radius r, the potential at all points outside the sphere is the same as though the charge were concentrated at the center. At all points inside the sphere, the potential is the same as it is at the surface, namely—

$$V = k \frac{Q}{r} \qquad (3)$$

It will be noted from Eq. (2) that, as d is made larger and approaches infinity, V becomes smaller and approaches zero. Mathematically speaking, then, the ground, referred to in the above definitions and statements, with its arbitrary assigned potential of zero, corresponds in Eq. (2) to $d = \infty$.

Example. A spherical conductor of 1-cm radius has a charge of $+25 \times 10^{-10}$ coulomb. Calculate the potential at a point 10 cm from the center.

Solution. Apply Eq. (2), and use mks units:

$$V = 9 \times 10^9 \frac{25 \times 10^{-10}}{0.10} = 225 \text{ volts}$$

Potential Difference. The potential of a body is defined as the work per unit positive charge done in carrying any charge from infinity to that body.

The difference of potential, V, between two bodies is defined as the work per unit positive charge done in carrying any charge from one of the bodies to the other.

For example, the potential difference between the two terminals of a car storage battery is 12 volts. This means that the work per unit positive charge done in carrying a charge from one terminal to the other is 12 joules/coulomb.

QUESTIONS

1. How could you determine whether an object with unknown charge had an excess or deficiency of electrons?
2. (a) What is meant by a nonconductor? (b) What kinds of charges move through solid conductors?
3. When a positively charged rod is touched to the knob of an electroscope, the gold leaf rises. When the rod is taken away, the leaf drops only part way back. Why?
4. When a negatively charged rod is brought up close to the knob of a negatively charged electroscope, what happens?
5. When a negatively charged rod is brought up close to the knob of a positively charged electroscope, what happens?
6. (a) Why are some substances good conductors of electrons and others not? (b) Do all substances contain electrons?
7. (a) What is electric potential? (b) How is it defined? (c) What are the units of potential?
8. (a) What is the potential of a point in space? (b) How is it defined? (c) Is it a vector or a scalar?

PROBLEMS

1. If 2.4×10^{-5} joule of work is done in carrying a charge of 5×10^{-8} coulomb up to a charged body, what is its potential?

2. A charge of 8×10^{-7} coulomb is carried from a distant point up to a charged body. What is the potential of that body if the work done is 2×10^{-4} joule?
3. How much work is done by a 12-volt storage battery if 5 coulombs of charge is moved by it?
4. How much work is done by a 6-volt battery that moves 1 coulomb per second through a lamp for 1 hour?
5. A spherical conductor 2 cm in diameter has a charge of 5×10^{-9} coulomb. Calculate the potential of (a) a point 8 cm from the center and (b) the sphere.
6. A spherical conductor 3 cm in diameter has a charge of 2×10^{-9} coulomb. Calculate the potential of (a) the sphere and (b) a point 5 cm from the center.
7. A metal sphere is suspended by a silk thread and charged negatively. In carrying a negative charge of 4×10^{-8} coulomb from a great distance to the metal sphere, an amount of work equal to 8×10^{-5} joule is done. What is the potential of the sphere?

PROJECT

Make a simple but effective electroscope as suggested by Fig. C.

ELECTRICITY

Lesson 72 THE ELECTRIC FIELD

Faraday Ice-pail Experiment. The distribution of charge over a metallic conductor can, in part, be demonstrated by an experiment first performed by Michael Faraday in 1810. This demonstration, known as *Faraday's ice-pail experiment,* involves a small metal ball, a hollow metal container such as a tin pail, and an electroscope, as shown in Fig. A.

If the ball is charged from another source and then lowered into the pail, the leaf of the electroscope rises. When the ball is moved around inside the pail and even when it touches the inside surface, no change in the potential is shown by the electroscope leaf. After the ball has been removed, the inner surface of the pail and the ball are found to be completely free of charge.

To explain what happens, let the ball be charged negatively and lowered to the position shown. Free electrons in the metal

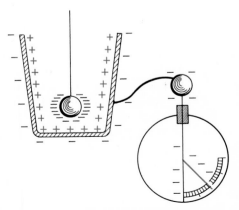

Fig. A. Diagram illustrating Faraday's ice-pail experiment.

pail are repelled to the outer surface and to the connecting electroscope, leaving positives on the inside unneutralized. When the ball touches the pail, all negatives leave the ball and neutralize an equal number of positives.

The fact that the electroscope leaf remains fixed when the ball is removed shows (1) that there is no redistribution of the negative charges on the outer pail surface and (2) that the number of induced positives is equal to the number of negatives on the ball.

When static charges are acquired by a nonconductor like hard rubber, glass, or amber, they remain where they were first located. When a conductor like copper, silver, or gold acquires a charge, however, the charge quickly spreads over the entire surface. With a metallic sphere, whether solid or hollow, the charge spreads uniformly over the surface as shown in Fig. B. On other shapes of conductors, the

gether at the point. Mutual repulsion ejects electrons from a negatively charged point and attracts electrons to a positively charged point.

The Electric Field. A useful way of describing the action at a distance of one charge upon another is through consideration of an electric field. The force on a given charge is determined by a two-step process as follows. First, an electric field around one or more charges is calculated for any point in space. Second, the force on a charge placed at that point is attributed to the electric field there. *The intensity of the electric field at any point in the neighborhood of a charged body is equal to the force per unit positive charge exerted on any charge placed at that point.*

Because force is a vector quantity, an electric field has magnitude and direction. The field about a positive charge is, therefore, radially outward, as shown in Fig.

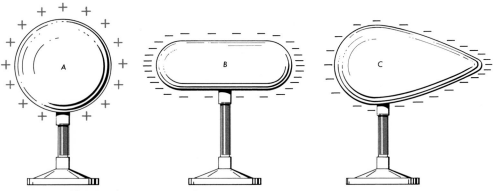

Fig. B. Charge density on conductors is greatest in regions of greatest curvature.

charge distributes itself according to surface curvature, concentrating more at points and less where the walls are more nearly straight.

On a charged conductor with a sharp point, the charges crowd very close to-

$C(a)$. It is radially outward because a positive charge placed at any point is repelled along a line through the two charges. By similar reasoning, the field about a negative charge is radially inward, as shown in diagram (b).

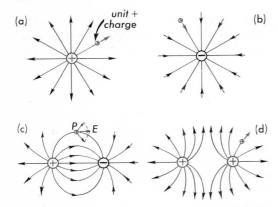

Fig. C. Diagrams of the electric field around charged bodies.

The electric field around two charged bodies is shown in diagrams (c) and (d). Each of these fields may be experimentally mapped by placing a positive charge at any one point and moving it always in the direction of the force F exerted on it. The lines traced out by such a charge are called *electric lines of force*. Note that as many lines as desired can be drawn and that no two lines ever cross. Furthermore, the lines themselves are imaginary and do not actually exist. They were first introduced by Michael Faraday about 1820 as an aid to the understanding of various electrical phenomena.

The direction of the lines of force is given by the arrowheads and the relative magnitude of the field at any region is given by the relative number of the lines passing through that region. In agreement with Coulomb's law, *the intensity of the field at any point near a single charged body is inversely proportional to the square of the distance between the point and the charged body.*

Because, E, the electric field intensity, is defined as the force per unit charge placed there, F/Q', Coulomb's law may be used to obtain a formula for the field intensity at any point near a small body of charge Q. Dividing both sides of Eq. (1) in Lesson 70 by Q' gives—

$$\frac{F}{Q'} = k\frac{Q}{d^2}$$

or—

$$E = k\frac{Q}{d^2} \qquad (1)$$

The charge, Q, is in *coulombs*, the distance, d, to the field point is in *meters*, the field, E, at that point is in *newtons per coulomb*, and $k = 9 \times 10^9$ newton meter^2/coulomb^2. See Eq. (2) in Lesson 70. Because E represents the force per unit charge, the force on any charge Q' placed at that point will be—

$$F = Q' \times E \qquad (2)$$

$$\left(1 \text{ newton} = 1 \text{ coulomb} \times 1\frac{\textbf{newton}}{\textbf{coulomb}}\right)$$

Example. A proton is an atomic particle having a mass of 1.672×10^{-27} Kg and a positive charge of 1.602×10^{-19} coulomb. Calculate the force on a proton in an electric field of 5000 newtons/coulomb and compare this with its weight.

Solution. To find the electrical force, apply Eq. (2):

$$F = Q'E = 1.602 \times 10^{-19} \times 5 \times 10^3$$
$$= 8.010 \times 10^{-16} \text{ newton}$$

To find the weight of a proton—

$$W = mg = 1.672 \times 10^{-27} \times 9.80$$
$$= 1.638 \times 10^{-26} \text{ newton}$$

A comparison of these two forces clearly indicates how negligibly small the gravitational force on atomic particles is when compared with the force due to electric fields commonly employed in the laboratory.

Uniform Electric Field. In many experimental studies of atomic structure a great deal of knowledge can be obtained by observing the behavior of charged atomic particles traversing a uniform electric field. To obtain such a field, that is, a field constant in magnitude and direction over a specified volume of space, two flat metal plates are set up parallel to each other as shown in Fig. D.

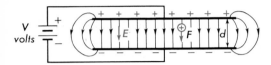

Fig. D. The electric field between two parallel charged plates is uniform.

When the terminals of a battery with a voltage V are connected to these plates, as indicated in the diagram, a uniform electric field, E, is produced between the plates. Outside the plates and near the ends, the field is not uniform.

In mechanics, *work done* is defined as *force times distance*, $W = F \times d$. The electrical equivalent of this equation follows, therefore, by direct substitution of the equivalent electrical quantities for W and F. Because work done per unit charge is potential difference, V, and the force per unit charge is the electric-field intensity, E, the work equation $W = F \times d$ becomes—

$$V = E \times d$$

or—

$$E = \frac{V}{d} \qquad (3)$$

If V is in volts and d is in meters, E is in *volts/m:*

$$1 \frac{\text{volt}}{\text{m}} = 1 \frac{\text{newton}}{\text{coulomb}}$$

QUESTIONS

1. (a) What is meant by an electric field? (b) How could one find the electric-field intensity at a point in space? (c) What are the units of the electric-field intensity, E?
2. (a) Is the electric field a vector or scalar quantity? (b) Is electric potential a vector or scalar quantity?
3. Which is the greater force, electrical or gravitational? Explain.
4. (a) If an egg-shaped conductor is charged negatively, where are the charges most concentrated? (b) Where are they least concentrated?
5. Suppose the point in space between two charges has zero electric field. What can be said about the charges?
6. Suppose the point in space between two charges has zero potential. What can be said about the charges?

PROBLEMS

1. What is the force on an electron in a field of 3000 newtons/coulomb?
2. What is the force on a hydrogen ion (an atom of hydrogen that has lost its electron) in a field of 8000 newtons/coulomb?
3. Two insulated metal spheres, 50 cm apart, each have a charge of 5×10^{-8}

coulomb. Calculate (a) the field intensity and (b) the potential at a point midway between them.

4. The high-voltage end of a Van de Graaff generator is a sphere 80 cm in diameter, upon which a charge of 10^{-4} coulomb has been placed. (a) What is the potential and the electric field at the surface? (b) What is the potential and electric field 40 cm from the surface?

5. An earth satellite 30 cm in diameter attracts a nearby speck of dust, which has a positive charge of 2×10^{-17} coulomb. This dust particle is accelerated toward the satellite, owing to the electrostatic attraction, and strikes the surface with a kinetic energy of 10^{-14} joule. (a) What is the potential of the satellite? (b) What is its charge? (c) What is the electric field at the surface?

6. Two flat metal plates 2 cm apart are connected to a 1000-volt battery. A proton, with its positive charge of 1.6×10^{-19} coulomb, is located between these plates. Find (a) the electric field intensity between the plates, and (b) the force on the proton in newtons.

7. Two flat metal plates 2 cm apart are connected to a 2000-volt source. A small charge, Q, of 5×10^{-9} coulomb is located in the field. Find (a) the electric-field intensity, and (b) the force on the charge, Q.

8. A potential difference of 5000 volts is applied to two parallel plates 2 cm apart. A small metal sphere with a charge of 1.8×10^{-10} coulomb is located midway between the plates. Find (a) the electric-field intensity between the plates, and (b) the force on the charged sphere.

9. A battery of 8000 volts is connected to two parallel plates 5 mm apart. What is the force of an electron of charge 1.60×10^{-19} coulomb when it passes through the uniform electric field between the plates?

PROJECT

Make a set of variously shaped conductors such as those in Fig. D. Charge them and, with your electroscope, measure the positions of maximum-charge concentration.

ELECTRICITY

Lesson 73 *CAPACITANCE*

The Capacitor. A capacitor is an electrical device for storing quantities of electricity in much the same way that a reservoir is a container for storing water. The general form of a capacitor is that of two parallel conducting plates, as shown in Fig. A.

Such plates are of relatively large area, close together, and separated by a nonconducting medium called the *dielectric*. Common dielectrics are *air, glass, mica, oil, Mylar,* and *vacuum.*

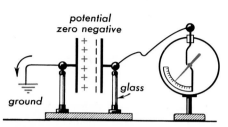

Fig. A. Demonstration of the principles of a capacitor.

Quantitatively, the capacitance of a capacitor is a measure of its ability to store electricity. To increase capacitance, one or more of the following things can be done: first, the area of the plates may be increased; second, the plates may be put closer together; and third, a more suitable dielectric may be inserted between the plates. If the plates of a capacitor are small in area and at the same time relatively far apart, the capacitance is small. If the area is large and the plates are close together, the capacitance is large.

The principles of the capacitor are illustrated in Fig. A. One plate of this capacitor is grounded and the other is insulated but connected to an electroscope or electrometer. If the right-hand plate is given a negative charge, as shown, electrons in the other plate are repelled into the ground, leaving that plate positively charged. If the insulated plate is given a positive charge (not shown), electrons from the ground are attracted to the other plate and it acquires a negative charge.

In either case, the grounded plate is, by definition, at *ground potential,* or *zero potential.* The right-hand plate is at negative potential, because if connected to the ground, its electrons would escape into the ground. As shown in the diagram, however, the capacitor is charged.

If, while in the charged condition, the two plates of a capacitor are suddenly connected by a conductor, the negatives can flow through the conductor to the positives, thus neutralizing the charges. The capacitor has thus been discharged.

During the time a capacitor is being charged, the plates acquire a greater and greater difference of potential. If in Fig. A more electrons are added to the insulated plate, the potential difference is increased. The amount of charge stored in this way is limited only by the breakdown of the dielectric between the two plates. When the charge becomes too great, a spark will jump between the plates, thus discharging the capacitor.

Capacitance is not determined by the amount of charge a capacitor will hold before sparking occurs; it is defined as the amount of charge, Q, on one plate necessary to raise the potential, V, of that plate 1 volt above the other. Symbolically—

$$C = \frac{Q}{V} \qquad (1)$$

The unit of capacitance, the *farad,* named in honor of Michael Faraday, is defined as the capacitance of a capacitor of such dimensions that *a charge of one coulomb will give the plates a difference of potential of one volt:*

$$1 \text{ farad} = \frac{1 \text{ coulomb}}{1 \text{ volt}} \qquad (2)$$

Whether one plate of a 1-farad capacitor is grounded or not, the potential difference between the plates will be 1 volt when one plate has a positive charge of 1 coulomb and the other plate has a negative charge of −1 coulomb. Grounding one plate simply brings that plate to zero potential without changing its charge.

A capacitance of 1 farad is very large and, for practical purposes, is not used. The *microfarad*, μF, is more convenient. The smaller unit is one-millionth of the farad. In other words, one million microfarads are equivalent to one farad. A still smaller unit, the *micromicrofarad*, or *picofarad*, is sometimes used. One picofarad is one-millionth of one microfarad and is abbreviated $\mu\mu$F, or pF:

$$1 \ \mu F = 10^{-6} \text{ farad} \qquad (3)$$

$$1 \ pF = 10^{-12} \text{ farad} \qquad (4)$$

The charging of a capacitor until the difference of potential is one volt is analogous to raising the level of water in a tank to one foot, whereas the charging of the same capacitor to the point where it sparks over is like filling the tank until water runs over the top. A large capacitance is like a tank of large cross-sectional area, and a small capacitance is like a tank of small area. It takes more charge to raise the potential of a large capacitance one volt, and it takes more water to raise the level in a large tank one foot.

Capacitors in common use today are of various kinds, sizes, and shapes. Perhaps the most common is the so-called "paper capacitor" often used in radio and television circuits and the ignition systems of automobiles. Two long strips of tin foil are glued to the two faces of a strip of thin paper. This paper is then soaked in paraffin or oil and rolled up with another paraffin-soaked strip of paper into a small compact unit. Each sheet of tin foil becomes one plate of the capacitor and the paper becomes the dielectric separating them.

Another type of capacitor is the variable capacitor commonly used in tuning radios. See Fig. B. The amount of capacitance of such a device can be varied at will by the turning of a knob. Turning the knob moves one set of plates between the other set, thus

Fig. B. Variable capacitor commonly used in radio sets. (Courtesy of Hammarlund Manufacturing Co.)

increasing or decreasing the effective plate area, and hence, the capacitance. The capacitance of such variable air capacitors is from zero to some 4000 pF.

Calculation of Capacitance. A general formula for calculating the capacitance of a parallel plate capacitor is the following:

$$C = \left(\frac{K}{4\pi k} \right) \frac{A}{d} \qquad (5)$$

where, as shown in Fig. C, A is the area of

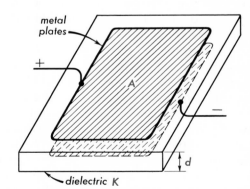

Fig. C. Diagram of the principal elements of a capacitor.

either of the parallel plates in meters^2, d is the distance between them in meters, k is the constant from Coulomb's law, and C is the capacitance in farads. The constant called K is the dielectric constant, or dielectric coefficient. Values of the dielectric constants of a few substances are given in Table 1.

Table 1. Dielectric Constants

Dielectric	K
vacuum.............	1.0000
air................	1.0006
glass..............	5-10
rubber.............	3-35
mica..............	3-6
glycerine..........	56
petroleum..........	2
water.............	81

Example. Two rectangular sheets of tinfoil 20 cm × 25 cm are stuck to opposite sides of a thin sheet of mica 0.1 mm thick. Calculate the capacitance if the dielectric constant is 5.

Solution. The given quantities are $K = 5$, $d = 1 \times 10^{-4}$ m, and $A = 0.20 \times 0.25 = 0.05$ m². By substituting in Eq. (5) and Eq. (4), Lesson 70, we obtain—

$$C = 5 \times 8.85 \times 10^{-12} \frac{0.05}{1 \times 10^{-4}}$$

$$= 221 \times 10^{-10} \text{ farad} = 0.0221 \ \mu F$$

parallel capacitors

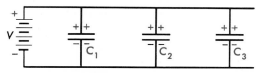

Fig. D. Circuit diagram of parallel capacitors.

When capacitors are connected in parallel, as shown in Fig. D, their combined capacitance is just the arithmetic sum of the individual capacities:

$$C = C_1 + C_2 + C_3 + \text{etc.} \qquad (6)$$

When capacitors are connected in series, as shown in Fig. E, the combined capacitance

series capacitors

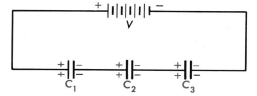

Fig. E. Circuit diagram of series capacitors.

is given by the reciprocal of the sum of the reciprocals:

$$\frac{1}{C} = \frac{1}{C_1} + \frac{1}{C_2} + \frac{1}{C_3} + \text{etc.} \qquad (7)$$

The first formula is derived from the principle that capacitors in a parallel combination each have the same potential difference, V, given by $V = Q/C$, while $Q = Q_1 + Q_2 + Q_3 + \text{etc.}$ The second of these formulas is derived from the principle that capacitors in a series combination acquire the same charge, Q, given by $Q = CV$, while $V = V_1 + V_2 + V_3 + \text{etc.}$

QUESTIONS

1. (a) What is a capacitor? (b) What three elements go to make up a capacitor?
2. (a) What is capacitance? (b) What are the units of capacitance? (c) What is the formula? (d) Is Q the sum of the charges on both plates?
3. (a) How does capacitance change when the plate area is doubled? (b) What happens when the plate separation is doubled?

4. How does capacitance change when air between the plates is replaced by glass?
5. What is the formula for capacitance in terms of its dimensions?
6. (a) What is the dielectric constant? (b) What is the dielectric constant for a vacuum?
7. (a) What is the equation for capacitors in parallel? (b) What is the formula for series connection?
8. If the negatively charged plate of a capacitor is connected to the ground, (a) do the electrons leave the plate? (b) Is the plate at zero potential?
9. (a) Could a capacitor plate have a net positive charge and a negative potential? (b) If so, how could you produce it?
10. Basically, what is the primary function of a capacitor?

PROBLEMS

1. A 1000-volt battery is connected to a 10-μF capacitor. What is the charge on each plate?
2. A 250-volt battery is applied to a 6-μF capacitor. Find the charge on each plate.
3. Two sheets of tinfoil 20 cm $\times$ 50 cm are glued to opposite faces of a glass plate 0.8 cm thick. Find the capacitance if the dielectric constant for glass is 5.
4. Two flat metal plates 40 cm $\times$ 100 cm are mounted parallel to each other and 1 cm apart. Find the capacitance when they are immersed in oil of dielectric constant 2.
5. A parallel-plate capacitor, with air as a dielectric, has a capacitance of 500 pF. What will be its capacitance if it is submerged in glycerine?
6. A parallel-plate capacitor, with glass as a dielectric, has a capacitance of 0.05 μF. What will be its capacitance if the glass (dielectric constant 8) is replaced by mica (dielectric constant 4.8)?
7. A capacitor is made up of 16 sheets of tinfoil each 4 cm $\times$ 15 cm, separated by mica sheets 0.25 mm thick. Find the capacitance in microfarads if alternate sheets of tinfoil are connected together. (Dielectric constant of mica = 4.8.)
8. Three capacitors of 8, 12, and 24 μF, respectively, are connected in series. Find the capacitance of the system.
9. Three capacitors of 4, 5, and 20 μF are connected in series to a 300-volt battery. Find (a) the capacitance, (b) the charge on each capacitor plate, and (c) the voltage across each capacitor.
10. Two capacitors of 5 μF and 20 μF, respectively, are connected in parallel. Then the combination is connected in series with a third capacitor of 10 μF. Find (a) the capacitance of the parallel circuit, (b) the total capacitance, and (c) the voltage across each capacitor, if the ends are connected to a 1000-volt battery.
11. A 4000-pF air capacitor has 2500 coulombs on each plate. The plates are 0.05 cm apart. What is the potential difference and the electric field in the gap?
12. The charge of +1 microcoulomb is placed on the right-hand plate of a 1200-pF capacitor. The left plate is grounded. (a) What is the charge and

potential of the left plate? (b) Give the charge and potential of each plate if the ground is removed from the left plate, and the right plate is then grounded.

13. A 400-pF air-gap capacitor has a charge on its plates so that the voltage across it is 100 volts. If the air is replaced by water, what is the capacitance, voltage, and charge?

14. Using the hint in the last paragraph of the text, show that three capacitors in parallel are equivalent to one capacitor whose capacitance is given by $C = C_1 + C_2 + C_3$.

15. Using the hint in the last paragraph of the text, derive the law of series capacitors.

PROJECTS

1. Make a collection of a variety of capacitors that have been and are being used in electronic equipment.
2. Build an impedance bridge for measuring capacitance.

ELECTRICITY

Lesson 74 *BATTERY CELLS*

To make an electron current flow continuously along a wire, a continuous supply of electrons must be available at one end and a continuous supply of positive charges at the other as shown in Fig. A. This is like the flow of water through a pipe: to obtain a continuous flow, a continuous supply of

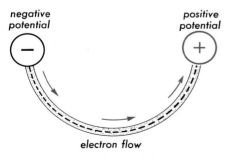

negative potential · positive potential

electron flow

Fig. A. Two terminals at different potentials and connected by a conductor give rise to an electric current.

water must be provided at one end and an opening for its escape at the other. The continuous supply of positive charge at the one end of a wire offers a means of escape for the electrons. If this is not provided, electrons will accumulate at the end of the wire and their repulsion back along the wire will stop the current flow.

There are two general methods by which a continuous supply of electrical charge is obtained: one is by means of a *battery* and the other is by means of an *electric generator*. The battery is a device by which chemical energy is transformed into electrical energy and the generator is a device by which mechanical energy is transformed into electrical energy.

Battery Cells. Battery cells, as continuous sources of electrical energy, are the result of a long series of experiments that started with the discoveries of Alessandro Volta* more than one hundred years ago. Today, battery cells are manufactured in two common forms: (1) dry cells, as used in flashlights, and portable radios and (2) wet cells, as used in automobiles, airplanes, and boats.

The Voltaic Cell. The voltaic cell, as shown in Fig. B, is composed of three parts,

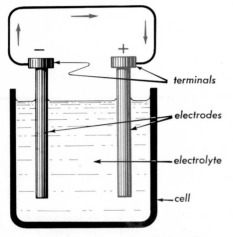

Fig. B. Diagram of a voltaic cell.

a pair of dissimilar metal plates called *electrodes*, a dilute acid solution called the *electrolyte*, and a nonconducting container called the *cell*. While many different combinations of materials have been tried and used in such cells, zinc and carbon as electrodes, dilute sulfuric acid as the electrolyte,

* Alessandro Volta (1745-1827), Italian scientist, was for more than twenty years professor of physics at Pavia. Traveling throughout Europe, he became acquainted with many celebrities. In 1801, he was awarded the Copley medal of the Royal Society of London. He was also called to Paris and awarded a medal by Napoleon. In 1815, the emperor of Austria made him director of the philosophical faculty of the University of Padua. A statue now stands in his memory at Como, his birthplace.

and a glass or hard-rubber container as the cell, are the most common.

Electrolytic Dissociation. Individual molecules of sulfuric acid (H_2SO_4) are composed of seven atoms each: two hydrogens, one sulfur, and four oxygens. When concentrated acid is poured into water to form a dilute solution, a small percentage of the molecules *ionize*, that is, they dissociate. The two hydrogens split off from the molecule, each leaving an electron behind with the remaining SO_4 molecule. Similarly, some of the water molecules, each composed of two hydrogens and one oxygen, dissociate when one of the hydrogen atoms splits off without an electron. See Fig. C.

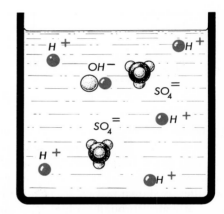

Fig. C. In a dilute solution, some of the sulfuric acid molecules and water molecules dissociate.

Because each hydrogen atom leaves an electron behind, its remaining charge is positive and the atom is called a *positive ion*. Each remaining SO_4 fragment from the acid, as well as the OH fragment from the water, has a surplus of negative charge and is called a *negative ion*.

Electrode Action. If we now insert a zinc rod into this electrolyte, chemical action is initiated, whereby individual zinc atoms break off from the surface leaving two electrons behind. See Fig. D. Going into solution as doubly charged positive ions, they strongly attract SO_4^{--} ions. With each

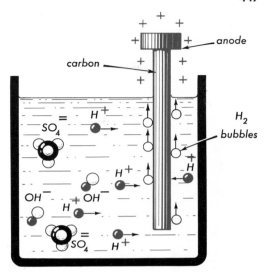

Fig. E. A carbon rod in dilute sulfuric acid.

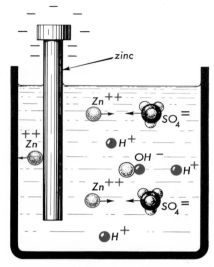

Fig. D. A zinc electrode in dilute sulfuric acid.

encounter of two such ions, combination takes place, resulting in the formation of neutral $ZnSO_4$ molecules.

$$Zn^{++} + SO_4^{--} = ZnSO_4$$

As more and more zinc ions go into solution, the negative charge on the zinc electrode increases and soon reaches a maximum.

If, instead of a zinc rod, we insert a carbon rod into the electrolyte, as shown in Fig. E, hydrogen ions are attracted to the electrode. There, each H^+ ion acquires an electron from the carbon, and two such particles form a neutral hydrogen molecule, H_2. Because hydrogen is a gas at normal temperatures, the accumulation of H_2 molecules results in the formation of bubbles of gas rising to the surface. In giving up electrons, the carbon electrode acquires a posi-

tive charge and a certain definite positive potential:

$$2(H^+) + 2(e^-) = H_2 \uparrow$$

The Cell Electromotive Force. If we now insert both the zinc and carbon electrodes into the electrolyte, as shown in Fig. F, each one acquires its appropriate charge. The positive electrode, called the *anode*, acquires a positive potential; the negative electrode, called the *cathode*, acquires a negative potential.

When a voltmeter is connected to the two terminals of the cell, the pointer indicates the *difference of potential* in volts, and this we call the *electromotive force*, or *emf*.

Because the voltmeter completes the electric circuit between cathode and anode, a small electron current will flow from cathode to anode through the connecting wires and the voltmeter. Electrons leaving the zinc metal surface change the cathode potential, and electrons arriving at the carbon neutralize positives, thereby changing the anode potential. With the tendency of the potential difference to fall, chemical ac-

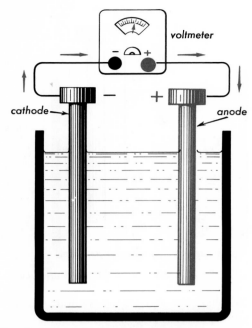

Fig. F. The emf of a voltaic cell is measured with a voltmeter.

and a little water. Surrounding the anode is a thin layer of powdered carbon and manganese dioxide.

When current is being supplied by the dry cell, zinc ions form at the cathode, while ammonium ions gain electrons at the carbon rod, forming hydrogen and ammonia gas.

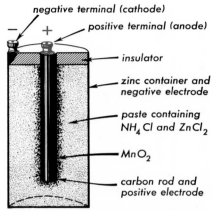

Fig. G. Cross-section diagram of a dry cell or "flashlight" battery, showing the essential elements.

tion takes place immediately and maintains a continuous supply of + and − charges at the terminals. When the circuit is opened, the terminals remain charged, but no current flows and no chemical action takes place.

The Dry Cell. Probably the most common form of battery used today is composed of dry cells. While these cells are manufactured in different shapes and vary in size from $\frac{1}{8}$ in. to many inches, they all produce the same emf of 1.5 volts between their two terminals.

One common form of dry cell is shown in Fig. G. The negative electrode is a zinc-coated metal container in which all chemical ingredients are sealed, and the positive electrode is a round carbon rod. In place of a liquid electrolyte, we have a paste containing ammonium chloride, zinc chloride,

The hydrogen reacts chemically with the manganese dioxide, and the ammonia gas with the zinc chloride. While the emf of all dry cells is 1.5 volts, the larger the cell the greater is the current and the total electrical energy that can be supplied.

Storage Batteries. When the electrical energy contained in a battery composed of dry cells has been exhausted, it is thrown away. A storage battery, on the other hand, is composed of what are called *wet cells* and, when exhausted of its stored up energy, such a battery can be rejuvenated or *recharged*.

The negative electrode of a storage cell, as shown in Fig. H, is composed of a set of parallel lead grills filled with *spongy lead* (Pb), while the positive electrode is an-

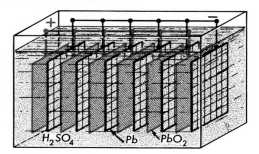

Fig. H. The cell of a storage battery has a number of plates.

other set of lead grills filled with porous *lead dioxide* (PbO_2).

When a current is supplied by the cell, PbO_2 in one set of grills and Pb in the other combine with the dissociated H^+ and SO_4^{--} ions of the electrolyte and form lead sulfate ($PbSO_4$) and water (H_2O). When the surfaces of all plates become coated with lead sulfate, they behave chemically alike, and no more current can be drawn from the cell.

To recharge a storage cell the two terminals are connected to a direct-current generator. The current flowing through the electrolyte reverses the chemical process, changing them back to their original form. Chemically, one writes—

$$PbO_2 + Pb + 2H_2SO_4$$
charge $\uparrow$ $\downarrow$ discharge
$$2PbSO_4 + 2H_2O$$

When a cell is charged too rapidly some of the dissociated water molecules of the electrolyte are converted into hydrogen gas at the cathode and oxygen gas at the anode. These rise to the surface as bubbles and necessitate the occasional addition of water to the cell.

Regardless of the size, each such cell develops an emf of 2.2 volts. While many other kinds of storage cells have been developed, the lead battery is still the most widely used in the United States.

The Battery. If two or more cells are connected together as shown in Fig. I, they

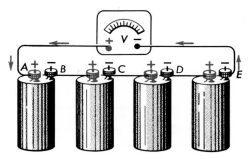

Fig. I. Four dry cells connected in series form a 6-volt battery.

form what is called a battery. In this diagram, the battery is composed of four dry cells connected *in series*. In series connections, the + terminal of one cell is connected to the − terminal of the next.

The purpose in connecting two or more cells in series is to obtain a higher emf than that available with one cell alone. The potential difference between the extreme end terminals, *A* and *E*, of any battery is just the sum of those for the individual cells.

Each dry cell produces an emf of 1.5 volts, so that, if the voltmeter is connected to two points, it will indicate 1.5 volts between *A* and *B*, 3.0 volts between *A* and *C*, 4.5 volts between *A* and *D*, and 6 volts between *A* and *E*.

The common flashlight contains several dry cells connected in series, as shown in Fig. J. When new cells are inserted, they are all turned in the same direction so that the + terminal at the center of each cell makes

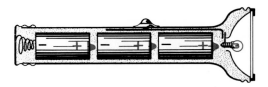

Fig. J. Cross section of a 3-cell flashlight.

good contact with the − case of the next cell. The closing of the switch shown in the figure applies the end-terminal voltage of 4.5 volts to the light bulb.

A storage battery commonly used in automobiles contains six wet-cells of 2 volts each, connected in series, as shown in Fig. K. Note how the heavy crossbars connect

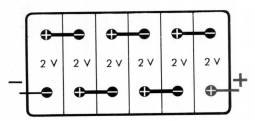

Fig. K. Series connections for a 12-volt storage battery.

the − terminal of any one cell with the + terminal of the next. With six cells in series, the end terminals produce a resultant of 12 volts, hence its name, *twelve-volt battery*.

It is customary in circuit diagrams to represent battery cells as shown in Fig. L.

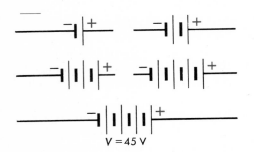

Fig. L. Circuit diagram indicating the cells of a battery.

The + and − terminals of each cell are indicated by long and short vertical lines, respectively. The first four diagrams shown represent one, two, three, and four cells, respectively, connected in series. If many cells are to be represented, four or five can be

drawn and the over-all terminal voltage written beneath it as shown by $V = 45$ volts.

Fuel Cells. The dry cell produces electricity only as long as there is a considerable amount of zinc available to furnish electrons. The storage battery will produce electricity for only a relatively short time before it must be recharged. This limits both to uses where small amounts of electricity are needed for short times. The fuel cell was developed in an attempt to make a portable source of electrical power with no such limitations.

When hydrogen and oxygen are burned, a great deal of energy is released at a very high temperature. In a typical fuel cell, these two gases are made to combine at room temperatures. See Fig. M. Hydrogen

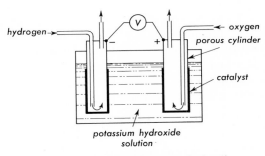

Fig. M. Hydrogen-oxygen fuel cell.

and oxygen are sent to two porous cylinders that have been treated with a special catalyst. The reaction between the two gases takes place here, producing an excess of electrons at the hydrogen electrode. At the oxygen electrode, the reaction produces a shortage of electrons. The reactions take place at room temperature because of the action of the catalyst. Water is produced as the result of the action of this cell just as if the gases were burned directly.

A great deal of research is currently in progress to improve the catalyst action and to utilize fuels that are cheaper than pure hydrogen.

QUESTIONS

1. (a) What is a voltaic cell? (b) What is a battery?
2. (a) What are ions? (b) Where are they produced?
3. (a) What is electromotive force? (b) In what units is it measured?
4. (a) What is the source of electrical energy in a cell? (b) What is the emf of a dry cell? (c) Of a storage cell?
5. (a) Of what is the storage-cell electrolyte composed? (b) Of what elements are the electrodes composed?
6. (a) What is meant by dissociation? (b) What is a terminal? (c) What is a cathode? (d) What is an anode?
7. What is the main disadvantage of using a dry cell as a main source of electric power?
8. What is gained by connecting dry cells (a) in series and (b) in parallel?
9. Does the size of a cell made of zinc and carbon have any effect on its voltage? Explain.
10. What is the basic principle of the fuel cell?

PROBLEMS

1. (a) Make a diagram of a voltaic cell composed of zinc and carbon electrodes with dilute sulfuric acid in water as an electrolyte. (b) Briefly explain what happens on a closed circuit.
2. Make a diagram of a dry cell showing the electrode and chemical materials used.
3. Make a diagram of a lead storage cell, label the essential elements, and write down the chemical reactions taking place on (a) charge and (b) discharge.
4. A student hooks up 12 dry cells in series to make a battery, but connects two of them backwards. What is the total resulting voltage?
5. Suppose one cell in the flashlight (Fig. J) was put in backward. What would be the total emf?
6. Suppose the cells in Fig. I were connected in parallel, i.e., all positive poles connected to one wire, and all negative poles to the other. (a) What would be the total emf? (b) What purpose would such an arrangement serve?

PROJECTS

1. Make a series of primary cells using different metals and solutions.
2. Make a simple fuel cell and test its efficiency.

ELECTRICITY

Lesson 75 *OHM'S LAW*

Electric current is measured in units called *amperes. The ampere,* named in honor of a French physicist,* *is defined as the flow of one coulomb of electric current per second.* In other words, one coulomb flowing past any given point in a wire in one second constitutes a current of one *ampere,* or *amp.*

$$\mathbf{1\ amp} = \frac{\mathbf{1\ coulomb}}{\mathbf{1\ sec}}$$

If twice this quantity passes by in 1 sec, the current is 2 amp. Thus, electric current is analogous to the rate of flow of water through a pipe:

$$\mathbf{current} = \frac{\mathbf{quantity\ of\ charge}}{\mathbf{time}}$$

$$I = \frac{\Delta Q}{\Delta t} \qquad (1)$$

Remembering that 1 coulomb $= 6.24 \times 10^{18}$ electrons, a current of 1 amp means a flow of 6.24×10^{18} electrons per second past any given point.

This enormous number does not mean that the electrons are moving with high speed through a conductor. Actually, the number of moving charges is so large that their average velocity is but a small fraction of a millimeter per second. When we picture a solid conductor as a crystal lattice, similar to that shown in Fig. E in Lesson 33, the electrons are thought of as moving

André M. Ampère (1775-1836), French physicist and mathematican, began his career as professor of physics and chemistry at Bourg at the early age of 26. Later, he established the relation between electricity and magnetism and helped to develop the subject he called electrodynamics. His only son, Jean J. Ampère, also became famous as a philologist, lecturer, and historian.

through the intervening spaces. This movement is not completely free, however, being influenced by the repulsion and attraction of like and unlike charges.

Many years ago, before it was known which of the electric charges, + or −, moved through a wire, there seemed to be some evidence that it was the positive charge and not the negative. This notion became thoroughly entrenched in the minds of those interested in electrical phenomena. In later years, when it was discovered that the negatives move in solid conductors and not the positives, it became difficult to change this convention.

The convention that electric current flow from plus to minus is still to be found in many books and is used by some electrical engineers in designing electrical machines and appliances. The rapid growth and the importance of radio engineering and electronics, however, has brought about a change in this practice, and we shall, hereafter in this text, speak of current as the electron flow from − to + and call it *electron current.*

Ohm's Law.* This is the well-known and fundamental law in electricity that

* George Simon Ohm (1787-1854), German physicist, was born at Erlangen and educated at the university there. After teaching mathematics in Cologne for sixteen years and in Nuremburg for sixteen more, he became professor of experimental physics in the Hoch Schule at Munich. His writings were numerous and, with one exception, were not of the first order. This single exception consists of a pamphlet on electric currents, the most important part of which is summarized in what is now called "Ohm's law." For this work he was awarded the Copley Medal of the Royal Society of London in 1841 and made a foreign member of the society one year later.

makes it possible to determine the current flowing through a circuit when the resistance of the circuit and the potential difference applied to it are known. Ohm discovered that the ratio of the potential difference between the ends of a metallic conductor and the current flowing through the metallic conductor is a constant. The proportionality constant is called the electrical *resistance:*

$$\text{resistance} = \frac{\text{potential difference}}{\text{current}}$$

Symbolically, Ohm's law is often written—

$$R = \frac{V}{I} \qquad (2)$$

In electrical units—

$$1 \text{ ohm} = \frac{1 \text{ volt}}{1 \text{ amp}}$$

Ohm's law is of great importance because of its very general application to so many electrical phenomena. One of its simplest applications is illustrated in Fig. A. A dry cell is directly connected by wires to a small light bulb. The battery maintains

a potential difference of 1.5 volts across the lamp. If the electron current flowing through the circuit is 0.5 amp, the resistance of the circuit is—

$$R = \frac{1.5 \text{ volts}}{0.5 \text{ amp}} = 3 \text{ ohms}$$

Although the resistance as found here is assumed to be the resistance of the light bulb, it really includes the resistance both of the connecting wires and of the battery. In practice, one usually uses wires of such low resistance that they can be neglected in most calculations. If they are not small, they cannot be neglected and must be added in as part of the R in Ohm's law.

Consider the illustration shown in Fig. B, where a battery of many cells maintains

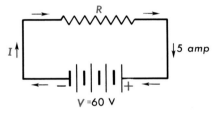

Fig. B. Circuit diagram of resistor, R, connected to a 60-volt battery.

a potential difference of 60 volts across a circuit and a current of 5 amp through it. By Ohm's law, the resistance of the circuit is given by Eq. (2) as—

$$R = \frac{V}{I} = \frac{60 \text{ volts}}{5 \text{ amp}} = 12 \text{ ohms}$$

Resistance in circuit diagrams is represented by a saw-toothed line as shown and the word *ohm* is represented by the capital Greek letter omega, Ω. In Fig. B, the resistance—

$$R = 12 \ \Omega$$

Resistance may be defined as the opposition offered to a flow of current through a circuit.

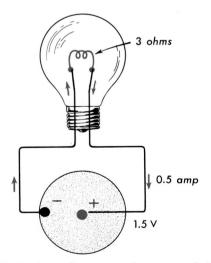

Fig. A. A dry cell connected to a small light bulb.

The Experimental Method. In determining the resistance of any electrical circuit, it is common practice to use a voltmeter and an ammeter. The voltmeter is applied across the circuit to measure the potential difference; the ammeter is connected in series to measure the current.

Fig. C represents a connector board ar-

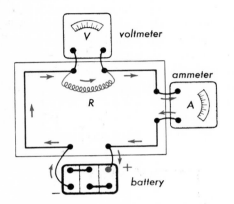

Fig. C. Connector board for determining electrical resistance.

ranged for measurements of this kind. An appliance, or unknown resistor, R, is connected between two terminals at the top, so that the current supplied by the battery below must pass through it as well as through the ammeter. The voltmeter is connected across R to measure the potential difference between its ends.

Suppose that three heating elements, commonly used as replacement elements for electrical kitchen utensils, are connected in turn to the two terminals at the top of the board and a 6-volt storage battery is applied to the terminals below. The voltage, V, and the current, I, from a sample set of measurements give the results listed in Table 1.

By Ohm's law, Eq. (2), the resistance of each element can be calculated. This is left as an exercise for the reader.

Table 1. Recorded Data

Element	Volts	Amp
toaster..........	6.1	2.3
waffle iron.......	6.2	1.6
iron.............	6.3	1.8

Resistivity. There are several factors that determine the electric resistance of any wire: (1) the material of which it is composed, (2) the size of the wire, and (3) its temperature. If the length of a wire is doubled, its resistance is likewise doubled; if the cross-sectional area is doubled, the resistance is halved. In more general terms, the resistance of a wire is proportional to its length and inversely proportional to its cross-sectional area. Symbolically—

$$R = \rho \frac{L}{A} \qquad (3)$$

where R is the resistance, L the length, A the cross-sectional area, and ρ the *resistivity* of the material in question. See Fig. D.

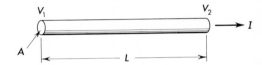

Fig. D. Conductor of constant cross section, A, and length, L.

Resistivity is defined as the resistance of a wire 1 m long and 1 m² in cross section. Values of this constant are given for several common metals in Table 2. The smaller the constant, ρ, the better is the substance as a conductor.

To find the resistance of any size of wire made of one of these metals, the value of ρ is inserted in Eq. (3) along with the length and cross-sectional area, and the

**Table 2. Resistivity of Metals in Ohm
Meters (at 20°C)**

Material	Resistivity
Nichrome	$100. \times 10^{-8}$
aluminum	3.2×10^{-8}
bismuth	119×10^{-8}
copper	1.69×10^{-8}
iron	10.0×10^{-8}
mercury	94.1×10^{-8}
silver	1.59×10^{-8}
tungsten	5.5×10^{-8}
platinum	10×10^{-8}

value of R is calculated. To illustrate the method, consider the following:

Example. Find the resistance of a copper wire 1 mm² in cross section and 300 m long.

Solution. If we use Eq. (3) and remember that there are 1000 mm in 1 m, we find that—

$$R = 1.69 \times 10^{-8} \frac{300 \text{ m}}{1 \times 10^{-6} \text{ m}^2} = 5.07 \ \Omega$$

Intrinsic and Extrinsic Quantities. Suppose you were asked for the resistivity of copper. The question concerns a general property of matter and is called an *intrinsic quantity.* Its value can be looked up in Table 2. If you were asked for the resistance of copper, no answer can be given, since it depends upon other quantities, such as length, area, and shape. Resistance is called an *extrinsic quantity.*

Potential Drop. When a current flows through a resistor, a potential difference exists across the resistor. This is called a *potential drop,* or *voltage drop.* The magnitude of the potential increases in the direction of the electron flow. See Fig. E.

Fig. E. Potential drop in a resistance circuit. V_4 is greater than V_3, etc.

QUESTIONS

1. (a) How is current defined? (b) What is the ampere? (c) How many electrons pass by any point in a wire when a current of 1 amp flows?
2. In what direction does current flow?
3. (a) What is Ohm's law? (b) In what units is each quantity measured?
4. What common electrical instruments are used to determine the factors in Ohm's law?
5. How is it possible to measure the resistance of an electric light bulb?
6. (a) What is the abbreviated notation for battery cells in series? (b) How is a resistor shown in a circuit diagram?
7. Does the same current flow through each resistor in series connections?
8. If the resistance of a circuit and the applied voltage were known, how could you determine the current?
9. Give two examples of intrinsic and extrinsic properties, other than the examples given in the text.
10. Describe how you would measure the resistivity of a metal.
11. Which would have the greater resistance, a 25-watt electric light bulb, or a 100-watt light? Explain.

12. In certain critical circuits, the parts are sometimes plated with silver. Why is this done?

13. Although aluminum has a higher resistance than copper, it has been used in power transmission lines. Can you explain?

PROBLEMS

1. A battery of 5 dry cells is used in series in a flashlight having a bulb with a resistance of 22 Ω. What electron current flows when the light is turned on?

2. A 12-volt storage battery supplies a current of 48 amp when the starter in a car is turned on. What is the resistance of the starter motor?

3. Three resistors, $R_1 = 7\ \Omega$, $R_2 = 4\ \Omega$, and $R_3 = 10\ \Omega$, are connected in series to a battery of 10 dry cells. Calculate the current.

4. An electric light bulb connected to a house-lighting circuit of 110 volts draws a current of 0.25 amp. (a) Calculate the number of coulombs/sec flowing through the wire. (b) How many electrons per second pass by any given point in the wire?

5. The heater wire in a small stove is made of iron ribbon wire, 0.01 cm by 0.05 cm in cross section and 2 m long. Calculate its resistance.

6. A fine platinum wire 0.4 mm in diameter and 200 cm long is used as the sensitive element in an electrical resistance thermometer. Find the resistance.

7. A battery of two dry cells in series is used in a flashlight having a bulb with a resistance of 25 Ω. Find the electron current when the light is turned on.

8. A wire 2 mm in diameter and 5 Km long has a total resistance of 26.9 Ω. (a) What is its resistivity? (b) Of what is it made?

PROJECT

Measure the cold and hot resistance of electric light bulbs by the ammeter voltmeter method.

ELECTRICITY

Lesson 76 *SERIES AND PARALLEL RESISTANCES*

The fundamental relation concerned with electrical circuits is Ohm's law:

$$R = \frac{V}{I} \qquad (1)$$

where R is the resistance of the circuit in ohms, V is the potential difference applied in volts, and I is the current in amperes.

Transforming this equation, one obtains two other forms of Ohm's law:

$$I = \frac{V}{R} \qquad (2)$$

and—

$$V = IR \qquad (3)$$

Resistors in Series. When several electrical devices are connected together in series, the resistance, R, of the combination is equal to the sum of the resistances of the individual resistors. Symbolically—

$$R = R_1 + R_2 + R_3 + R_4 + \text{etc.} \qquad (4)$$

This, the *law of series resistances*, is illustrated by an application of Ohm's law to the complete electric circuit in Fig. A.

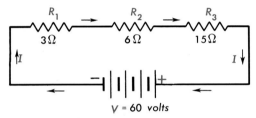

Fig. A. The same current flows through all resistors when connected in series.

Three resistors, $R_1 = 3\,\Omega$, $R_2 = 6\,\Omega$ and $R_3 = 15\,\Omega$, are connected in series with a battery of 30 storage cells. The sum of the resistances given by Eq. (4) is—

$$R = 3 + 6 + 15 = 24\,\Omega$$

and the potential difference supplied by the battery is 60 volts.

Applying Ohm's law, Eq. (2), the electron current flowing through the circuit is—

$$I = \frac{60 \text{ volts}}{24\,\Omega} = 2.5 \text{ amp}$$

This means that the same electron current of 2.5 amp flows through the high resistance of 15 Ω, as well as through the 6-Ω and 3-Ω resistors. Like water flowing through pipes of different sizes connected one after the other, just as much water passes through one pipe per second of time as through any other, and none can accumulate at any point. The battery acts like a pump and keeps a constant and steady current flowing in the circuit.

A circuit diagram showing how an ammeter and a voltmeter are connected to the series circuit is given in Fig. B. If the two

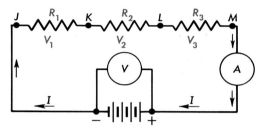

Fig. B. Circuit diagram of three resistors in series.

leads of a voltmeter are connected to the two points J and K, the potential difference across R_1 is measured. Knowing the resistance of R_1 and the current, I, through it, one can calculate this potential difference by using Eq. (3):

$$V_1 = I_1 R_1$$
$$V_1 = 2.5 \text{ amp} \times 3\,\Omega = 7.5 \text{ volts}$$

Because the potential falls by 7.5 volts from one side of the resistor to the other, this potential difference is commonly called the *IR drop*. In a similar way, the *IR* drop across R_2 or R_3 can be measured by connecting the voltmeter to K and L, or L and M, or computed by means of Eq. (3):

$$V_2 = 2.5 \text{ amp} \times 6\,\Omega = 15 \text{ volts}$$
$$V_3 = 2.5 \text{ amp} \times 15\,\Omega = 37.5 \text{ volts}$$

If we find the sum of all the *IR* drops around the circuit, we obtain—

$$7.5 + 15 + 37.5 = 60 \text{ volts}$$

This is known as *Kirchhoff's voltage law* and is usually written—

$$V = V_1 + V_2 + V_3 + \cdots \qquad (5)$$

Parallel Circuits. Fig. C is a circuit diagram of three resistors, R_1, R_2, and R_3, con-

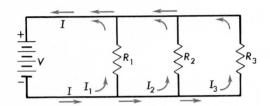

Fig. C. Parallel circuit for three resistors R_1, R_2, and R_3.

nected in parallel. The electron current, I, leaving the battery at the lower left, divides at the first junction, part I_1, going through R_1, and the remainder goes on to the next junction. Part of this current, I_2, goes through R_2, and the remainder goes on and through R_3. These three currents recombine at the top junctions and form, finally, the same total current, I, returning to the battery.

It is clear from this explanation that, for any number of resistors in parallel—

$$I = I_1 + I_2 + I_3 + \text{etc.} \qquad (6)$$

where I is the total current and I_1, I_2, I_3, etc., are the separate currents through the resistors. Eq. (6) is the second of Kirchhoff's laws.

An excellent demonstration of Eq. (6) is shown in Fig. D, where four ordinary tungsten-filament light bulbs are connected in parallel to a house-lighting circuit of 120

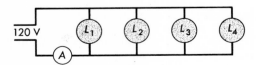

Fig. D. Parallel circuit of four light bulbs.

volts. The lamps may be the same or all different.

Suppose the lamps are rated as 25, 50, 75, and 100 watts, respectively, and we begin with all lamps sufficiently loose in their screw bases to be disconnected. Each lamp in turn should now be tightened in its socket, the ammeter current read and recorded, and then that lamp loosened again. Suppose these recorded currents are those shown at the left in Table 1.

Table 1. Recorded Data

$I_1 = .24$ amp	$I_1 = .24$ amp
$I_2 = .44$ amp	$I_1 + I_2 = .68$ amp
$I_3 = .65$ amp	$I_1 + I_2 + I_3 = 1.33$ amp
$I_4 = .85$ amp	$I_1 + I_2 + I_3 + I_4 = 2.18$ amp

As the second step, tighten each lamp in turn without loosening any, and as each new lamp comes on, record the current. These current totals could well appear like those shown in Table 1.

Such sums of currents represent an experimental confirmation of Kirchhoff's law, as given by Eq. (6).

The Law of Parallel Resistances. Another type of diagram frequently drawn for parallel circuits is shown in Fig. E. Three

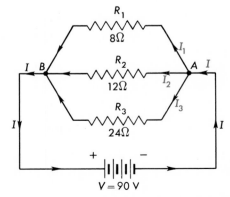

Fig. E. Three resistors in parallel, illustrating Kirchhoff's law.

resistors, R_1, R_2 and R_3, are connected in parallel to a 90-volt battery. To find the total current through such a circuit, we proceed to find a single resistance, R, that, when substituted for the parallel combination of R_1, R_2, and R_3, will result in the same current. This equivalent resistance is given by *the law of parallel resistances*, as—

$$\frac{1}{R} = \frac{1}{R_1} + \frac{1}{R_2} + \frac{1}{R_3} + \text{etc.} \quad (7)$$

To illustrate its use, let $R_1 = 8\ \Omega$, $R_2 = 12\ \Omega$, and $R_3 = 24\ \Omega$ as shown in Fig. E. By direct substitution in Eq. (7)—

$$\frac{1}{R} = \frac{1}{8} + \frac{1}{12} + \frac{1}{24}$$

Because the common denominator is 24—

$$\frac{1}{R} = \frac{3}{24} + \frac{2}{24} + \frac{1}{24} = \frac{6}{24}$$

from which—

$$R = \frac{24}{6} = 4\ \Omega$$

If we now imagine the parallel combination of three resistors replaced by a single

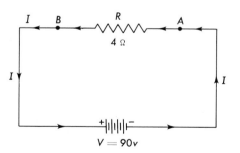

$V = 90v$

Fig. F. Resistor equivalent to the parallel resistor network in Fig. E.

resistor $R = 4\ \Omega$, the circuit will have the same general form as Fig. F, and the current, I, will be given by Ohm's law as follows:

$$I = \frac{V}{R} = \frac{90\text{ volts}}{4\ \Omega} = 22.5\text{ amp}$$

This is the total current, I, supplied by the battery to the parallel circuit of Fig. E.

To find how this current divides at A into three parts, I_1, I_2, and I_3, we note that the full 90 volts are directly applied to the opposite ends of each resistor. Therefore, Ohm's law can be applied to each resistor separately as follows:

$$I_1 = \frac{90\text{ volts}}{8\ \Omega} = 11.25\text{ amp}$$

$$I_2 = \frac{90\text{ volts}}{12\ \Omega} = 7.50\text{ amp}$$

$$I_3 = \frac{90\text{ volts}}{24\ \Omega} = 3.75\text{ amp}$$

If we now apply Kirchhoff's law, Eq. (6), we find—

$$I = 11.25 + 7.50 + 3.75 = 22.5\text{ amp}$$

and this is a check upon the previous total current. Note that the largest of the three currents, $I_1 = 11.25$ amp, flows through the smallest resistance, and the smallest current, I_3, flows through the highest resistance.

Kirchhoff's Law of Currents is frequently stated as follows: *The sum of all the currents flowing into any junction point is equal to the sum of all the currents flowing out.*

An inspection of junction A or junction B in Fig. E will show how this definition gives us Eq. (6).

QUESTIONS

1. What is the equivalent resistance of two or more resistors connected in series?
2. (a) How can you find the equivalent resistance of a parallel circuit? (b) How does this differ from the series-circuit formula?

3. (a) How does the current divide in a parallel circuit? (b) Which resistor carries the largest current? (c) Which carries the smallest current?

4. (a) If several resistors are in parallel and connected to a battery, how is the current through each resistor calculated? (b) What is the same for all resistors?

5. What is meant by the *IR* drop?

6. Will the voltage drop be the same across each resistor if the resistors are of different values connected in series to a dry cell? Explain.

7. Will the voltage drop be the same across each resistor if the resistors are of different values connected in parallel to a dry cell? Explain.

8. Three electric lights, one 15 watts, one 25 watts, and one 60 watts, are connected in series. (a) Will they all light up? (b) Which light will be the brightest? Explain.

9. Why is it preferable to have Christmas tree lights connected in parallel than in series?

PROBLEMS

1. Three resistors of 10 Ω, 15 Ω, and 20 Ω, respectively, are connected in series to a battery composed of 45 dry cells. Calculate the current through the circuit.

2. Six resistors of 5 Ω, 10 Ω, 18 Ω, 24 Ω, 38 Ω, and 12 Ω, respectively, are connected in series to a storage battery of 12 cells. Find the current through the circuit.

3. Three resistors of 4 Ω, 5 Ω, and 6 Ω are to be taken two at a time and connected in series to a 120-volt battery. Find the current for each of the three cases.

4. A string of seven Christmas tree lights, each with a resistance of 60 Ω, are connected in series to a house lighting circuit of 110 volts. Find the current.

5. Two coils of an electric-stove element are so connected that, with proper switches, either one or the other can be connected alone to the house-lighting voltage of 120 volts or they may be connected in series. Find all three possible currents if their resistances are 4 Ω and 8 Ω, respectively.

6. Four resistors of 4 Ω, 5 Ω, 6 Ω, and 9 Ω, respectively, may be connected three at a time only, in series with a 90-volt battery. Find all possible currents from the allowed combinations.

7. Two resistors of 6 Ω and 12 Ω, respectively, are connected in parallel to a battery supplying a potential difference of 20 volts. Find (a) the equivalent resistance of the parallel circuit, (b) the total current, and (c) the current through each resistor.

8. Two resistors of 10 Ω and 30 Ω, respectively, are connected to a 45-volt battery. Find (a) the equivalent resistance of the parallel circuit, (b) the total battery current, and (c) the current through each resistor.

9. Three appliances of 6 Ω, 18 Ω, and 36 Ω, respectively, are connected in parallel to a 90-volt battery. Find (a) the equivalent resistance of the parallel circuit, (b) the total current supplied by the battery, and (c) the electron current through each appliance.

10. Three hot plates of 4 Ω, 5 Ω, and 20 Ω, respectively, are connected in parallel

to a 48-volt battery. Find (a) the circuit resistance, (b) the total current, and (c) the current through each hot plate.

11. Four appliances of 5 Ω, 6 Ω, 10 Ω, and 30 Ω, respectively, are connected in parallel to a house-lighting circuit capable of maintaining $V = 120$ volts. Find (a) the equivalent resistance of the parallel circuit, (b) the total current supplied by the battery, and (c) the electron current through each appliance.

12. Prove the law of series resistances.

13. Prove the law of parallel resistances.

PROJECTS

1. Make an apparatus to demonstrate the law of parallel resistance.
2. Make an apparatus to demonstrate the current flow and the voltage drops when resistors of different value are in series.

ELECTRICITY

Lesson 77 *COMPOUND CIRCUITS*

Because of the numerous uses of electrical devices involving resistors in series and parallel, it is important to understand thoroughly their electrical characteristics. For this reason, we shall study several common circuits using these electrical devices.

Series-Parallel Networks. A circuit involving a combination of series and parallel resistors is shown in Fig. A. This particular circuit is composed of two resistors, R_1 and R_2, in parallel, and this combination in series with a third resistor, R_3.

If we apply the parallel-resistor formula to R_1 and R_2 alone, we find—

$$\frac{1}{R'} = \frac{1}{R_1} + \frac{1}{R_2} \qquad (1)$$

where R' is the equivalent resistance of the parallel combination only. Because this part of the circuit is in series with R_3, the law of series resistances is applied and we find—

$$R = R' + R_3 \qquad (2)$$

where R is the equivalent resistance of the entire circuit. Ohm's law can then be applied to this R and to the applied potential difference, V, to obtain the total current, I.

To find how the current divides at the

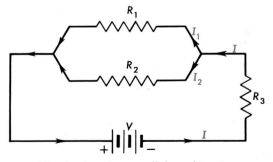

Fig. A. A series-parallel combination.

center junction, the potential difference across the parallel circuit is calculated from Ohm's law:

$$V' = IR' \qquad (3)$$

Then, with this value of V' as the potential difference between the ends of R_1, as well as of R_2, Ohm's law can be applied to each resistance separately:

$$I_1 = \frac{V'}{R_1}$$

and—

$$I_2 = \frac{V'}{R_2} \qquad (4)$$

Example. A battery supplies a potential difference of 180 volts to the ends of a circuit containing four resistors of 5 Ω, 6 Ω, 8 Ω, and 20 Ω, as shown in **Fig. B.** Calculate (a) the

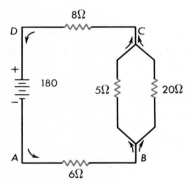

Fig. B. Series and parallel resistances in the same circuit.

equivalent resistance of the 5 Ω and 20 Ω parallel combination, (b) the electron current supplied by the battery, and (c) the electron current through each resistor.

Solution. (a) Apply the law of parallel resistances:

$$\frac{1}{R} = \frac{1}{5} + \frac{1}{20} = \frac{4}{20} + \frac{1}{20} = \frac{5}{20}$$

from which, by inverting, we obtain—

$$R = 20/5 = 4 \ \Omega$$

(b) Since the parallel combination of 5 Ω and 20 Ω is equivalent to 4 Ω and it is in series with the other two of 6 Ω and 8 Ω, respectively, the three are added by the law of series resistance:

$$R = 6 + 4 + 8 = 18 \ \Omega$$

Apply Ohm's law:

$$I = \frac{V}{R} = \frac{180 \text{ volts}}{18 \ \Omega} = 10 \text{ amp}$$

(c) The electron current of 10 amp flows through the 6-Ω resistor and divides at *B* of the parallel circuit. Combining again at *C*, the total electron current flows through the 8-Ω resistor. To find how the current divides in the parallel circuit, the *IR* drop across that circuit is found.

$$IR = 10 \text{ amp} \times 4 \ \Omega = 40 \text{ volts}$$

This value of 40 volts is the potential difference between *B* and *C*. If we apply Ohm's law to each of the two resistors separately, we obtain—

$$I_1 = \frac{40 \text{ volts}}{5 \ \Omega} = 8 \text{ amp}$$

and

$$I_2 = \frac{40 \text{ volts}}{20 \ \Omega} = 2 \text{ amp}$$

Hence, 8 amp flow through the 5-Ω resistor, and 2 amp through the 20-Ω resistor. Note that these currents are in inverse ratio to their resistances.

Potential Divider. The *potential divider* is an electrical circuit constructed around a variable resistor, or rheostat, with a sliding contact. When such a device, sometimes called a potentiometer, is connected to a battery as shown in Fig. C, the sliding contact makes it possible to obtain any desired potential difference from zero up to the full voltage, *V*, of the battery.

Suppose, as shown in Fig. C, that a bat-

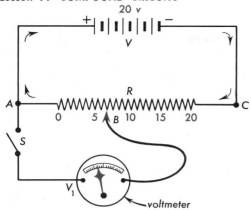

Fig. C. Potentiometer circuit for obtaining variable voltage.

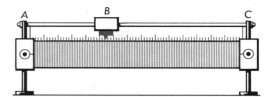

Fig. D. Diagram of a slide-wire rheostat.

tery supplies 20 volts to the extreme ends of a resistance wire, AC, and a voltmeter, V is connected to one end, A, and to a sliding contact, B. When the slider B is at A, the voltmeter will read zero, but as it moves down toward C, the reading will steadily rise. At one-quarter of the way to C, the voltmeter will read 5 volts; half way, 10 volts; three-quarters of the way, 15 volts; and finally at C, it will read 20 volts. As a general rule, the potential difference is directly proportional to the length of the resistance wire between A and B.

As a sample calculation, let the total resistance A to C in Fig. C be 100 Ω. By Ohm's law, the current through AC will be—

$$I = \frac{20 \text{ volts}}{100 \text{ Ω}} = 0.2 \text{ amp}$$

Let B be located three-quarters of the way to C so that the resistance A to B is $100 \times \frac{3}{4}$, or 75 Ω. The IR drop across this portion is, therefore—

$$IR = 0.2 \times 75 = 15 \text{ volts}$$

as also shown by the voltmeter.

A slide-wire rheostat of a conventional type is shown in Fig. D. This is a porcelain tube about 2 in. in diameter and 12 in.

long, with a long, uniform resistance wire wrapped around it in the form of a coil of only one layer.

The slider at the top is mounted on a conducting rod and, when moved along, it makes contact with the resistance wire at any desired position. A short section of a meter stick can be mounted close to the slider to help determine the distance from either end of the rheostat to any contact point.

Wheatstone Bridge. The Wheatstone bridge is a widely used electrical circuit that determines with high precision the electrical resistance of any wire or appliance. Such a circuit involves several electrical resistors and may take any one of several forms.

The Wheatstone bridge is shown schematically in Fig. E. A battery of but a few volts is connected in parallel with a circuit

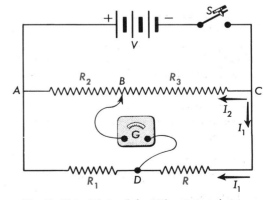

Fig. E. The circuit of the Wheatstone bridge.

involving a resistance wire with a sliding contact and two other resistors, R and R_1. A switch, S, is connected into the battery circuit for applying the potential whenever desired, and a galvanometer is connected to the sliding contactor and the junction between R and R_1.

A galvanometer is a sensitive current-reading instrument, with the zero point at the center of its scale, as shown in Fig. F.

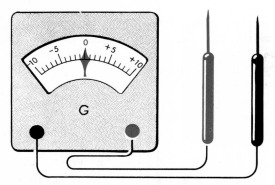

Fig. F. Galvanometer with two insulated probes.

If the current flows one way through the instrument, the needle deflects to the right. If the current flows in the other direction, the needle deflects to the left. If the probes make contact at two points in a circuit and the needle shows no current one way or the other, those two points are at the same potential. If there were a difference of potential, a current would flow.

Of the different resistors shown in Fig. E, R represents the unknown resistance to be determined, R_1 a precisely known resistance, and R_2 and R_3 the sections of a uniform slide wire.

When the switch is closed, a current, I_2, flows through the slide wire and a current, I_1, through R and R_1. If the sliding contact is moved along until a point B is reached where the galvanometer shows no current, the points B and D will be at exactly the same potential.

Under these balanced conditions, the potential difference between A and B will be the same as between A and D, and the potential difference between C and B will be the same as between C and D. Because these differences in potential are given by the respective IR drops, we can write—

$$I_1 R_1 = I_2 R_2$$

and—

$$I_1 R = I_2 R_3$$

Because equals divided by equals give equals, we find—

$$\frac{I_1 R}{I_1 R_1} = \frac{I_2 R_3}{I_2 R_2}$$

or—

$$\frac{R}{R_1} = \frac{R_3}{R_2}$$

Solving for the unknown resistance R, we have—

$$R = R_1 \frac{R_3}{R_2} \qquad (5)$$

Because the resistance of a uniform wire is proportional to its length, we can use the measured lengths of the slide wire between A and B and between B and C, and substitute these for R_2 and R_3 in Eq. (5).

Internal Resistance. Although the terms *electromotive force* and *potential difference,* as applied to electrical circuits in general, are both measured in *volts,* there is a real distinction between them. This difference may be illustrated by a demonstration experiment shown by a circuit diagram in Fig. G.

A battery of four dry cells is connected to a resistor, R, of about 3 Ω. When the switch, S, is open, no current will flow around the circuit. The voltmeter, however, with its very high resistance of several thousand ohms will draw a negligibly small current from the battery, yet one

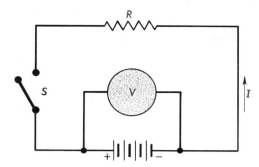

Fig. G. The measured voltage, V, changes when the switch is closed.

that will indicate the electromotive force $\mathcal{E}$. For the four dry cells, it would read 6.0 volts.

When the switch, S, is closed to complete the electric circuit, a current I of about 2 amp will flow around and through R, and the voltmeter will show a potential difference, V, between the battery terminals of about 5.4 volts.

The drop in battery voltage from 6.0 volts on open circuit to 5.4 volts on closed circuit is due to the *internal resistance* of battery cells. This internal resistance behaves as though it were in series with the battery and may be illustrated schemati-

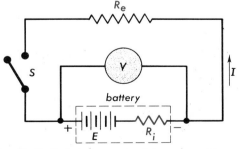

Fig. H. Batteries have an internal resistance, R_i.

cally as in Fig. H. The total resistance of this circuit is composed of the external resistance, R_e, in series with the battery's internal resistance, R_i. When the switch is closed, the current, I, flowing through the circuit is given by Ohm's law as—

$$I = \frac{\mathcal{E}}{R} \tag{6}$$

where, by the law of series resistances—

$$R = R_e + R_i \tag{7}$$

and $\mathcal{E}$ is the internal electromotive force of the battery ($\mathcal{E} = 6.0$ volts).

If the internal resistance $R_i = 0.3\ \Omega$ and $R_e = 2.7\ \Omega$, the total resistance $R = 3.0\ \Omega$, and a current of 2 amp will flow through the circuit. The IR drop across R_i will be $2 \times 0.3 = 0.6$ volt and the voltmeter will indicate $V = 5.4$ volts instead of the 6.0 volts it indicates on open circuit.

The emf, $\mathcal{E}$, may be thought of as the driving force of the battery acting on the electrons in the circuit conductors. A voltmeter always measures the potential difference between the two points to which it is connected. This is true whether they are battery terminals or two points anywhere in the circuit. We see, therefore, that the effective V across a battery will depend upon the battery emf, the current being drawn from that battery, and the internal resistance.

Instead of applying Eq. (6) to a circuit, it is customary to measure or specify V on closed circuit and then apply Ohm's law in the form—

$$I = \frac{V}{R} \tag{8}$$

where R is the external resistance only.

QUESTIONS

1. (a) What is a potential divider? (b) What is it used for?
2. (a) What is a Wheatstone bridge? (b) What is it used for?
3. Why is a galvanometer used in a Wheatstone bridge, rather than an ordinary ammeter?
4. (a) What is meant by the emf of a battery? (b) How is it measured?
5. What is the difference between electromotive force and potential difference?
6. (a) What is meant by the potential difference? (b) How is it measured? (c) Is the potential difference across battery terminals always the same?
7. How is Ohm's law applied to a circuit if the emf and internal resistance are given?
8. How is Ohm's law applied when the potential difference of the battery on closed circuit is specified?
9. How should the internal resistance of the voltmeter in Fig. G be related to the resistance, R, to insure that accurate measurements are made?
10. Why is the Wheatstone bridge a more accurate method for measuring resistance than the voltmeter-ammeter method?

PROBLEMS

1. Two resistors of 5 Ω and 20 Ω are connected in parallel. This parallel circuit is in series with an 8 Ω resistor and the entire circuit is connected to a 60-volt battery. Find the equivalent resistance of (a) the parallel combination and (b) the entire circuit. (c) Find the electron current through each resistor.
2. Three light bulbs of 50 Ω, 75 Ω, and 150 Ω, respectively, are connected in parallel. This combination is connected in series with a 15 Ω appliance and the entire circuit is connected to a 120-volt line. Find the equivalent resistance of (a) the parallel combination and (b) the entire circuit. (c) What current flows through each device?
3. A battery has an emf of 26 volts and an internal resistance of 0.4 Ω. (a) Find the current supplied when the battery is connected to a 10 Ω appliance. (b) What is the IR drop within the battery? (c) What is the potential difference across the battery?
4. A battery has an emf of 45 volts and an internal resistance of 1.0 Ω. (a) What current is supplied when it is connected to a 24 Ω resistor? (b) What is the potential difference across the battery? (c) What is the IR drop across the resistor?
5. A battery has an emf of 22 volts and an internal resistance of 0.5 Ω. What is the potential difference between the battery terminals when connected to an external resistance of 5 Ω?
6. An unknown resistor is connected to a Wheatstone bridge and the variable resistances are adjusted until the galvanometer, G, shows no current. See Fig. E. The

resistors R_1, R_2, and R_3 have values of 100 Ω, 650 Ω, and 2470 Ω, respectively. Find the unknown resistance.

7. An unknown resistor, X, is connected to a slide-wire Wheatstone bridge as shown in Fig. E. When the galvanometer, G, shows no current, $R_1 = 92$ Ω, the wire AC is 100 cm long, and the wire section AB is 65 cm. Find the resistance of X.

8. Two resistors, $R_1 = 15$ Ω and $R_2 = 24$ Ω, are connected in series to a battery whose voltage on open circuit is 120 volts. If the internal resistance of the battery is 1 Ω, find (a) the resistance of the circuit, (b) the electron current in the circuit, (c) the drop in potential across R_1 and R_2, and (d) the voltage across the battery.

9. Two resistors of 20 Ω and 80 Ω, respectively, are connected in parallel, and the combination then connected to a 70-volt battery with internal resistance of 1.5 Ω. Find (a) the resistance of the external circuit, (b) the electron current supplied by the battery, (c) the electron current through the external resistance, and (d) the voltage across the battery.

PROJECT

Make a Wheatstone bridge to measure resistance. If ac is used, instead of a battery as shown in Fig. E, and an earphone substituted for the galvanometer, the bridge can also be used to measure capacitors and inductors.

ELECTRICITY

Lesson 78 *ELECTRIC ENERGY AND POWER*

Everyone is more or less familiar with the electrical appliances of the modern household such as the electric light, electric toaster, iron, refrigerator, vacuum cleaner, and washing machine. All of these devices depend for their operation upon one or more of four general effects produced by electric currents; these are (1) *the heating effect*, (2) *the magnetic effect*, (3) *the mechanical effect*, and (4) *the chemical effect*. It is the purpose of this lesson to consider the first of these different phenomena and to take up in some detail the important principles involved.

Electric Energy. Consider the two terminals of a battery as shown in Fig. A and the mechanical work that would be required to move a negative charge from the + terminal to the − terminal. The amount of work done per unit charge in carrying any charge, Q, from one terminal to the other is called the *difference of potential*. Symbolically—

$$V = \frac{E}{Q} \qquad (1)$$

where V is in volts, E is in joules, and Q is in coulombs.

Instead of carrying a charge from one terminal to the other and thereby doing

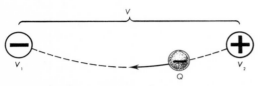

Fig. A. The work done per unit charge in carrying any charge, Q, from one terminal to the other is called the difference of potential, V.

work, let us connect the two terminals with a conductor. A current, I, will then flow and the battery will be doing work for us in creating heat. By definition, *the current, I, is defined as the amount of charge, Q, flowing per second of time:*

$$I = \frac{Q}{t} \qquad (2)$$

If we solve this equation for Q—

$$Q = It$$

and substitute It for Q in Eq. (1), we obtain—

$$V = \frac{E}{It} \qquad (3)$$

or—

$$E = VIt \qquad (4)$$

joules = volts × amperes × seconds

The Heating Effect of an Electric Current. When an electron current is sent through a wire, heat is generated and the temperature of the wire rises. If the current is increased, the rate at which heat is generated increases rapidly until the wire itself glows a deep red. A still further increase in current will heat the wire to a yellow or

white heat. Beyond this point, if it has not already done so, the wire will reach a temperature where it will melt.

Whether a wire is only warmed by an electron current or heated to incandescence depends upon several factors, the principal ones being current and voltage. By the law of conservation of energy, each calorie of heat produced will require the expenditure of a definite amount of electrical energy. The electrical energy, E_H, consumed by the circuit in producing heat is given by—

$$E_H = VIt \qquad (5)$$

where V is in volts, I is in amperes, and t is in seconds.

If Ohm's law is introduced in the form $V = IR$, we can substitute IR for V and obtain—

$$E_H = I^2Rt \qquad (6)$$

This is known as *Joule's law.*

Electrical energy, like mechanical energy, is measured in joules. Heat energy is often measured in calories. These units are related by a constant, J, called the *electrical equivalent of heat:*

$$J = 4.18 \frac{\text{joules}}{\text{cal}}$$

which is exactly the same as the mechanical equivalent of heat.

Example 1. If the heating element of an electric toaster draws an electron current of 5 amp when connected to a 110-volt line, how much heat will be generated in one minute?

Solution. By direct substitution in Eq. (6)—

$$E_H = 5 \times 110 \times 60 = 33,000 \text{ joules}$$
$$= 7920 \text{ cal}$$

For some electric appliances, heating is a desired effect, while in others, it is a source of trouble and even danger. In an electric iron, hot plate, or toaster, for example, heat is the main objective of the device.

In such appliances, a relatively large current of several amperes is sent through a coil or element of special wire having a resistance of several ohms. As a rule the wire is of some alloy, such as nichrome, and of such a size that the heat developed will not raise the temperature higher than red hot. Diagrams of typical heating elements used in three different household appliances are shown in Fig. B.

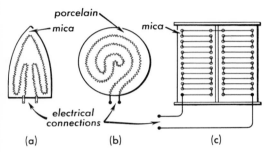

porcelain
mica
mica
electrical
connections

(a)   (b)   (c)

Fig. B. Diagrams of the heating elements of various common electrical appliances: (a) electric iron, (b) electric stove, and (c) electric toaster.

Electric Power. Power is defined in mechanics, as well as in electricity, as the rate at which energy is developed or expended. $P = E/t$. Dividing each of the above energy equations by t, we find that—

$$P = I^2 R \qquad P = V^2/R$$

and—

$$P = VI \qquad (7)$$

where P is in *watts*. These are practical equations, because with most electrical equipment, the *voltage, current,* and *resistance* are usually known from voltmeter and ammeter readings. The last equation is well worth memorizing: *Power in watts is equal to potential difference in volts times current in amperes.* The other two follow by a direct substitution from Ohm's law.

Energy as expressed in Eq. (4) is power,

VI, multiplied by the time t. *Power in kilowatts multiplied by the time in hours gives the energy in kilowatt-hours.* The kilowatt-hour is the unit of electric energy by which all electric energy is calculated and paid for (1 kilowatt = 1000 watts). The watt-hour meter placed on the premises of every consumer is a slowly revolving motor, having a low-resistance winding, which is in series with the line, and which, therefore, conducts the current in the line. The meter also has a high-resistance winding, which is across the line and which, therefore, conducts a small current proportional to V. The time factor, t, is accounted for by the automatic recording of the total number of rotations of the armature by a small clocklike mechanism with dials and pointers.

Example 2. Two resistors of 3 Ω and 5 Ω, respectively, are connected in series with a battery of 20-volt terminal voltage (see Fig. C).

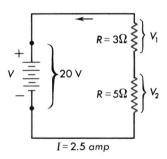

$R = 3\Omega$ V_1

V 20 V

$R = 5\Omega$ V_2

$I = 2.5$ amp

Fig. C. The power consumed by any resistance is calculated by multiplying the voltage across it by the current.

Calculate (a) the electron current through the circuit, (b) the potential difference across each resistor, (c) the power consumed by each resistor, (d) the total energy consumed in 2 hr of operation, and (e) the total cost of operation for 40 hr at 3 cents per Kw-hr.

Solution. Connected in series, the two resistors, $R_1 = 3$ Ω and $R_2 = 5$ Ω, have a total resistance of $R = 8$ Ω.

(a) If we apply Ohm's law, the electron current through the circuit is found to be—

$$I = V/R = 20/8 = 2.5 \text{ amp}$$

(b) The drop in potential across any resistor is given by IR:

$$V_1 = I_1R_1 = 2.5 \times 3 = 7.5 \text{ volts}$$
$$V_2 = I_2R_2 = 2.5 \times 5 = 12.5 \text{ volts}$$

(c) The power consumed is given by VI, the potential drop across each resistor, multiplied by the electron current through it:

$$P_1 = V_1I = 7.5 \times 2.5 = 18.75 \text{ watts}$$
$$P_2 = V_2I = 12.5 \times 2.5 = 31.25 \text{ watts}$$

(d) The power supplied by the battery is VI, the voltage across its terminals multiplied by the total electron current in amperes:

$$P = VI = 20 \times 2.5 = 50 \text{ watts}$$

in agreement with the sum of the two values in (c).

To find the energy, multiply by the time in seconds:

$$W = 50 \text{ watts} \times 7200 \text{ sec} = 360,000 \text{ joules}$$

(e) The power, 50 watts, should next be expressed in kilowatts and multiplied by the time in hours, to give—

$$W = 0.05 \text{ Kw} \times 40 \text{ hr} = 2 \text{ Kw-hr}$$

At 3 cents per Kw-hr, the total cost will be 6 cents.

QUESTIONS

1. (a) What are the four effects of electric currents? (b) What, specifically, is the heating effect?
2. (a) Does the same amount of electrical energy always produce the same amount of heat? (b) What is Joule's law?
3. (a) What three factors determine the electrical energy converted into heat? (b) What are the units of heat energy? (c) What are the units of electrical energy?
4. How is power related to energy?
5. What kind of quantity is a kilowatt-hour?
6. Ten cm of copper wire and 10 cm of iron wire, both of the same diameter, are connected in series to a dry cell. Which will heat up more? Explain.
7. How is the electrical energy consumed in a home measured by the electric company?

PROBLEMS

1. An electric toaster draws a current of 4 amp when connected to the house-lighting circuit of 120 volts. How many calories of heat are produced in 1 min?
2. The heating element of an electric heater draws a current of 10 amp when connected to 110 volts. How many calories of heat are produced in one hour?
3. An electric toaster with a resistance of 25 Ω draws a current of 5 amp when connected to a house-lighting circuit. If it takes 2 min running to make dark toast, how many calories are required?

4. The heating element of an electric stove connected to a 220-volt line draws an electron current of 5 amp. Find the amount of heat produced in 10 min.

5. An electric iron having a resistance of 15 Ω is connected to a 110-volt supply. Find the heat developed in 5 min.

6. (a) Calculate the heat developed by an electric soldering iron in 10 min if it draws 3.5 amp on a 120-volt line. (b) What power is being developed?

7. A teakettle containing 1 gal of water (3785 cm³) at a temperature of 10°C is heated on an electric stove. If the heating element draws an electron current of 8 amp from a 220-volt line, and one-half of the heat generated goes to heat the water, how long will it take for the water to reach the boiling point?

8. An electric coffee pot containing 1000 cm³ of water at 15°C is connected to a 110-volt line. If the electron current drawn is 4.5 amp and 65% of the heat developed goes into the water, how hot will the water be in 8 min?

9. Three resistors, 5 Ω, 8 Ω, and 12 Ω, respectively, are connected in series to a battery. If these resistors are immersed in a glass containing 500 cm³ of water and a current of 5 amp sent through them, how long will it take to raise the water from 25°C to the boiling point of 100°C?

10. (a) What is the resistance of a 60-watt lamp and a 40-watt lamp operating on 110-volt house lines? (b) If these two lamps are placed in series across the 110-volt line, calculate the current through them. (c) What is the power developed in each?

PROJECT

Measure the heat produced by an electric heater of the type sold for heating a cup of water for coffee. Measure the power consumed and calculate its efficiency.

Magnetism

Wherefore I say that in the magnet is a trace of the world, wherefore there is in it one part having in itself the property of the west, another of the east, another of the south, another of the north. And I say that in the direction north and south it attracts most strongly, little in the direction east and west.

John of St. Amand, *Antidotarium Nicolai.* XIII Century.

◀ This skilled craftsman is insulating the field poles of a large electric motor with the synthetic fabric Lecton.

Dupont Magazine

Lesson 79 *MAGNETISM*

Magnetism was known to the early Greek philosophers. One story goes that Magnes, a shepherd,·when on Mt. Ida of the island Crete, was so strongly attracted to the ground by the tip of his staff and the nails in his shoes that he had difficulty in getting away. Upon digging into the ground to find the cause, he discovered a stone with the most amazing properties of attracting iron. This stone is now called *lodestone* or *magnetite.*

The idea that a lodestone can be used as a compass is a very old one. There is some evidence that the Chinese had a knowledge of this as far back as A.D. 121. At any rate, a Chinese author writing as early as the beginning of the twelfth century explains that a needle, rubbed with lodestone and suspended free to turn, will point toward the south. This appears to be the first evidence that a piece of iron could be magnetized by a lodestone and used as a compass. The action of a lodestone or a bar magnet when suspended free to turn about a vertical axis is illustrated in Fig. A.

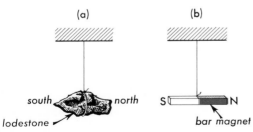

Fig. A. A lodestone and a bar magnet point north and south.

A compass, as it is often made for demonstration purposes, consists usually of a steel needle that has been magnetized and mounted free to turn on a sharp pointed rod as shown in Fig. B.

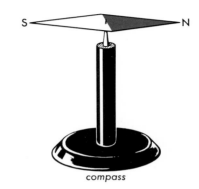

Fig. B. A compass needle points toward the north.

The Power of Attraction. Nearly everyone has at sometime or other played with a small horseshoe magnet and discovered for himself that it attracted mostly things containing iron. Upon drawing the magnet through dry sand or dirt, you probably discovered that it will pick up small grains of iron ore. While a few metals, such as cobalt and nickel, are known to be feebly attracted by a magnet, most substances like aluminum, copper, silver, gold, wood, glass, and paper, do not exhibit any noticeable effect.

If more extensive experiments are carried out, a magnet can be shown to attract magnetic substances at a distance even though other matter lies in the intervening space. In other words, magnetic attraction acts right through matter of all kinds. This can be demonstrated, as shown in Fig. C, by picking up iron filings on one side of a thin wooden board by holding a magnet

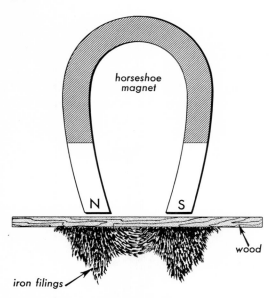

horseshoe
magnet

N   S

wood

iron filings

Fig. C. The attraction of a magnet for iron acts through all substances.

These preferred regions of attraction are called *magnetic poles*. If this same magnet is supended by a thread, as shown in Fig. A(*b*), it will come to rest in a position close to the north-south geographic direction. The end toward the north is, therefore, called the N or *north-seeking pole* and the other end the S or *south-seeking pole*.

That the N and S poles of a magnet are different may be shown by bringing the magnet close to a compass needle. Such an experiment is illustrated in Fig. E. When the

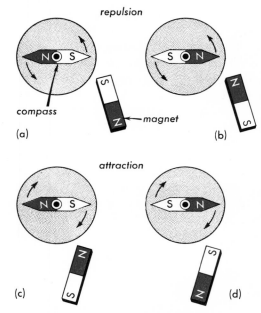

repulsion

compass

magnet

(a)   (b)

attraction

(c)   (d)

Fig. E. Unlike magnetic poles attract each other, while like magnetic poles repel each other.

close to the other side. If a sheet of copper, brass, or any nonmagnetic substance, is placed over the magnet, the power of attraction is not destroyed. A magnetic material, however, will attenuate the magnetic attraction. In fact, a small region of space can be partially shielded from magnetic fields if it is entirely surrounded by layers of soft iron.

Magnetic Poles. When an ordinary straight bar magnet is dipped into a box of iron filings, the tiny bits of iron are observed to cling to the ends as shown in Fig. D.

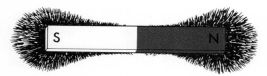

S   N

Fig. D. The attraction of iron filings by a bar magnet shows greater attraction near the ends. These regions of greatest attraction are called magnetic poles.

S pole of the magnet is brought close to the S pole of the compass needle, as in diagram (*a*), there is a force of repulsion that turns the compass needle away. A similar repulsion occurs between the two N poles, as shown in diagram (*b*). If the N and S poles are brought near to each other, however, a very strong attraction arises and the compass needle turns toward the other as shown in diagrams (*c*) and (*d*). These experiments show, therefore, that *two kinds of magnetic poles exist* and that *like poles repel and unlike poles attract*.

Permanent magnets can now be made so strong that one magnet can be lifted by the repulsion of another. This is illustrated in Fig. F. Unless guide rods of glass or some

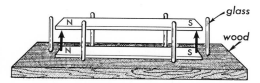

Fig. F. One magnet may be suspended in mid-air by the strong repulsion of like poles from another magnet.

other substance are used, however, the floating bar will move to one side and then fall. In other words, the forces of repulsion are such that the upper bar is not in stable equilibrium.

It should be pointed out that each magnetic pole in a magnetized body is not confined to a single point but extends over a finite region. If the magnet is long and thin, however, each polar region acts as though it were concentrated at a point, similar to that of the center of mass in mechanics.

Poles Exist in Pairs. If a magnet is broken in the middle in an attempt to separate the poles, one finds new poles formed at the broken ends. If one of these pieces is again broken, each piece is again found to contain two poles of opposite kind. As long as this process is repeated the same result is obtained—a magnetic pole of one kind is always accompanied by a pole of opposite polarity.

This is conveniently illustrated by magnetizing a hacksaw blade and breaking it successively into smaller and smaller pieces,

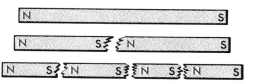

Fig. G. The poles of a magnet cannot exist alone. When a bar magnet is broken, poles appear on either side of the break, and each piece has two opposite poles.

as shown in Fig. G. Each time a piece is broken, each fragment, upon being tested with a compass, is found to have an *N* pole on one side and an *S* pole on the other. A hacksaw blade is readily magnetized by stroking it from one end to the other with one of the poles of a magnet.

It is possible to magnetize a bar of steel so that it has three or more polar regions. This is illustrated in Fig. H where a hack-

Fig. H. Diagram of a bar magnet with iron filings showing three polar regions.

saw blade has been magnetized with an *N* pole at each end and an *S*-polar region in the center. The combined strength of the *N* poles is seen by the quantity of iron filings to be equal to the *S*-pole strength in the center. We might say, therefore, that the magnet has four poles: an *N* pole at either end and two *S* poles at the center.

Molecular Theory of Ferromagnetism. The modern theory of magnetism, which is now quite firmly established, is that a piece of iron consists of millions of tiny elementary magnets called *domains*. These domains can often be seen with a microscope and consists of atoms aligned to form small elementary iron crystals. How single atoms act as magnets will be explained later. Before a piece of iron or steel has been magnetized, the domains are oriented more or orientations. The frictional forces between domains in hardened steel makes it more difficult to induce magnetization. However,

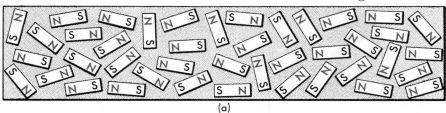

(a)

(b)

Fig. I. Schematic diagrams of the elementary magnets within a piece of iron, (a) unmagnetized and (b) magnetized.

less at random throughout the metal as shown in Fig. I(a).

In the process of magnetizing a piece of iron, the domains are rotated and lined up parallel to each other, as shown by the schematic representation in diagram (b). Lined up in this way, the small N and S poles are adjacent to each other and cancel each other's effect on external objects. At one end there are many free N poles and at the opposite end an equal number of free S poles.

When a magnet is broken at any point, free S poles are exposed at one side of the break and free N poles at the other. It is clear, therefore, why poles always exist in pairs and why, no matter how many times a magnet is broken, each piece will contain an N pole at one end and an S pole at the other.

When soft iron is magnetized by induction and the permanent magnet taken away, the domains return to their original random when hardened steel becomes magnetized, the domains remain aligned after the magnetizing field is taken away.

Other Types of Magnetism. If a ferromagnetic material is heated above a certain temperature called the *Curie temperature,* the thermal motion causes the atoms or molecules to become randomly oriented, the ferromagnetism disappears, and the material becomes *paramagnetic.* If an external magnet is held near the paramagnetic material, the atoms will weakly attempt to line up, resulting in a small magnetization.

The atoms or molecules of an *antiferromagnetic* material line up, but with every other atom reversed in position. The atoms of a *diamagnetic* material cannot be aligned because they do not act as small magnets. These latter two types of material have an extremely small reaction to an external magnet and, for all practical purposes, are considered nonmagnetic.

QUESTIONS

1. (a) What is a bar magnet? (b) What is a horseshoe magnet?
2. (a) What are magnetic poles? (b) How many kinds of poles are there? (c) What are their names? (d) What is the origin of these names?
3. Can magnets be made strong enough to lift one another by repulsion?
4. (a) Is a magnetic pole a point or a distributed area on the surface of a magnet? (b) Can a magnet have one pole only? (c) Can the two poles of a magnet be broken apart?
5. (a) Can a magnet have more than two poles? (b) Can a magnet have 1000 poles?
6. (a) What is magnetic induction? (b) How can it be demonstrated?
7. (a) What is the molecular theory of magnetism? (b) How does soft iron differ in behavior from steel?
8. Suppose you have discovered some bar magnets but their poles are not labeled. How can you show that like poles repel and unlike poles attract?
9. Nickel is paramagnetic at room temperature. (a) To what different form of magnetism could you change it? (b) How?
10. Iron sulfide is antiferromagnetic. (a) Draw a picture showing the orientation of the molecules. (b) Why is the effective magnetization small?
11. How can you prove that a piece of iron is magnetized?
12. What do you think would happen if you ran a length of recorded magnetic tape past a permanent magnet? Explain.

PROJECTS

1. Make an apparatus similar to Fig. F to show the force between like poles.
2. Make tape recordings of different low-frequency notes at high speed. Show the location of the poles on the tape with very fine iron filings.

MAGNETISM

Lesson 80 *MAGNETIC FIELDS*

The Magnetic Field. In the space surrounding every magnet, there exists what we call a magnetic field. Although this field cannot be seen, it can be demonstrated and mapped out in the following way.

A very small compass is placed at some point near the N pole of a bar magnet and then moved in the direction the compass is pointing. The center of the compass will trace out a smooth line called a magnetic line of force. Starting at various points, many such lines may be drawn as shown in Fig. A. Each line starts as some point near the N pole and ends at a corresponding point near the S pole.

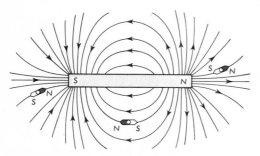

Fig. A. Diagram of the magnetic field and magnetic lines of force about a bar magnet, as obtained with a small compass needle.

These magnetic *lines of force* do not really exist, but they are useful concepts that may be used in describing the many different magnetic phenomena to be taken up in later lessons. It should be noted that, where the magnet exerts its strongest attraction near the poles, the lines are closest together and that each line points away from the N pole and toward the S pole. This latter is an arbitrary assignment, being the direction indicated by the N pole of the compass.

A close examination of the iron filings clinging to a magnet shows that each tiny, needlelike piece of iron lines up in the direction of the magnetic lines of force. The reason for this is that each filing has become magnetized by the magnet and, having its own N and S poles, acts like a compass. An excellent demonstration of the field and its direction can be performed by laying a plate of glass or a sheet of paper over a magnet and then sprinkling iron filings over the top. When the glass or paper is gently tapped, the filings turn and

line up, as shown in the photograph in Fig. B.

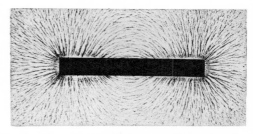

Fig. B. Photograph of the iron filings lined up by the magnetic field of a permanent bar magnet.

The Earth's Magnetic Field. To Sir William Gilbert we owe the view that the earth is a great magnet. To prove his theory, Gilbert shaped a lodestone into a sphere and demonstrated that a small compass placed at any spot of the globe always pointed, as it does on the earth, toward the North pole.

The earth, therefore, has been schematically pictured in Fig. C as a large magnetized sphere of iron or as though it con-

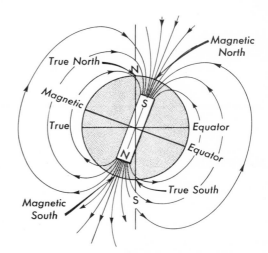

Fig. C. Schematic diagram illustrating the earth as a huge magnet surrounded by a magnetic field extending far out into space.

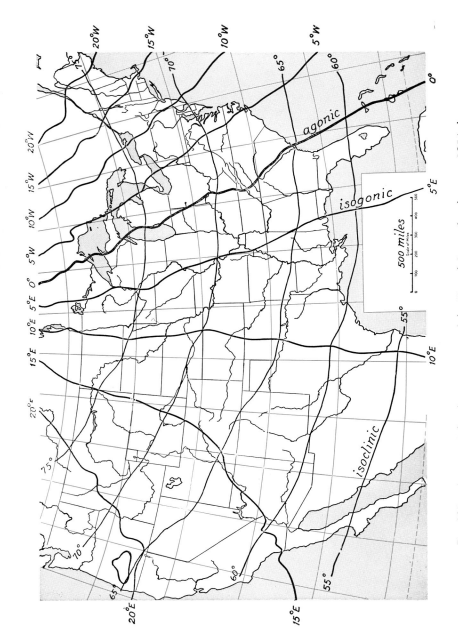

Fig. 80D. A terrestrial magnetism map of the United States for the year 1954 showing the declination of a compass from true north and the angle of dip of a dip needle. Such maps are drawn from data assembled by the U.S. Coast and Geodetic Survey.

tained a huge permanent magnet. Because the magnetic axis is at an angle with the polar axis, the earth's magnetic poles are not at the *true North* and *true South poles.* The true North and true South poles are points located on the earth's rotational axis.

The *North Magnetic pole* is located in far northern Canada, while the *South Magnetic pole* is located almost diametrically opposite it, in the southern hemisphere. As for polarity, the North Magnetic pole is an S pole and the South Magnetic pole is an N pole. This becomes apparent from the magnetic lines of force that always start from an N pole and are directed toward, and end at, an S pole.

Although the cause for the earth's magnetism is not completely understood, several reasonable theories have been proposed. The earth is known to contain large iron-ore deposits, some of these deposits being almost pure iron. One theory proposes that during the ages past, all these iron deposits gradually became magnetized in very nearly the same direction and that, together, they act like one huge permanent magnet.

Another theory, and a very plausible one, is that the magnetism is due to large electric currents, which are known to be flowing around the earth, not only in the earth's crust but also in the space above. These earth currents may be connected in some direct way with the earth's rotation. This appears to be corroborated by the fact that the earth is magnetized in a direction almost parallel to the earth's polar axis.

Magnetic Declination. Since the earth's magnetic and polar axes do not coincide, a compass needle does not, in general, point toward true North. Because of the influence of the irregular iron deposits near the earth's surface, the magnetic field is not as regular as it is pictured in Fig. C, and a compass needle may deviate considerably from magnetic north. The angle that a compass needle deviates from true North is called the *angle of declination.*

A map showing the angle of declination for the United States is shown in Fig. D. The more or less vertical, generally irregular, north-south lines are lines of equal declination and are called *isogonic lines.* At every point along the line marked 20°E, for example, a compass needle actually points 20° east of true North. In the region of San Francisco, the declination is seen to be about 18°E, while in the region of New York it is about 11°W. The line through points where a compass points true North, 0°, is named the *agonic line.*

Magnetic Dip. If a compass needle is mounted to turn freely about a horizontal axis, as shown in Fig. E, it will not come to

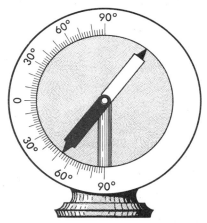

Fig. E. A magnetic dip needle.

rest in a horizontal position but will dip down at some angle with the horizontal as shown. This direction, called the *dip,* is the angle the earth's field makes with the earth's surface at that point. In Fig. C, it is seen that, in the far north and south, the angle of dip is large, whereas near the equator it is small. Fig. F indicates the approximate dip at different latitudes for one cross section of the entire globe.

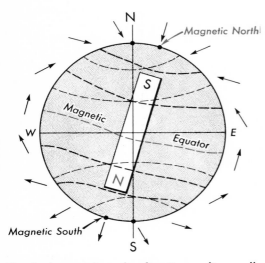

Fig. F. Arrows show the direction a dip needle takes at different parts of the earth's surface.

In the strait between Bathurst and Prince of Wales islands, north of central Canada and about 15° south of the geographic North pole, a dip needle points straight down, perpendicular to the earth's surface, and locates the North Magnetic pole. In Australian Antarctic Territory, about 25° from the geographic South pole, a dip needle points straight up, at 90° from the horizontal, and locates the South Magnetic pole.

On maps of terrestrial magnetism, all points that have equal dip angles are connected by a line called an *isoclinic* line. Such lines for different angles form a set of nearly parallel east-west lines as shown on the map of the United States in Fig. D. (In San Francisco, for example, the angle of dip is about 62°.)

Careful and accurate measurements of

the *declination* and *dip* show that the earth's magnetic field is continually changing. Although these changes are extremely small, they are somewhat periodic and, at times, quite erratic. Within geologic time, the earth's magnetic field has shifted greatly and actually reversed its direction completely.

Effect of a Magnetic Field on a Moving Charge. On Christmas Day, 1821, Michael Faraday discovered that, when a wire carrying a current is placed in the field of a magnet, a mechanical force is exerted on the wire. This is the principle upon which the modern electric motor is based.

A demonstration of Faraday's discovery is shown in Fig. G, where a flexible cop-

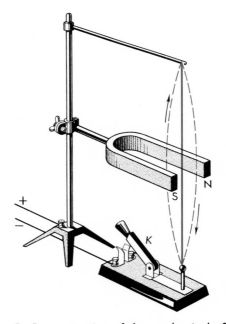

Fig. G. Demonstration of the mechanical effect of an electric current in a magnetic field.

per wire about 1 m long is suspended from a support. A U-shaped magnet straddles the wire somewhere near the middle.

Upon closing the switch, K, an electron current flows up through the wire and the wire moves to the left. If the battery connections are reversed, thereby reversing the electron current, the deflection of the wire will be to the right.

We can more easily study the force that the magnet produces on the electrons in the wire if we isolate the streams of electrons from the wire. This can be done by the use of a special tube as shown in Fig. H.

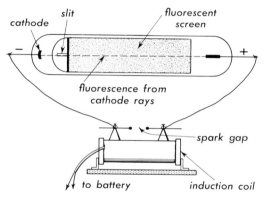

Fig. H. Special tube to make visible the path of a stream of electrons.

An evacuated tube containing a fluorescent screen is provided with two electrodes and a metal barrier with a small slit to admit a fine stream of electrons.

The path of the rays is made visible by allowing them to strike a long strip of metal painted with zinc sulfide, a fluorescent paint. High voltage from an induction coil is connected to the two electrodes, one at either end of the tube.

Although an induction coil does not deliver direct current, its characteristics are such that the potentials are higher on half of the alternations than they are on the other half and that the two electrodes act

nearly the same as if a high-voltage direct current were used. The negative electrode under these circumstances is called the *cathode* and the positive electrode the *anode*.

When the battery is connected to the induction coil, a bright green line is observed on the screen. By placing a horseshoe magnet over the outside of the tube, as illustrated in Fig. I, the path of the

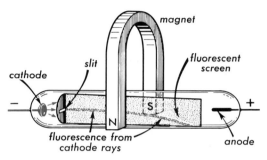

Fig. I. Effect of a magnetic field on the path of an electron stream.

electrons is bent down. If the polarity of the magnet is reversed, the path is bent up.

Experiments with tubes similar to this but in which accurate measurements could be made, show that the force exerted on the electrons depends directly on their charge and velocity and on the strength of the magnetic field. This can be formulated as—

$$F \propto qvB$$

or—

$$F = kqvB \tag{1}$$

In the mks system, the force, F, is measured in newtons, the charge, q, in coulombs, and the velocity, v, in meters per second. The units of the magnetic field or magnetic induction, B, as it is commonly called, can then be chosen to make the constant of proportionality equal to one.

$$F = qvB \tag{2}$$

Rearranging Eq. (2) we get—

$$B = \frac{F}{qv} \qquad (3)$$

The units of B are, therefore, seen to be—

$$\frac{\text{newton}}{\text{coulomb} \times \dfrac{\text{m}}{\text{sec}}}$$

Because an ampere is a coulomb per second, the units of magnetic induction, B, are usually written as—

$$\frac{\text{newton}}{\text{amp-m}}$$

Example. What force would be exerted on electrons moving with a velocity of 2×10^4 m/sec in a magnetic field with a strength of 0.2 newton/amp-m?

Solution. By direct substitution in Eq. (2), and remembering that the charge on the electron is 1.6×10^{-19} coulomb—

$$F = 1.6 \times 10^{-19} \times 2 \times 10^4 \times 0.2$$
$$= 6.4 \times 10^{-16} \text{ newton}$$

QUESTIONS

1. (a) Does a compass point true North at all times? (b) Does it ever point true North?
2. (a) What is magnetic declination? (b) Why does it arise?
3. (a) What is meant by magnetic dip? (b) How is it determined?
4. (a) What is the agonic line? (b) What is an isogonic line? (c) What is an isoclinic line?
5. Does the earth's magnetic field remain always the same?
6. Why are the isogonic lines so irregular from point to point?
7. (a) What is a magnetic field? (b) Can it be seen? (c) Can it be detected? (d) Can a magnetic field be mapped out?
8. Draw from memory the magnetic field around a bar magnet with two poles.
9. If a negatively charged particle enters a uniform magnetic field, moving perpendicularly to the magnetic induction, B, what will happen to it?
10. If a current-carrying wire is placed in a uniform magnetic field parallel to the magnetic induction, B, what force acts upon it?

PROBLEMS

1. What force would be exerted in electrons if their velocity were 6.0×10^6 m/sec in a field of 0.7 newton/amp-m?
2. Suppose we have a beam of electrons moving at a velocity of 2.0×10^6 m/sec. What is the force on the electrons if they pass through a field of 0.15 newton/amp-m?
3. An electron, with its charge of 1.6×10^{-19} coulomb, moves with one-tenth the speed of light across a magnetic field of 0.01 newton/amp-m. Find the magnitude of the mechanical force acting on the electron.
4. What force would be exerted on protons if their velocity were 3.0×10^6 m/sec in a field of 0.65 newton/amp-m?

5. By measuring the deflection of a stream of electrons moving in a field of 0.12 newton/amp-m, a force of 1.5×10^{-15} newton is found. What is the velocity of the electrons?

PROJECTS

1. Construct a unit that woud make it possible to study the effect of a magnetic field on a wire-carried current.
2. Using a small cathode-ray tube, which is another form of the tube described in Fig. H, study the effects of a magnetic field on the path of the electrons.
3. Make blueprints of the lines of force surrounding various combinations of magnetic and nonmagnetic substances, using fine iron filings.
4. Make a model of the earth that would demonstrate its magnetic properties. Try to make it as close to the way it is as possible.

MAGNETISM

Lesson 81 *MAGNETIC FIELD OF A CURRENT*

We have seen in the preceding lessons how the atomic arrangement within certain materials can produce a magnetic field. The atoms themselves owe their magnetic properties to the microscopic currents produced by the motion of their own electrons. It is now of interest to see how magnetic fields can be produced by macroscopic currents.

Magnetic Effect; Oersted's Experiment. The first discovery of the connection between electricity and magnetism was made by Oersted * in 1820. Often during his

lectures, at the University of Copenhagen, Oersted had demonstrated the nonexistence of a connection between electricity and magnetism. His usual custom was to place a current-carrying wire at right angles to and directly over a compass needle and show that there was no effect of one on the other. On this one occasion at the end of his lecture, when several of the audience came up to meet him at the lecture-room desk, he placed the wire parallel to the compass needle and, not the least expecting it, saw the needle move to one side. See Fig. A. Upon reversal of the current in the wire,

* Hans Christian Oersted (1777-1851), Danish scientist, was the son of an apothecary. He spent part of his boyhood teaching himself arithmetic and, at the age of twelve, he assisted his father in his shop and there became interested in chemistry. Passing the entrance examinations at the University of Copenhagen at the age of seventeen, he entered the medical school to graduate six years

later with his doctorate in medicine. At twenty-nine he came back to the university, but this time as professor of physics. It was at one of his demonstration lectures on chemistry and metaphysics that he discovered the magnetic effect bearing his name. The discovery not only brought him many endowments and prizes but made him one of the most eminent personalities in his own country.

the needle, to Oersted's amazement and perplexity, deviated in the opposite direction. Thus, this great discovery was made quite by accident, but, as Lagrange once

netism can always be relied upon to give the direction of the magnetic field induced by an electron current in a wire. *If the current-carrying wire were to be grasped with*

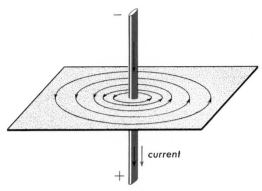

Fig. A. Diagram of Oersted's experiment illustrating the effect of an electric current upon a compass needle.

Fig. B. Experiment demonstrating the magnetic field about a straight wire carrying an electron current.

said of Newton on a similar occasion, "such accidents come only to those who deserve them."

The Left-Hand Rule. Oersted's experiment is interpreted as demonstrating that *around every wire carrying an electric current there is a magnetic field.* The direction of this field at every point, like that around a bar magnet, can be mapped by means of a small compass or by iron filings. A wire is mounted vertically through a hole in a plate of glass or other suitable nonconductor. Then iron filings are sprinkled on the plate. When current is fed into the wire, the filings line up parallel to the magnetic field. The result shows that the magnetic lines of force, or *lines of induction,* are concentric circles whose planes are at right angles to the current. This is illustrated by the circles in Fig. B.

The left-hand rule used in electromag-

the left hand, the thumb pointing in the direction of the electron current, − to +, the fingers will point in the direction of the magnetic induction.

Magnetic Induction. The strength of the magnetic field at any point in and around any electrical equipment is represented by the letter B, *the magnetic induction.* For example, the magnetic induction around a long, straight wire is everywhere perpendicular to the wire, and the magnetic lines of force representing B are drawn as concentric circles as shown in Fig. C. While the direction of B, as represented by the arrowheads, is given by the left-hand rule, the magnitude of B, for long straight wire at any point, is given by—

$$B = \mu_o \frac{I}{2\pi r} \qquad (1)$$

where I is the electron current in amperes, r is the perpendicular distance from the point

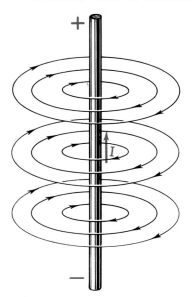

Fig. C. The magnetic field around a long, straight conductor.

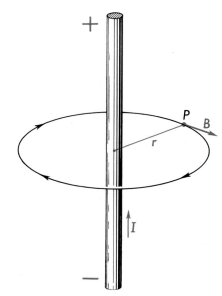

Fig. D. Magnetic induction, B, around a straight conductor carrying an electron current.

in question in meters, and μ_o is a proportionality constant whose value is exactly—

$$\mu_o = 4\pi \times 10^{-7} \frac{\text{newton}}{\text{amp}^2} \qquad (2)$$

See Fig. D.

Example. A current of 75 amp flows through a long straight wire. Find the magnetic induction 1 cm from the wire.

Solution. By direct substitution in Eq. (1), we obtain—

$$B = \left(4\pi \times 10^{-7} \frac{\text{newton}}{\text{amp}^2}\right) \frac{75 \text{ amp}}{2\pi \times 0.01 \text{ m}}$$

$$= 0.0015 \frac{\text{newton}}{\text{amp-m}}$$

Magnetic induction, B, is measured in newton/amp-m, and, having both magnitude and direction, is a vector quantity.

Circular Turns of Wire. As the current, I, flows through a circular loop of wire, as

shown in Fig. E, each part of the wire contributes to the magnetic induction, B, at

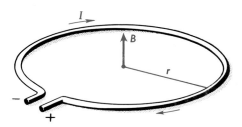

Fig. E. Magnetic induction, B, in a current-carrying loop of wire.

every point in the space inside or outside the loop. The direction of B at all points in the surrounding space is shown in Fig. F, and the closeness of the lines in any region is a measure of the magnitude of B.

The field strength is greatest at the center of a circular turn of wire and is given by—

$$B = \mu_o \frac{I}{2r} \qquad (3)$$

The magnetic induction, B, is in newtons/amp-m, the current, I, is in amperes, r is the radius in meters, and μ_o is given by Eq. (2).

The Solenoid. When a coil of wire is wrapped in the form of a helix, it is called

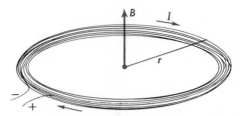

Fig. G. Magnetic induction, B, in a coil of N turns of wire.

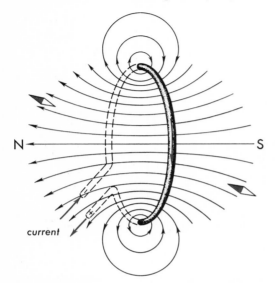

Fig. F. Diagram of the magnetic field through and around a single loop of wire carrying an electron current.

a solenoid. The general shape of the magnetic field in a solenoid is shown in Fig. H. The magnetic induction is fairly uniform throughout the center of the solenoid, and

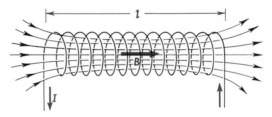

Fig. H. A solenoid of N turns of wire.

If, instead of a single loop of wire, the coil has a number of turns, each turn contributes the same field at the center, and the resultant magnetic induction will be given by N times that of Eq. (3). Hence—

$$B = \mu_o \frac{NI}{2r} \qquad (4)$$

N in this equation represents the number of turns, as in Fig. G, and the product NI represents what is called the *ampere turns*.

its magnitude at the center is given, for a long solenoid, by—

$$B = \mu_o \frac{NI}{l} \qquad (5)$$

were l is the length of the solenoid in meters.

We shall see the importance of the solenoid when the subject of electromagnets is treated.

QUESTIONS

1. (a) Who discovered the magnetic effect on an electric current? (b) What did he do? (c) What happens when the current is reversed?

2. (a) To what kind of current does the left-hand rule apply? (b) How does the rule apply to a straight wire?

3. (a) What is meant by magnetic induction? (b) In what units is B measured? (c) Does B have direction? (d) Is B a vector quantity?

4. How does the magnetic induction, B, at a point vary with distance from a long straight wire carrying an electron current?

5. How does B at the center of a circular coil vary (a) with the current; (b) with the radius; (c) with the number of turns?

6. How will the magnetic induction, B, at the center of a coil be altered if (a) the current is doubled and (b) the current is reversed in direction?

7. How does B at the center of a long solenoid vary (a) with the current; (b) with the radius?

8. Why was Oersted unsuccessful for such a long time in observing the connection between electricity and magnetism?

9. How could you experimentally determine the direction of the magnetic field around a wire carrying an electric current?

10. How can the magnetic effect of a current flowing in a wire be increased?

11. What is the relation between the magnetic induction inside a solenoid and the length of the solenoid for a fixed number of turns?

12. Is the magnetic field that surrounds the electric wires in a house strong or weak? Explain.

PROBLEMS

1. Calculate the magnetic induction at a distance of 1 cm from a long straight wire carrying an electron current of 200 amp.

2. Two long straight parallel wires 6 cm apart each carry an electron current of 40 amp. Calculate the magnetic induction at a point between the wires, 2 cm from one and 4 cm from the other, when the currents are (a) in the same direction and (b) in opposite directions.

3. What is the magnetic induction 50 cm from a wire that is carrying a current of 7.5 amp?

4. How much current would have to flow in a wire to produce a magnetic induction of 1.0×10^{-3} newton/amp-m at a distance of 1.0 cm from the wire?

5. What is the magnetic induction in the center of a 20-cm diameter coil of 10 turns with 4.0 amp flowing in it?

6. A solenoid with 100 turns of wire is 25.0 cm long. What is the magnitude of the magnetic induction at its center when 3.5 amp is flowing through it?

7. A solenoid 60 cm long has 1000 turns of wire. What electron current is required to produce a magnetic induction of 2×10^{-2} newton/amp-m at its center?

8. It is desired to have a solenoid with a magnetic induction of 2.5×10^{-3} newton/amp-m at its center. How many turns would be needed if the solenoid is to be 15.0 cm long and limited to a current of 5.0 amp?

PROJECTS

1. Develop a method to measure the magnetic induction of a solenoid. Check your results with calculations made with Eq. 5.
2. Make an apparatus using a relatively long wire and small compasses placed around it to show the lines of induction and how they change with a change in the direction of current flow.

MAGNETISM

Lesson 82 **MAGNETIC FORCES**

Interaction Between Magnetic Fields. To gain some understanding of the mysterious invisible force acting on a current-carrying wire in a magnetic field, consider the diagrams in Fig. A.

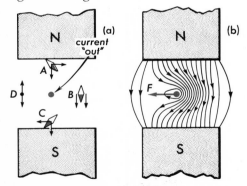

Fig. A. Magnetic fields owing (a) to an electron current and (b) to magnetic poles.

The circles in diagram (a) represent the circular magnetic lines of force around a straight wire carrying a current. The directions of the arrows are given by the left-hand rule, shown here for an electron current up and out of the page. The lines of force in diagram (b) represent the mag-

netic field between two opposite poles of a magnet.

If we place the current-carrying wire between the poles of the magnet, the two fields interact on each other. The interaction is such that a newly formed field, as that shown at the right in Fig. B, is obtained. Im-

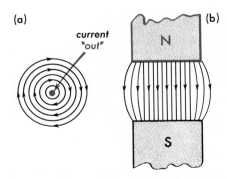

Fig. B. Diagrams of two interacting magnetic fields.

agining that the magnetic lines of force act like stretched rubber bands, one can predict from this diagram that the wire should experience a force, F, to the left.

To understand how such a field can arise out of two interacting symmetrical fields, it should be remembered that the field direction at any point is that taken by a small magnetic *dipole* placed there. (A dipole is any body having two oppositely charged poles.) Consider as examples the points *A*, *B*, *C*, and *D* of diagram (*a*). At *A*, the field owing to the current in the wire is to the right, and that owing to the magnetic poles is down. Because the two fields exert torques on the tiny, dipolar compass needle, the needle will point along a direction between the two.

At *B* the field owing to the current is down, and so is the field owing to the magnet. A compass at this point would point down. At *C* the fields are again at right angles, and the compass points halfway between, down and left. At *D* the fields are oppositely directed and, if they are equal in magnitude, cancel each other's effect. In practice, a compass needle at *D* wavers erratically as the current in the wire varies. This process, repeated for many other points, will lead to the field shown in diagram (*b*).

It is important to note that the direction of the current, *I*, in the wire, the direction of the magnetic field, *B*, at the wire due to the magnet, and the direction of the force, *F*, acting on the wire are all at right angles to each other.

Force on a Current-carrying Wire. We found earlier that electrons moving in a magnetic field have a force exerted on them. When electrons move in a wire in a magnetic field, this same force exerted on them will move the wire, because the electrons are confined to this wire.

An electron at rest in a magnetic field experiences no force from the magnet. An electron moving across magnetic lines of force experiences a force at right angles to

both the field and the direction of motion, as shown in Fig. C. To find the force on a

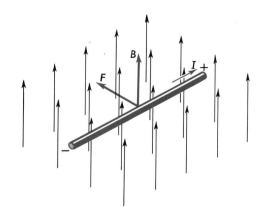

Fig. C. The force on a current-carrying wire in a magnetic field.

current-carrying wire in a magnetic field, we make use of Eq. (2) in Lesson 80, previously developed for electrons:

$$F = qvB \qquad (1)$$

A single moving charge, *Q*, constitutes a current, $I = Q/t$. Moving with a velocity, *v*, it will, in a time *t*, travel a distance $l = vt$. Substituting It for Q and l/t for *v* in Eq. (1), we obtain—

$$F = It \times \frac{l}{t} \times B$$

or—

$$F = IlB \qquad (2)$$

In the mks system, *F* is in newtons, *B* is in newtons per ampere meter, *I* is in amperes, and *l* is in meters.

A current-carrying wire, making an angle θ with the field, experiences a force proportional to $\sin \theta$:

$$F = IlB \sin \theta \qquad (3)$$

Example. A wire 40 cm long and carrying an electron current of 2.5 amp is located in a uniform magnetic field in which $B = 10^{-2}$

newton/amp-m. Calculate the force on the wire when it makes an angle of 60° with the field direction.

Solution. Since θ is measured from the direction of B, $\theta = 60°$, and substitution in Eq. (3) gives—

$$F = 2.5 \times 0.40 \times 10^{-2} \times 0.866$$
$$= 8.66 \times 10^{-3} \text{ newton}$$

Force Between Parallel Wires. We have just seen that a wire carrying a current experiences a force when in a magnetic field. When two parallel wires both carring current are near one another, they both experience a force, because they both are surrounded by a magnetic field. By experiment, it has been found that the force depends directly on the currents in the two wires and their lengths and varies inversely as the distance between them. The formula for finding the force between two parallel wires carrying current is given by the equation—

$$F = \text{constant} \times \frac{I_1 I_2 L}{d} \qquad (4)$$

where the force, F, between the wires is in newtons, the current in both wires is in amperes, the length, L, of the wires is in meters, and the distance, d, between the wires is also in meters.

Definition of the Ampere. In our discussion of Coulomb's law for electrostatic charges, we stated that the coulomb is the unit of charge that represents 6.24×10^{18} electrons. We also defined the ampere as the rate of flow of charge in a conductor. One ampere is equal to one coulomb per second. In the mks system, the force between parallel wires is used as the basic definition of the ampere.

When the distance between the two current-carrying wires is equal to their length

and when the same current flows in both, Eq. (4) reduces to—

$$F = \text{constant} \times I^2 \qquad (5)$$

The ampere is defined so that this constant is given by—

$$\text{constant} = \frac{\mu_0}{2\pi} = 2 \times 10^{-7} \text{ newton/amp}^2$$

It would seem at first that, for simplicity, the constant should be called μ_o rather than $\mu_o/2\pi$. However, many equations derived from Eq. (5) will involve a 2π or 4π in the numerator. Therefore, with the 2π occurring in the denominator of the definition, the πs will cancel, leaving more simply derived equations. See Eqs. (4) and (5) of Lesson 81.

As shown in Fig. D, two wires 1 m long

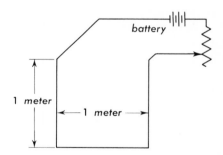

Fig. D. Dimensions of wire and spacing to define ampere in the mks system.

and 1 m apart are arranged so that the same current flows in both and so that the force between the wires can be measured. The current is adjusted by the variable resistor so that the force between the wires is exactly 2×10^{-7} newton. When this occurs, then, by definition, 1 amp of current is flowing in both wires.

The DC Electric Motor. An electric motor is a device by which electrical energy, in the form of an electric current, is transformed into mechanical energy. The principle of the motor is illustrated in Fig. E. A wire carrying an electron current is bent

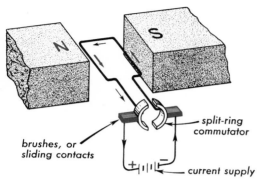

Fig. E. Principal elements for demonstrating the principles of an electric motor.

into a loop and placed between two magnetic poles, as shown. In this horizontal position, the resultant magnetic field is warped, as shown in Fig. F, forcing one wire down and the other up.

Mounted free to turn about an axis, the loop rotates until it is in a vertical plane. At this point, the current in the loop is re-

versed in direction by means of sliding contacts, or *brushes,* and a *split-ring commutator.* The reversal of the electron current reverses the forces so that the side of the loop that was previously pushed up is now pushed down. The side previously pushed

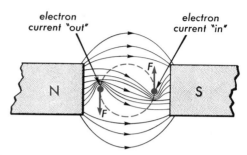

Fig. F. Diagram of the magnetic field around the current-carrying loop found in the electric motor.

down is now pushed up. The loop, therefore, rotates through half a turn more and the current again reverses.

A repetition of this reversing process at each half turn gives rise to a continuous rotation, the left side of the coil or loop always moving down and the right side always moving up.

QUESTIONS

1. (a) Who discovered the mechanical effects of electric currents? (b) What are the necessary conditions for producing the mechanical effect of an electric current?
2. Are the wires of a current-carrying coil being pushed apart or pulled together?
3. If a current-carrying wire is parallel to the magnetic induction, is there a mechanical force?
4. (a) How is the mechanical effect used in the electric motor? (b) What is the split ring used for? (c) Why are sliding contacts needed?
5. Upon what factors does the mechanical force on a current-carrying wire in a magnetic field depend?
6. Is the force on a current-carrying wire in a magnetic field basically different from the force exerted on free electrons? Explain.

7. What angle between a wire and a magnetic field gives the maximum force between them? What angle would give exactly half this value?
8. Of the two definitions given in the text for the ampere, which is the more fundamental? Why?
9. Briefly explain how a dc electric motor works.
10. What would happen to a dc electric motor if the two ends of the armature coil were connected to insulated rings instead of the opposing parts of a commutator?

PROBLEMS

1. A straight wire, 6 in. long and carrying an electron current of 25 amp, is placed in a field where the magnetic induction is 1 newton/amp-m, where the wire and the field are perpendicular to each other. Find the force on the wire.
2. An electron current of 50 amp flows through a straight wire 15 cm long. If this wire is placed in a field of 2×10^{-2} newton/amp-m, making an angle of 90° with the field direction, what is the force on the wire?
3. A wire 60 cm long and carrying a current of 20 amp is located in a uniform magnetic field of 6×10^{-3} newton/amp-m. Calculate the force on the wire when it makes an angle of 45° with the field directions.
4. A wire 10 cm long is in a uniform magnetic field of 1.5 newtons/amp-m. What current would have to flow in the wire to produce a force of 0.1 newton?
5. Two parallel wires 3.0 m long are 20 cm apart. (a) What force will be exerted on the wire if 3.0 amp flow through the wires? (b) In what direction will the force be if the current is flowing in the same direction in both wires?
6. Two parallel wires 2.0 m long carry a current of 10 amp. How close would they have to be for them to experience a force of 5×10^{-5} newton?
7. Two wires 10.0 m long are at right angles to each other. How much force would they exert on each other if they were 10 cm apart and carried 5.0 amp?

PROJECT

Make a simple dc motor to illustrate the theory of its operation.

MAGNETISM

Lesson 83 *ELECTROMAGNETS*

Magnetic Properties of a Solenoid. Not long after the announcement of Oersted's discovery of the magnetic effect of a current-carrying wire, Ampere found that a loop, or coil, of current-carrying wire acted as a magnet. When wound as a solenoid (see Fig. A), the coil's magnetic lines of force are such that one end of the coil acts as an N magnetic pole, and the other end as an S magnetic pole.

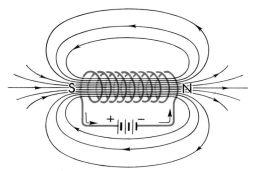

Fig. A. Diagram of the magnetic field around a solenoid carrying an electric current.

At all points in the region around a current-carrying coil, the direction of the magnetic field, as shown by a compass, can be predicted by the left-hand rule. Inside each loop or turn of wire, the lines point in one direction, whereas outside, they are oppositely directed. Outside the coil, the lines go from N to S in quite the same way they do about a permanent bar magnet, whereas inside, they go from S to N.

Not only does one coil of wire act like a magnet, but two coils may be used to demonstrate the repulsion and attraction of like and unlike poles.

The Electromagnet. Five years after Oersted's discovery and Ampere's demonstration of the magnetic properties of a solenoid, William Sturgeon filled the center of a coil of wire with soft iron and thereby produced a powerful magnet. See Fig. B. Since electromagnets are so much stronger than solenoids, they have a great many applications. Doorbells, chimes, vibrators, relays, telephone headsets, and electric meters are just a few of their uses.

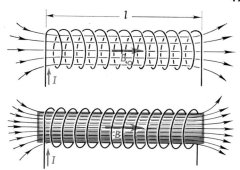

Fig. B. An iron core greatly strengthens the magnetic induction in a solenoid.

Permeability. We have seen in Lesson 81 how the magnetic induction, B_o, at the center of a solenoid is given by—

$$B_o = \mu_o \frac{NI}{l} \qquad (1)$$

When an iron core is inserted into this magnetic field, as shown in Fig. B, the magnetic induction, B, increases many fold, and we write—

$$B = K_m \mu_o \frac{NI}{l} \qquad (2)$$

where K_m is the *relative permeability* of the iron core and is typically around 2000. (Values of K_m for several substances are given in Table 1.) The magnetic induction,

Table 1. Relative Permeability of Several Materials

Material		Permeability
Copper	(diamagnetic)	.99999
Oxygen liquid	(paramagnetic)	1.0040
Oxygen gas	(paramagnetic)	1.0013
Iron	(ferromagnetic)	2000.

B, beyond, but near, the coil ends is not greatly different from that at the coil center.

Magnetic Properties of Matter. We have seen from Oersted's experiment that magnetic forces originate from electric currents. We shall now see how the magnetic properties of materials such as iron are also due to currents.

The atom, which will be studied later, can be pictured as a number of electrons moving about a central nucleus. Most of the motions tend to cancel each other. Often, however, one or more of the outer valence electrons will have a motion that is not compensated. Such a motion is equivalent to a circular turn of current (see Fig. E in Lesson 81).

The magnetic field of a current is very similar to the field of a small magnet. See Fig. C. For this reason, such a current loop

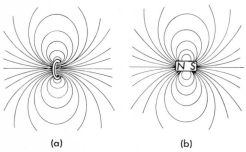

(a)   (b)

Fig. C. The field of a magnetic dipole. (a) A loop of current or an electron in a circular orbit, as a source of field. (b) A small bar magnet.

is called a *magnetic dipole*. When an external magnetic field is applied to a piece of soft iron, as in Fig. B, the submicroscopic currents, or dipoles, line up so as to enhance the applied field. Following the same reasoning, the attraction between two magnets can be attributed to the attraction of all the dipoles in one magnet to all the dipoles in the other.

Superconductivity. Certain conductors, when cooled to 1°K or 2°K, lose their resistance completely. Under these conditions, they are called superconductors. By

starting a current in a superconducting coil of wire, a magnet will be produced that will last indefinitely, provided that the refrigeration is maintained. Many large superconducting electromagnets have recently been made for particle accelerators, etc., using wire made of such material as niobium or tin alloy, cooled by liquid helium. Fields have been produced up to 100,000 newtons/amp-m, which last a long time and require no continuous input power.

Ammeters and Voltmeters. Electrical instruments designed to measure an electric current are called *ammeters,* and those designed to measure potential difference are called *voltmeters.* The principle upon which both of these devices operate is essentially the same as that of the electric motor. They differ from the motor, however, in the delicateness of their construction and the constrained motion of the rotating armature.

For either meter, a coil of fine copper wire is mounted between the two poles of a permanent magnet so that its rotation, as shown in Fig. D, is constrained by a hair-

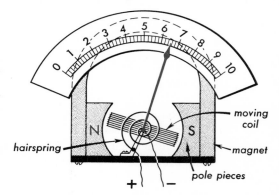

Fig. D. Diagram of the essential parts of an ammeter or voltmeter.

spring. The farther the coil is turned from its equilibrium, or zero, position, the greater is the restoring force. To this coil is fastened a long pointer, at the end of which is a fixed scale reading amperes, if it is an ammeter, or volts, if it is a voltmeter.

Upon increasing the current through the moving coil of an ammeter or voltmeter, the resultant magnetic field between coil and magnet is distorted more and more. The resulting increase in force, therefore, turns the coil through a greater and greater angle, reaching a point where it is just balanced by the restoring force of the hairspring.

Whenever an ammeter or voltmeter is connected to a circuit to measure electron current or potential difference, the ammeter must be connected in series and the voltmeter in parallel. As illustrated in Fig. E,

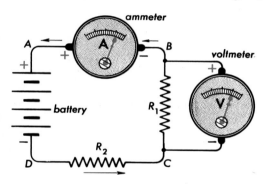

Fig. E. Circuit diagram showing the connections for an ammeter and voltmeter.

the ammeter is connected so that all of the electron current passes through it. To prevent a change in the electron current when such an insertion is made, all ammeters must have a low resistance. Most ammeters, therefore, have a low-resistance wire, called a *shunt*, connected across the armature coil inside.

A voltmeter, on the other hand, is connected across that part of the circuit for which a measurement of the potential difference is required. If the potential difference between the ends of the resistance R_1

is wanted, the voltmeter is connected as shown. If the potential difference across R_2 is desired, the voltmeter connections are made at C and D. If the potential difference maintained by the battery is desired, connections are made at A and D. To prevent the connection of a voltmeter to a circuit from changing the electron current in the circuit, the voltmeter is given a relatively high resistance. If the armature coil does not have a large resistance of its own, additional resistance is added in series.

Very delicate ammeters are often used for measuring very small currents. A meter whose scale is calibrated to read thousandths of an ampere is called a *milliammeter*. One whose scale is calibrated in millionths of an ampere is called a *microammeter* or *galvanometer*.

Ammeter Shunts. Suppose we have an instrument capable of a full-scale deflection when only one milliamp or $\frac{1}{1000}$ amp goes through its armature coil and we would like to use it to read currents in the order of 10 amp. Obviously, we would have to divert most of the current around the meter to prevent its burning up the delicate wire. We would connect a shunt resistor R_s as shown in Fig. F. At full scale, the meter

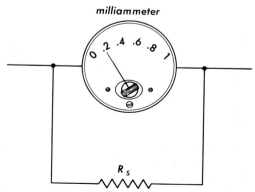

Fig. F. Diagram showing how a shunt resistor converts a milliammeter into an ammeter.

would take 0.001 amp, and R_s would take the remainder, or 9.999 amp. The value of R_s will depend on the value of the meter coil; let us assume it is 50 Ω.

Because the meter and R_s are in parallel, the voltages dropped across both of them are equal:

$$V_{meter} = I_{meter} \times R_{meter}$$
$$V_{Rs} = I_{Rs} \times R_s$$

Substituting the values given and equating the two equations gives—

$$.001 \times 50 = 9.999R_s$$

Solving for R_s:

$$R_s = \frac{.001 \times 50}{9.999} = 0.005 \ \Omega$$

With this value of resistance across the meter, all readings on the scale would have to be multiplied by 10 to give the correct value in amperes.

Voltmeter Multipliers. It is possible to convert this same milliammeter into any range voltmeter we wish. Let us say we need a voltmeter with a 10-volt, full-scale deflection. This time, we use a series resistor as shown in Fig. G. When the meter and resistor are connected to 10 volts, only

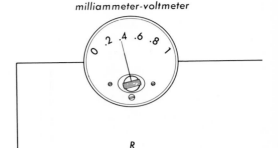

milliammeter-voltmeter

Fig. G. Diagram showing how a series resistor converts a milliammeter into a voltmeter.

0.001 amp of current need flow to cause full-scale deflection of the needle. The total resistance of the circuit can be calculated by Ohm's law:

$$R_t = \frac{V}{I}$$
$$= \frac{10}{.001} = 10,000 \ \Omega$$

However, the meter has an internal resistance of 50 Ω and, therefore, only 9,950 Ω need be added to convert this meter to a 10-volt voltmeter. Either the meter scale would have to be changed or all readings be multiplied by 10.

QUESTIONS

1. Is there any difference in the magnetic behavior of an electromagnet and a permanent magnet? Explain.
2. How does the left-hand rule (see Lesson 81) apply to a coil of wire?
3. (a) What effect does a soft-iron core have upon the strength of the magnetic field around a solenoid? (b) Does a current have to flow to produce the field?
4. What is the origin of the force between a current-carrying wire and a bar magnet?
5. What is the origin of the force between two bar magnets?
6. (a) Where does the term "magnetic dipole" come from? (b) What would be meant by an electric dipole?

7. (a) How is an ammeter constructed? (b) What is the spiral spring for? (c) Why are the poles curved?

8. (a) Can an ammeter be converted into a voltmeter? (b) If so, how?

9. In what general way does a voltmeter differ from an ammeter?

10. (a) Why should an ammeter have a low resistance? Why should a voltmeter have a high resistance?

11. What would happen to an ammeter if it were connected directly across a source of voltage? Why?

12. Would an electrical circuit work well if a voltmeter were connected in series with the other elements in the circuit? Explain.

13. (a) What would happen to the accuracy of the readings of a voltmeter if its internal permanent magnets were weakened? (b) Would the readings be too high or too low?

14. What is the present theory as to why some atoms are magnetic and others are not?

PROBLEMS

1. A voltmeter with a resistance of 100 Ω shows a full-scale reading when 5 volts are applied to its terminals. What resistance connected to this instrument will give it a full-scale reading when connected to 120 volts?

2. A voltmeter with a resistance of 200 Ω shows a full-scale reading when 1 volt is applied to its terminals. What resistance connected to this instrument will give it a full-scale reading of (a) 5 volts (b) 50 volts, and (c) 150 volts?

3. A voltmeter with a resistance of 5000 Ω shows a full-scale reading at 25 volts. What resistance should be connected to this instrument to have it give a full-scale reading of 500 volts?

4. If the voltmeter in Problem 1 is used as a milliammeter, what current will give a full-scale deflection?

5. What shunt resistance across the voltmeter in Problem 1 will make it into an ammeter with a full-scale deflection for 5 amp?

6. What shunt resistance across the voltmeter in Problem 2 will make it into an ammeter with a full-scale deflection for 5 amp?

7. What shunt resistance across the voltmeter in Problem 3 will make it into an ammeter with a full-scale deflection of 25 amp?

8. A voltmeter with a resistance of 500 Ω shows a full-scale reading when an electron current of 10 milliamp flows through it. What shunt resistance across this instrument will enable it to be used as an ammeter indicating 5 amp on full-scale deflection?

9. A solenoid has a magnetic field of 0.035 newton/amp-m. (a) What is the magnetic field inside a piece of iron placed in the solenoid? (b) What would it be inside a bar of copper?

PROJECTS

1. Make a working model of an electrical meter. It does not have to be sensitive to small currents but should show how it operates.
2. Make a volt-ammeter, using resistors and shunts, from a 0-1 milliammeter.

MAGNETISM

Lesson 84 *INDUCED ELECTRIC CURRENTS*

Magnetic Flux. In diagrams of magnetic fields, lines are used to represent the field. The direction of the lines shows the direction of the field; the strength of the field is represented by the density of the lines. See Fig. A.

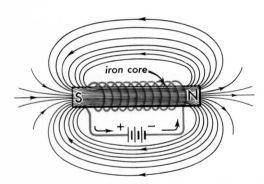

Fig. A. Lines of force around an electromagnet.

The total number of such lines crossing any area normal to a magnetic field is called the *magnetic flux*, ϕ. This is simply the product of the magnetic field and the area:

$$\phi = B \times A \qquad (1)$$

Example. A solenoid with a radius of 6 cm has a magnetic field of 0.05 newton/amp-m. What is the flux through the solenoid?

Solution. The flux is—

$$\phi = .05 \times \pi \times (.06)^2$$
$$= 5.65 \times 10^{-4} \text{ newton-m/amp}$$

Induced Electric Currents. The discovery of induced electric current goes back about one hundred twenty-five years, to 1831, and the well-planned experiments of Michael Faraday.[*] A bar magnet plunged

[*] Michael Faraday (1791-1867), English experimental physicist was the son of a blacksmith. Faraday's early life was spent earning his living as a bookbinder's apprentice. Taking time from his work to read some of the books passing through his hands, Faraday became intensely interested in science. With a passionate desire to make science a life work, his chance finally came when he was made a valet and assistant to the great English scientist Sir Humphrey Davy of the Royal Institute. As a young man, he openly proclaimed that women were nothing in his life, and even wrote and published a poem in criticism of falling in love. At the age of twenty-nine he saw, fell desperately in love with, and married Sarah Barnhard, who become a devoted and inspiring companion for the nearly fifty remaining years of his life. Four months after his marriage, he made the famous discovery of the motion of a wire carrying a current in the field of a magnet. Because a current-carrying wire would move in a magnetic field, should not the reverse be true and a magnet be made to produce current in a wire? For days he experimented with magnets and coils of wire until, in desperation, he plunged a magnet down into a

into a coil of wire was found to produce an electric current. The experiment is illustrated in Fig. B. As the N pole of the mag-

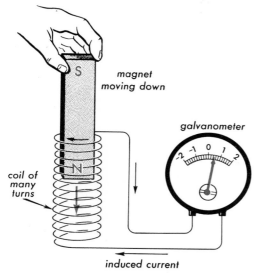

Fig. B. Diagram of Faraday's experimental discovery of induced electric currents.

net is plunged into the coil, a galvanometer needle deflects to the *right;* when it is withdrawn, the needle deflects to the *left,* indicating a current in the opposite direction. If the S pole is moved down into the coil, the needle deflects to the *left;* and as it is withdrawn, the deflection is to the *right.*

The relative motion of the coil and magnet is what produces the current. It makes no difference whether the coil alone moves, whether the magnet alone moves, or

coil and observed that a current was generated in the coil. Why had he not discovered this before? The motion was the thing; it was the connecting link he had failed to realize. For this discovery, the whole scientific world sought to honor him. So many universities gave him honorary degrees that he soon had to turn down such honors. He refused the presidency of both the Royal Institute and the Royal Society of London and also refused to be knighted.

whether they both move. In any case, when the relative motion ceases, the current stops. A "somewhat old-fashioned" way of describing the action is to say that only when a wire is cutting the lines of flux is there an induced emf. A somewhat more acceptable statement at the present time is, in effect, that only when the total magnetic flux linking a closed electrical circuit is changing is there an induced emf. To demonstrate this concept, a simple experiment like that shown in Fig. C may be performed.

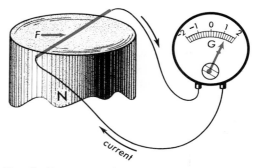

Fig. C. Experimental arrangement for demonstrating induced electron currents.

A flexible wire, connected to an ammeter and held in the hands, is moved in various ways across the pole of a magnet. When a straight section of the wire is held over the N pole and moved to the right with force F, an electron current flows in the direction shown by the arrows. If the wire is moved in the opposite direction, the induced emf (and current) reverses direction. If the wire is moved vertically upward or downward, parallel to the magnetic induction, no current flows. In other words, *there is an induced emf only when the total number of lines of induction (flux) through the closed circuit is changing.*

The *left-hand rule* may be used to predict the direction of the induced emf in any section of wire. If we imagine grasping the wire in the left hand, as it moves through the magnetic field, with the fingers pointing in the direction of the magnetic induction immediately in front of it, the thumb will point in the direction of the induced emf.

Induced Electromotive Force. It was shown, in Lesson 80, how an electric charge, Q, moving with a constant velocity, v, through a magnetic field where the flux density is B, experiences a force, F, upon it given by—

$$F = QvB \qquad (2)$$

where F, B, and v are all mutually perpendicular.

When, therefore, a single wire is made to cross magnetic lines of induction, as shown in Fig. D, every atomic charge within the

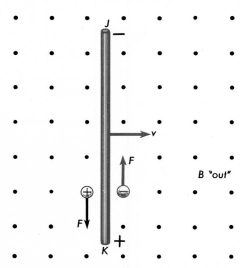

Fig. D. Forces on the charges in a conductor moving through a magnetic field.

metal experiences a force upon it parallel to the conductor. The direction of the force on the $+$ charges is from J to K, while the force on the $-$ charges is from K to J. Because only the electrons are free to move in a metallic conductor, the negative charges mi-

grate along the wire building up a negative potential at one end and a positive potential at the other.

Consider the straight conductor, JK, sliding along a U-shaped conductor to form a closed circuit, as shown in Fig. E. The

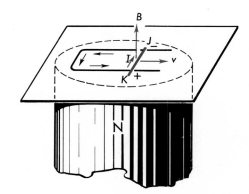

Fig. E. Inducing a current by the motion of a conductor.

potential difference created between the ends forces electrons through and around the circuit in the direction indicated. In other words, the moving conductor becomes the source of an *electromotive force*, or *emf*.

The electromotive force developed within a moving conductor of length l is defined as the work per unit charge done in carrying any charge from one end to the other. From mechanics, we draw upon the principle that work done, W, is equal to *force times distance moved*. With the force given by Eq. (2) and the distance moved by l, the work done on a charge, Q, is—

$$W = QvBl \qquad (3)$$

If we now divide both sides of the equation by Q, the work per unit charge becomes—

$$V = vBl \qquad (4)$$

where V is the *emf*, or work per unit charge done on the charges in this section of the moving conductor.

In the mks system, B is in *newtons amp-m*, v is in *meters/second*, l is in *meters*, and V is in *volts*. It should be pointed out that it makes no difference in the above treatment whether the wire moves through a stationary magnetic field or whether the field moves across a stationary conductor. It is the relative motion giving rise to crossing of lines of induction that produces the *emf*.

The Electric Generator. The construction of an electric generator is the same as that of an electric motor, with a rotating armature containing coils of wire, pole pieces, field windings, brushes, and a commutator. Instead of being supplied with an electron current to produce mechanical rotation, mechanical work is done to turn the generator's armature, thus producing an electron current.

If, in the construction of a generator, two solid rings are used as a commutator, as shown in Fig. F, the current delivered to the

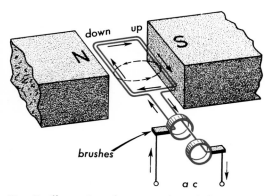

Fig. F. Illustrating the principles of the electric generator.

brushes flows first in one direction, then in the other. The reversal of current with each half turn of the armature is due to the fact that each wire moves up across the field at

one instant and down across at the next. At one instant, the one terminal is positive and the other negative; at the next instant the first terminal is negative and the second positive. This periodically reversing emf produces what is called *an alternating emf*. The machine is called an *alternating-current*, or *ac*, *generator*.

If a direct current is desired, the commutator of the generator must be of the split-ring type illustrated in Fig. G. It can be

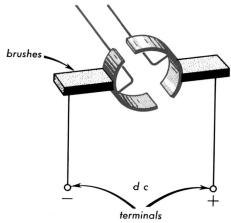

Fig. G. Split-ring commutator for a direct-current generator.

seen that, with this arrangement, one brush is at all times in contact with wires moving up across the field while the other is in contact with wires moving down across the field. This produces a unidirectional electron current and the whole machine is called a *direct-current*, or *dc*, *generator*.

It is important to note that a generator does not make electricity. The electricity, or electric charge, is always in the wire, and a generator sets it into motion. A generator produces an electric current.

Alternating Current. The magnitude of the voltage induced in a generator coil rotating as shown in Fig. F is given by the relation—

$$V = NBA\omega \sin \omega t \qquad (5)$$

where N is the number of turns in the coil, B is the magnetic induction in newtons per ampere-meter, A is the cross-sectional area of the wire coil in meters^2, ω is the angular speed in radians per second, and t is the time in seconds.

If f represents the frequency of rotation—

$$\omega = 2\pi f \qquad (6)$$

The frequency, f, has the unit of cycles per second called *Hertz* or *Hz*.

Hz = cycle/sec
KHz = kilocycle/sec = 10^3 cycles/sec
MHz = megacycle/sec = 10^6 cycles/sec

A 60-cycle/sec, or 60 Hz, 110-volt alternating emf, for example, is one in which the potential difference reverses direction 120 times per second. The rating of 110 volts (see Fig. H) specifies a sort of average voltage called the *root-mean-square, rms,* volt-

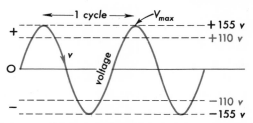

Fig. H. Voltage graph for an alternating-current generator coil.

age and not the so-called *peak voltage* of 155 volts.

The maximum voltage is obtained when the plane of the coil is parallel to the field ($\omega t = 90°$ or $270°$) and zero when it is perpendicular ($\omega t = 0°$ or $180°$). When $\omega t = 90°$, $\sin \omega t = 1$, and Eq. (5) gives—

$$V_{max} = NBA\omega \qquad (7)$$

The root-mean-square voltage is given by—

$$V_{rms} = .707V_{max} \qquad (8)$$

and the root-mean-square current supplied to any circuit is given by—

$$I_{rms} = .707I_{max} \qquad (9)$$

QUESTIONS

1. (a) Who discovered induced electric currents? (b) How was the phenomenon produced?
2. What are the basic principles of induced currents?
3. Can a current be induced in a wire that is stationary?
4. Can a current be induced in a wire by a stationary magnetic field?
5. If a wire moves through a magnetic field parallel to the lines of induction, is there an emf developed within the wire?
6. Upon what four factors does the induced emf in a wire depend?
7. How can an alternating current be induced in a wire?
8. How are alternating currents generally produced?
9. Upon what four factors does the emf produced by an alternating-current generator depend?
10. (a) What is magnetic flux? (b) Give two totally different ways in which flux through a loop might be changed.

PROBLEMS

1. A wire 20 cm long moves with a speed of 25 m/sec through a uniform magnetic field where the magnetic induction is 0.3 newton/amp-m. If the wire, field, and motion are all mutually perpendicular, what emf is produced in the wire?

2. A wire 10 m long is located in the wing of an airplane traveling at 720 km/hr. If the magnetic induction due to the earth's field has a value of 5×10^{-4} newton/amp-m, what is the maximum possible induced emf?

3. A wire 1 m long moves with a speed of 15 m/sec through a uniform magnetic field where the flux density, B, is 0.2 newton/amp-m. If the wire, field, and motion are all perpendicular to each other, what emf is produced in the wire?

4. A wire 20 cm long is moved with a speed of 4 m/sec through a uniform magnetic field where the magnetic induction, B, is 0.25 newton/amp-m. Find the emf produced in the wire.

5. At what speed should a wire 50 cm long be moved through a magnetic field where $B = 0.5$ newton/amp-m if it is to produce an emf of 1 volt?

6. A flat rectangular coil, 10 cm by 20 cm, made of 50 turns of wire, is rotating at the constant speed of 3000 r/min in a magnetic field where the magnetic induction is 0.2 newton/amp-m. Calculate (a) the maximum voltage and (b) the root-mean-square voltage.

7. A flat circular coil, 20 cm in diameter and containing 100 turns of wire, is rotating at 2400 r/min in a magnetic field where $B = 0.25$ newton/amp-m. Find (a) the maximum emf produced and (b) the root-mean-square voltage.

8. A rectangular coil of 100 turns is 10 cm wide and 20 cm long. What is the speed at which this coil should rotate in the earth's magnetic field ($B = 5 \times 10^{-4}$ newton/amp-m) to produce a peak emf of 0.10 volt?

9. A flat circular coil of 50 turns is 20 cm in diameter. If this coil is to be rotated in a uniform magnetic field to produce a root-mean-square voltage of 100 volts at 1000 Hz, what must be the value of the magnetic induction?

10. An electric heater with a resistance of 30 Ω is connected to a house-lighting outlet of 120 volts ac. Find (a) the peak voltages and (b) the peak current.

11. An ac generator whose terminal root-mean-square emf is 110 volts is connected to a resistance of 20 Ω. If the internal resistance of the generator is 2.5 Ω, what is the peak electron current?

12. A resistance of 12 Ω is connected to an ac generator whose internal resistance is 1.2 Ω. If the rms current in the circuit is 8.5 amp, find the peak emf of the generator on open circuit.

13. An electric toaster with a resistance of 16 Ω is connected to a 220-volt ac line. Find (a) the peak voltage, and (b) the peak electron current.

14. An electric iron with a resistance of 15 Ω is connected to a 220-volt ac line. Find (a) the peak voltage, and (b) the peak electron current.

PROJECT

Make a simple ac generator. Drive it with a variable-speed motor, if possible, so that the voltage produced at various speeds can be measured.

MAGNETISM

Lesson 85 LENZ'S LAW AND SELF-INDUCTANCE

Lenz's Law. Recalling both Faraday's and Oersted's findings, we know (1) that an electron current is induced in a conductor moving through a magnetic field and (2) that a current produces around its conductor a magnetic field with a direction determined by the direction of the induced current. Thus, *when a conductor moves through a magnetic field, the direction of the induced current's own magnetic field conflicts with the direction of the original magnetic field, opposing the motion of the conductor.* Stated for the first time by H. F. E. Lenz in 1833, this is known as *Lenz's law.* The action of the two magnetic fields upon each other is always such as to oppose the motion or any change in conditions already existing, for if they assisted the change we would have perpetual motion and a violation of the law of conservation of energy.

If the *N* pole of a bar magnet is approaching a solenoid, as shown in Fig. B in Lesson 84, the induced electron current in the coil is in such a direction as to produce an *N* pole near the top of the coil. The two *N* poles, therefore, repel each other, tending to stop the motion. To keep the current flowing, a force, *F*, must continually be supplied to the moving magnet. It is this force, *F*, moving through a given distance that determines the amount of mechanical work done in producing a given current.

If now the *N* pole is withdrawn from the solenoid, the induced current in the coil reverses in direction and produces an *S* pole at the top end. The opposite poles, therefore, attract each other, tending to stop the motion. Again, to keep the current flowing, a force *F* must be continually supplied and thus work is done.

There are numerous ways of demonstrating Lenz's law. One common experiment is to move a flat copper or aluminum plate rapidly through a strong magnetic field, as shown in Fig. A. As each part of the plate enters the field between the poles of the magnet, a strong opposing force tends to stop it. What happens electrically is that strong eddy currents of electricity are produced in the metal. The magnetic field arising from these eddy currents opposes the field through which it is moving. If the plate is held in the hand the sensation is that of movement through thick molasses.

If the solid disk is replaced by a slotted disk, as shown in Fig. B(*a*), strong currents are induced in the vertical bars as they enter the field, and the disk stops quickly. If the slots are open at one end, as in diagram (*b*), each bar is an open circuit and

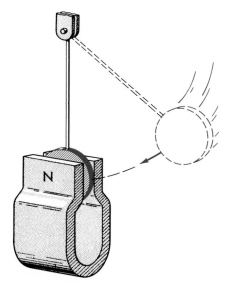

Fig. A. Induced currents in the copper-disk pendulum quickly stop its swing.

no large induced currents can be produced. Consequently, the disk is not strongly retarded but swings through the magnetic field rather freely.

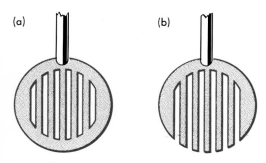

Fig. B. Slotted copper disks for the demonstration of induced eddy currents.

Levitation. The phenomenon known as levitation is another illustration of Lenz's law. A metal bowl, *B*, as in diagram (*a*) of Fig. C, is supported in stable equilibrium in midair just above an electromagnet, *M*, of special design. Top and side views of the iron core and coil windings are shown in

diagrams (*b*) and (*c*). Excited by an alternating current, the raised iron knobs labeled *N* and *S* reverse their polarity periodically with the current. As the electron current

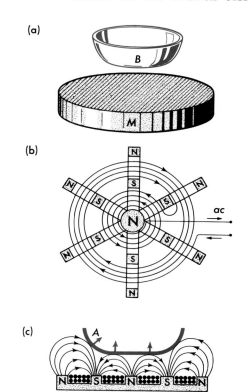

Fig. C. A metal bowl is suspended in midair.

builds up in the direction indicated in diagram (*b*), the magnetic induction grows as in diagram (*c*). With the aluminum bowl in place, the growing field induces strong eddy currents in the aluminum conductor. These currents, in turn, give rise to opposing fields. Because the primary field being created by an alternating current increases and decreases rapidly, the bowl always experiences an upward force.

Should the bowl move to one side, as, for example, to the left in diagram (*c*), the changing field at *A* will induce stronger electron currents on that side of the bowl and give rise to an increased repulsion, pushing the bowl back toward the center as indicated. The strong induced currents give rise to so much heat that the bowl soon becomes hot.

Self-induction. When a battery is first connected to the ends of a long straight copper wire, the electron current rises quickly to the value given by Ohm's law, as shown by curve (*a*) in Fig. D. When

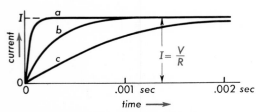

Fig. D. Current-time graph for a long copper wire in the form of (a) a straight wire, (b) a coil, and (c) a coil with an iron core.

the same wire is wound into a coil or solenoid, however, the current rises more slowly, as shown by curve (*b*). If an iron core is inserted to make of the solenoid an electromagnet, the current rises much more slowly, as shown in curve (*c*).

The cause for this lagging of the current is attributed to an emf, induced in the wire, that is opposite in direction to the rising current. This *back emf*, as it is sometimes called, is extremely small if the wire is straight, is large if it is a coil, and still larger if a soft-iron core is inserted. To understand the existence of a back emf, consider a small section of one turn of wire in a solenoid of many turns. As the current rises in this section, the growing magnetic induction developing around it threads through neighboring loops of wire inducing in them an emf. These induced emf's and their corresponding currents run counter to

the impressed emf and current. This property is called *self-induction*.

The unit by which one measures the self-induction of a coil is the *henry*, in honor of the American scientist, Joseph Henry.* *A coil having an inductance of one henry is one in which a change in the current of one ampere per second produces a back emf of one volt.* The definition for induction may be written—

$$L = \frac{V}{\Delta I/\Delta t} \qquad (1)$$

A coil with a large number of turns is one that has a large inductance, L, whereas one with but a few turns has a small inductance. The higher the inductance, the more slowly does the current rise or fall within the coil.

The establishment of a steady current in an inductance requires work, since the back emf's must be overcome. Not all of the electrical energy expended in reaching the steady-current state is lost. Some is stored up in the form of a magnetic field. When the source emf is disconnected from the circuit, the magnetic induction decreases, thereby inducing an oppositely directed emf and corresponding current.

* Joseph Henry (1797-1878), American physicist and scientific administrator, was born in Albany, New York, in 1797. Henry attended a country school, but quit at the age of thirteen. Later, he attended the Albany Academy. Becoming interested in electricity and magnetism he invented the magnetic telegraph and the electric relay, and he discovered the phenomenon of self-induction. In 1832, he became professor of natural philosophy at Princeton and, in 1842, was elected by Congress as first secretary of the Smithsonian Institution in Washington, D.C. In this capacity, he founded the U.S. Weather Bureau and inaugurated the idea of distributing scientific publications to libraries and scientific bodies all over the world. He was the principal figure in the organization of the National Academy of Sciences, of which he was the second president. By general agreement, Henry was the foremost American physicist of his time.

An experiment demonstrating the property of self-induction is illustrated in Fig. E. A solenoid of many turns of wire is connected in parallel with an electric lamp

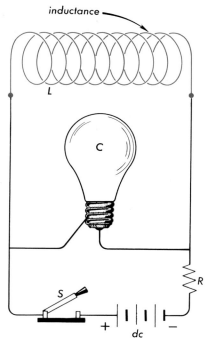

inductance

L

C

S

R

+ dc −

Fig. E. An experimental demonstration of the self-induction of a coil of wire.

to a 110-volt battery, B. When the switch, S, is closed, the light flashes brightly for an instant and then becomes dim. When the switch is opened, the light again flashes brightly for a moment and then goes out.

When the switch was closed, the back emf in the inductance prevented the current from building up rapidly through the inductance. The inductance, therefore, acted as though it had a very high resistance, so that practically all of the current went through C. When the current became steady, there was no back emf in L, and

part of the current flowed through C and part through L. When the switch was opened, the magnetic field rapidly diminished, inducing a current in L. This current flowing through the lamp C caused it to light up momentarily.

Calculation of Inductance. In many instances, the inductance of a solenoid can be calculated from its geometry. For a long solenoid of uniform cross section (see Fig. H in Lesson 81, the inductance, L, in *henries*, is given by—

$$L = K_m \mu_o \frac{N^2 A}{l} \qquad (2)$$

where N is the number of turns of wire, A is the cross-sectional area of the core in square meters, K_m is the relative permeability of the core, μ_o is the constant $4\pi \times 10^{-7}$, and l is the length of the coil in meters.

Example. A round iron bar, 4 cm in diameter and 20 cm long, is wrapped with one layer of copper wire. The coil has 200 turns and the relative permeability of the iron is 2000. Find the inductance.

Solution. The given quantities are just those occurring on the right in Eq. (2): $N = 200$, $K_m = 2 \times 10^4$, $l = 0.20$ m, and $A = \pi r^2 = 0.00126$ m^2.

$$L = \frac{2000 \times 4\pi \times 10^{-7} \times (200)^2 \times .00126}{0.2}$$

$$= 0.634 \text{ henry}$$

Without the iron core, the solenoid would have a very much smaller inductance. For an air core, K_m would be equal to 1, and the inductance would be only 0.317 millihenry. The *millihenry*, is a smaller unit of inductance and is equal to one-thousandth of a henry, while a still smaller unit, the *microhenry*, is equal to one-millionth of a henry.

It should be noted that, if the core is air or a vacuum, L is a constant independent of the electron current. If the core is a ferromagnetic material, however, L will vary because the relative permeability varies.

QUESTIONS

1. (a) What is self-induction? (b) How does self-induction depend on the shape of a conductor?
2. In what units is self-induction measured?
3. Upon what factors does the inductance of a long solenoid depend?
4. How does the inductance of a coil change when an iron core is inserted?
5. (a) What is Lenz's law? (b) How can the law be demonstrated?
6. Explain why the magnetic field induced in a wire moving in a magnetic field must oppose its motion through the field.
7. (a) What are eddy currents? (b) How can they be reduced?
8. (a) What is the principle of the magnetic levitator? (b) Would it work if direct current were used in the coils? Explain.
9. (a) How would you make a coil with a large value of inductance? (b) What one factor would influence the inductance the most?
10. An inductor in a circuit has no emf developed across it. What can be said concerning the current through it?
11. It has been said that the formula representing Lenz's law consists of a single minus sign. Explain what this means.

PROBLEMS

1. An oscillator coil is wound on a glass tube 4 cm in diameter and 20 cm long. How many turns of copper wire must it have to give it an inductance of 250 microhenries?
2. What would the effect be on the inductance of a coil if its diameter were halved?
3. A coil wound on a bar of magnetic material has an inductance of 0.8 henry when it is 30.0 cm long with a 4.0 cm radius. It has 1500 turns of wire. What would its inductance be if its length were changed to 40.0 cm, its radius to 3.0 cm radius, and the number of turns to 75?
4. A round iron bar, 4 cm in diameter and 20 cm long, is wound with copper wire. If the iron has a relative permeability of 10^3, and the inductance is 0.45 henry, how many turns of wire does it have?
5. A solenoid, 2.0 cm in diameter and 50 cm long, has 420 turns of wire. Find its inductance when it has (a) an air core and (b) an iron core of relative permeability 2000.
6. A small solenoid, 1 cm in diameter and 10 cm long, has 500 turns of fine wire. Calculate its inductance when it has (a) an air core and (b) an iron core of relative permeability 180.

7. An inductor develops a back emf of 10 volts when the current through it is changing by 100 amp/sec. What is its inductance?

8. A 10-millihenry inductor develops a back emf of 50 volts. How fast is the current changing in it?

PROJECTS

1. Make an apparatus to demonstrate Lenz's law.
2. Make an apparatus to demonstrate self-induction in a solenoid.
3. Make a levitator as suggested by Fig. C. Plans for a small one are available from the Lawrence Hall of Science, Berkeley, California.

MAGNETISM

Lesson 86 *TRANSFORMERS*

Because of the widespread use of transformers in long-distance power transmission, as well as in telephones, television transmitters and receivers, satellite communications, and the like, it is of interest to consider the elementary principles upon which these instruments operate. A transformer is an electrical device by which the electromotive force of a source of alternating current may be increased or decreased.

The Primary Circuit. To study the actions and principles of a transformer, we must return to the *electromagnet,* treated in Lesson 83. Before an electron current is

started through the coil of an electromagnet, no magnetic field whatever exists. This is illustrated by the diagram in Fig. A. When the switch, K, is first closed, completing the electric circuit, the electron current does not rise immediately to its full value, but requires a certain amount of time to build up (see Fig. B). Starting at zero at the time

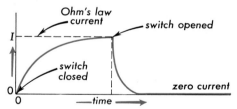

Fig. B. Current-time graph for an electromagnet, as illustrated in Fig. A.

the switch is closed, the current increases rapidly at first, then more slowly, reaching finally its full value, the value given by Ohm's law.

During the time the electron current is increasing, the magnetic induction, B, in

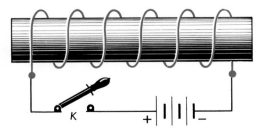

Fig. A. Electromagnet on open circuit. No current and no field.

and around the coil, is increasing, as shown in Fig. C. This field continues to grow in

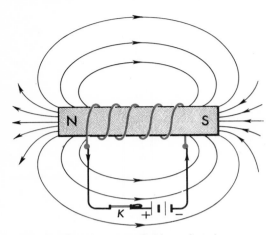

Fig. C. Electromagnet field on closed circuit.

strength until the current reaches its maximum value, whereupon both current and field become constant. In most circuits, this whole process requires but a small fraction of a second. A constant current is indicative, therefore, of a constant unchanging magnetic field.

When the switch is opened, the current will not stop instantly, nor will the surrounding field vanish instantly. The current will decrease with time by forming an electric arc across the opening switch terminals, as shown in the graph of Fig. B. The magnetic induction will decrease accordingly. When the current reaches zero, once more the field will simultaneously vanish as in Fig. A. Thus, by opening and closing a switch, a magnetic field of increasing and decreasing strength is produced.

The Secondary Circuit. If a loop of wire is placed around an electromagnet, as shown in color in Fig. D, and the switch in the circuit is closed and opened as described in the preceding section, an electromotive

force, and hence an electron current, will be induced in the loop. Immediately after the switch has been closed and the current and magnetic induction begin to rise, the total flux through the loop increases and we obtain an induced emf. An induced emf

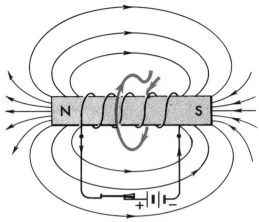

Fig. D. Diagram illustrating an electron current induced in a loop of wire placed in the changing field of an electromagnet.

means that, if the loop ends are connected so as to form a closed circuit, a current will flow in the loop as shown by the arrows in the diagram.

When the electromagnet current reaches a steady state, the field becomes constant. This means that the total flux through the loop is no longer changing and the loop emf has dropped to zero.

If the switch is opened at this time, allowing the electromagnet current to decrease, the magnetic induction will decrease, and the total flux through the loop will fall. This decreasing flux, linking the loop circuit, induces an electron current that is opposite in direction to that shown in the diagram. When the current in the electromagnet winding drops to zero, the field vanishes and so does the induced emf. The properly timed closing and opening of a switch can, therefore, induce one complete cycle of an alternating current in a loop of wire.

To increase the emf in the outside circuit, many loops of wire are usually employed. Such an arrangement becomes similar to that shown in Fig. E and is called an

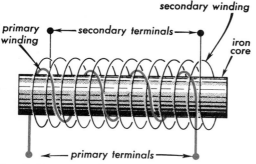

Fig. E. Diagram of an open-core transformer.

open-core transformer. The inside winding, connected to a source of current, is called the *primary* and the outside winding is called the *secondary.* As the magnetic induction increases, the total flux through each loop of the secondary increases, and approximately the same emf is induced in each turn of the secondary coil. Because the turns are all in series with each other, the total emf between the outside ends is the sum of the individual emfs for each turn.

It is customary for both the primary and secondary windings of a transformer to be wound with well-insulated copper wire and for the windings to be electrically insulated from each other.

Alternating Current. It is inconvenient to operate a transformer on a dc supply, because the primary circuit must be rapidly opened and closed by some mechanical means, such as a vibrator.

Rather than use dc, it is convenient and practical to connect the primary winding to

a source of alternating current. In this way, the rapidly increasing and decreasing field induces a corresponding alternating emf in the secondary.

As a consequence, most transformers operate from alternating-current sources, rather than from batteries or dc generators.

Step-up and Step-down Transformer. Nearly all transformers come under one of the two following classes: (a) *step-up,* or (b) *step-down transformers.* As shown in Fig. F, the step-up transformer is one in

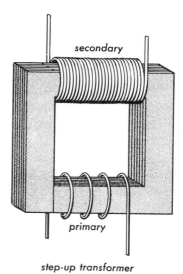

step-up transformer

Fig. F. A step-up transformer with a closed core.

which the secondary winding has more turns of wire than the primary. In the step-down transformer the reverse is true. The importance of this distinction is based upon the general and well-established principle that the ratio of the number of turns of wire in the primary and secondary windings is the same as the ratio of the respective voltages in each. This may be stated as an equation:

no. of primary turns
──────────────────────
no. of secondary turns

$$= \frac{\text{primary voltage}}{\text{secondary voltage}} \quad (1)$$

Thus, if a step-up transformer has 100 turns in the primary and 100,000 turns in the secondary, the voltage delivered at the secondary terminals will be 1000 times the voltage impressed upon the primary. If this same transformer were connected to the ordinary house-lighting circuit of 110 volts ac, the voltage at the secondary terminals would be 110,000 volts ac.

Another type of step-up transformer in common use has a tapped secondary. A tapped secondary is one in which different secondary voltages can be obtained by making connections to different numbers of secondary turns, as shown in Fig. G. If second-

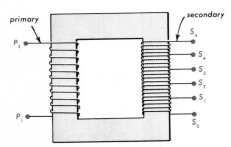

Fig. G. Transformer with a tapped secondary.

ary connections are made to S_0 and S_1, a relatively low voltage is obtained. If the upper connection is shifted to S_2, S_3, etc., more and more secondary turns are included, and the secondary voltage is proportionally larger. The effect is similar in many ways to the potential divider.

A type of step-up transformer of widespread use has two or more independent secondary windings. See Fig. H. Electrically insulated from each other, these secondaries produce their own voltages as given by Eq. (1).

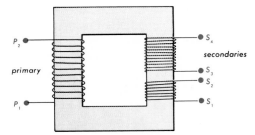

Fig. H. Transformer with two secondaries.

The step-down is just the reverse of the step-up transformer: the secondary voltage is lower than the primary voltage. As an illustration, suppose the primary of a transformer has 2000 turns of fine wire and the secondary has 100 turns. Having a turn ratio of 20 to 1, this transformer connected to the 110-volt ac line will deliver at its secondary a difference of potential of one-twentieth of 110 volts, or 5.5 volts. Such transformers are used in electric welding, for doorbells, for toy electric trains, for lighting the filaments in vacuum tubes, and for other low-voltage applications.

Power. The increase in voltage of an alternating current by means of a step-up transformer appears, at first sight, to be a violation of the law of conservation of energy, *i.e.*, it appears as though a large amount of energy could be obtained at the expenditure of a smaller amount. This is really not the case, for when the voltage is increased, the current is simultaneously decreased by the same proportion.

The power developed in any electric circuit is given by the product of voltage times current:

$$P = VI \quad (2)$$

If V is in volts and I is in amperes, the power, P, is in watts. One thousand watts is called one *kilowatt*.

When, for example, a transformer is used to step up the voltage to 100 times that supplied to the primary, the current in the secondary becomes only one one-hundredth of the current in the primary. In keeping with the law of conservation of energy, therefore, the power supplied at the primary $(V_p I_p)$ is just equal to that delivered at the secondary $(V_s I_s)$. In general, when the voltage is stepped up by a transformer, the current is stepped down by the same proportion.

In practice, this is not exactly true, because a transformer is not quite 100 percent efficient. A small amount of electrical energy is continually expended, principally in the form of heat. In a well-designed trans-

pensable. At a powerhouse in the distant mountains, for example, electric current is generated by huge ac generators at the relatively low voltage of several thousand volts. If an attempt were made to transmit this electrical energy, at a voltage of say 2200 volts, over many miles of wire cable to a distant city, the current would be so large that nearly all of the power would be consumed in heating the power line. The heat generated is, according to Eq. (6) in Lesson 78, proportional to the square of the current: heat energy $= I^2 Rt$.

To avoid large heat losses, transformers at a powerhouse (see Fig. I) step the volt-

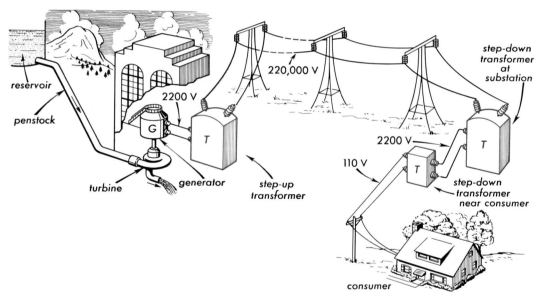

Fig. I. Illustrating the use of transformers in the transmission of electrical energy from the powerhouse in the mountains to the consumer in the distant city.

former such losses do not exceed 2 or 3%, so that a transformer is often considered as almost 100% efficient.

Power Transmission. In the transmission of electrical energy over wires for long distances, transformers are practically indis-

age up to some 220,000 volts before switching the current onto the power line. Because the voltage in the case cited is increased one-hundred fold, the current drops by the same proportion to one one-hundredth. Because the square of 1/100 is 1/10,000, the heat loss along the transmission line is only one ten-thousandth of what it would have been had the transformer not been used.

At the city end of the power line, a transformer substation steps the voltage down to something like its original value of 2200 volts. From there, branch lines distribute the power to various sections of the city where smaller transformers, one near each group of several houses, step it down again to the relatively safe voltage of 110 and 220 volts.

QUESTIONS

1. (a) What is a transformer? (b) What are its three principal components?
2. (a) Can direct current be applied to a transformer? (b) If so, how?
3. What advantages are there in applying an alternating, rather than a direct, current to a transformer?
4. (a) What is a step-up transformer? (b) What is a step-down transformer?
5. If a transformer increases the voltage tenfold, how does the secondary current compare with the primary current?
6. (a) How is the power supplied to a circuit computed? (b) What is a watt? (c) What is a kilowatt?
7. Why are high-voltage transformers used in power transmission?
8. (a) Why are the high voltages from power lines reduced to lower voltages in the city? (b) What kind of transformers are used?
9. What is the relation between transformer voltages and the windings of the primary and secondary coils?
10. Would transformers with identical primary and secondary coils, but constructed as shown in Figs. E and F, have the same voltage? Explain.

PROBLEMS

1. A step-up transformer has 150 turns in the primary coil and 25,000 turns in the secondary coil. If the primary is connected to a 110-volt ac line, find the voltage delivered at the secondary terminals.
2. The primary of a step-up transformer having 125 turns is connected to a house-lighting circuit of 115 volts ac. If the secondary is to deliver 15,000 volts, how many turns must it have?
3. The secondary of a step-down transformer has 25 turns of wire and the primary is connected to a 110-volt ac line. If the secondary is to deliver 2.5 volts at its output terminals, how many turns should the primary have?
4. The primary of a step-down transformer has 600 turns and is connected to a 120-volt ac line. If the secondary is to supply 5 volts at its terminals and an electron current of 3.5 amp, find (a) the number of turns in the secondary and (b) the electron current in the primary.
5. A step-up transformer with 350 turns in the primary is connected to a 120-volt

ac line. The secondary delivers 10,000 volts at its terminals and a current of 40 milliamp. (a) How many turns are in the secondary? (b) What is the current in the primary? (c) What power is drawn from the line?

6. The primary of a step-up transformer is connected to a 110-volt ac line. The secondary with 8600 turns delivers 10,000 volts and a current of 20 milliamp. Calculate (a) the number of turns in the primary and (b) the current drawn from the line.

7. One end of a power transmission line of 6 Ω is connected to a 220-volt line and the other end to a load resistance of 16 Ω. Find the power consumed by (a) the line and (b) the load. (Each of the two wires is 3 Ω.)

8. If by means of transformers the source voltage in Problem 7 is stepped up to 2200 volts and then down to 160 volts at the load, find the power consumed by (a) the line and (b) the load. Assume both transformers to be 100% efficient.

PROJECTS

1. Make an experimental transformer, that is, one whose primary and secondary coils can be changed.
2. Make a labeled collection of a variety of different transformers and their uses. Surplus transformers are often available.

MAGNETISM

Lesson 87 *ALTERNATING CURRENT*

Capacitor Time Constant. When a capacitance, C, is connected in series with

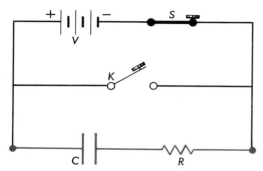

Fig. A. Series circuit containing capacitance and resistance.

a resistance, R, and a battery emf, V (see Fig. A), an electron current flows for a short period of time because it takes time for the plates of the capacitor to acquire charge. The rate at which a capacitor charges depends upon how full it is. The time to fill it completely is infinite. The rate at which a capacitor charges is shown graphically in Fig. B. If now the switch, S, is opened, thus disconnecting the battery, and then the switch, K, is closed, the capacitor will discharge, and again an electron current will flow through R. Because the time it takes to discharge it totally is infinite, it is necessary to choose some ar-

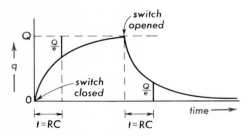

Fig. B. Capacitance time constant.

bitrary criterion to describe how fast the charge and discharge occurs.

The time taken for the charge on the capacitor to reach within $1/e$ of its full charge, Q, while charging, and the time taken to drop to $1/e$ of its full charge while discharging, is called the circuit *time constant:*

$$\text{time constant} = RC \qquad (1)$$

The constant, e, equals 2.718 ($1/e$ = 0.368) and is the base of natural logarithms. The greater the resistance and the larger the capacitance, the greater is the time required to charge or discharge a capacitor. The simplicity of Eq. (1) results from choosing $1/e$ to describe the time for charging.

Inductance Time Constant. When an inductance, L, is connected in series with

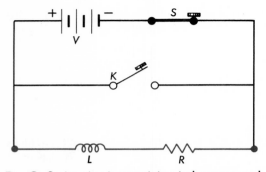

Fig. C. Series circuit containing inductance and resistance.

a resistance, R, and a battery emf, V (see Fig. C), it takes time for the electron current, I, and the accompanying magnetic field to build up to a steady state. When the switch, S, is opened and the switch, K, closed, the field decreases and the electron current falls, approaching zero as t approaches infinity. The time constant of the circuit, that is, the time for the electron current to rise to within $1/e$ of its final value (see Fig. D), is given by—

$$\text{time constant} = \frac{L}{R} \qquad (2)$$

Currents of these types are called *transient currents.*

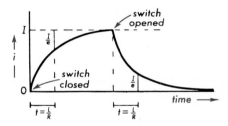

Fig. D. Inductance time constant.

Alternating Voltages. As we have seen in Lesson 51, a sine wave can be generated by a rotating vector. Fig. E shows that the amplitude of the wave at any angle is the height of the vector above the x-axis. This height is just the length of the vector times the sine of its angle ϕ. By plotting the amplitude against ϕ, a graph of a sine wave is formed.

The angle of the vector, as measured from the horizontal axis, is called the *phase* of the wave. This corresponds to various positions along the sine wave and may be measured in either degrees or radians.

If the vector is rotated at a uniform speed, the phase, ϕ, is directly proportional to the time. Thus, the amplitude — time

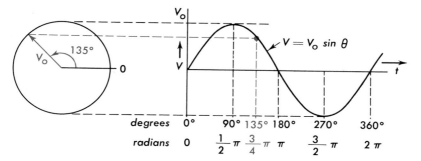

Fig. E. Generation of a sinusoidal wave by projection of a uniformly rotating vector.

graph is also a sine wave. Voltages or currents whose graphs are such sine waves are called *alternating voltages* or *currents*.

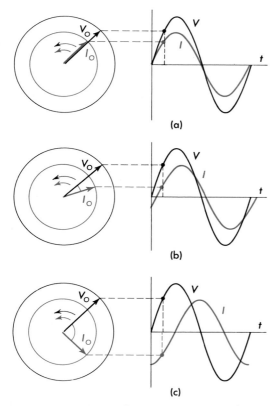

(a)

(b)

(c)

Fig. F. Generation of two sine waves with: (a) no phase difference, (b) phase difference of 20°, (c) phase difference of 90°.

If the alternating voltage, such as that in Fig. E, is applied to a circuit containing resistors, capacitors, inductors, and other such devices, an alternating current will result. However, there will often be a *phase difference* between the voltage and the current. If the current and voltage happen to be in phase ($\Delta\phi = 0$), the wave forms can be represented by two vectors moving together, as shown in Fig. F(a). If the phase difference is not zero, such waves may be represented by two vectors moving at the same speed, but with the fixed-phase angle between them. See Fig. F(b) and F(c). This voltage-current relationship may be simply represented by drawing just the voltage and current vectors alone, with the proper phase angle between them.

All electrical devices connected to a source of alternating emf contain a certain amount of *resistance, inductance,* and *capacitance*. If the total inductance and capacitance of the circuit are small compared to the resistance, Ohm's law can be applied to find the current in the various parts. In this case, the voltage is proportional to the current at every instant of time. See Fig. G(a).

If the inductance and capacitance are not relatively small, they will introduce phase differences, or time lags, between current and voltage, and Ohm's law will

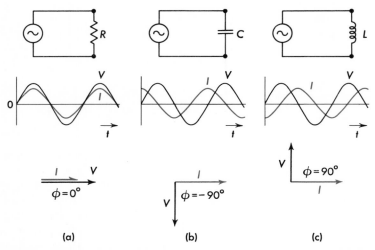

Fig. G. Graph showing the voltage-current relationships across circuit elements in alternating-voltage circuits.

not apply in the ordinary way. See Fig. G(*b*) and (*c*).

Capacitive Reactance. When a capacitor is inserted into a *dc circuit*, the plates charge up and the electron current drops to zero. The capacitor thereafter acts as though it has an infinite resistance. Connected to an alternating emf, however, it may act quite differently. As the frequency, *f*, rises in an *ac circuit*, the resistive effect of a capacitor decreases. The reversing of the emf reverses the flow of electrons to and from the plates of the capacitor, and the alternating flow of charge constitutes an *alternating current*. Because a capacitor differs from a pure resistance in that it stores electrostatic energy, its resistive effect is called *capacitive reactance*, given by—

$$X_C = \frac{1}{2\pi f C} \qquad (3)$$

The voltage across the capacitor does not build up until the current has been flowing for a while. Therefore, the voltage across a capacitor lags after the current.

The phase angle, measured from the current vector, is −90°. See Fig. G(*b*).

Inductive Reactance. Because an emf suddenly applied to an inductance requires a certain time for the electron current to build up to a fixed value, the application of an alternating emf finds that the voltage leads the current across the inductor in its rapid changes and reversals. The phase angle is +90°; see Fig. G(*c*). Furthermore, if the frequency is very high, there is not time enough for the electron current to rise very far from zero toward its Ohm's-law value.

Because the inductance effect reduces the electron current, it may be thought of as something analogous to a resistance. The measure of this effect is called *inductive reactance*, X_L, to distinguish it from a true resistance where electrical energy is converted into heat:

$$X_L = 2\pi f L \qquad (4)$$

where *f* is the frequency in cycles per second, or hertz (Hz).

AC Series Circuit. When an inductance, L, capacitance, C, and a resistance, R, are connected in series to an ac generator, as shown in Fig. H, the electron current in the

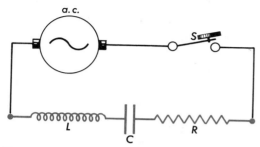

Fig. H. Series circuit containing inductance, capacitance, and resistance.

circuit can be determined by the following equation:

$$I = \frac{V}{\sqrt{R^2 + (X_L - X_C)^2}} \qquad (5)$$

where I and V are the root-mean-square, or rms, of the electron current and voltage, respectively. The quantity $X_L - X_C$ in this equation is often called the *reactance* and is represented by X.

$$X = X_L - X_C$$

so that

$$I = \frac{V}{\sqrt{R^2 + X^2}}$$

The whole denominator is called the *impedance* and is represented by Z:

$$Z = \sqrt{R^2 + (X_L - X_C)^2} \qquad (6)$$

and—

$$I = \frac{V}{Z} \qquad (7)$$

Note the identical form of this last equation to Ohm's law for direct currents. The resistance, R, in Ohm's law has here been replaced by the impedance, Z.

The Vector Impedance Diagram. The relations between R, X_L, and X_C and the

resultant impedance, Z, of a series circuit containing them may be represented graphically by treating all quantities as vectors. As shown in Fig. I, the resistance,

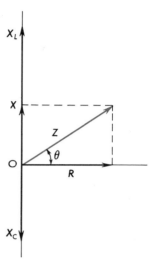

Fig. I. Impedance diagram for ac series circuit.

R, is represented by a vector along the x-axis, the reactances, X_L and X_C, by vectors up and down on the y-axis, and the impedance, Z, as the vector resultant of X and R. In practice, R includes the resistance of the inductance winding, as well as of all the connecting wires of the circuit.

Phase Relations Between I and V. As we have seen, the effect of an inductance and a capacitance on an *ac series circuit* is such as to alter the phase of the electron current, I, with respect to the applied alternating voltage. If the inductive reactance, X_L, is greater than the capacitive reactance, X_C, the impressed voltage will lead the electron current, while if X_C is greater than X_L, the impressed voltage will lag behind the electron current.

The phase angle may be found from the impedance diagram:

$$\tan \phi = \frac{X}{R} \qquad (8)$$

The relation between the voltages, the current, and the impedance diagram may be seen by multiplying each term in the impedance diagram by the current through the series circuit:

$$V_R = IR$$
$$V_C = IX_C$$
$$V_L = IX_L$$
$$V = IZ$$

Fig. J shows how the voltages across each element are related. Because the cur-

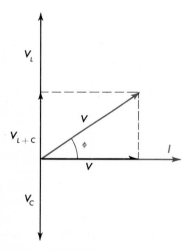

Fig. J. Voltage diagram for ac series circuit.

rent and voltage are in phase across a resistor, the current vector may be placed on the same diagram as shown.

Example. A series circuit contains a 300-Ω resistor, a 5-millihenry inductor, and a 0.01 μF capacitor. If 100 volts is applied at 15 KHz, find (a) the reactance of each element, (b) the total impedance, (c) the phase angle, (d)

the rms current, and (e) the voltage across each element.

Solution. (a) The reactances are —

$$R = 300 \ \Omega$$
$$X_L = 2\pi f L$$
$$= 2\pi \times (15 \times 10^3) \times (5 \times 10^{-3})$$
$$= 471 \ \Omega$$

$$X_C = \frac{1}{2\pi f C}$$

$$= \frac{1}{2\pi \times (15 \times 10^3) \times (0.01 \times 10^{-6})}$$

$$= 1052 \ \Omega$$

(b) The total impedance is given by—

$$Z = \sqrt{R^2 + (X_L - X_C)^2}$$
$$= \sqrt{300^2 + (-581)^2}$$
$$= 657 \ \Omega$$

(c) The phase angle is given by—

$$\tan \phi = \frac{X}{R}$$

$$= \frac{-581}{300} = -1.94$$

$$\phi = -62.7° \text{ (voltage lags the current)}$$

(d) The current is given by—

$$I = \frac{V}{Z}$$

$$= \frac{100}{657}$$

$$= 0.152 \text{ amp (rms)}$$

(e) The voltages are given by—

$$V_R = IR = 0.152 \times 300 = 45.6 \text{ volts}$$
$$V_L = IX_L = 0.152 \times 471 = 71.6 \text{ volts}$$
$$V_C = IX_C = 0.152 \times 1052 = 159.8 \text{ volts}$$

Do these voltages add up to equal the total voltage across the three elements?

QUESTIONS

1. How long would it take to completely charge a capacitor? Explain.
2. (a) What is the dc resistance of a good capacitor? (b) Is this the same as its resistance to the flow of ac? Explain.
3. Will a light go on if it is connected to ac voltage in series with a capacitor? Explain.
4. How could a coil be used to discover whether a source of power were ac or dc?
5. In airplanes, where there are many capacitors and inductors, why is it an advantage to use 400- or 800-Hz ac instead of the 60-Hz ac used on the ground?
6. (a) What is meant by the time constant of a RC circuit. (b) Of a RL circuit?
7. (a) What is inductive reactance? (b) Does it depend upon the frequency of the applied emf? (c) In what units is it measured?
8. (a) What is capacitive reactance? (b) Does it depend on the frequency of the applied emf? (c) In what units is it measured?
9. What is the reactance of a circuit?
10. (a) What is impedance? (b) Upon what circuit factors does it depend? (c) In what units is it measured?
11. What does a vector-impedance diagram illustrate?
12. If the vector impedance of a RLC circuit points down and to the right, what is the relation between the reactances of the inductance and the capacitance in the circuit?
13. Explain how you would use Fig. J. to generate graphical wave-pictures of the voltages and current in a series circuit.

PROBLEMS

1. A 10-megohm resistor is in series with a 20-pF capacitor. What is the time constant?
2. A 20-K (20,000 Ω) resistor is in series with a 3-microhenry inductance. What is the time constant?
3. An inductance of 60 microhenries is connected to a 60-Hz ac line. Calculate the inductive reactance.
4. A capacitance of 250 μF is connected to a 60-Hz ac line. Find the capacitive reactance.
5. An inductance of 240 microhenries is connected to a 500-Hz ac line. Calculate the inductive reactance.
6. A capacitance of 180 μF is connected to a 500-Hz ac line. Find the capacitive reactance.
7. A circuit contains a 10-Ω resistor, a 0.5 μF capacitor and a 0.3 millihenry inductor, in that order, in series. A 10,000-Hz voltage is applied. Draw the circuit and the impedance diagram. Calculate the impedance of each element separately,

the resistor and capacitor together, the capacitor and inductor together, and the whole network. Find the phase angle for each case.

8. What would the impedance of a coil of wire be if the resistance of the coil were 10 Ω and its inductive reactance at a given frequency 25 Ω?

9. What resistance should be used to give a time constant of 1 sec with a 0.25-μF capacitor?

10. What capacitor should be used to give a time constant of 0.1 sec if a 10,000-Ω resistor is to be used?

11. A vacuum tube requiring 6.3 volts and 0.30 amp for its heater is connected to 120 volts ac. A capacitor is used to drop the extra voltage and to prevent burning out the tube. (a) What value capacitor must be used? (b) Is this better than using a dropping resistor? Explain.

PROJECTS

1. Set up an apparatus for measuring the time it takes to charge capacitors through a million or so ohms of resistance.

2. Make a saw-tooth oscillator using a neon-bulb capacitor and resistor in a relaxation circuit. This can be used as a timer.

MAGNETISM

Lesson 88 *RESONANT CIRCUITS*

Power Factor. For direct-current circuits, the power is given by the product $V \times I$ and is measured in *volt-amperes*, or *watts*. In alternating-current circuits, the instantaneous rate at which energy is supplied is equal to the product of the instantaneous voltage and the instantaneous current. Because both of these are sometimes zero, it is clear that the power consumption varies over each cycle and that some sort of average power must be taken.

The power from across a resistor, a resistor and inductance, and a pure inductance is shown in Fig. A. At each point in time, the instantaneous power is found by multiplying the voltage times current. From Fig. A(*a*), we see that the power is always positive or zero, showing that power is expended in a resistor when a current flows through it.

Although power flows in and out of the inductor-resistor combination, there is still a net power flow (see diagram (*b*) in Fig. A). Power also flows in and out of the pure inductance (see diagram (*c*) in Fig. A), but the average power expended is seen to be zero. The inductor, and, similarly, the capacitor will temporarily store energy but will not convert it into heat.

We see then that the expenditure of

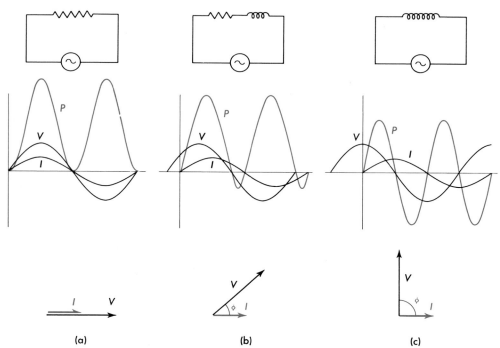

Fig. A. Power in an ac series circuit containing: (a) a resistor, (b) a resistor and an inductance, and (c) a pure inductance.

power depends upon the phase of the current and voltage. The average useful power delivered by any ac circuit is equal to the rms voltage times the rms electron current multiplied by the cosine of the angle of lag:

$$P = VI \cos \phi \qquad (1)$$

The quantity $\cos \phi$ is called the *power factor*. A low power factor in *ac circuits* is to be avoided, because, for a given supply voltage, V, a large current would be needed to transmit appreciable electrical energy. Because heat losses are given by I^2R, currents should be held to a minimum by making the power factor as near unity as possible. This means that ϕ should be as near zero as possible.

Examination of the impedance diagram,

Fig. I in Lesson 87, will show that a circuit containing a relatively large inductive reactance should contain an equally large capacitive reactance to make $\phi = 0$ and the power factor $\cos \phi = 1$.

Example 1. A 60-Ω resistor is connected in series with a 0.25-henry inductor, a 50-μF capacitor, and an ac generator delivering 110 volts (rms) at 60 Hz. Find (a) the reactance, (b) the impedance, (c) the electron current in the circuit, (d) the power factor, and (e) the power.

Solution. By direct substitution in Eqs. (3), (4), (5), and (6) in Lesson 87—

$$X_L = 2\pi fL = 2\pi \times 60 \times 0.25 = 94.25 \ \Omega$$
$$X_C = 1/(2\pi fC)$$
$$= 1/(2\pi \times 60 \times 50 \times 10^{-6})$$
$$= 53.05 \ \Omega$$

(a) $X = X_L - X_C = 94.25 - 53.05$
    $= 41.20\ \Omega$

$Z = \sqrt{R^2 + X^2} = \sqrt{(60)^2 + (41.2)^2}$
  $= 72.8\ \Omega$

(c) $I = V/Z = 110/72.8 = 1.51$ amp

Fig. I in Lesson 87 is drawn to scale as a graphical solution for part of this problem. By direct substitution in Eq. (8) in Lesson 87—

(d) $\tan \phi = \dfrac{X}{R} = \dfrac{41.2}{60} = 0.687$ or $\phi = 34.5°$

$\cos \phi = 0.824 =$ power factor

By Eq. (1)—

(e) $P = VI \cos \phi = 110 \times 1.51 \times 0.824$
    $= 137$ watts

The power expended in a circuit containing inductance and capacitance cannot be measured with a voltmeter and ammeter. To measure power, one uses a *wattmeter*. Such an instrument takes the emf, current, and power factor into account and reads the power directly. By reading a wattmeter, an ammeter, and a voltmeter, the power factor of a circuit can be determined by Eq. (1):

$$\text{power factor} = \cos \phi = \frac{P}{VI} \qquad (2)$$

The Resonant Frequency. By choosing the proper value of capacitance, the net reactance can be made zero, thereby maximizing the power flow. For the case of a fixed inductance and capacitance, however, the power flow can be made a maximum by choosing the proper frequency. Consider a series circuit (Fig. B) containing a small resistance. The impedance is given by—

$$Z = \sqrt{R^2 + X^2} \qquad (3)$$
$$X = X_L - X_C$$
$$= 2\pi f L - \frac{1}{2\pi f C} \qquad (4)$$

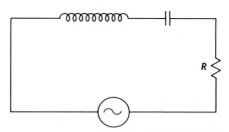

Fig. B. An ac series circuit with a small series resistance.

For a low frequency, the impedance is mainly due to the capacitance. See Fig. C(*a*). As the frequency is increased, X_C decreases while X_L increases. At some frequency, these will be equal, giving zero total reactance:

$$2\pi f L = \frac{1}{2\pi f C} \qquad (5)$$

See Fig. C(*b*). Under these conditions, the impedance is a minimum and is equal to the resistance, and the phase angle is zero:

$$X = 0$$
$$Z = R \qquad (6)$$
$$\phi = 0$$

Such a frequency is called the *resonant frequency* and is obtained by solving Eq. (5) for the frequency:

$$f = \frac{1}{2\pi\sqrt{LC}} \qquad (7)$$

where L is the inductance in henries, C is the capacitance in farads, and f is the number of oscillations per second. As the frequency is increased above the resonant frequency, the reactance will increase owing to the inductance. See Fig. C(*c*).

We see that the current at the resonant frequency is determined purely by the voltage and resistance:

$$I_R = \frac{V}{R} \qquad (8)$$

and can be very large for a small resistance,

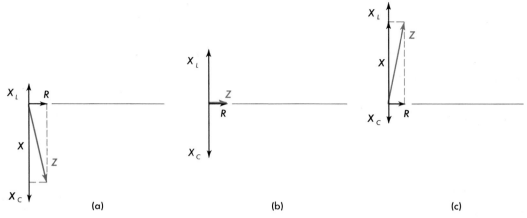

Fig. C. Vector impedance diagram for (a) a low frequency, (b) resonant frequency, and (c) a high frequency.

as seen in Fig. D. Such a circuit is said to have a high *Q-value* or *selectivity*.

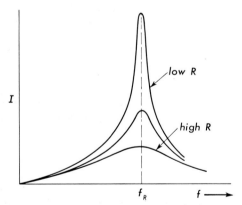

Fig. D. Current-vs-frequency graph for series L-R-C circuit for various resistances.

Example 2. A series circuit contains a 10-μF capacitor, a 4-millihenry inductance and a 5-Ω resistor. If 110 volts ac is applied, find (a) the resonant frequency, (b) the current at resonance, and (c) the voltages across each element.

Solution. The resonant frequency is given by—

(a) $f = \dfrac{1}{2\pi\sqrt{LC}}$

$= 1/2\pi\sqrt{4 \times 10^{-3} \times 10 \times 10^{-6}}$

$= 796 \text{ Hz}$

(b) $I = V/Z$

$= V/R$

$= 110/5 = 22 \text{ amp}$

(c) $V_C = IX_C$

$= I \times \dfrac{1}{2\pi fC}$

$= 22 \times \dfrac{1}{2\pi \times 796 \times 10 \times 10^{-6}}$

$= 440 \text{ volts}$

$V_L = IX_L$

$= I \times 2\pi fL$

$= 22 \times 2\pi \times 796 \times 4 \times 10^{-3}$

$= 440 \text{ volts}$

$V_R = IR$

$= 22 \times 5$

$= 110 \text{ volts}$

Notice that the voltages across the capacitor and the inductor are greater than the total applied voltage. Because of the phase effects, however, the voltage across the capacitor is always opposite, but equal, to that across the inductor. See Fig. E.

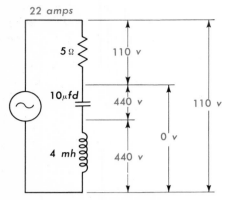

Fig. E. Voltages across elements of a series resonant circuit.

Natural Oscillations. A child on a swing is an illustration of a simple mechanical oscillator whose frequency is determined by

tralize the charge. Owing to the inductance of the coil, the electrons will take a certain time before they will flow freely. Once the current is established, the coil resists the slowing down until the other plate of the capacitor is filled. The process then reverses.

The frequency of natural oscillation is just the resonant frequency, given by Eq. (7), which may be compared with the analogous formula for the frequency of a vibrating spring (see Fig. G):

$$f = \frac{1}{2\pi\sqrt{m/k}} \qquad (9)$$

The mass, m, of the spring is analogous to the inductance, L, for the circuit, and the stiffness, $1/k$, is analogous to the capacitance, C. An increase of the inductance, L,

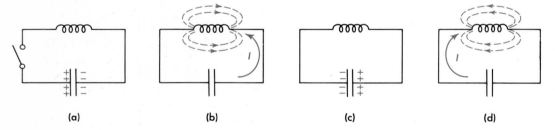

(a)　　　　　　(b)　　　　　　(c)　　　　　　(d)

Fig. F. Circuit showing four parts of a single cycle of natural oscillation.

the length of the supporting ropes. If the swing is given a push, it will continue to oscillate until friction slows it down. It can be kept going indefinitely if, periodically, it is given a push at the proper time to overcome the losses due to friction.

An inductor, connected in parallel to a capacitor, acts in a similar fashion with respect to the flow of electrons. Let us assume that we charge a capacitor by connecting it to a suitable battery. Now let us connect the capacitor to an inductor. See Fig. F. The electrons from one plate of the capacitor will begin to flow to the other plate to neu-

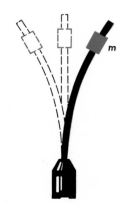

Fig. G. A vibrating spring is like an electrical oscillating circuit.

or capacitance, C, or both, decreases the frequency of the oscillating circuit.

Damped Oscillations. If the series circuit contained no resistance, the oscillations

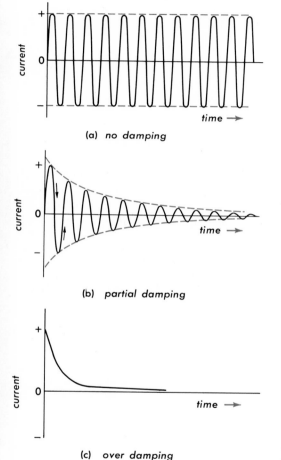

(a) no damping

(b) partial damping

(c) over damping

Fig. H. Current in a naturally oscillating circuit.

would continue indefinitely, as seen in Fig. H(a). An actual circuit, however, will have some resistance (see Fig. I). This resistance

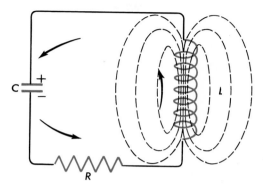

Fig. I. Schematic diagram of a damped oscillating circuit.

will slowly expend the electric energy as heat, just as the vibration amplitude of the spring slowly decreases because of *friction*. A graph showing how current slowly dies out in an electric circuit is given in Fig. H(b). These are called *damped vibrations*, or *damped oscillations*. Such a plot of damped oscillations is a combination of an *alternating* and *transient current*.

If the resistance of the circuit is high, the damping is high, and the current quickly dies out after but few oscillations. If the resistance is low, however, the damping is small, the amplitude decreases slowly, and there are many oscillations. If the resistance is large enough, compared to the reactances, the transient part will dominate, resulting in an *overdamped* circuit. See Fig. H(c).

QUESTIONS

1. (a) What is meant by the power factor? (b) What is its significance?
2. (a) Upon what three factors does the useful power delivered by an ac circuit depend? (b) What is the formula for power? (c) What are the units of power?

3. (a) What is meant by a resonant circuit? (b) How can a nonresonant circuit be made to resonate without changing any components?

4. (a) As the frequency is raised through the resonant frequency, how does the current behave? (b) How does the total reactance behave? (c) How does the impedance behave?

5. (a) What is meant by natural oscillations? (b) Name or describe two different mechanical systems that undergo natural oscillations.

6. What is meant (a) by damping, (b) by overdamping? (c) Describe what would be meant by damping and overdamping in the mechanical systems of the previous question.

7. How much power would be consumed by a good capacitor if it were left connected to a 120-volt ac power line?

8. How much power would a perfect capacitor consume if it were connected to a dc source? Explain.

9. Why doesn't a capacitor use much power when it is in an ac circuit?

10. Which is more apt to use more power, an inductor or a capacitor when connected to an ac source? Explain.

11. In an ac circuit that services many motors, large banks of capacitors are connected across the line. Explain what value this might have.

12. (a) Why can't a voltmeter and ammeter be used to measure the power used by an alternating circuit? (b) Under what conditions might their use be satisfactory?

13. Explain how the electrons oscillate when an inductor is connected in parallel with a capacitor.

14. In an oscillator consisting of an inductor and capacitor in parallel, how could you raise the frequency of oscillation?

15. What could you do to make a parallel inductor-capacitor resonant circuit with the highest Q?

16. Is it possible for the voltage across an element in a series circuit to be greater than the applied voltage? Explain.

17. At what point during oscillation in a resonant circuit is maximum potential energy stored (a) in the capacitor, (b) in the inductor? (c) Explain what is meant by potential energy in these cases.

PROBLEMS

1. A 60-Ω resistor is connected in series with a 0.25-henry inductor, a 50-μF capacitor, and an ac generator delivering 110 volts (rms) at 60 Hz. Find (a) the reactance, (b) the impedance, (c) the electron current in the circuit, (d) the power factor, and (e) the power.

2. An inductance of 60 millihenries is connected in series with a resistance of 90 Ω, a capacitance of 50 μF, and a generator delivering a 60-Hz rms voltage of 30 volts at its terminals. Find (a) the reactance, (b) the impedance, (c) the

rms current, (d) the phase angle, (e) the power factor, and (f) the useful power developed.

3. A 3-millihenry inductor is in series with a 4-μF capacitor. What is the resonant frequency of the circuit?

4. A 60-Hz transmission line has an inductance of 50 millihenry. What capacitance is needed to transmit maximum power?

5. An ammeter reads 2.4 amp in a circuit when connected to a 120-volt ac source. A wattmeter in the same circuit gives a reading of 150 watts. What is the power factor of the circuit?

6. A 2-millihenry inductor is in parallel with a 2-μF capacitor. What is the resonant frequency of the circuit?

7. A series circuit contains a 2-μF capacitor, a 3-millihenry inductance, and a 3-Ω resistor. If 120 volts ac is applied, find (a) the resonant frequency, (b) the current at resonance, and (c) the voltage across each element.

8. An atomic-particle accelerator, called a synchrotron, consists of a large electromagnet wound with large copper wire. The magnetic field is caused to rise and fall at a frequency of 6 Hz by connecting the magnet coil to a 5000-μF capacitor bank and allowing the system to oscillate. What is the inductance of the synchrotron magnet coil?

PROJECT

Develop an apparatus for demonstrating resonance using a suitable coil, capacitor, and 60-Hz alternating current. Show how you can vary the Q with a resistor.

MAGNETISM

Lesson 89 ELECTROMAGNETIC WAVES

The Leyden Jar. A cross section of a Leyden jar of the type invented by the Dutch mathematician, Pieter van Musschenbroek, in 1746, is shown in Fig. A. Two metallic conductors forming the plates of a capacitor are separated by a glass bottle as a dielectric insulator. When such a capacitor is connected to a source of high potential, one plate will become positively charged and the other will be negative. If the source voltage is high enough, an electric spark will jump between the terminals indicating a sudden discharge of the capacitor, and an electron current will surge first one way then the other around the circuit.

This oscillatory current was first postulated by Joseph Henry, then derived from theory by Lord Kelvin, and later proved experimentally by Feddersen. Feddersen, looking at a spark discharge with a rotating mirror, observed that each initial

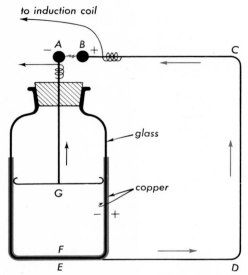

Fig. A. The discharge of a Leyden jar is oscillatory.

breakdown spark was followed by a succession of fainter sparks. The initial spark ionizes the air, making of it a good conductor and of the entire system, *ABCDEFGA*, a complete electrical circuit.

The Oscillatory Circuit. The Leyden-jar circuit in Fig. A contains, in addition to a *capacitance*, an *inductance* and a *resistance* as well. The single loop *FGABCD* and *E* forms practically one turn of a coil. Such a circuit will oscillate at a natural frequency given by Eq. (7) in Lesson 88:

$$f = \frac{1}{2\pi\sqrt{LC}} \qquad (1)$$

Example. A Leyden jar with a small capacitance of 0.01 μF is connected to a single turn of wire (about 6 in. in diameter) having

an inductance of 1 microhenry. Calculate the natural frequency of the circuit.

Solution. Because 1 henry = 10^6 microhenries and 1 farad = 10^6 μF, direct substitution for L and C in Eq. (1) gives—

$$f = \frac{1}{2\pi\sqrt{LC}} = \frac{1}{2\pi\sqrt{1 \times 10^{-6} \times 1 \times 10^{-8}}}$$

$$= 1,590,000 \text{ Hz}$$

or

1.59 MHz

Electrical Resonance. One of the earliest experiments on electrical resonance originated by Sir Oliver Lodge, is known as Lodge's experiment. The phenomenon is analogous to the sympathetic vibrations of two tuning forks, as demonstrated in Lesson 53. Two similar electrical circuits, each containing a Leyden jar of the same capacity, are set up parallel to each other and some 5 to 10 ft apart, as shown in Fig. B. The circuit *T* on the left acts as a

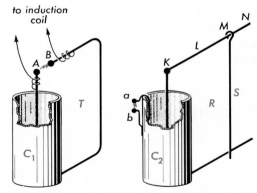

Fig. B. Diagram of experiment demonstrating electrical resonance.

source of oscillations, or as a transmitter, and the circuit *R* on the right acts as a resonator, or receiver.

Connected to a source of high potential, the capacitance C_1 charges and sparks are seen jumping the gap *AB*. If the cross-bar, *S*, of the receiver is moved to position *M*, thus making *R* a duplicate of *T*, resonance will occur and small sparks will also be observed jumping the gap *ab*. If *S* is moved toward *L* or *N*, however, no sparks are observed at *ab*. In other words, to respond to the oscillations, the receiver, *R*, must be tuned to the same frequency of the transmitter, *T*.

With the first rise of the current in the transmitting circuit, a magnetic field develops in and around the loop *T*. With each reversal of the current, the field falls off and builds up again in the opposite direction, just as it does with the primary winding of a transformer. Reaching out in all directions from *T*, this changing field induces a weak but alternating current in *R*. If the natural vibration frequency of *R* is the same as that of the induced current, the amplitude of the oscillations will quickly rise to a high value and cause sparks to jump the gap *ab*.

Hertzian Waves. In 1888 a young German scientist, Heinrich Hertz,* began a series of experiments in which he not only produced and detected electromagnetic waves, but also demonstrated their properties of reflection, refraction, and interference. One of his experimental arrangements is diagramed in Fig. C.

The transmitter consists of two spheres, *Q* and *Q′*, located near the ends of two

* Heinrich Rudolf Hertz (1857-1894), German physicist born at Hamburg, February 22, 1857, studied physics under Helmholtz in Berlin, at whose suggestion he first became interested in Maxwell's electromagnetic theory. His researches with electromagnetic waves that made his name famous were carried out at Karlsruhe Polytechnic between 1885 and 1889. As professor of physics at the University of Bonn, after 1889, he experimented with electrical discharges through gases and narrowly missed the discovery of X-rays described by Röntgen a few years later. By his premature death, science lost one of its most promising disciples.

straight rods, *M* and *N*, separated by a spark gap, *S*. With the two rods connected to transformer *I*, sparks jump across the gap, giving rise to oscillating currents in

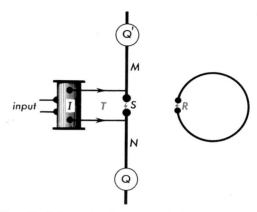

Fig. C. Schematic diagram of the apparatus with which Hertz produced and detected the first radio waves.

MN. That such a generator is an oscillating circuit can be seen from the fact that the spheres form the plates of a capacitor and the rods form the inductance.

The receiver, or detector, consists of a single loop of wire with a tiny spark gap at *R*. This circuit, also, is an oscillating circuit with the spark gap as a capacitance, *C*, and the loop as an inductance, *L*. Tuning the transmitter frequency to that of the receiver is accomplished by sliding the spheres along the rods, resonance being indicated by the appearance of sparks at *R*.

Electromagnetic Waves. To visualize the production of waves by a Hertzian oscillator, consider the schematic diagram in Fig. D. Let the rods, *M* and *N*, and spheres, Q_1 and Q_2 be charged initially as indicated, and consider the electrostatic action of the charges on a small charge, *C*, located some distance away. The negative charge, Q_1, attracts C with a force a and the positive charge, Q_2, repels it with a force b. Because by symmetry these two forces are of equal magnitude, their resultant CE is parallel to MN. If the isolated charge is farther away, as at D, the

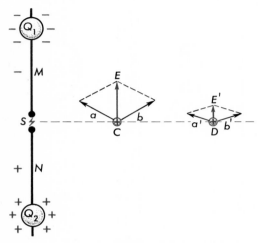

Fig. D. Hertzian dipole.

resultant force is also parallel to MN but weaker. In other words, the electric field, E, at points C and D is upwards and parallel to MN, decreasing in intensity as the distance from the transmitter increases.

Suppose that a spark jumps the gap, S, and oscillation sets in. One-half cycle after the condition shown in Fig. D, electrons have surged across the gap charging Q_1 positively and Q_2 negatively. With reversed charges, the resultant force on C and D will be downwards instead of upwards. Thus, it is seen how oscillations in the transmitter, which constitute a surging of electrons back and forth between M and N, give rise to a periodically reversing electric field at distant points.

In addition to an electric field at C and D, the surging electrons in MN give rise

to a magnetic field as well. When the electron current is downwards (using the conventional left-hand rule), the magnetic induction, B, at C or D is perpendicular to and into the plane of the page; when the electron current is upwards, the magnetic induction is directed out from the page. The surging of the charges, therefore, gives rise to a periodically reversing magnetic induction, the direction of which is at right angles to the electric intensity at the same points.

According to Maxwell's theory, the E and B fields do not appear instantly at distant points; time is required for their propagation. The speed of propagation, according to Maxwell (and this has been confirmed by numerous experiments) is the same as the speed of light. The changing E and B fields at C therefore lag behind the oscillating charges in MN, and those at D lag behind still farther.

Fig. E is a graph of the instantaneous

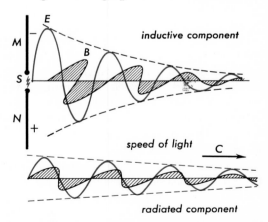

Fig. E. Graph of the electromagnetic waves emitted by a Hertzian dipole.

values of the electric and magnetic fields as they vary with distance from the transmitter. At certain points the fields are a maximum and at other points they are zero. As time goes on, these electric and magnetic waves move away from the transmitter with a speed of 186,300 mi/sec.

The mathematical theory of electromagnetic radiation shows that close to the transmitter, the E and B fields, called the *inductive components,* are 90° out of phase and that their magnitudes fall off very rapidly with distance. Farther out, however, the two get in phase with each other and their amplitudes fall off more slowly as shown in the lower diagram. The latter are called the *radiated components* and are the ones detected at great distances. These waves are used in radio, radar, and television.

QUESTIONS

1. (a) What is a Leyden jar? (b) What is it used for?
2. (a) What is an oscillatory circuit? (b) What are its three principal elements?
3. (a) Upon what does the natural frequency of a circuit depend? (b) What is the formula for the frequency?
4. (a) What is electrical resonance? (b) Under what conditions does it arise?
5. (a) What are Hertzian waves? (b) What is a Hertzian dipole?
6. (a) What are electromagnetic waves? (b) What is their nature? (c) With what speed do they travel?
7. (a) What are damped oscillations? (b) How can damping be reduced?
8. What prevents the oscillations in an oscillatory circuit from going on forever?
9. What will be the effect on the frequency of an oscillatory circuit by (a) making the Leyden jar larger, (b) making the loop of wire smaller?
10. What is the significance of electrical resonance for radio and television receivers?

PROBLEMS

1. Calculate the frequency of an oscillating circuit composed of a 1-μF capacitor and a 1-microhenry inductor.
2. Calculate the frequency and period of an oscillating circuit containing two 3-μF capacitors and an inductance of 3.4 microhenries if all three are connected in parallel.
3. What inductance connected to a capacitor of 0.25 μF will give the circuit a natural frequency of 4 MHz?
4. What capacitance, if connected in parallel to an inductance of 6 microhenries, will give an oscillating circuit a frequency of 250 KHz?
5. Determine the frequency of an oscillating circuit composed of two capacitors and one inductor, all connected in parallel: $C_1 = 2$ μF, $C_2 = 3.5$ μF, and $L = 6.6$ microhenries.
6. Two capacitors of 10 μF each are first connected in series and then the combination is connected across an inductor of 2 microhenries. Calculate the frequency of the oscillating circuit.

7. What capacitance, in parallel with an inductance of 0.1 microhenry, will have a frequency of 1 MHz?

8. A capacitance of 0.1 μF is connected to an inductance of 8×10^{-8} henry. Find (a) the frequency and (b) the wave length of the electromagnetic waves emitted.

9. What capacitance should be used with an inductance of 0.09 microhenry to produce electromagnetic waves having a wave length of 10 cm?

10. What inductance should be used with a capacitance of 0.04 μF to produce electromagnetic waves of wave length 1 m?

PROJECTS

1. Make a small tube transmitter to show production of electromagnetic waves. Show how power can be coupled to a light that has a complete loop connected to it. *The Amateur Radio League Handbook* is an invaluable source of information for this project.

2. Develop an apparatus for demonstrating resonance using a coil, capacitor, and 60-Hz ac.

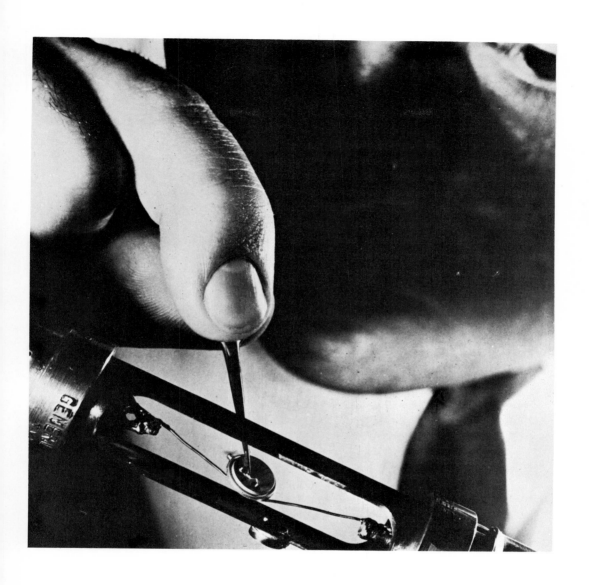

Electronics

The young Italian observed a marked difference between Hertzian oscillations and ordinary alternating currents which had attracted the attention of several experimenters. This was the Marconi explanation:

An analogy may be found in the case of a sound wave in the air. The swing of a bell in a church steeple to and fro will produce no wave and further no sound. But if the rim of the bell is struck with a hammer, it affects the air with sufficient suddenness to make a sound.

Hence it appears absolutely clear to me that there is no Hertzian wave telegraphy without the essential feature for producing Hertzian waves, which is the Hertzian spark.

Orrin E. Dunlap, Jr., *Marconi—The Man and His Wireless*, New York, Macmillan Co., 1937, pp. 10-11.

". . . To Mr. Hertz, of course, belongs the distinction of having discovered the electric waves, and by his experiments he proved that electricity in its progress through space, follows the law of optics," said Signor Marconi. "Many others have made experiments in the same direction as I, but so far no one has obtained such results at anything approaching the distances I have done with these Hertzian waves. Fog has no effect upon the signals, nor has even the most solid substance. The waves can penetrate walls and rocks without being materially affected."

The New York Times, December 15, 1901.

◄ A scientist at RCA Laboratories points a tweezer at a novel FM radio transmitting device so small it is almost invisible. The "transmitter" is a tiny speck of gallium arsenide centered between and attached to the two electrical terminals on the disk-shaped holder above. When plugged into an electrical circuit and activated, the experimental device makes it possible to generate microwaves and to transmit voice and sound. It has been used to broadcast high-quality music across a laboratory room. The device could lead to new types of hand-held, ground-to-ground, and ground-to-air communications systems.

R.C.A. Electronic Age

_tronics" means a _____ and its mass. To oth___ _____ ___cifically refers to a study of electronic devices and circuits. In this section, both topics will be taken up in order to examine the many properties of the electron and its applications.

Electrical Discharge Through a Gas. In 1853, an obscure French scientist by the

diverse sizes, shapes, and colors of glass, and resembling the modern neon and argon signs used in advertising, attracted the attention of physicists in the leading scientific institutions and universities of the world, who purchased many of these "Geissler tubes" and used them for study and lecture demonstrations.

In 1869, Johann W. Hittorf of Munster, with improved vacuum pumps, made sev-

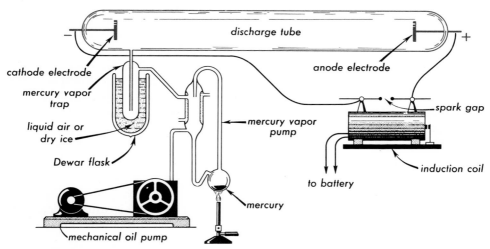

Fig. A. Diagram of a gaseous discharge tube showing the electrical connections, as well as the vacuum pumps and accessories.

name of Masson sent the first electric spark from a high-voltage induction coil through a partially evacuated glass vessel and discovered that instead of the typical spark observed in air the tube was filled with a bright glow.

Several years later, Heinrich Geissler, a German glass blower in Tübingen, developed and began the manufacture of gaseous discharge tubes. These tubes, made in

eral observations on gaseous discharge. These studies were extended several years later by Sir William Crookes.*

In Fig. A, a long glass tube, about 4

* Sir William Crookes (1832-1919), English physicist and chemist, at twenty-two became an assistant at the Radcliff Observatory in Oxford. He was knighted in 1897, received the Order of Merit in 1910, and was president of the Royal Society from 1913 to 1915. He invented and made the first focusing type of X-ray tube.

cm in diameter and 150 cm long, is shown connected to a mercury diffusion pump and a mechanical vacuum pump. The purpose of the pumps is to enable one to observe continuously the changes in the electrical discharge as the air is slowly removed from the tube. The purpose of the *trap* is to freeze out any mercury vapor and prevent it from reaching the discharge. High voltage from an induction coil is shown connected to the two electrodes, one at either end of the tube.

Although an induction coil does not deliver direct current, its characteristics are such that the potentials are higher on half of the alternations than they are on the other half and that the two electrodes act nearly the same as if a high-voltage direct current were used. The negative electrode under these circumstances is called the *cathode* and the positive electrode the *anode*.

As the long tube is slowly pumped out, an emf of 10,000 to 15,000 volts will produce the first discharge when the pressure has dropped to about one one-hundredth of an atmosphere, *i.e.*, at a barometric pressure of about 10 mm of mercury. This first discharge, as illustrated in diagram (*a*) of Fig. B, consists of long thin bluish-colored

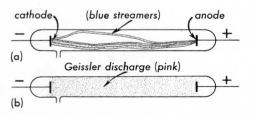

Fig. B. Sketches of the general appearance of a high-voltage electric discharge through rarefied air at various stages of evacuation.

streamers. As the gas pressure drops to about 5 mm of mercury, sometimes called a Geissler-tube vacuum, the discharge

changes to pink and, at the same time, widens until it fills the whole tube as shown in diagram (*b*). At still lower pressures, the discharge patterns change and become fainter until, at a pressure of about 0.01 mm Hg, the gas glow disappears. At this point a new feature appears: the whole glass tube itself glows with a faint greenish light.

Cathode Rays. The green glow in the final stage of the gaseous discharge just described was soon found to be a *fluorescence of the glass produced by invisible rays emanating from the cathode itself*. These *cathode rays*, as they are called, believed by Crookes to be an "ultra gaseous state" and by Hittorf to be a "fourth state" of matter, turn out to be tiny corpuscles that we now call *electrons*. In the relatively free space of a highly evacuated tube, cathode particles, torn loose from the atoms of the cathode, stream down the length of the tube, seldom colliding with a gas molecule until they hit the glass walls.

The first important discovery concerning the nature of cathode rays was that they travel in straight lines. This was first revealed by Hittorf in 1869 by casting shadows of objects placed inside the discharge tube. This is usually demonstrated by a tube of special design as shown in Fig. C.

Where the rays strike the walls of the tube the glass fluoresces green, while in the shadow it remains dark.

That *cathode rays have momentum and energy* was first demonstrated by Crookes in 1870 using a tube of special design as illustrated in Fig. D. Leaving the cathode and acquiring a high speed on their way toward the anode, the rays strike the mica vanes of a small pinwheel and exert a force, causing it to turn and thus roll along a double track toward the anode. When it reaches the end of the track a reversal of

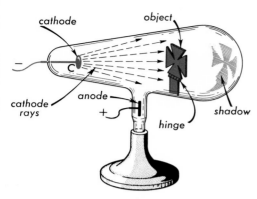

Fig. C. A Crookes' discharge tube for demonstrating that cathode rays travel in straight lines.

the potential, making the right-hand electrode the cathode, will send it rolling back toward the anode, now at the left. From this experiment, Crookes concluded that cathode particles have *momentum* and that, therefore, they have *mass, velocity,* and *kinetic energy,* $\frac{1}{2} mv^2$.

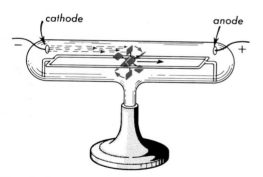

Fig. D. Demonstration of experiment showing that cathode rays have momentum and energy. Cathode rays striking the vanes of a small pin wheel cause it to roll from one end of the tube to the other.

That *cathode rays are negatively charged particles* was first discovered in Paris in 1895 by Jean Perrin. A discharge tube of special design usually used to demonstrate this property is illustrated in

Fig. E. A beam of cathode rays is narrowed down to a thin pencil or ribbon of rays by a narrow slit near the cathode. The path of the rays is made visible by allowing them

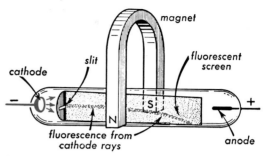

Fig. E. The bending of a beam of cathode rays in the field of a magnet demonstrates that cathode rays are negatively charged particles.

to strike a long strip of metal painted with zinc sulfide, a fluorescent paint. By placing a horseshoe magnet over the outside of the tube, the path of the cathode rays is bent down. If the polarity of the magnet is reversed, the path is bent up. The bending shows the cathode rays to be charged, and the direction of bending shows the kind of charge. Being charged, a stream of particles is like an electric current.

The penetrating power of cathode rays was first demonstrated by Heinrich Hertz and his assistant P. Lenard by passing cathode rays through thin aluminum foils. In air, the rays were found to retain sufficient power to cause fluorescence and phosphorescence.

Millikan's Oil-Drop Experiment. Millikan* began his experiments on the elec-

* Robert Andrews Millikan (1868-1953), American physicist, educated at Oberlin College and Columbia University, was for twenty-five years professor of physics at the University of Chicago and for thirty years president of the Norman Bridge laboratory at the California Institute of Technology in Pasadena. He served during World War I in the research division of the Signal Corps

tronic charge, *e*, in 1906. His apparatus is illustrated by a simple diagram in Fig. F.

of gravity, has a constant velocity. This *terminal velocity*, as it is called, is reached

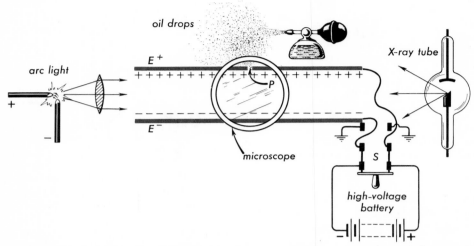

Fig. F. Schematic diagram of Millikan's oil-drop experiment. From this experiment the charge of the electron was determined.

Minute oil drops from an atomizer are sprayed into the region just over the top of one of two circular metal plates, E^+, and, E^-. Shown in cross section, the upper plate is pierced with a tiny pinhole, P, through which an occasional oil drop from the cloud will fall. Once between the plates, such a drop, illuminated by an arc light from the side, is observed by means of a low-powered microscope.

With the switch, S, in the up position, the capacitor plates are grounded so that they are not charged. Under these conditions, the oil drop, falling under the pull

by the drop before it enters the field of view and is of such a value that the downward pull of gravity, F_G, is exactly equalized by the upward resisting force of the air. By measuring this velocity of fall, the force, F_G, can be calculated, and from it the mass of the oil drop determined. The velocity of the drop can be determined by using a stop watch and measuring the time it requires to fall the distance between the two cross hairs illustrated in Fig. G.

As the drop nears the bottom plate, the switch, S, is thrown down, charging the two parallel plates positively and negatively. If the drop has a negative charge, as illustrated in Fig. H, there will be an upward electrostatic force, F_E, acting to propel the drop up across the field of view. The drop will move upward with a constant velocity if F_E is greater than the gravitational force, F_G. Again using the stop watch, this time to measure the velocity of rise, the up-

with the rank of lieutenant colonel. His principal contributions to science have been his measurement of the charge on the electron, his photoelectric determination of the energy in a light quantum, and his precision study of cosmic rays. He was the second American to be awarded the Nobel Prize in physics (1923). He was also awarded the Edison Medal, the Hughes Medal of the Royal Society, the Faraday Medal, and the Mattenci Medal.

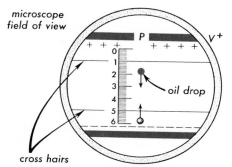

microscope
field of view

cross hairs

Fig. G. Microscope field-of-view showing oil drop.

ward force, F_E, can be calculated. Knowing the force and the voltage on the plates, one can compute the charge on the drop.

As the drop nears the top plate, the switch, S, is thrown up, and the plates are again grounded. Under these conditions, the drop falls again under the pull of gravity alone. Upon the oil drop's nearing

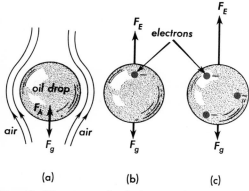

electrons

(a)   (b)   (c)

Fig. H. Diagrams of oil drop with extra electronic charges.

the bottom plate, the switch is again thrown down and the drop rises once more. When this process is repeated, a single drop may be made to move up and down many times across the field of view. Each time it falls, the velocity is measured and the mass of the oil drop computed; while each time it rises, the velocity is measured and the charge computed.

Millikan found that, if X-rays were allowed to pass through the apparatus while an oil drop was being observed, the charge on the drop could be increased or decreased almost at will. One time on rising, the velocity would be low due to a small charge, see diagram (b) in Fig. H, while the next time, the velocity would be high due to a larger charge, as in diagram (c). Regardless of the amount of charge, the rate of fall for a given oil drop is always the same. The reason for this is that the total mass of a number of electrons is so small, compared with the mass of the oil drop, that their added mass is not perceptible.

Millikan, and numerous other experimenters who have repeated these experiments, have found that the charge on a drop is never less than a certain minimum value and is always some integral multiple of this value. In other words, any one electron is like every other electron, each carrying this minimum charge called e:

$$e = -1.6021 \times 10^{-19} \text{ coulomb} \quad (1)$$

This is the most recent and probable value of the electronic charge.

QUESTIONS

1. (a) What is a cathode? (b) What is an anode?
2. What is the general appearance of the first vacuum discharge in a tube when the pressure is lowered?
3. (a) How can it be shown that cathode rays travel in straight lines? (b) Where do cathode rays originate?

4. (a) How can it be shown that cathode rays have momentum and energy? (b) Do cathode rays have mass?

5. How can it be shown (a) that cathode rays are charged particles and (b) that the charge is negative?

6. Do cathode rays have penetrating power?

7. What evidence is there in the experiments described here that cathode rays probably are all alike and have the same mass and charge?

8. (a) Upon what does the color of the light from the positive column of an electrical discharge tube depend? (b) How is this related to present-day "neon signs"?

9. (a) What is Millikan's oil-drop experiment? (b) What was its purpose?

10. (a) What determines the speed of fall of an oil drop? (b) Is the velocity of fall constant?

11. (a) What determines the speed of rise of an oil drop? (b) Is the velocity the same each time the same drop rises?

12. (a) What is determined by the rate of fall of an oil drop? (b) What is determined by the rate of rise?

13. What was the purpose of the X-rays in the oil-drop experiment?

14. What conclusions can be drawn from the Millikan oil-drop experiment?

PROBLEMS

1. (a) How many coulombs of charge does a proton have? (b) How many coulombs of charge does an alpha particle have?

2. How many electrons flow into a toaster that is drawing 4.5 amp?

3. How many electrons are needed to make one unit of electric charge?

4. What is the nuclear charge of the uranium atom in coulombs?

5. A student measured the charge on an oil drop and deduced that the electron charge is -8.0085×10^{-19} coulomb. (a) What mistake did he make? (b) What value should he have obtained?

6. Two measurements of the electronic charge on an oil drop gave charges of -4.8066×10^{-19} coulomb, and -6.4040×10^{-19} coulomb, respectively. What value of the electronic charge should be inferred?

7. A measurement of the charge on an oil drop gave a value of -19.2192 ± 0.0048, where the number following the plus-or-minus sign represents the estimated error of the experiment. (a) What value of the electronic charge, along with its error, should be inferred? (b) Is this value consistent with its assigned error (compare with Eq. 1)? Explain.

PROJECTS

1. Make a collection of a variety of gas-discharge tubes, arranged so they can be exhibited with no danger from the high voltages needed to display them.

2. Measure the charge on an electron using recently developed student equipment that simplifies the procedure over that used by Millikan.

ELECTRONICS

Lesson 91 *ELECTRONIC CHARGE-TO-MASS RATIO*

When, in 1895, it was discovered that cathode rays were negatively charged particles, the question immediately arose as to whether or not they were all alike. It was clear from the beginning that two things would have to be done: one was to measure the amount of charge on the particles and the other was to measure the particles' mass.

Although the first attempts to measure the electronic charge and mass were not entirely successful, J. J. Thomson* did succeed, in 1897, in determining the velocity of the rays and in measuring the ratio between their charge and mass.

The discharge tube designed for these experiments is shown in Fig. A. Cathode rays, originating at the left-hand electrode and limited to a thin pencil of rays by two pinholes in diaphragms DD, are made to pass between two parallel metal plates and between the magnetic field of two external solenoids to a fluorescent screen at the far end.

* Sir Joseph John Thomson (1856-1940), English physicist, was educated at Owens College, Manchester, and at Trinity College, Cambridge. He was appointed Cavendish professor at Cambridge in 1884 and professor of physics at the Royal Institution, London, in 1905. He was awarded the Nobel Prize in physics in 1906, was knighted in 1908, and elected to the presidency of the Royal Society in 1915. He became master of Trinity College in 1918 and helped to develop at Cambridge a great research laboratory attracting scientific workers from all over the world.

When the two metal plates, P, are connected to a high potential, the particles experience a downward force and their path curves to strike the screen at N. Without a charge on the plates, the beam passes straight through undeviated and strikes the screen at S.

When the magnetic field alone is applied, so that the magnetic lines are perpendicular to the plane of the page, the path of the rays curves upward to strike the fluorescent screen at some point M. If both the electric field and the magnetic field are applied simultaneously, a proper adjustment of the strength of either field can be made so that the deflection downward by the one is exactly counteracted by the deflection of the other upward. When this condition is attained a measurement of the magnetic induction, B, and the electric intensity, E, permits a calculation of the velocity of cathode rays.

Deflection in an Electric Field. In Lesson 72, it is shown that, if e is the charge on a body located in an electric field of strength E, the force exerted on the particle is given by—

$$F_E = eE \qquad (1)$$

As a charged particle like an electron enters the electric field between two charged plates, as shown in Fig. B, this force acts straight downward, parallel to the field lines

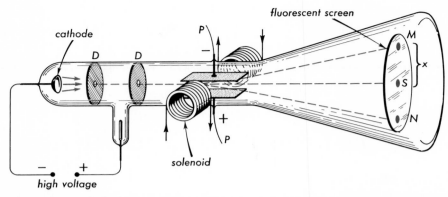

Fig. A. Diagram of discharge tube used by J. J. Thomson to measure the velocity of cathode rays.

at all points. The net result is that the particle traverses a parabolic path in much the same way that a projectile follows a parabolic path in the earth's gravitational field.

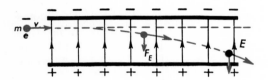

Fig. B. Electrons in a uniform electric field, E, follow a parabolic path.

Deflection in a Magnetic Field. In Lesson 80, it is shown that, if e is the charge on a body moving through a magnetic field, the force acting upon it is given by—

$$F_B = evB \qquad (2)$$

Because this force is always at right angles to both the magnetic induction, B, and the direction of motion, v, the particle will traverse a circular path, as shown in Fig. C.

Electron Velocity. When both the electric and magnetic fields act on the stream of electrons, as in Thomson's experiment, Fig. A, the two opposing forces are adjusted until the beam travels straight through. Under

these conditions the two forces, F_E and F_B, are equal in magnitude, and we can write—

$$eE = evB$$

or

$$E = vB$$

from which—

$$v = \frac{E}{B} \qquad (3)$$

where E is in volts per meter, B is in newtons per ampere-meter, and v is in meters per second. Inserting the known values of

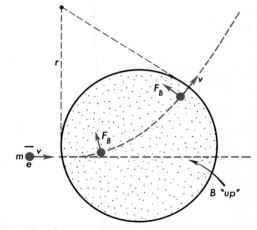

Fig. C. Electrons in a uniform magnetic field, B, follow a circular path.

E and B, the velocity v can be calculated. Thomson's early results showed that cathode rays travel with a speed of several thousand miles per second, about one-fifth the velocity of light. Furthermore, the velocity is not always the same, but depends upon the voltage applied between the anode and cathode. By increasing this voltage, the velocity of the rays is increased.

It is of interest to point out here that the picture tubes used for television receivers are quite similar in shape and principle to J. J. Thomson's cathode-ray tube of Fig. A.

The Ratio of Charge to Mass. Having found the velocity of electrons for a particular applied high voltage, Thomson next proceeded to measure the deflection of the beam produced by the magnetic field alone and to calculate the radius, r, of the beam's path. See Fig. C.

The force F_B is simply the centripetal force, and we can make use of the mechanics relation for centripetal force and write—

$$F_B = m \frac{v^2}{r} \qquad (4)$$

or—

$$evB = m \frac{v^2}{r} \qquad (5)$$

The electron charge-to-mass ratio is, therefore, given by—

$$\frac{e}{m} = \frac{v}{Br} \qquad (6)$$

Upon substitution of the velocity, v, the magnetic induction, B, and the radius, r (all measurable quantities), Thomson found a value for the ratio e/m.

This ratio is called the *electronic charge-to-mass ratio*. The most probable value of this important constant for electrons is—

$$\frac{e}{m} = 1.7588 \times 10^{11} \frac{\text{coulombs}}{\text{Kg}} \qquad (7)$$

Such a large number means that the mass of an electron in Kg is extremely small as compared with the charge it carries in coulombs.

The Mass of the Electron. From Millikan's determination of the charge on the electron and Thomson's measurement of e/m, the mass of the electron can be calculated by dividing one value by the other. Using the most accurately known values for both e and e/m, we obtain—

$$m = \frac{e}{e/m} = \frac{1.6021 \times 10^{-19} \text{ coulomb}}{1.7588 \times 10^{11} \text{ coulombs/Kg}}$$

$$m = 9.1091 \times 10^{-31} \text{ Kg} \qquad (8)$$

This mass is unbelievably small, yet its value has been determined many times and by many experimenters, and it is always the same.*

* For a more complete and elementary treatment of these early experiments see "Electrons + and —," by R. A. Millikan, University of Chicago Press.

QUESTIONS

1. What is the path taken by a charged particle in traversing a magnetic field at right angles to B?

2. What is the path taken by an electron as the result of entering a uniform electric field perpendicular to the electric lines of force?

3. What was the approximate speed of the cathode rays in J. J. Thomson's experiment?

4. (a) How is the mass of the electron determined? (b) Why is it done in such an indirect way?

5. (a) Is it easy to measure the velocity of electrons? (b) What is the method used?

6. What conclusions can be drawn from J. J. Thomson's experiment?

7. Why do we believe that electrons, from whatever source, are identical?

8. (a) What determines the velocity of the electrons in the tube used by J. J. Thomson? (b) How could he change their velocity?

PROBLEMS

1. How many electrons would it take to equal a mass of 1 gm?

2. Suppose you had a mole of water (18.0 gm). (a) How many electrons would there be in this much water? (b) How much would they weigh?

3. Electrons with a velocity of one-tenth the velocity of light enter a uniform magnetic field at right angles to the magnetic induction. What will be the radius of their circular path if $B = 2.0 \times 10^{-3}$ newton/amp-m?

4. Electrons, entering a uniform magnetic field in a direction at right angles to the lines of induction where $B = 4 \times 10^{-4}$ newton/amp-m, have a velocity of 6.5×10^8 cm/sec. Calculate the radius of their circular path.

5. In J. J. Thomson's experiment, a magnetic induction field of 1.9×10^{-2} newton/amp-m is employed. If electrons entering this field have a velocity of 2×10^9 cm/sec, what potential difference applied to the parallel plates will keep their path straight? Assume the plates to be 0.5 cm apart.

6. Electrons, moving in a uniform magnetic field where $B = 1 \times 10^{-3}$ newton/amp-m, follow a circular path of 46.5-cm radius. Calculate their velocity.

7. Electrons, moving in a uniform magnetic field where $B = 4.5 \times 10^{-4}$ newton/amp-m, follow a circular path of 20-cm radius. Find their velocity.

8. Electrons are injected with a speed of 5×10^6 m/sec into a uniform magnetic field at right angles to the lines of induction. If the flux density is 2×10^{-3} newton/amp-m, find the diameter of their circular path.

9. If a beam of electrons with a speed of 3×10^7 m/sec enters a uniform magnetic field at right angles to B and describes a circular path of 10-cm radius, what is the value of B?

10. A 100-volt battery is connected to two parallel metal plates 15 cm long and 2 cm apart. If electrons enter this field from one end, moving with a constant velocity of 3×10^7 m/sec, how far will they be deviated from their original straight-line path when they reach the other end?

PROJECT

Using a three- or five-inch cathode-ray tube and a pair of Helmholz coils, measure the e/m ratio for electrons.

ELECTRONICS

Lesson 92 *ELECTRON OPTICS*

A remarkable similarity exists between optical systems of prisms and lenses as they act upon light rays and between electric and magnetic fields as they act upon streams of electrons. It is the purpose of this lesson to consider some of these similarities and to treat several practical applications of *electron optics*.

An Electron Accelerator. A schematic diagram of an electron accelerator is shown in Fig. A. The source of electrons is a fila-

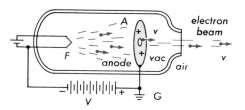

Fig. A. Electrons are accelerated by an applied potential, V.

ment, F. The filament is connected to the negative terminal and the circular disk at the center to the positive terminal of a high-voltage battery, V. Starting essentially from rest at the filament, the electrons are accelerated along the electric lines of force, acquiring a velocity v at the anode, A.

By connecting the + terminal to the ground, the anode is brought to the potential of the surrounding walls of the room and the electrons are not attracted back toward A, but continue on with constant velocity. With a thin aluminum foil at the end and a high applied voltage, V, electrons may be projected into the air beyond.

One result of J. J. Thomson's experiments with cathode rays was the discovery that the velocity of electrons depends upon the potential applied between the anode and the filament. The higher the voltage, the higher is the electron velocity.

We have seen in Lesson 71 that, if the difference of potential between two terminals is V, the work done on each charge e in going from one to the other is given by Ve. Because this work is converted into kinetic energy by giving electrons a velocity, v, we can write—

$$Ve = \tfrac{1}{2}m_0v^2 \qquad (1)$$

Usually, V is in volts, m_0 (the rest mass of the electron) is in Kg, v is in meters per second, and e is in coulombs.

Example. Calculate the velocity of electrons accelerated by a potential of 10,000 volts. (The electronic charge e = 1.60×10^{-19} coulomb, and $m_0 = 9 \times 10^{-31}$ Kg.)

Solution. Direct substitution in the above equation gives—

$$10,000 \times 1.6 \times 10^{-19} = \tfrac{1}{2}(9 \times 10^{-31}) \times v^2$$

from which—

$$v = \sqrt{\frac{10,000 \times 1.6 \times 10^{-19} \times 2}{9 \times 10^{-31}}}$$

$$= 0.6 \times 10^8 \text{ m/sec}$$

This is just one-fifth the velocity of light. (Velocity of light: c = 3×10^8 m/sec.)

Refraction of Electrons. When a moving electron, entering an electric field, makes an angle with the electric lines of force, it is bent as shown in Fig. B. Consideration of the x- and y-velocity components reveals

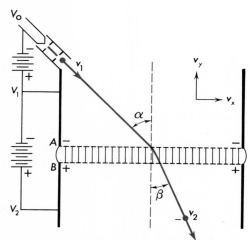

Fig. B. Refraction of electrons.

that v_{2y} is greater than v_{1y}, because the electric field accelerates the y-component. Because there is no force acting in the x-direction—

$$v_{1x} = v_{2x}$$

To relate the velocities with the corresponding angles, we note that—

$$\frac{\sin \alpha}{\sin \beta} = \frac{v_{1x}/v_1}{v_{2x}/v_2}$$

which reduces to—

$$\frac{\sin \alpha}{\sin \beta} = \frac{v_2}{v_1} \qquad (2)$$

which is known as Bethe's law of refraction.

This relation is observed to be very similar to Snell's law of refraction in optics (see Fig. C):

$$\frac{\sin i}{\sin r} = \frac{v_1}{v_2}$$

Note the reverse order of the velocities v_1 and v_2. When a ray of light enters a more dense medium like glass, it is slowed down and, at the same time, bent toward the normal. Electrons, on the other hand, are deflected toward the normal when, in crossing a potential layer, they are speeded up.

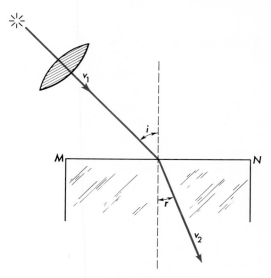

Fig. C. Refraction of light.

If the grid potentials are reversed, the electrons will be retarded in crossing the potential layer and they will be deflected away from the normal. In other words, *reverse the direction of the electrons, keeping their speed the same, and they will retrace their paths exactly.* Such a behavior is analogous to the very useful principle in geometrical optics that *all light rays are retraceable.*

To carry the refraction analogy a little further, consider the bending of electron paths by electrically charged bodies, as shown in Fig. D. Attraction by the posi-

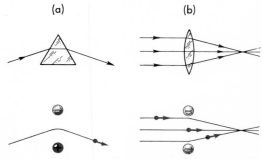

Fig. D. Comparison of light optics with electron optics.

tively charged wire and repulsion by the negative produces a prism-like action in case (*a*). A negatively charged metal ring produces a converging lens-like action in case (*b*).

Electron Lenses. An electron lens, known as a double-aperture system, is shown in Fig. E and is to be compared in

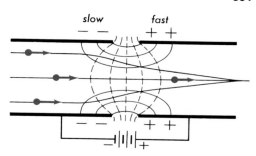

Fig. F. Symmetrical electron lens.

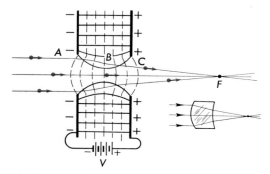

Fig. E. Double-aperture electron lens and its optical analog.

its action to parallel rays of light incident on a converging glass lens as shown at the lower right. While both are converging systems, the essential difference between the two is that, whereas light rays are bent only at the two surfaces, electrons are refracted continuously as they pass through the electric field between the two coaxial disks.

If the electrons are reversed in direction on the right, they will retrace their paths and emerge parallel at the left; but if the electric field is reversed in direction, the electron paths will not be the same, but the system will still act as a converging lens.

A second type of electron lens, known as a double-cylinder system, is shown in Fig. F. In passing through the potential gap, the electric field has a converging action for the first half of the distance and a diverging action during the second half. Because they spend a greater time in the first half of the

converging field and because the force on a charged particle is independent of velocity, the impulse (force × time) is greater for the convergence interval than it is for the divergence interval.

By making the second cylinder larger than the first, as in Fig. G, the electric lines

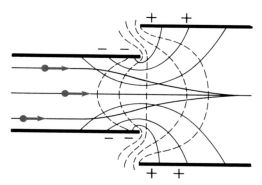

Fig. G. Asymmetrical electron lens.

of force spread out more in the second cylinder. Such spreading weakens the field in the larger cylinder and reduces the divergent action to bring the electrons to a shorter focus.

An Electron Gun. A narrow beam of high-speed electrons, all having as nearly as possible the same velocity, has many practical applications in the field of electronics and atomic research. A device for producing such beams is based on the principle of the electron accelerator and is called an *electron gun* (see Fig. H).

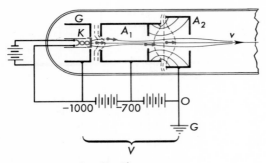

Fig. H. Electron gun.

Electrons from a small filament-heated cathode, *K*, are accelerated by a difference of potential, *V*, applied to the cylinders of an electrostatic lens system, A_1 and A_2. The purpose of the guard ring maintained at the potential of the cathode is to improve the properties of the lens action of the first

straighten the beam out into a narrow pencil. The velocity of the emergent beam is given by Eq. (1), where *V* is the over-all voltage from cathode *K* to anode A_2.

One of the simplest applications of an electron gun is to be found in every *cathode-ray oscilloscope*, an instrument whose purpose it is to reveal the detailed variations in rapidly changing electric currents, potentials, or pulses. Because of its importance in research, television, and radar, the oscilloscope will be studied separately in detail in Lesson 97.

Magnetic Lenses. When electrons cross a magnetic field and their paths make an angle with the magnetic lines, they are deflected in spiral-like paths, which, if properly controlled, may bring them to a focus. Such focusing properties of magnetic fields, illustrated by the cross section of a flat coil in Fig. I, were first demonstrated and

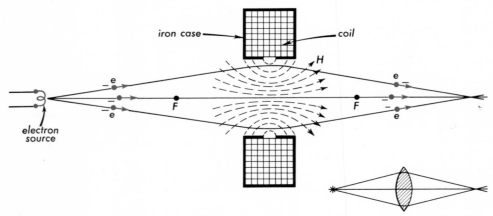

Fig. I. Magnetic lens for electrons. (Optical analog, lower right.)

aperture and, thereby, collect a maximum number of emitted electrons into the collimated beam.

The function of the second lens is to converge the bundle toward a focus and then introduce enough divergence to

proved mathematically by Busch in 1926. It can be shown that the focal length, *f*, of such a lens, the magnetic induction, *B*, and the electron velocity, *v*, fit into well-known formulas in optics.

By encasing a flat coil in a hollow iron

ring, the magnetic field becomes more concentrated and the refraction of electrons becomes more abrupt as they pass through the field. As a consequence, the refraction more nearly resembles that of optical lenses. Still greater concentration is brought about by providing a small, narrow gap on the inside of the iron casing as shown in the diagram.

Electron Microscope. The electron microscope, like the optical microscope, is an instrument used principally in the research laboratory for magnifying small objects to such an extent that their minutest parts may be observed and studied in detail.

Like the optical microscope, it contains two principal lens elements: an objective lens for the initial magnification and an ocular lens for the final magnification.

The importance of this device in the field of medical and biological research cannot be overestimated. To illustrate, many viruses known to medical science as being responsible for certain human diseases lie beyond the range of the optical microscope. With the electron microscope, magnifications of from 10 to 100 times that of the finest optical microscopes make many of these viruses and some of their detailed structure observable. While the highest magnification obtained with the best optical microscope is about 2000X, electron microscopes have already been made that give magnifications as high as 100,000X.

QUESTIONS

1. (a) What is Bethe's law? (b) In what way is it like Snell's law in optics? (c) In what way is it different?
2. What kind of electric field will deviate an electron beam the way a glass prism deviates a light beam?
3. (a) What are electron lenses? (b) How are they made?
4. (a) What is an electron gun? (b) What can it be used for? (c) Does it employ electron lenses?
5. (a) What is a cathode-ray oscilloscope? (b) What is its purpose?
6. What are the principles of a magnetic lens?
7. (a) What is an electron microscope? (b) Is it capable of magnifying very small objects?
8. Can you think of some practical application for an electron gun other than its use in an oscilloscope?
9. What would be meant by the "index of refraction" as it applies to an electric-potential gap?
10. In an electron accelerator, how can the velocity of the electrons produced be varied easily?
11. Could electrons be made to go faster than the speed of light? Explain.
12. (a) In what way do moving electrons act like like rays? (b) In what way do they behave differently?
13. Suppose the electrons in Fig. I went through the lens backward. What would happen?

14. Why is the electron microscope better for some purposes than the optical one?
15. An electron microscope operates in a vacuum. Why is this necessary?
16. How is it possible to slow down electrons in a vacuum tube after they have been accelerated?

PROBLEMS

1. Make a diagram of an electron gun, using two hollow tubes of the same diameter. Show the electric field and the paths of electrons in passing through.
2. (a) Make a diagram of an electron gun, using two hollow tubes of different diameter. Show the electric field and electron paths. (b) Reverse the potentials and assume a parallel beam again coming in from the left.
3. Make a diagram of an electron gun. Label the principal elements. Briefly describe its action.
4. Make a diagram of your idea of an electron microscope. Label the principal elements.
5. An electron leaves the high-voltage end of a 1-million-volt Van de Graaff generator. What is its kinetic energy when it reaches the grounded end?
6. An electron leaves a charged sphere at −2000 volts and is attracted to a charged sphere at +4000 volts. What velocity will it attain?
7. How fast are the electrons moving just before striking a television screen if the accelerating voltage is 18,000 volts?
8. In vacuum tubes, the accelerating voltage used is in the order of 180 volts. What velocity do electrons attain in these tubes?
9. A beam of electrons enters an electric field at an angle of 20°. At what angle will it leave if its velocity is increased 50%?
10. A beam of electrons enters an electric field normally. Its velocity is doubled by the field. At what angle will it leave?
11. A beam of electrons makes an angle of 35° with an electric field. After leaving, its angle is 50°. What is the ratio of its entering velocity to its emerging velocity?

PROJECTS

1. Make a collection of the latest photographs made with an electron microscope. Correlate these with recent advances in biology and medicine.
2. Very carefully break the glass envelope of a small cathode-ray tube. This should be done under supervision, because on shattering, glass may fly in all directions with considerable velocity. Dissect the electron gun and mount the parts.

ELECTRONICS

Lesson 93 **VACUUM-TUBE RECTIFIERS**

Thermionic Emission. When any substance is heated to incandescence in a vacuum, it not only gives off visible light radiation, it also emits electrons as well. Such action is illustrated in Fig. A and is called *thermionic emission.*

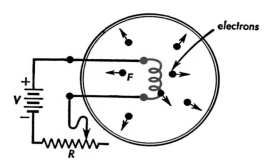

Fig. A. Thermionic emission.

The thermal emission of electrons by a hot tungsten filament, F, heated to incandescence by the current from a battery, is analogous to the steam boiling off from a tea kettle. The higher the current, the higher is the surface temperature of the metal and the greater are the numbers of electrons emitted. The surface temperature required for the copious emission of electrons is greater for some materials than for others.

Rectifiers. Electronic devices generally require direct current for their proper operation. With few exceptions, however, most electrical mains supply alternating current. We will now see how it is possible to convert ac to dc. The process is called *rectification.*

The Vacuum-tube Rectifier. While the great American inventor, Thomas A. Edison, was striving by a process of trial and error to produce a satisfactory electric light bulb, he made an accidental discovery, the importance of which was first recognized and used successfully by Sir John Fleming. Now called a vacuum-tube rectifier or diode, the Fleming "valve" was used in nearly every radio and television transmitter and receiver to change ac to dc.

The Fleming valve, as shown in Fig. B,

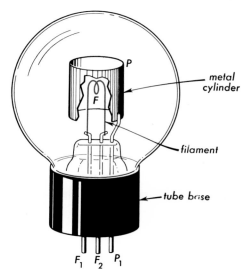

Fig. B. Diagram of a Fleming valve, or rectifier tube. Such tubes are now called diodes.

consists of a highly evacuated glass bulb containing a wire filament that is heated electrically to incandescence. Surrounding the filament and connected to the outside through the tube base and a prong, P_1, is a cylindrical metal plate, P. When the filament is heated to incandescence, it gives off large quantities of electrons by thermionic emission.

The principal action of the *filament* and *plate* is explained by means of a typical electric circuit shown schematically in Fig. C. The circuit consists of a *transformer*

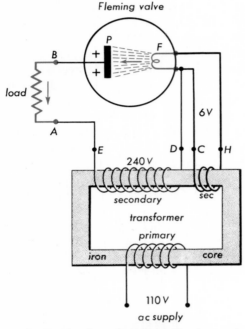

Fig. C. Circuit diagram of a Fleming valve rectifier.

having *two secondary windings*, a *Fleming valve*, and a *load*. The latter, shown as a resistance, represents any electrical device requiring unidirectional current for its operation. With an alternating current of 110 volts supplied to the primary, a high voltage, 240 volts for example, is delivered by one secondary to the terminals *ED* and a low voltage of 6 volts ac is delivered by the other secondary to the terminals *CH*. The latter, called the *filament winding*, is for the purpose of heating the filament.

When for a fraction of a second the plate, P, of the tube is positively charged and the filament, F, is negatively charged, the electrons from F are attracted to the plate P and constitute a current flowing across the vacuum space, PF, and through the load from B to A. One-half cycle later, when the potential is reversed and P becomes negatively charged and F positively charged, the electrons from F are repelled by P, and very little current flows.

The emfs in each part of the rectifier circuit are shown by graphs in Fig. D: the

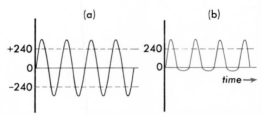

Fig. D. Alternating current as rectified by a Fleming valve, or diode.

secondary emf of 240 volts in (*a*) and the *rectified*, or *pulsating emf*, through the load *AB* in (*b*).

Full-wave Rectifier. A full-wave rectifier tube, sometimes called a *duo-diode*, is essentially a double Fleming valve with two plates and two filaments. (See Fig. E.) The two prongs F_1 and F_2 in the base are connected to both filaments in series while the prongs P_1 and P_2 are connected one to each plate.

A schematic diagram of a rectifier circuit employing such a tube is shown in Fig. F. Here, an iron-core transformer with one primary and two secondary windings is used, differing from the single-phase rectifier in Fig. C in that the center of the secondary high-voltage winding is now connected to the load. *CJ* is the filament

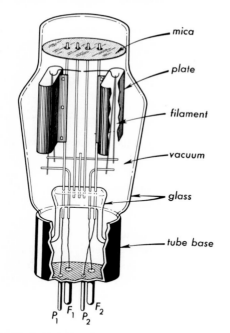

Fig. E. Drawing of a full-wave rectifier tube.

P_2 is +, electrons from the filament are attracted to P_2.

In the first instance, a current flows around the circuit $F_1P_1GEABHF_1$, and in the second it flows around the circuit $F_2P_2DEABHJCF_2$. In each case, the current has gone through the load, AB, in the same direction and has pulsating characteristics, as shown in Fig. G(a).

A Filter Circuit. If such a pulsating current were used to supply the dc needed in every radio receiver, a loud objectionable hum with a frequency of 120 Hz would be heard. To make this current approach a steady, smooth dc, as illustrated by the straight line in the same graph, and thus eliminate the hum, a *filter circuit*, as shown in Fig. H, is used. The terminals A and B are connected to and replace the load, AB, in Fig. F. K is an iron-core inductance, and C_1 and C_2 are capacitors of large capacitance.

The action of the filter circuit relies on the fact that changes in current through the inductance are inhibited by the induced back emf. Therefore, the rectifier output

winding and supplies current to both filaments (shown as one bent wire), while GED is the high-voltage winding. The latter supplies an alternating potential to the

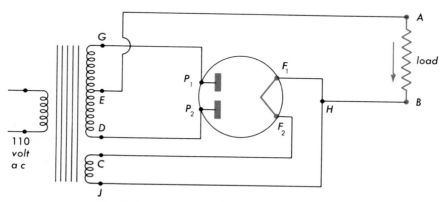

Fig. F. Diagram for a full-wave rectifier circuit.

plates so that when P_1 is + and P_2 is −, electrons from the filament are attracted to P_1, and when a moment later P_1 is − and

deposits charge in the capacitor C at a variable rate, whereas the charge is removed from C through K at a relatively

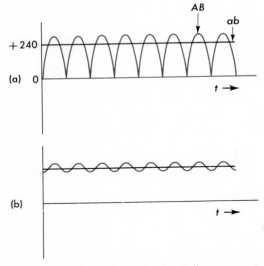

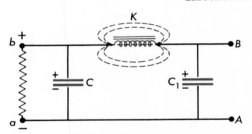

Fig. H. Electrical filter circuit for "smoothing out" pulsating direct current.

Fig. G. Rectified voltage from a full-wave rectifier circuit: (a) before filter, (b) after filter.

steady rate. The capacitor C_1 serves to keep the voltage across AB approximately constant.

Moderate capacities and self-inductances will not filter perfectly, but will leave a voltage ripple, as shown in Fig. G(b). Large capacities and large self-inductance deliver more constant voltage.

QUESTIONS

1. (a) What is a rectifier? (b) Why are rectifiers important?
2. Modern tubes give off very little light compared to those of forty years ago. Why is this so?
3. The plate of most rectifier tubes is black. Can you give a reason for making them this way?
4. What is the advantage of a full-wave rectifier compared to a half-wave rectifier?
5. (a) What is the function of the capacitor in the filter system? (b) Is it better to have a large or small value?
6. (a) What is a filter system? (b) What would happen if either capacitor were removed or if the inductance were shorted?

PROBLEMS

1. Draw from memory a schematic wiring diagram of a full-wave rectifier showing the vacuum tube, transformer, and load.
2. Make a schematic diagram combining a full-wave rectifier consisting of a transformer and a vacuum tube with a filter circuit consisting of an inductance, two capacitors, and a load.
3. What sound would you hear if earphones were connected to the output of (a) a half-wave rectifier, (b) a full-wave rectifier, and (c) the filter circuit?
4. With an ac voltmeter, you have determined that the center-tapped secondary

of a transformer has 500 volts across it. What is the minimum value of voltage that the first filter capacitor would have to be able to stand if this transformer were used in a full-wave rectifier?

PROJECT

Make a power supply suitable for an electrophoresis, or similar, experiment, using a vacuum-tube rectifier.

ELECTRONICS

Lesson 94 **THE TRIODE**

De Forest's Audion. Although the Fleming valve was originally developed for the purpose of detecting wireless waves, its operation as such did not prove to be very satisfactory until, in 1906, De Forest[*] invented the *audion*. By inserting a *grid* wire between the *plate* and *filament* of a Fleming valve, he created a device capable not only of detecting wireless waves but of amplifying the signals as well. The purpose of the grid (see Fig. A) is to control the flow of electrons from the hot filament, F, to the plate, P.

During the time the grid, G, is negative, electrons from the filament are repelled and are unable to reach the plate, P. When the

grid is positive, however, the electrons from the filament are accelerated toward the plate and constitute a flow of current.

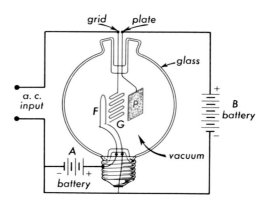

Fig. A. Diagram of the De Forest audion.

Not only does the grid act as a rectifier valve and let the electron current flow in one direction only, from filament to plate, but it acts as an amplifier, allowing large currents from the high-voltage *B-battery* to flow through when it is slightly positive and practically no current when it is slightly negative.

[*] Lee De Forest (1873-1961), American scientist, Ph.D. from Yale University, 1899, was most famous for the audion, considered by many to be the most important invention ever made in radio. He designed and installed the first five high-power radio stations for the U.S. Navy. After 1921, he devoted his time to the development of talking motion-picture film. He was awarded gold medals at the St. Louis Exposition in 1904, the Panama Pacific Exposition in San Francisco in 1915, and the Institute of France in 1923. He received the Cresson Medal of the Franklin Institute in 1921 for his important contributions to wireless.

The Modern Triode. Every radio en- thusiast today knows there are hundreds of different kinds of radio tubes. Some contain two filaments and two plates, while others contain as many as three or four separate grids. Although a treatment of such com- plex tubes is out of place here, the funda- mental principles of all of them are little different from De Forest's audion. One im- portant difference, however, is illustrated in Fig. B, and that is the employment in some

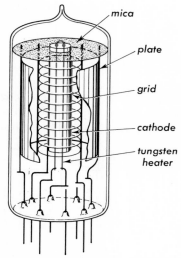

Fig. B. Modern vacuum tube with a cesium- coated cathode as a source of thermal elec- trons. The heater heats the cathode.

tubes of a cathode in place of a filament as a source of thermal electrons.

A fine tungsten-wire heater is threaded through two small holes running lengthwise through a porcelain-like insulating rod. Fit- ting snugly around this rod is the cathode, a metal cylinder coated on the outside with a thin layer of thorium, strontium, or cesium oxide. These particular oxides are copious emitters of electrons when heated to a dull red heat. Insulated from the cathode, the

heater is generally connected directly to an appropriate transformer winding.

A schematic diagram of the cathode type of tube containing one plate and one grid is given in Fig. C.

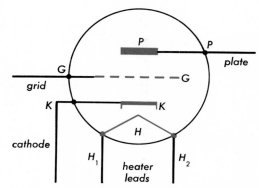

Fig. C. Schematic diagram of a cathode type of radio tube.

Triode Characteristics. A circuit dia- gram showing the electrical connections and instruments needed to measure the *grid- voltage vs plate-current* curve for vacuum tubes in general is given in Fig. D. The battery supplying the heater current is the *A-battery,* that supplying the plate is the *B-battery,* and that supplying the grid is the *C-battery.* A variable voltage is applied to the plate, P, by a potential divider and a B-battery, and a variable voltage is ap- plied to the grid, G, by another potential divider and a C-battery. The various ap- plied voltages are read from voltmeters, V_P and V_G, respectively, and the corre- sponding plate current is read from a mil- liammeter, MAp.

Three characteristic curves taken with the above circuit connections are repro- duced in Fig. E, one for each of three plate voltages, 80, 90, and 100 volts, respectively.

The foot of each curve, near -6 to -9 volts, indicates that, with these negative po- tentials on the grid, very few electrons are

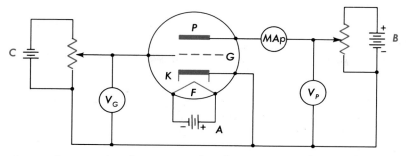

Fig. D. Circuit diagram for determining the characteristics of a triode vacuum tube.

able to reach the plate. As the grid is made less and less negative, more and more electrons get through, thereby increasing the current to the plate. The higher the positive potential on the plate, the higher is the plate current and the more negative must be the grid to stop the electrons.

The dotted lines near the center of the curves illustrate the meaning of what is called the voltage amplification factor, μ, of the tube. *The change in plate voltage giving rise to a change in plate current divided by the change in grid voltage that will give rise to the same change in plate current is called the voltage amplification factor, μ.*

To illustrate the meaning of μ, consider the point A on the 90-volt curve where the grid voltage is −3 volts. Where the vertical line through A intersects the upper and lower curves at B and C, horizontal dotted lines are drawn as shown. Where these lines intersect the 90-volt curve at D and E, vertical dotted lines are drawn downward, intersecting the baseline at F and G.

It can now be seen from the graph that, if we maintain the plate voltage at +90 volts and then change the grid voltage from F to G—a change of about 2.4 volts—the plate current will rise from J to H. To change the plate current this same amount by keeping the grid voltage at −3 volts, the plate voltage must be increased from 80 volts at C to 100 volts at B, or 20 volts. Hence, the voltage amplification factor is—

$$\mu = \frac{20 \text{ volts}}{2.4 \text{ volts}} = 8.3$$

Vacuum-tube Amplifier. One of the most important functions of the vacuum tube is its use as an amplifier of pulsating voltages. A diagram of a single vacuum-tube phonograph amplifier is shown in Fig. F.

When certain crystals are mechanically distorted, they generate a small voltage.

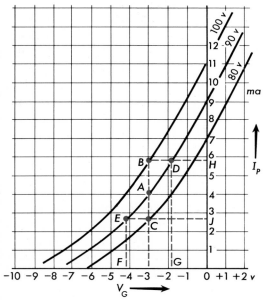

Fig. E. Characteristic curves for a triode vacuum tube.

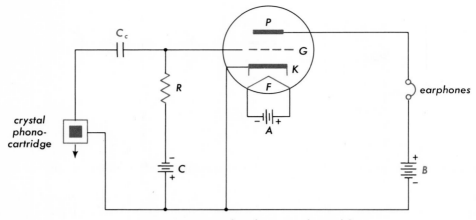

Fig. F. Vacuum tube phonograph amplifier.

This is known as the piezoelectric effect. Rochelle salts, which show marked piezoelectric effects, have been used for many years in microphones and in phonograph cartridges. A voltage that varies with the variations in the phonograph groove is produced by the crystal as the attached needle alternately compresses and decompresses it. This voltage is impressed on the grid through the coupling capacitor, C_c. The coupling capacitor offers negligible impedance to the pulseating voltage produced by the crystal but keeps the negative direct voltage of the *C-battery* confined to the grid. This makes possible the addition of the ac and dc voltages to the grid without interference with each other. The grid then controls the much larger current flow through the earphones. The source of the additional energy is the *B-battery* plate supply.

In amplifying any given signal voltage, a faithful reproduction of the wave form must occur; otherwise distortion will result. Let us assume that 2 volts of pulseating voltage is available from the crystal cartridge and that the grid of the tube is at zero potential, *i.e.*, there is no C-battery in the circuit. An inspection of Fig. G shows that,

with 200 volts on the plate of the tube and 0 volt on the grid, 24 milliamp of plate current flows. If the voltage from the crystal is applied to the grid, the plate current will

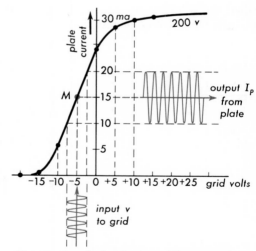

Fig. G. Graph showing amplifier operation.

drop to about 20 milliamp when the grid is −2 volts and rise to about 26 milliamp when it is +2 volts. The reason for this nonsymmetrical change in plate current is that, when the grid is positive, some of the electrons accelerated by the grid to the plate are attracted to the grid. This causes a grid current to flow. This cannot happen when the grid is negative, because electrons are then repelled by the negative charge.

To amplify without distortion requires a tube that has a long straight section in its *characteristic curve* (see Fig. G), and it should be operated at the center of this straight portion. Such operation is shown by the graph. To make the tube operate at M, a small battery (a *C-battery* or *grid-bias* battery) can be inserted in the grid circuit to maintain the grid at a negative potential. For the curve and tube shown, this requires −5 volts, while for other types of tubes, it might well require greater or smaller potentials.

The Earphone. When the crystal is not producing a voltage, the grid is held at −5 volts and a steady current of 15 milliamp flows through the plate and the earphones. No sound will be heard in the earphones, because they respond only to variations in current.

An earphone, as shown in Fig. H, consists of a coil of many turns of fine wire wound on a small permanent magnet. A thin sheet of iron called the *diaphragm* is held by the permanent magnet in the center and by the plastic case on its outer rim. When ac is applied to the coil, it alternately adds and subtracts magnetic flux to that of the permanent magnet. This causes the diaphragm to vibrate as it is pulled by a

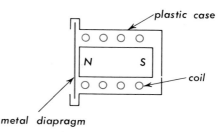

Fig. H. Cross section of an earphone.

stronger and weaker magnetic force. The air in contact with the diaphragm will be alternately compressed and released, producing sound waves.

Now when the voltage produced by the crystal is applied to the grid, it will vary according to our example from −7 to −3. The plate current will vary symmetrically, as shown in Fig. G, from about 10 to 20 milliamp. The earphone will now respond to the variations in plate current. Because this is an amplified, but faithful, copy of the grid-voltage variation, the music on the record will be heard with little or no distortion.

It should be noted that, if the impressed grid-voltage variations are too large, say −20 to +10 volts, the amplified currents will reach the curved portions of the curve above and below. *Distortion* of the *wave form* will result. As long as the tube is operated on the straight portion of the curve, plate current is directly proportional to the impressed grid potential and faithful amplification takes place.

QUESTIONS

1. (a) What is an audion? (b) What are the three elements of such a vacuum tube? (c) Who invented the tube?
2. (a) What is a vacuum-tube amplifier? (b) Where does the added electrical energy come from?
3. What is the purpose of the coupling capacitor in Fig. F?

4. What would happen if the crystal were connected directly without a coupling capacitor?
5. (a) What is the piezoelectric effect? (b) How can it be used in a microphone?
6. Why is the amount of energy available from a crystal cartridge so small?
7. (a) What would happen to the sound of an audio amplifier if the C-battery were to go dead? (b) Why?
8. What is the primary function of the grid in a triode?
9. What is the major difference between the modern triode and De Forest's audion?
10. (a) What is meant by the amplification factor of a tube? (b) What could be done in the manufacture of a tube to increase its amplification factor?
11. (a) How is an earphone made? (b) Explain how it can change electricity into sound.
12. What would you hear if you connected an earphone to a dry cell, left it on, and then disconnected it?

PROBLEMS

1. Draw the diagram for an amplifier with one vacuum tube.
2. The following measurements were made on a triode.

$$\text{plate voltage} = 150 \text{ volts}$$
$$\text{grid voltage} = -6 \text{ volts}$$
$$\text{plate current} = 2.5 \text{ milliamp}$$

When the plate voltage was raised to 180 volts the grid voltage had to be changed to -6.5 to bring the plate current back to 2.5 milliamp. What is the amplification factor?
3. A triode has an amplification factor of 15.6. What change in grid voltage will keep the plate current constant if the plate voltage is dropped 50 volts?
4. (a) What would the plate-current variations be in the tube, shown graphed in Fig. G, if the grid varied + and − 10 volts from a starting voltage of −10 volts? (b) Would the plate-current wave form be distorted? Explain. (c) Draw a graph like Fig. G showing the input and output wave forms.

PROJECT

Make a single vacuum-tube amplifier. Change grid and plate voltages, and note the effect on sound intensity (or gain) and fidelity.

ELECTRONICS

Lesson 95 **SEMICONDUCTOR JUNCTIONS**

Semiconductors. There are many solids that are neither good conductors of electricity nor good insulators. These materials are called *semiconductors*. Of the large number of semiconductors known to science, certain ones are of considerable importance. Typical examples are the crystalline forms of the elements listed in the fourth column of the periodic table (see Appendix). Two important ones are *silicon* and *germanium*.

In the pure state, both silicon and germanium are nonconductors at reasonable temperatures and voltages. If a crystal of either is heated, the resistance of the material decreases. The resistance of metallic conductors behaves in just the opposite way; their resistance increases with a rise in temperature. In order to explain this behavior, we must consider the crystal structure of semiconductors.

Silicon and germanium atoms each have what the chemists call four *valence electrons*, that is, four electrons that enter into the chemical binding in solids. The atomic pattern of atoms in both crystals is a tetrahedral structure, as shown in Fig. A. In Fig. B, each atom shares one of its electrons with each neighbor; the neighbor in turn shares one of its four with it. Such a sharing of electrons between two atoms is called a *covalent bond*.

Because of the difficulty of drawing a three-dimensional tetrahedral lattice structure, it is convenient to flatten the diagram out and represent the bonding as a square lattice, as shown in Fig. C.

At temperatures close to absolute zero,

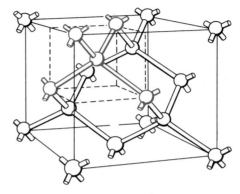

Fig. A. Diamond crystal structures of carbon, silicon, and germanium.

all electrons in a crystal are tied up strongly by these chemical bonds. When the crystal is raised to room temperature, however, the thermal vibrations of the atoms are sufficient to break some of the bonds and free some of the electrons to wander throughout the crystal. Where an electron has broken free, as shown at the upper right and lower

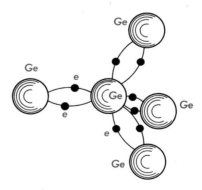

Fig. B. Each atom in a germanium crystal is bound at the center of a tetrahedron formed by its four nearest neighbors.

left in Fig. C, a "hole" has been created and the process is referred to as *dissociation*. Because that part of the crystal was neutral beforehand, it now lacks an electron, and the vacant hole is equivalent to a net positive charge.

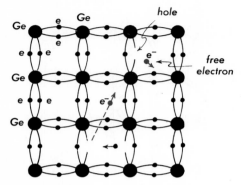

Fig. C. Schematic diagram of the covalent bonding of atoms in a germanium crystal. Thermal agitation breaks some bonds and liberates electrons.

Owing also to thermal agitation, a *bound* electron next to a hole can move across to fill the gap, the net motion of the negative charge from one bonded position to another being in effect equivalent to the motion of a hole in the opposite direction. The motion of a hole is, therefore, equivalent to the motion of a positive charge. This action is shown at the lower center in Fig. C.

N-Type and P-Type Crystals. The resistance of a cube of pure germanium about 1 cm on each side is several hundreds of thousands of ohms. If a small speck of arsenic or aluminum is added before molten germanium recrystallizes, the resistance now would be less than 100 ohms. Evidently something has happened to the crystal structure making many electrons available to carry current.

If crystals are formed with *arsenic* as an impurity, the arsenic atoms, with five valence electrons each, provide a crystal lattice with extra electrons. Such a crystal, as shown in Fig. D, is therefore one in which each arsenic atom donates one free electron to the system. With arsenic pres-

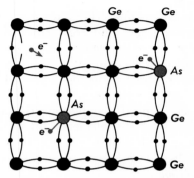

Fig. D. N-type crystal lattice with arsenic atoms as an impurity.

ent in quantities of one in a million, *donor atoms* are, on the average, about 100 atoms apart, or there are about 10^{17} arsenic atoms and 10^{17} free electrons per cubic centimeter. Because there is now a considerable number of electrons available for conduction, the germanium's resistance to current flow is reduced. This type of crystal is called *N-type*, because the excess free electrons have a *negative charge*. If an electric field is established across this crystal by a battery, electrons will leave the negative electrode of the battery and enter the crystal. Simultaneously, electrons will leave the crystal and then go into the positive electrode of the battery. In the crystal, electrons will drift from the negative to the positive end.

If crystals are grown with *aluminum* as an impurity, the aluminum atoms, with only three valence electrons each, form a crystal lattice with an *electron deficiency*, that is, *with holes*. Fig. E shows that, to form normal bonds with germanium atoms, the

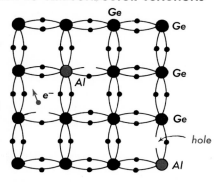

Fig. E. P-type crystal lattice with aluminum atoms as the impurity.

in an N-type crystal is compensated for by the positive charges on the arsenic nuclei, while the surplus of holes in the P-type crystal is compensated for by the deficiency in positive nuclear charge of the aluminum nuclei.

The PN Junction. When two semiconductors of the P and N types are brought into contact, as shown in Fig. F, they form

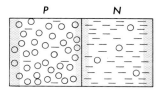

Fig. F. PN junction showing diffusion boundary.

aluminum atom would have to have four electrons to match. Because the aluminum atom is short one electron, a space or a *hole* exists for an additional electron. Because there is a deficiency of electrons in the crystal lattice, it is called a *positive*, or *P-type*, crystal. An electron from an adjacent electron-pair bond may absorb enough energy to break its bond and move through the crystal lattice to fill the hole. This leaves another hole that another electron can fill and so forth. Notice that the flow of electricity in the crystal is still electron flow and that the flow of holes is opposite to that of the electrons. For every electron that enters this crystal from the negative electrode of a battery, another electron must leave and go to the positive electrode. In the crystal, the electrons move from hole to hole.

Another way to explain conduction in a P-type crystal is to think of holes as real positive particles, just as electrons are real negative particles. Bubbles rising in a soft drink are an excellent analogy of holes that move. As far as the external circuit is concerned, there is no way of knowing whether holes or electrons are moving in the crystal.

Neither of these crystals, by itself, has a net charge. The surplus of free negatives

what is called a *PN junction,* or *diode.* In the region of contact, a cloud of free electrons in the N crystal diffuse across the boundary, filling the holes to the left, much the same as gas atoms diffuse through a porous ceramic material.

Because electrons leave the N crystal, that side of the junction acquires a positive potential, while the P crystal gains electrons and acquires a negative potential. As this diffusion of electrons continues, the potential difference between the two sides rises. The filling of holes in the P crystal gives rise to more holes developing in the N crystal, and this action is the same as though holes had diffused across the boundary to the right.

As the N crystal becomes more positive, and the P crystal more negative, electrons will be attracted back toward the right, and an equilibrium condition will develop in which equal numbers of electrons will be crossing the boundary in opposite directions.

Current Flow Through a PN Junction. There are two ways to connect a voltage to a PN junction. We will start by applying a positive voltage to the N-type, as shown in Fig. G. The ammeter in this case will show little or no current flowing. The battery

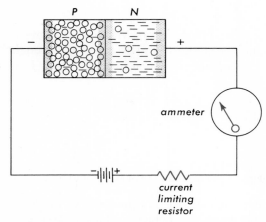

Fig. G. Reverse-biased PN junction. Very little current flows.

establishes an electric field through the crystal. Electrons are attracted to the positive pole of the battery and holes are attracted to the negative pole. This leaves no current carriers in or near the junction and, therefore, the junction acts as a high resistance. When the junction is connected to

the battery with this polarity, it is said to be *reverse biased.*

Now let us reverse the battery connections, as shown in Fig. H. With the electric field reversed, electrons and holes are driven to the junction where they combine, making room for more electrons and holes. At the N-type contact, the battery supplies electrons to make up for those lost at the junction. At the P-type contact, the extra electrons are given up to the positive side of the battery. When the PN junction is connected to a battery in this manner, it is said to be *forward biased.*

PN Junction as a Rectifier. We have seen how a vacuum tube can rectify, because it is capable of conducting current only when the plate is positive with respect to the filament. The semiconductor PN junction behaves in a similar fashion, since it conducts only in the forward-biased direction. In addition, it has the advantage of requiring no filament power, is very small, and produces very little heat. Fig. I shows the simple connections for a half-wave semiconductor rectifier. Current flows through the PN junction only when it is forward biased, which occurs only on every other part of the ac cycle. Full-wave rectifi-

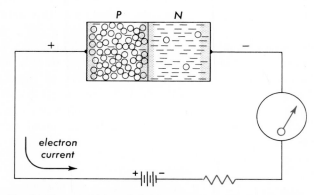

Fig. H. Forward-biased PN junction. High current flows.

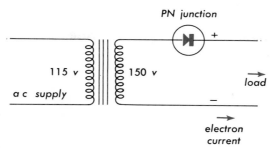

PN junction

115 v
a c supply

150 v

+

load

−

→
electron
current

Fig. I. Schematic diagram of a half-wave rectifier circuit using a semiconductor diode.

cation can be done in the same way as a full-wave tube rectifier, using a transformer with a center-tapped secondary coil or by the use of a bridge circuit. The same filter as was used for the vacuum tube can be used to smooth out the pulsations.

QUESTIONS

1. (a) What is a covalent bond? (b) How is it useful in explaining the N-type crystal?
2. Why does the original germanium or silicon used to make semiconductor devices have to be so pure to start with?
3. (a) Are there other impurities that could be used, besides the ones mentioned in the text, to make P and N crystals? (b) What would be an easy reference to find them?
4. (a) What is a semiconductor? (b) What is a P-type crystal? (c) What is a PN junction?
5. Because an N-type semiconductor crystal has more free electrons than holes, why is it electrically uncharged?
6. Because a P-type semiconductor crystal has more holes than free electrons, why is it electrically uncharged?
7. (a) Explain what is meant by a "hole." (b) Why does it move through a semiconductor just like a charged particle?
8. (a) If gallium were added to germanium, what type semiconductor would be produced? (b) What kind of carrier (electron or hole) would carry the current?
9. What is meant by reverse biasing?
10. What are the advantages of using a PN-junction rectifier compared to a vacuum-tube diode?
11. With the help of a diagram, explain how a PN junction rectifies alternating current.
12. Draw a diagram of a full-wave rectifier using PN-junction diodes.
13. A solar cell is a PN junction that generates current when sunlight causes ionization in the junction. Explain in detail how this would produce a direct current.

PROJECT

Make a power supply using a full-wave solid-state rectifier suitable for use in the chemistry or physics laboratory. Exact instructions for making these power supplies may be obtained in elementary textbooks on electronics or in magazines about electronics.

ELECTRONICS

Lesson 96 **THE TRANSISTOR**

In the preceding lesson, we saw how a PN junction may be used as a rectifier. If we take two PN junctions and join them so that the two P sections are fused and made very thin as shown in Fig. A, we would have a basic transistor. Even though actual transistors are not made by this method, it simplifies our discussion of transistor action if we think of them as two diodes back to back. N_1 is known as the *emitter*, P, as the *base*, and N_2 is called the *collector*.

Let us now connect a battery between the emitter and the base and measure the

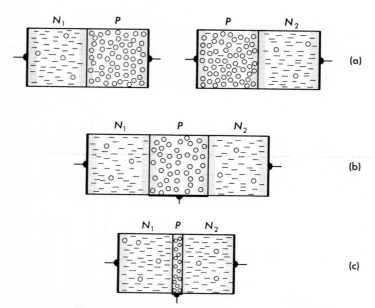

Fig. A. Development of a transistor from two PN diodes.

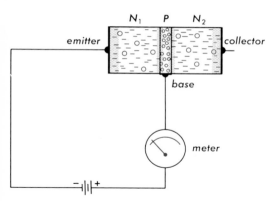

Fig. B. Connections to measure current flowing between emitter and base with forward bias applied to emitter.

current flow as shown in Fig. B. The negative end of the battery is connected to the emitter so that it is forward biased. This should result in a large current flow, except that the base is very thin and very lightly doped so that there are very few holes for electrons to combine with. For this reason, only a very small current flows in spite of the forward bias.

The collector circuit is connected to its battery with reverse bias, as shown in Fig. C. As we expected from our knowledge of diode action, very little current flows, be-

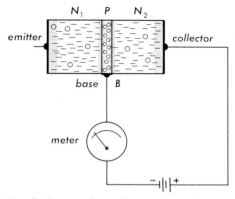

Fig. C. Reverse-biased connection between collector and base.

cause the positive charge of the battery pulls electrons away from the junction.

Meaning of "Alpha." Fig. D shows the normal biasing for an NPN transistor. Notice that a large current flows in the collector circuit even though it is reverse biased. This can only be because the emitter current is flowing to the collector instead of the base. This clearly shows that the emitter battery may be used to control collector current.

Let us assume that, because of the resistance and voltage in the emitter-base circuit, 20 milliamp flows into the emitter. At the emitter-base junction, some of the electrons combine with holes in the base. This causes only 1 milliamp to flow in the base circuit. This current is low, because the P section is very thin and very lightly doped so there are few holes for the electrons to combine. A large electric field exists between the emitter and the collector, owing to the voltages of two batteries and the extreme closeness of the emitter and collector regions to each other. This causes most of the electrons from the emitter to go on to the collector from which they enter the collector circuit. In other words, 95% of the emitter current becomes collector current.

Alpha is defined as the ratio of a change in collector current to a change in emitter current. In symbols—

$$\alpha = \frac{\Delta I_c}{\Delta I_e} \qquad (1)$$

where ΔI_c is the change in collector current and ΔI_e is the change in emitter current. α must always be less than unity, because a few electrons will combine with holes in the base region to contribute to the base current.

Voltage Amplification. Having just seen that α is always less than one, it would

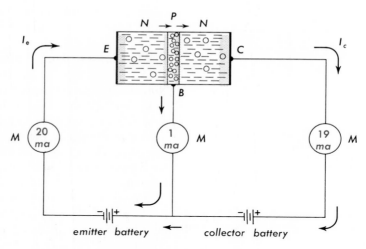

Fig. D. Biasing of transistor.

seem that a transistor could not be used as a device to amplify, because we appear to lose rather than to gain current. However, the manner in which the transistor is biased makes a very important difference. The emitter is forward biased, which means current can flow easily, indicating low resistance. The emitter battery can have a very low voltage and still produce a reasonable current flow. As shown in Fig. E, the generator resistance, R_1, will also have to be low (in the order of about 100 ohms) so as not to restrict the flow of current. The collector is reverse biased, which means that, even with a large battery, little or no current will flow. To match this condition of high resistance of the transistor, a high resistance, R_L, is used. It is easy to show

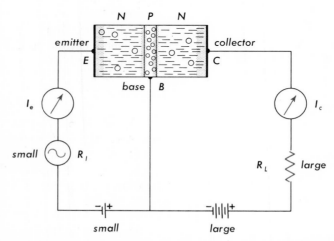

Fig. E. Relation between resistance and voltages in emitter and collector circuits.

that, to get the most power out of a power source, the load resistance must match the resistance of the source. The resistance of R_L might be as high as 100,000 ohms.

Voltage amplification is defined as the ratio of the change in output voltage to input voltage. In symbols—

$$VA = \frac{\Delta V_O}{\Delta V_I} \qquad (2)$$

where ΔV_O is the change in output voltage and ΔE_I is the change in input voltage. From Ohm's law, $V = IR$, we get—

$$VA = \frac{\Delta I_c R_L}{\Delta I_e R_I} \qquad (3)$$

From Eq. (1),

$$VA = \alpha \frac{R_L}{R_I} \qquad (4)$$

Referring to our previous example in Fig. D and substituting the values of R_L and R_I and α, we get—

$$VA = 0.95 \times \frac{100,000}{100}$$
$$VA = 950$$

It is obvious that a difference in the input and output resistance makes possible a large voltage amplification.

Power Amplification. Power amplification may be defined as the ratio of the change in output power to change in input power. In symbolic form—

$$PA = \frac{\Delta P_O}{\Delta P_I} \qquad (5)$$

We remember that $P = I^2R$, so we can rewrite the formula as—

$$PA = \frac{\Delta I_c^2 \times R_L}{\Delta I_e^2 \times R_I}$$

or—

$$PA = \alpha^2 \times \frac{R_L}{R_I} \qquad (6)$$

Using the data from the previous examples gives—

$$PA = (0.95)^2 \times \frac{100,000}{100} = 903$$

Single-stage Transistor Amplifier. Transistors are made, as we have seen, with the emitter and collector of N-type crystal and the base of P-type. They are also made in the opposite way. They are abbreviated *NPN* and *PNP*, respectively. Symbols for these two types are shown in Fig. F. In use,

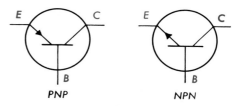

Fig. F. Schematic diagrams of transistors. Arrows are opposite to electron flow.

the only difference between the two is that the applied voltages must be reversed when using a PNP transistor instead of an NPN transistor.

In the operation of a simple phonograph amplifier, the output of a Rochelle-salt crystal cartridge is connected to the primary winding of a step-down matching transformer, as shown in Fig. G. This transformer is necessary in order to match the high impedance of the cartridge with the low impedance of the forward-biased emitter-base circuit. The collector is also connected to a step-down transformer to match the high impedance of the reverse-biased collector-base circuit to the low impedance of the earphone. As was explained in the lesson on tube amplifiers, the phonograph cartridge generates a voltage pulsating as the playback needle moves along the phonograph groove, which is proportional in amplitude and

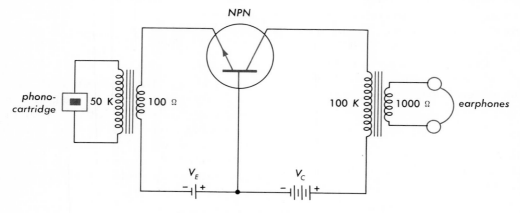

Fig. G. Transistor amplifier.

frequency to the music recorded. This voltage in the primary appears in the secondary and adds to and subtracts from the voltage of the battery, V_E. This in turn creates a change in emitter current. Most of this current change shows up in a change in collector current. Because the impedance in the collector circuit is so much higher, a voltage and power gain is achieved and a much louder sound is then heard in the earphones.

Notice that we have been talking about impedance instead of resistance in our discussion of the amplifier. This is necessary, because we are now dealing with ac instead of dc as we were previously. However, our calculations of voltage and power amplification still apply as before.

QUESTIONS

1. What is the normal biasing for a transistor?
2. What is the difference between an NPN and a PNP transistor?
3. (a) What is the meaning of alpha? (b) Why is it always less than one?
4. Why is the base current so small in a transistor circuit?
5. How can the emitter voltage control the collector current?
6. Explain how a transistor can amplify.
7. How can you tell by looking at a transistor diagram whether a PNP or NPN transistor is used?
8. Why is a transformer needed between the collector circuit and the earphone?
9. Why must the base section of any transistor be made as thin as possible?

PROBLEMS

1. (a) What would the alpha be for a transistor if emitter current is 16 milliamp and base current 2 milliamp? (b) What would the collector current be?

2. What would be the voltage amplification of the transistor in Problem 1 if the emitter resistance were 50 Ω and collector resistance 90,000 Ω.

3. What would the power amplification be of the transistor described in Problems 1 and 2?

4. A phonograph cartridge generates 1 volt as it moves in the groove of a record. It is connected to a transistor amplifier that has an alpha of 0.92. The impedance of the emitter circuit is 75 Ω, while the collector circuit is in the order of 1500 Ω. What voltage will appear across the output?

PROJECT

Make a number of simple transistor projects, such as a radio receiver, amplifier, code-practice oscillator, etc. Many manufacturers of transistors sell inexpensive booklets with instructions for simple transistor projects.

ELECTRONICS

Lesson 97 *OSCILLOSCOPE, TELEVISION, AND RADAR*

Cathode-ray Tube. The cathode-ray tube is a special vacuum tube similar to that used by J. J. Thomson in his studies of the electron. Electrical voltages of almost any frequency can be displayed on its screen. This ability to convert electricity to a visual pattern makes it particularly useful in the oscilloscope and for television and radar. A cathode-ray tube contains an electron gun for producing a stream of electrons, a grid for controlling the intensity of the beam, and a screen coated with a chemical that gives off light when electrons strike it. Tubes, 7 in. in diameter and smaller, focus and deflect the beam electrostatically, with internal electrodes. Larger tubes, such as are used in television receivers, are both focused and deflected magnetically. Coils for this purpose are placed externally around the neck of the tube.

The Deflection System. To make the tube useful, two horizontal plates, labeled x in Fig. A, and two vertical plates, labeled y, are on each side of the path of the electron beam. Voltages applied to these plates can be used to move the electrons to any spot on the screen.

When the electrons impinge on the screen, a portion of their kinetic energy is converted into light by the *phosphor* on the screen. Phosphors are available in almost any color, green being the color most used in oscilloscopes and white for television. An emulsion of carbon black is painted on the inside of the tube to pick up the electrons and complete the circuit to the cathode, and prevent charge build-up on the screen.

Oscilloscope. One of the simplest applications of the cathode-ray tube is to be

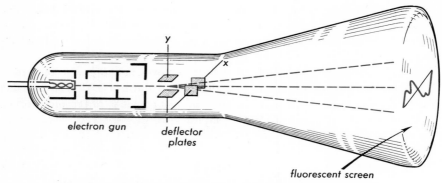

Fig. A. Cathode-ray tube with electrostatic deflector plates.

found in the *cathode-ray oscilloscope*, an instrument whose purpose is to reveal the detailed variations in rapidly changing electric currents or potentials. A *block diagram* of a simple oscilloscope is shown in Fig. B. The

causes the beam spot to move from left to right across the screen at constant speed and then jump quickly back from right to left to repeat the motion, (*c*).

The saw-tooth generator develops the

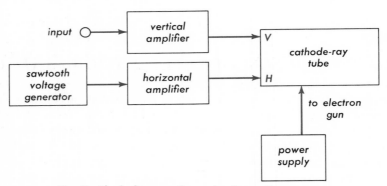

Fig. B. Block diagram for a simple oscilloscope.

electron gun is supplied suitable voltages by the power supply to produce a bright spot in the approximate center of the screen. Appropriate controls are brought out to the front of the instrument to adjust the brightness, focus, etc. of the spot.

It is customary to apply a *saw-tooth potential difference* to the x-plates, as shown in Fig. C(*a*), and the unknown potential difference to be studied, (*b*), to the y-plates. The saw-tooth potential difference supplied by a special circuit, called a "sweep circuit,"

voltage for the sweep circuit at a rate that can be varied from the control panel from

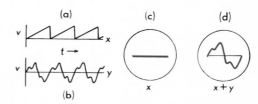

Fig. C. Potentials applied to a cathode-ray tube, and graphs appearing on a fluorescent screen.

zero to about one million hertz. This voltage is then amplified by the horizontal amplifier before being applied to the horizontal deflector plates. By varying the amplification of this voltage from the control panel, it is possible to stretch out the horizontal line drawn out by the moving spot.

Voltages whose wave form is to be examined, as in Fig. C(b), are applied to the vertical input. They are then amplified by the vertical amplifier before being applied to the vertical deflection plates. If an alternating voltage were applied only to the vertical plates, the electron beam would go up and down. Owing to the persistence of vision, the spot would appear to be a line if it were oscillating at least 16 Hz. When the vertical and horizontal deflections occur at the same time, the spot draws out a graph of the varying potential difference as in diagram (d). By varying the sweep-circuit frequency until it matches the frequency of the studied signal, repeated graphs will be drawn out, one on top of the other, and persistence of vision and the fluorescent screen will present a stationary graph.

Green fluorescent screens are used for visual observation, because the eye is most sensitive to this color; blue screens are used for photographic purposes, because films and plates are most sensitive to blue.

The oscilloscope has many practical applications and is to be found in every research laboratory, as well as in every radio and television repair shop. Its principal function is to analyze, or diagnose, rapidly changing potential differences whose frequencies may be as low as a fraction of a hertz or as high as thousands of megahertz. Periodic or transient potential differences as small as a fraction of a microvolt may also be studied by first amplifying them with standard vacuum-tube or transistor circuits.

Another valuable feature of the oscilloscope is its ability to measure time intervals between electrical impulses less than a microsecond apart.

The Scanning Process in Television. For years, the sending of pictures by wire or radio has been an everyday occurrence. The fundamental principle involved in this process, which is illustrated in Fig. D, is known as *scanning*. Every picture to be transmitted is scanned by an *exploring spot* which, starting at the top, moves in straight lines over

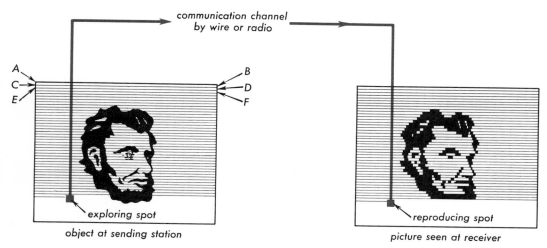

communication channel
by wire or radio

A
C→
E↗
B
D
F

exploring spot

reproducing spot

object at sending station

picture seen at receiver

Fig. D. Illustrating the process of picture scanning.

the entire picture. The spot first moves from A to B, then from C to D, then E to F, etc., until the entire picture has been covered. Each time the spot reaches the right-hand side it jumps back to the left and starts on the next line. This process is called *field sequential-scanning.*

The exploring spot in any scanning device is so constructed that it generates an electric current proportional to the brightness of its instantaneous position. Such a pulsating current, called the *video signal,* is transmitted over wires or radio waves to the receiving station. There in a specially designed instrument, a *reproducing spot,* whose brightness is proportional to the video-signal amplitude, moves over a viewing screen in a path similar to that of the exploring spot. In this way, the reproducing spot reconstructs the original picture.

It will be realized that the smaller the scanning and reproducing spots and the greater the number of lines, the better will be the details of the scanned picture being reproduced at the receiving end. The diagram shown here includes only 50 lines per picture as compared with 525 lines used in some standard (black and white) broadcasts.

In order to reduce flicker, the process of *interlacing* is employed. By this process each picture is scanned twice, first by running the exploring spot over the odd numbered lines, 1, 3, 5, 7, etc., and then over the even numbered lines, 2, 4, 6, 8, etc.

Television Receiver. In many respects, the construction of a television receiver and its operation is similar to an ordinary radio receiver. After being tuned in, detected, and amplified with conventional radio-tube circuits, the carrier wave from a nearby transmitter is fed as a video signal into a cathode-ray tube in place of a loud-speaker.

The operation of a small cathode-ray

tube in a television receiver is very similar to its use in an oscilloscope. The saw-tooth generator is adjusted to a frequency of approximately 15,750 Hz, as shown in Fig. E.

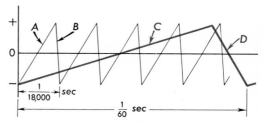

Fig. E. Saw-tooth potentials applied to plates of the television tube to produce horizontal scanning A and B, and vertical scanning C and D. A, horizontal deflection; B, horizontal return; C, vertical deflection; and D, vertical return.

Another saw-tooth generator adjusted to approximately 60 Hz is connected through an amplifier to the vertical-deflection plates. Without a signal from the transmitter the spot of light will move across the screen 15,750 times a second, while at the same time, moving up and down 60 times per second. This forms a pattern called a *raster.*

For a small fraction of a second, between successive pictures being scanned for transmission, current pulses of a certain type and frequency are sent out from the sending station as part of the video signal. These, picked up by the receiver, act as a trigger-like mechanism to bring the reproducing spot to the top left of the screen at the proper time to start the next picture. In other words, the transmitter sends out signals that enable the receiver to automatically keep "in phase" with the pictures as they are sent.

The proper fluctuations in the intensity of the luminescent spot are brought about by applying the video signal shown in Fig. F to the *grid* of the electron gun. This grid

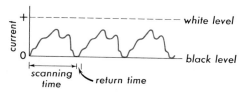

Fig. F. Video signal current for three lines of a single picture.

controls the flow of electrons through to the anode in the same way that the grid controls the current to the plate in an ordinary three-element vacuum tube.

The wave lengths used in transmitting TV signals lie in the VHF and UHF regions of the electromagnetic spectrum. These two wave-length bands extend from 10 cm to 10 m.

Color Television. In Lesson 66, it was shown that most of the colors in a scene can be reproduced with the primary colors red, blue, and green. In color television, three cameras are used, each of which is sensitive to only one of these colors. Each camera records the amount of the corresponding primary color in the scene.

A sequence of each color is scanned in turn. The transmitted carrier then consists of separate segments of red, green, and blue amplitude information. These segments are interspersed with necessary pulses to tell the receiver where one color stops and the next begins. The carrier is then picked up by the antenna at the receiving location, and the receiver must then unscramble the color segments.

The color television receiver is similar to the black and white set in many respects. However, the tolerances are much more critical, and additional circuits must be present to separate the color segments.

Perhaps the biggest difference, in both design and cost, is the special picture tube that is required. The conventional black

and white tube contains only one electron gun. Most of the color receivers that have been marketed have employed three separate electron guns, one for each color. The screen, in turn, possesses three different color-emitting phosphors.

These phosphors are arranged in an orderly array of small triangular groups, each group containing a green, red, and blue emitting dot. See Fig. G. There are about

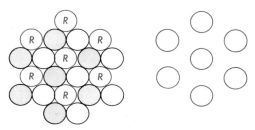

Fig. G. (a) Section of a phosphor-dot screen and (b) a corresponding section of the aperture mask.

1,000,000 such dots for a 21-inch screen. To insure that each beam strikes only its corresponding phosphor, an *aperture mask* is placed between the screen and the electron guns. This mask contains holes, each corresponding to a color group. Each hole is so aligned with respect to its group that each of the approaching beams can strike only one color of phosphor. See Fig. H.

If only one gun is actuated, then only the color that it excites will appear on the screen. Although only one gun is on at a given instant of time, the sequential switching from one color to the next is so rapid that the colors blend with no noticeable flicker. If all the guns are operating in quick succession with equal intensity, then white will appear.

Radar. Radar is one of the most important electronic developments of World War II and may be defined as the art of deter-

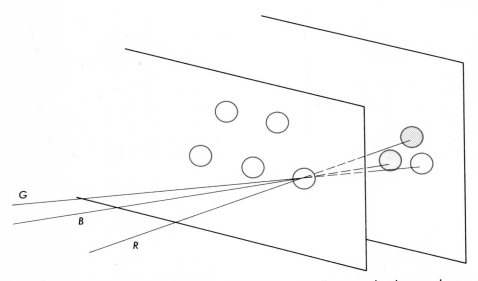

G

B

R

Fig. H. Diagram illustrating how the aperture mask allows each electron beam to strike the proper phosphor dot.

mining by means of *radio echoes* the presence, distance, direction, and velocity of distant aircraft, ships, land masses, cities, and other objects. Radar derives its name from the longer title "*RAdio Detection And Ranging.*"

Basically, a complete radar station consists of a *transmitter*, a *receiver*, and an *indicator*. As shown by a schematic diagram in Fig. I, the transmitter sends out high-frequency radio waves that, traveling outward with the velocity of light, are reflected from a distant object. That small portion of the reflected waves returning toward the station is picked up and amplified by the receiver. The signal is then fed into any one of a number of indicating devices, some of which are so complete as to give continuously the instantaneous *distance, direction,* and *relative velocity* of the object. With one type of air-borne unit, ground objects can be observed on the screen of a cathode-ray

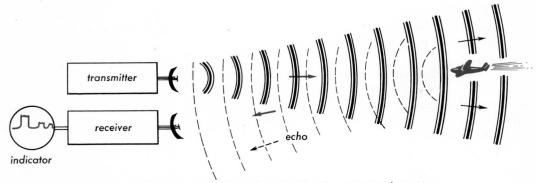

transmitter

receiver

indicator

echo

Fig. I. Illustrating the principles of radar detecting and ranging.

tube even though fog or clouds intervene. Such systems are extremely useful in reducing flying hazards during inclement weather.

The lengths of the waves used in radar are in the *microwave* region of the electromagnetic spectrum, the range of 1 cm to 10 cm.

The Pulsed System. Because a powerful transmitter must operate side by side with a supersensitive receiver, some provision is always made whereby the power from the transmitter is blocked out of the receiver. In most radar equipment, this is accomplished by means of intermittent transmission commonly called the *pulsed system*. In this operation, the transmitter is turned *on* for only a fraction of a second to send out a train of waves while the receiver is made very insensitive. When the transmitter goes *off*, the receiver is turned *on* to full sensitivity to receive the faint echo signal returning. When the receiver goes *off*, the transmitter comes *on* again to send out another wave train and repeat the above process hundreds of times per second.

A graph of the received pulses from an object 9 mi away is shown in Fig. J. Be-

distance. If a frequency of 30,000 MHz is used, the wave length is 1 cm and each pulse will contain thousands of waves. Rectified by the receiver, an entire wave train appears as a voltage pulse as in the graph.

One type of *indicator* used for determining this time interval is a *cathode-ray oscilloscope*, or *kinescope*, of the type shown in Fig. A. While the scanning spot is kept at constant intensity, a saw-tooth potential is applied to the horizontal sweep to make it move with constant speed across the fluorescent screen.

Electrical circuits are so arranged that the spot starts at the left just prior to the transmitter's emission of a pulse. When, a fraction of a second later, a pulse is initiated, a small part of the energy is applied as a vertical deflection of the spot, thereby producing a trace, *T*, as shown in Fig. K.

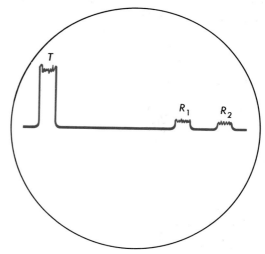

Fig. K. Trace of spot on cathode-ray tube as used in radar ranging.

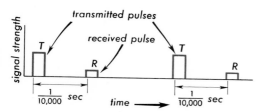

Fig. J. Graph of transmitted pulses showing received pulse, or echo, from an object 9 mi distant.

cause the velocity of radio waves is 186,300 mi/sec, the same as light, the time interval between each transmitted pulse, *T*, and its echo, *R*, returning is a direct measure of the

When the returning echo signal arrives at the receiver, it too is applied as a vertical deflection, and a peak like the one at R_1 is produced. Upon reaching the right-hand end of the screen the spot is extinguished and returned to the left, where it is again turned on and the above process repeated. As the spot retraces the same line many times every second, persistence of vision gives rise to the appearance of a steady trace.

If several different objects reflect waves of sufficient intensity to be picked up by the receiver, several peaks, R_1, R_2, etc., will be seen on the indicator screen. In radar parlance, each such peak on the trace is called a *pip*. Its distance along the horizontal line from T is a direct measure of the time required for the signal to go out and return and is, therefore, a measure of the range of the object that reflected the signal. Various methods of accurately measuring the distance interval have been developed.

If an object is coming toward or receding from a radar station, the frequency of the waves reflected from it will be increased or decreased respectively, as in the Doppler effect. Hence, by measuring the frequency change between the waves going out and those coming back, the velocity of approach or recession becomes known.

Wave Guides. The term *wave guide* is generally applied to a special class of metallic conductors having the property of conducting high-frequency oscillations from one place to another. To be more specific, it is a radio transmission line by which power generated at an oscillator can be transmitted to some utility point with little or no loss along the line.

Two types of wave guide commonly used at present are shown in Fig. L. The first, called a *coaxial cable* or *concentric line,* consists of a wire conductor insulated from and running lengthwise through the center of a tubular conductor. Power from any high-frequency source, when connected to the central wire and tubular sheath, is

propagated as waves through the dielectric between the two conductors.

The second is a hollow rectangular pipe, which is usually what is meant by the term wave guide. Power introduced as electromagnetic waves at one end is guided by the conducting walls to the other end. Each conductor is shown with a 90° bend to show that waves can be guided around corners.

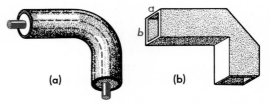

Fig. L. Wave guides commonly used in radar and television transmission lines: (a) coaxial cable and (b) hollow conductor.

While there is no limit to the frequency transmitted by coaxial lines, there is a lower limit for hollow wave guides. This lower limit, called the *cut-off frequency* or critical frequency, is the limiting case of a so-called

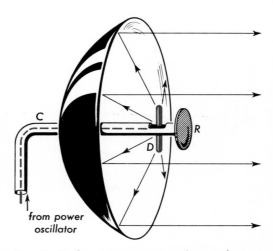

Fig. M. Radar antenna system for producing a parallel beam.

dominant mode of vibration inside the guide. It is analogous in some respects to the *fundamental vibration* of a given air column in sound. The dominant mode occurs in a rectangular pipe when the wider of the two dimensions, *b*, is one-half a wave length. The narrow dimension of the latter is not critical but in practice is made to be about ½ *b*.

Because wave guides are comparable in cross section to the waves they propagate, and a coaxial cable will transmit any frequency no matter how low, the latter is generally used for waves longer than 10 cm, whereas hollow pipes are used with waves shorter than 10 cm. The power capacity of a hollow pipe, transmitting at its dominant mode, is greater than a coaxial cable of the same size.

Fig. M shows an arrangement in which the high-frequency oscillations from an oscillator tube source (not shown) are fed through a coaxial cable, *C*, to a single dipole, or Hertzian doublet, *D*. Radiated waves from the doublet are reflected into a parallel beam by the mirror. Because the over-all length of a dipole must be equal to one-half a wave length, the two small rods for 10 cm waves would each be 2.5 cm, or 1 in., long.

By using arrays of such beamed antennas for both transmitted and received waves, radar waves have been reflected from both Venus and Mars.

QUESTIONS

1. (a) What is radar? (b) What do the letters stand for?
2. (a) What is a pulsed radar system? (b) Why is the operation intermittent?
3. (a) How is the distance of an object determined? (b) How is the velocity of a moving object determined?
4. (a) What is a wave guide? (b) How many kinds are there?
5. (a) What is the process called scanning? (b) What is a video signal?
6. (a) What is a cathode-ray tube? (b) How is the electron beam deflected for scanning the screen of the picture tube?
7. (a) What is meant by field sequential scanning? (b) What is interlacing?
8. What would you see on a TV screen (a) if the horizontal oscillator stopped functioning? (b) If the vertical oscillator stopped?
9. (a) Why is the cathode-ray tube so useful? (b) Would it be just as good if protons were used instead of electrons? Explain.
10. Can you give a reason why very large cathode-ray tubes are focused and deflected magnetically instead of electrostatically, as are the small tubes?
11. (a) Why is a saw-tooth voltage applied to horizontal plates in an oscilloscope instead of alternating voltage? (b) Trace out the motion of an electron using both voltages.
12. (a) Why are most oscilloscope screens green? (b) Could they be made of another color?
13. (a) What are the "ghosts" that are often seen on a TV receiver? (b) Would it be possible to calculate how far away the obstructions are that are causing the ghosts? Explain.

14. How is the position of the dot controlled by the transmitting station in a TV receiver?
15. Why are color television sets more costly than black and white?

PROBLEMS

1. Radar waves of frequency 5×10^3 MHz are reflected from a paraboloidal metal reflector. Calculate the over-all length of the dipole used at its focal plane.
2. The dipole of a radar transmitter has an over-all length of 1.63 cm. Calculate the frequency in MHz.
3. Find the time required for a radar signal to go out and return from an object 15 mi away.
4. What is the minimum microwave frequency that can be transmitted through a hollow rectangular wave guide if the inside cross section is 1 cm by 0.5 cm?
5. If each scanned picture in TV requires 325 lines and if 30 pictures per second are used, how many times per second does the electron beam sweep across the picture tube?
6. If the video signal for each line of a TV picture requires 10,000 waves of the carrier wave, and each picture requires 350 lines, what minimum frequency is required to send 30 pictures per second?
7. Make a diagram of a cathode-ray tube. Label the principal parts. Briefly describe its action.
8. American TV uses 525 horizontal lines to scan the picture and repeats the complete picture 30 times a second. This requires that the horizontal oscillator have a frequency of 15,750 Hz. What would the horizontal frequency have to be if the scanning were increased to 850 lines?

PROJECTS

1. Make an oscilloscope from one of the many excellent kits available. Use it to examine the wave form of human speech or music.
2. Make a sonar system that you can use to measure relatively short distances.

ELECTRONICS

Lesson 98 *TRANSMISSION OF ELECTROMAGNETIC WAVES*

Early in the summer of 1895 a young Italian inventor, Guglielmo Marconi,* happened upon a scientific article describing Hertz's experiments with electromagnetic waves (see Lesson 89). After reading the article with great interest, Marconi, then only twenty-one years of age, conceived the idea of using Hertzian waves as a means of communication. Beginning experiments immediately, he soon found that by (1) increasing the power of the transmitter, (2) stretching a wire high in the air for an antenna, and (3) improving upon Hertz's

could be greatly increased. So successful was he with these improvements that, by 1898, he had spanned a distance of 12 mi and, by 1900, had communicated successfully with another station 200 mi away.

The first authentic broadcast of the human voice by wireless waves took place on Christmas day in 1906. The feat was accomplished by Prof. F. A. Fessenden of the University of Pittsburgh. Using the continuous oscillating currents from a high-frequency electrical generator of his own design, instead of the damped oscillations of

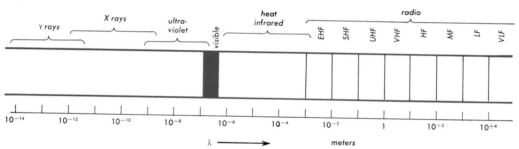

Fig. A. Electromagnetic spectrum showing wave lengths of radio bands.

methods of detection, distances over which signals could be transmitted and received

* Guglielmo Marconi (1874-1939), Italian inventor, famous for establishing wireless telegraphy on a commercial basis, was born at Bologna on April 25, 1874. Privately educated, he became interested in electrical phenomena at the age of twenty. During his lifetime he initiated many new ideas in wireless telegraphy, each one of which contributed to greater and greater range. In World War I, he served in the Italian Army and Navy as a technical expert. In 1909 Marconi, jointly with Ferdinand Braun, was awarded the Nobel Prize in physics, the Albert Medal of the Royal Society of Arts and, in the United States, the Franklin and the John Fritz Medals.

a discharging capacitor circuit, he was able to broadcast music from an experimental station at Brant Rock, Massachusetts, and have it heard by U.S. naval ships nearby. It is a most incredible fact that the importance of this great event and its future possibilities were not generally recognized.

The Electromagnetic Spectrum. A chart of the electromagnetic spectrum extending from the shortest known waves, the γ rays, to the longest known waves of radio is given in Fig. A. The long wave-length end

Table 1. Radio Wave Bands

Band Designation		Function	ν	λ
VLF	very low frequency	———	3 KHz	100 Km
LF	low frequency	Aircraft beacons	30 KHz	10 Km
MF	medium frequency	AM Radio	300 KHz	1 Km
HF	high frequency	Short-wave Radio	3,000 KHz	100 m
VHF	very high frequency	FM, Television	30 MHz	10 m
UHF	ultra high frequency	Hi-band Television	300 MHz	1 m
SHF	super high frequency	Radar	3,000 MHz	10 cm
EHF	extremely high frequency	———	30,000 MHz	1 cm
			300,000 MHz	.1 cm

of this chart is seen to be divided into equally spaced bands with the designations shown in Table 1.

The SHF and EHF bands are frequently referred to as *microwaves*.

Amplitude modulation, AM, broadcasting in the United States is restricted to frequencies between 550 KHz to 1550 KHz. *Frequency modulation, FM,* stations broadcast between 88 MHz to 108 MHz. Television stations operate in the very high frequencies starting about where the FM band ends and continuing into the higher frequencies.

The relation between the frequency and wave length of radio waves is given by the equation—

$$c = \nu\lambda \qquad (1)$$

where ν is the frequency, λ the wave length, and c the speed of the waves. In a vacuum, c is the same for all electromagnetic waves and is equal to the speed of light:

$$c = 3 \times 10^8 \, \frac{\text{m}}{\text{sec}} \qquad (2)$$

Example. What is the wave length of a station that is broadcasting on a frequency of 640 KHz?

Solution. From Eq. (1):

$$\lambda = \frac{c}{\nu}$$

$$\lambda = \frac{3 \times 10^8 \, \frac{\text{m}}{\text{sec}}}{640,000}$$

$$\lambda = 469 \text{ m}$$

Vacuum-tube Oscillator. To broadcast the human voice by radio, a generator of alternating current of extremely high frequency and constant amplitude is required. In commercial broadcasting stations and amateur transmitters, this function is performed by a vacuum tube in a circuit designed to be extremely stable in regard to its frequency.

One type of oscillator circuit is shown in Fig. B. The variable capacitor, C_1, is tuned so that the L_1C_1 circuit resonates at the desired frequency given by Eq. (7), in Lesson 88. When the switch, S, in the plate circuit is closed, the sudden flow of electrons in L_2 will induce an electron flow in

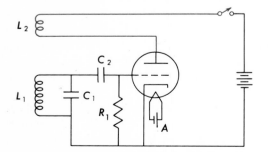

Fig. B. Vacuum-tube oscillator circuit for generating radio waves of constant amplitude.

L_1. Once this current is set oscillating at its natural frequency, the varying voltage on the capacitor C_1 will appear across the grid through capacitor C_2 and will cause an oscillating current to flow in the plate circuit. See Fig. C. The coil winding L_2

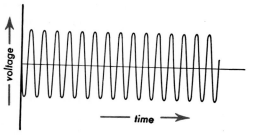

Fig. C. Continuous oscillations in a vacuum-tube oscillator circuit like that in Fig. A.

acts like a transformer to allow part of the oscillating energy in the plate circuit to be fed back into the grid LC circuit to keep it going. Such a *feedback* system is neces-

plate. Capacitor C_2 prevents these electrons leaving the grid. If it did not, in a short time, the grid would become so negative that the entire flow of electrons to the plate would stop. Therefore, a value of R_1 is selected so that the leakage of electrons from the grid is such that a small but constant value of negative charge remains on the grid at all times. This permits the tube to operate more efficiently and with less distortion, as was explained in the section on amplifiers.

Radio Transmitter. To use an oscillating tube circuit, of the kind described above, as part of a radio transmitter, the high-frequency oscillations in the L_2C_2 circuit must be modified by sound waves and then applied to an antenna and ground system for broadcasting as electromagnetic waves. A simplified circuit diagram showing one of the many ways of doing this is given in Fig. D. There are three parts to this particular

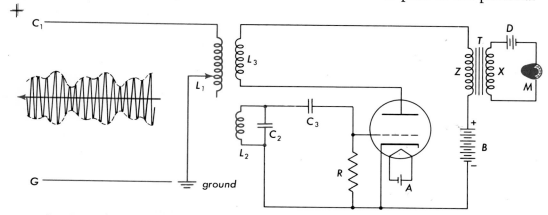

Fig. D. Radio transmitter employing a microphone and only one tube as an oscillator.

sary to prevent the oscillations from damping out due to ohmic resistance in the grid circuit.

On each half cycle, when the grid is positively charged, it would attract some electrons from the main stream going to the

"hook up": (1) *the microphone circuit* containing a battery D and a transformer T, (2) *the oscillator circuit* in the middle, and (3) *the antenna circuit*, C_1L_1G, at the left.

By talking or singing into the microphone, the diaphragm inside moves back and forth with the sound vibrations, thus altering the steady current previously flowing around the circuit DMX. An illustration of the pulsating current is shown in Fig. $E(a)$. Current pulsations in X, the trans-

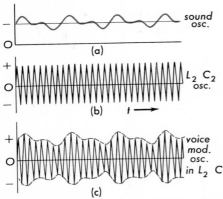

(a) sound osc.

(b) $t \longrightarrow$ $L_2 C_2$ osc.

(c) voice mod. osc. in L_2 C_2

Fig. E. Graphs of (a) sound waves, (b) continuous oscillations in L_2C_2, and (c) voice-modulated oscillations in L_2C_2.

former primary, cause similar pulsations in Z, the secondary circuit carrying the plate current. The effect of the relatively low-frequency audio currents on the high-frequency oscillations already there is to alter, or *modulate*, their amplitude, as shown in diagram (c).

The continuous wave produced by the radio-frequency oscillations alone is called the *carrier wave*, and the variation of its amplitude by audio frequency is *amplitude modulation*. *Frequency modulation* of the carrier wave is produced when the audio frequency is made to vary the frequency of the carrier wave around a central value. FM offers freedom from "static" as one of its advantages over AM.

Through the *coupling* of L_3 with L_1 the modulated oscillations are induced in the antenna circuit by resonance and are radiated as electromagnetic waves of the same

frequency and form. Although radio transmitters with one vacuum tube have been used by radio amateurs, it is customary to find transmitters with half a dozen or more tubes or transistors. The principal function of additional tubes or transistors in receivers, as well as in transmitters, is to amplify currents wherever they are needed and thereby give greater transmitting range and clearer reception.

Radio Receiver. The electromagnetic waves broadcast by the transmitter induce a very small voltage in every length of wire encountered as they spread out from the transmitting antenna. If a fairly long length of wire is placed high in the air and insulated at both ends, a reasonable voltage will be induced in this wire. It might be expected that, if this wire were connected to an earphone and the ground, as shown in Fig. F, that the station should be heard.

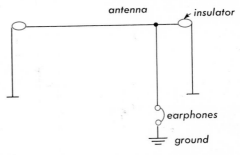

antenna   insulator

earphones

ground

Fig. F. Earphones connected between antenna and ground.

However, the alternating current produced by the radio station in the antenna is in the order of many thousands or millions of hertz and so the inertia of the metal earphone diaphragm prevents it from moving at all.

The simple circuit shown in Fig. F also suffers from another difficulty. All stations either powerful or close enough to the radio antenna to produce a voltage in it would be heard simultaneously. In order to make a practical receiver, a circuit that is able to pick out one station from the others is required. This needed selectivity is provided by the transformer and variable capacitor, C_1, as shown in Fig. G. The voltage pro-

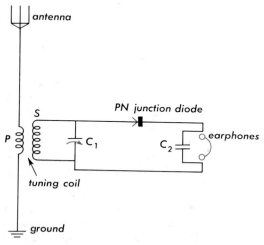

Fig. G. Diagram for a simple radio receiver.

duced in the antenna sends an ac through the primary coil, P, and to the ground. By transformer action, a higher voltage will be induced in the secondary winding, S, of the tuning coil. To select the frequency of the desired transmitting station requires the addition of capacitor C_1. This capacitor and the secondary coil form a series resonant circuit. Capacitor C_1 is adjusted so that its reactance at the desired radio frequency is equal to the inductive reactance. When this condition of resonance is established, the flow of current for this frequency will be limited only by the resistance of the circuit. Frequencies higher than the resonant one will encounter a high inductive reactance in the coil, while lower frequencies will produce a high capacitive reactance in the capacitor. In either case, the current in the circuit will be much lower than when resonance is established. With a high cur-

rent flowing through the coil at resonance, a large voltage will be developed across it. This voltage is now applied to the PN junction.

The PN junction is used as a rectifier or *detector* to change the ac to pulsating dc, as shown in Fig. G. The current flowing through the coil of the earphone is now in only one direction. However, because the PN junction is used as a half-wave rectifier, the earphone diaphragm will be pulled and released by each pulse of current. Capacitor C_2, acting with the inductance of the coil in the earphones, acts as a filter to smooth or average out the pulsating dc. The diaphragm can very easily follow the variations in amplitude, shown in color in Fig. H,

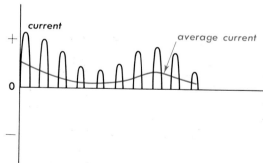

Fig. H. Rectified or detected AM radio wave.

which corresponds to the original amplitude variations added to the carrier at the transmitting station. This detector can also be connected to a suitable audio amplifier so that there will be sufficient power to operate a loudspeaker.

The Dynamic Loudspeaker. A loudspeaker of conventional design is shown in cross section in Fig. I. Its function is the same as that of a telephone receiver: to change audio-frequency currents from the last amplifier in a radio receiver or public-address system into sound waves of the same form.

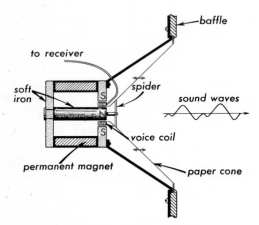

Fig. I. Cross-section diagram of dynamic loud-speaker.

There are two main parts to every loud-speaker. First, there is a strong shell-type magnet whose function it is to provide a field radially outward from a central N pole, across a narrow air gap, to a ringlike S pole. In most speakers this field is provided by a *permanent magnet*. The second element is a small cylindrical *voice coil* consisting of a dozen or so turns of wire fixed near the apex of a *paper cone* and centered in the narrow field gap by a springy fiber disk called a *spider*.

When a varying current from the amplifier passes through the voice coil, varying forces are exerted causing it to vibrate back and forth along its axis. As the cone is driven back and forth, it acts like a plunger, its large area setting considerable air into vibration. The walls of the room or cabinet behind which the speaker is mounted act as a *baffle*, preventing sound waves from the back surface of the cone from getting around to interfere destructively with the waves from the front surface. A good demonstration is to be had by removing a speaker from its normal mounted position and listening to the distorted sounds it seems to produce. The low-pitched sounds in particular are noticeably absent.

Large-sized speakers with a suitably large baffle area are particularly good at reproducing and dispersing low-pitched sounds. Because of diffraction and interference, however, high-pitched sounds are emitted in a narrow beam and in a forward direction only. Speakers with small cones, on the other hand, are particularly good on the high-pitched notes but are generally poor at reproducing the lows.*

* For a detailed treatment of the principles of radio see "Basic Radio," by J. Hoag, D. Van Nostrand Co., Inc.

QUESTIONS

1. (a) Who is credited with the invention of wireless telegraphy? (b) What kind of waves were used?
2. (a) What is a vacuum-tube oscillator? (b) What does it produce? (c) What determines the oscillation frequency?
3. Where does the energy come from that keeps the amplitude of the oscillations constant?
4. Name the basic elements of a simple radio transmitter.
5. (a) What is a carrier wave? (b) What is an audio frequency? (c) What is a radio frequency?

6. (a) What determines the frequency of a transmitter? (b) How can you change stations on a radio set?

7. (a) What is modulation? (b) What is distortion?

8. (a) What is the difference between AM and FM? (b) Which method is better and why?

9. Why are most radio sets more complicated than the one described in the text?

10. (a) How does a PN junction make the radio wave audible? (b) Could you use a vacuum tube to do this as well? (c) Which would you prefer? Why?

11. What are the principal elements of a dynamic loudspeaker?

12. Why is a baffle required for a dynamic loudspeaker?

13. Is the design of a good loudspeaker easy? Explain.

PROBLEMS

1. Draw a circuit diagram for a vacuum-tube oscillator for generating radio frequencies of constant amplitude.

2. What is the wave length of a station that is broadcasting on a frequency of 1500 KHz?

3. What is the frequency of a station that is broadcasting on a wave length of 100 m?

4. Radio telescopes are often tuned to the frequency of the radiation from atomic hydrogen, which is distributed through outer space. If the hydrogen wave length is 21 cm, to what frequency should the radio telescope be tuned?

PROJECTS

1. Make a simple crystal radio receiver.

2. Make a simple one- or two-tube radio receiver.

Atomic Physics

The present state of atomic theory is characterised by the fact that we not only believe the existence of atoms to be proved beyond a doubt, but also we even believe that we have an intimate knowledge of the constituents of the individual atoms.

According to our present conceptions, an atom of an element is built up of a nucleus that has a positive electrical charge and is the seat of by far the greatest part of the atomic mass, together with a number of electrons, all having the same negative charge and mass, which move at distances from the nucleus that are very great compared to the dimensions of the nucleus or of the electrons themselves. In this picture we at once see a striking resemblance to a planetary system, such as we have in our own solar system. Just as the simplicity of the laws that govern the motions of the solar system is intimately concerned with the circumstance that the dimensions of the moving bodies are small in relation to the orbits, so the corresponding relations in atomic structure provide us with an explanation of an essential feature of natural phenomena in so far as these depend on the properties of the elements.

To the first class belong most of the ordinary physical and chemical properties of substances, such as their state of aggregation, colour, and chemical reactivity. These properties depend on the motion of the electron system and the way in which this motion changes under the influence of different external actions. . . . On the other hand, the structure of the nucleus will be responsible for the second class of properties that are shown in the radioactivity of substances. In the radioactive processes we meet with an explosion of the nucleus, whereby positive or negative particles, the so-called α- and β-particles, are expelled with very great velocities.

Prof. Niels Bohr: "The Structure of the Atom," *Nature,* vol. 112, 1923, p. 29.

◄ **Pittsburgh is the first city to be powered by the first atomic-electric generating station that was built for exclusively civilian needs. The plant is located at Shippingsport, Pennsylvania.**

Westinghouse Electric Corp.

Lesson 99 *THE ELEMENTS AND THEIR ISOTOPES*

Although no one has ever seen an atom, there is no doubt in the mind of the scientist

the cathode. A tube designed to illustrate this is shown in Fig. A.

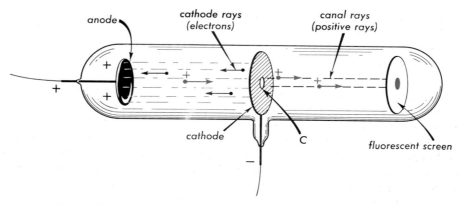

Fig. A. Experiment illustrating canal rays discovered by Goldstein.

that such particles really exist. To the physicists and chemists who have built up and established the current theories of the structure of matter, atoms are as real as any material objects that are large enough to be seen with the eyes or to be felt with the hands. Their reality is evidenced by hundreds of experiments that can be planned and executed in the laboratory.

The Discovery of Positive Rays. During the latter part of the nineteenth century, many physicists were investigating the various properties of cathode rays. In 1886, Eugene Goldstein in Germany designed a special discharge tube and with it discovered new rays called *canal rays*. The term is derived from the fact that the rays, traveling in straight lines through a vacuum tube in the opposite direction to cathode rays, pass through and emerge from a canal or hole in

Shortly after the measurement of the electronic charge by J. J. Thomson in 1896, Wilhelm Wien, a German Nobelist, deflected a beam of canal rays in a magnetic field and came to the conclusion that the rays consisted of positively charged particles. Because of this and other experiments, canal rays have become more commonly known as *positive rays*.

Since the time of Goldstein's discovery, positive rays have been found to be charged atoms of different weights. The origin of the charge carried by such atoms is explained briefly as follows. As the electrons from the cathode stream down the tube toward the anode, they occasionally collide with the atoms and molecules of the small quantity of remaining gas, knocking electrons from them.

This process, called *ionization*, is illustrated by a schematic diagram of a single oxygen atom in Fig. B. Before the collision, the atom as a whole, with its eight electrons and eight equal positive charges on the nucleus, has no net charge. After one of the electrons is removed by collision, it has only seven electrons and, therefore, a net positive charge equivalent in amount to the charge of one electron.

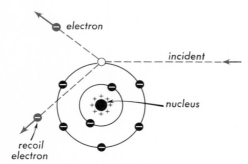

Fig. B. Schematic diagram of an oxygen atom in the process of becoming ionized by a collision with a high-speed electron.

Because the atom is now positively charged, the anode repels and the cathode attracts such atoms, accelerating them toward the cathode. There exists, therefore,

between the anode and cathode, two streams of particles: electrons moving toward the anode and positively charged atoms or molecules moving toward the cathode.

Any process by which an electron is removed from an atom or molecule is called *ionization*. The resulting charged particle is called a *positive ion*.

The Thomson Mass Spectrograph. In 1911, J. J. Thomson developed a method of measuring the relative masses of different atoms and molecules by deflecting positive rays in a magnetic and an electric field. The apparatus he developed for doing this is shown schematically in Fig. C and is called *Thomson's mass spectrograph*.

The entire spectrograph is enclosed in an airtight glass chamber, which is thoroughly evacuated. Then, a small quantity of the gas, the masses of whose atoms are to be measured, is admitted to the bulb at the left. When a high voltage is applied, electrons from the cathode ionize atoms and molecules in the region between the anode, A, and the cathode, C. Traveling to the

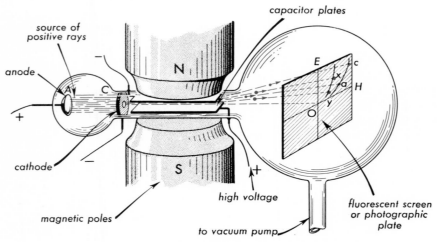

Fig. C. Diagram of J. J. Thomson's mass spectrograph.

right, many of these positively charged particles pass through the narrow hole in the cathode, thus forming a very narrow pencil of rays. Leaving the cathode with a constant velocity, they then pass between the poles of an electromagnet and the parallel plates of a capacitor, and thence to a fluorescent screen at the right end of the spectrograph.

The two capacitor plates, when charged, exert an upward force on the particles, deflecting them from the point O toward E by an amount—

$$\Delta y = k \frac{q}{m} E \left(\frac{1}{v}\right)^2 \qquad (1)$$

where E is the electric field, q is the charge of the particle, and k is a constant depending upon the dimensions.

The magnetic field, on the other hand, with its magnetic lines vertically downward and in the plane of the page, exerts a force at right angles to this, deflecting the particles into the page from the point O toward H by an amount—

$$\Delta x = k \frac{q}{m} B \left(\frac{1}{v}\right) \qquad (2)$$

where B is the magnetic field.

In order to determine the relation between x and y, we first rewrite Eq. (2) as follows:

$$\frac{1}{v} = \frac{\Delta x}{k \frac{q}{m} B} \qquad (3)$$

and insert it into Eq. (1), giving—

$$\Delta y = k \frac{q}{m} E \left(\frac{\Delta x}{k \frac{q}{m} B}\right)^2$$

or—

$$\Delta y = \left(\frac{E}{k \frac{q}{m} B^2}\right) \times \Delta x^2$$

Because all the terms within the parentheses are constants, and recalling that pa-

rabola is given by $y = cx^2$, we see that particles with a fixed charge and mass will fall along a parabola.

If the gas in the apparatus is not pure, but contains two kinds of atoms, the positive ions passing through the cathode will have two different masses. Each ion will contain the same positive charge and will, therefore, experience the same electric and magnetic forces when passing through the fields. However, the heavier particles will not be deflected as much as the lighter ones. The net result is that the heavier particles form one parabolic arc, and the lighter particles another.

By substituing a photographic plate for the fluorescent screen and exposing it to the rays for several minutes, photographs like those reproduced in Fig. D are obtained. The continual bombardment of the photographic plate by atoms and molecules has the same effect as does light, and images are produced upon development of the plate. The upper half of each picture is taken with the connections as shown in Fig. C and the lower half by reversing the polarity of the electromagnet and exposing for an equal length of time.

When this photograph was taken, the spectrograph contained *hydrogen, oxygen,* and *mercury,* and the magnetic field was relatively weak. From the known strengths of both the electric and magnetic fields and from the assumption that each atom carries a unit positive charge, the mass of the atoms producing each parabola can be calculated. The largest parabola is made by ionized hydrogen atoms (H^+). Hydrogen, being the lightest of elements, is assigned a relative mass, or mass number, of 1; $A = 1$.

The next largest parabola is shown by the calculations to be ionized hydrogen molecules (H_2^+) of mass 2. The next three are made by ionized atoms (O^+) of mass

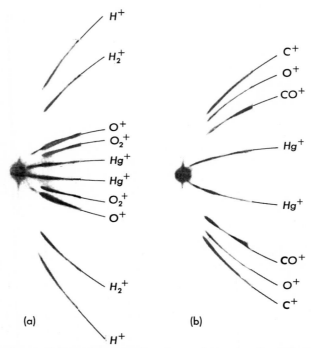

Fig. D. Reproductions of the photographs of parabolas made with Thomson's mass spectrograph.

16, ionized oxygen molecules of mass 32, and ionized mercury atoms (Hg^+) with a mass of approximately 200.

Thomson's Discovery of Isotopes. In 1912, Thomson, in comparing the mass of the neon atom with the known masses of other elements, discovered two parabolic curves for neon in place of one. Upon computing the masses of the particles involved, the stronger of two parabolas was found to be traced by particles of mass 20 and the other, a fainter parabola, by particles of mass 22.

Because the atomic weight of neon was then known to be 20.2, Thomson expressed the belief that neon is composed of two kinds of atoms, 90% of which have a mass of 20 and the other 10% a mass of 22. Because these two kinds of atoms exist as a mixture

and cannot be separated chemically, their atomic weight, when measured by chemical methods, is found to be their average value 20.2.

The discovery of two kinds of neon atoms, identical chemically but differing in atomic weight, suggested the possibility that all other elements whose atomic weights were not whole numbers might also be mixtures of atoms which do have whole number weights. Not only has this been confirmed by experiment, but a large majority of the elements have been found to be mixtures of from two to ten different kinds of atoms.

To all atoms of different weight belonging to the same element Soddy gave the name *isotopes*. The external structures of all isotopes of a given element are identical. The two atoms Ne-20 and Ne-22, shown in

Fig. E, are neon isotopes. Each of these neutral atoms, before it is ionized to become a positive ray, has ten external electrons and ten positive charges on the nucleus. They differ only in the weight of the nucleus.

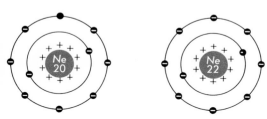

Fig. E. Schematic diagrams of the two different kinds of neon atoms, one of mass 20 and the other of mass 22. The external electron structure of two such isotopes are identical.

Atoms having different weights, but of the same chemical element, have the same atomic number and are called isotopes.

Aston's Mass Measurements. Immediately following World War I in 1919, F. W. Aston developed a new and improved type of mass spectrograph. Employing both electric and magnetic fields, the device presented an improvement over Thomson's mass spectrograph by focusing rays of different velocities but of the same mass to the same point. This had two important effects: (1) it was now possible to observe rare isotopes that might otherwise escape detection and (2) it produced sharper images of the different masses on the photographic plate, so that their masses could be more accurately measured.

An Aston mass *spectrogram* is reproduced at the top of Fig. F. In taking this particular photograph Aston had introduced into his apparatus, among other things, a little *hydrochloric acid* (HCl), *carbon monoxide* (CO), and *sulfur dioxide* (SO_2). Being close together in the periodic table, the elements of these compounds furnish an excellent demonstration of the linear shift of atoms and molecules differing in mass by one unit. It is found from this and other photographs that sulfur has three isotopes

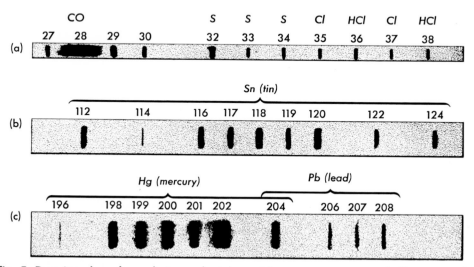

Fig. F. Drawings based on photographs taken with a mass spectrograph illustrating the linear shift of atoms differing by one unit of mass. (a) Carbon monoxide, sulfur, chlorine, and argon lines. (b) and (c) Isotopes of mercury, tin, and lead.

with masses 32, 33, and 34, and that chlorine has two isotopes of masses 35 and 37.

Because the atomic weight of chlorine is 35.46, then for every atom of mass 37 in a given quantity of chlorine gas there are four of mass 35. Mixed together in these proportions they give an average mass of 35.4.

The photographic lines corresponding to masses 28, 36, and 38 are due to diatomic molecules CO and HCl, each molecule having the combined weight of its constituent atoms. Because there are two relatively abundant chlorine isotopes, there are two kinds of HCl molecules. One type, H^1Cl^{35}, has a mass of 36, and the other type, H^1Cl^{37}, a mass of 38.

So successful was Aston with his mass measurements and his determination of isotopes of different elements that he attempted an investigation of the entire periodic table. All of the known elements are listed in Appendix II, with all of their observed isotopes. In each case, the most abundant isotope is given in heavy type, while the very rare isotopes, *i.e.*, those present to less than 1%, are given in parentheses. Where more than one isotope is given in heavy type, the isotopes occur with almost equal abundance. The isotopes given in italics represent unstable atoms, which are responsible for *radioactivity*, the subject of another lesson.

Recent developments in mass spectroscopy have made it possible to detect exceptionally rare isotopes. In neon, for example, an isotope of mass number 21 has been found, making three in all, with relative abundances as follows:

isotope	Ne-20	Ne-21	Ne-22
abundance, %	90.4	0.6	9.0

Isobars. *Atoms having the same atomic weight, but of different chemical elements are called isobars.*

The first pair of isobars (see App. II)

occurs in argon and calcium. The principal isotope of argon, atomic number 18, has a mass of 40, as does also the principal isotope of calcium, atomic number 20. Other examples are Cr-54 and Fe-54, Ge-76 and Se-76, Rb-87 and Sr-87, Zn-92 and Mo-92. The isobars Hg-204 and Pb-204 are illustrated in Fig. F(c).

Atomic Mass. For many purposes it is convenient to know the masses, M, of atoms in kilograms. For easy calculations, the following value may be used:

$$M = 1.660 \times 10^{-27} \text{ Kg} \qquad (4)$$

This number, multiplied by the "atomic weight" of any atom, will give its mass in kilograms.

Compared with the mass of the electron, namely—

$$m = 9.1091 \times 10^{-31} \text{ Kg} \qquad (5)$$

an atom of unit mass would be 1823 times as heavy. *The hydrogen atom is slightly heavier than one unit mass and is about 1840 times as heavy as the electron.* This latter number is convenient to remember for it is often quoted to illustrate the enormous difference between the mass of the nucleus of a hydrogen atom and the mass of its one and only electron.

Actually, the atomic masses of all isotopes, except for the standard mass (carbon-12), deviate very slightly from the mass number. The significance of this mass defect will be studied later.

Atomic number is defined as that number of electrons in the atom and specifies its position in the periodic table of elements. (See the first column of App. II.)

Atomic mass is defined as the mass of any isotope on a scale in which carbon-12 has a mass of exactly 12.0000.

Mass number is defined as that whole number nearest the actual mass of an isotope measured in atomic mass units. (See column four of App. II.)

Atomic weight is defined as the average weight of all the isotopes of an element weighed according to relative abundance and expressed in atomic mass units.

QUESTIONS

1. (a) What are canal rays? (b) Who discovered them? (c) How are they detected?
2. (a) What is a mass spectrograph? (b) Make a diagram of one and explain how it operates.
3. (a) Who discovered isotopes? (b) What are isotopes?
4. What is meant by (a) atomic number, (b) mass number, and (c) atomic mass?
5. How do isotopes of any given element differ from each other?
6. What is meant by relative abundance?
7. What are isobars? Give an example.
8. What do the more or less equal spacings of the mass spectrograms shown in Fig. F suggest regarding the relative masses of atoms?
9. Name five members of (a) the alkali metals and (b) the alkaline earths. (See Appendix.)
10. What chemical element has the greatest number of isotopes? (See Appendix.)
11. Make a list of elements having (a) atoms of one mass only and (b) only two isotopes. (See Appendix.)
12. Why were chemists unable to discover isotopes with the usual chemical methods?
13. Would salt made of chlorine-35 taste differently from that made with -37? Explain.
14. What is the difference between the atomic number and atomic mass of the atom?

PROBLEMS

1. The atomic mass of aluminum is 26.98. Find the mass, in grams, of one aluminum atom.
2. The atomic mass of cobalt is 58.93. How many atoms are there in one gram of cobalt metal?
3. The atomic mass of manganese is 54.94. How many atoms are there in one gram of manganese metal?
4. The atomic masses of carbon and oxygen are 12.00 and 16.00, respectively. Find the mass, in grams, of a carbon dioxide molecule. (See Fig. A in Lesson 33.)
5. The atomic masses of hydrogen, carbon, and oxygen are 1.01, 12.00, and 16.00, respectively. How many ethyl alcohol molecules are there in one gram of ethyl alcohol? (See Fig. A in Lesson 33.)
6. The two isotopes of lithium have masses of 6 and 7 atomic mass units. If the

normal mixture of these atoms has an atomic weigtht of 6.94, what is the relative abundance of the two isotopes?

7. The normal mixture of chlorine found in nature has an atomic weight of approximately 35.5. What is the relative abundance of the two chlorine isotopes 35 and 37?

8. Boron has two stable isotopes, 10 and 11. Find their relative abundance in a normal mixture if the atomic weight is 10.82.

PROJECTS

1. Measure the e/m ratio of electrons using readily available surplus 5-in. cathode-ray tubes. An oscilloscope can be modified to do the same thing and is easier because all the power-supply voltages are already present.

2. Make a chart showing all the naturally occurring isotopes of the elements.

ATOMIC PHYSICS

Lesson 100 STRUCTURE OF THE ATOM

The structure of the atom was a complete mystery at the beginning of the twentieth century, and represented an enticing challenge to the scientists of that time. The solution of this mystery was achieved by the piecing together of many indirect bits of evidence.

Models. Because the atom cannot be seen, one can never be sure what its structure is. The best that can be done is to propose a model. The acceptance of the model will then depend upon whether or not the experimental evidence is consistent with the model. If there is consistency, the model is accepted. If later inconsistent evidence is found, the model must be either replaced or modified. In the following lessons, we shall study the evidence that leads to the Bohr model of the atom.

The Thomson Atom. Early in the twentieth century J. J. Thomson proposed a type of electron-shell structure for all atoms. His model structures were worked out by mathematics from Coulomb's law for charged particles and soon became known as the *plum-pudding atom*.

Thomson visualized all the positive charge of an atom as being spread uniformly throughout a sphere about 10^{-8} cm in diameter, with the electrons as smaller particles distributed in shells somewhat as shown in Fig. A. While the net force exerted by the positively charged sphere on each electron is toward the center of the sphere, the electrons mutually repel each other and form rings.

An excellent demonstration of the tendency to form rings can be obtained as shown in Fig. B. A glass dish, 15 to 20 cm

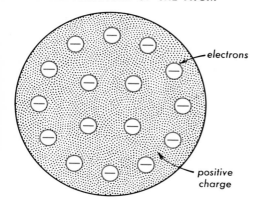

Fig. A. Diagram of the Thomson atom model.

in diameter, is wound with about 30 turns of No. 14 insulated copper wire. Common steel sewing needles are then mounted in small corks (8 mm diam. and 8 mm long),

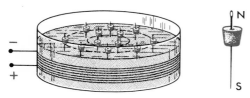

Fig. B. Floating needles in a magnetic field demonstrating electron shell structure of Thomson atom.

as shown at the right, and magnetized by stroking them from top to bottom with the N pole of a strong magnet.

With water in the dish and a current of 1 to 2 amp through the coil, a single needle is placed upright in the water. Released, it will migrate to the center where the magnetic field is strongest. The addition of needles, one after another, near the edge of the dish will result in the formation of geometrically symmetrical patterns and rings.

An increase or decrease in current will cause any given pattern to shrink or expand, corresponding to a greater or lesser positive charge. The stability of such ring

patterns undoubtedly influenced the later extension by Bohr and Stoner of the Bohr model of the hydrogen atom to all atoms.

Rutherford's Scattering Experiments. During the years 1905-1913, while Thomson was working out his model of the atom, Sir Ernest Rutherford, and his collaborators H. Geiger and E. Marsden, performed in England a series of ingenious experiments on the scattering of α particles. From the results of these studies it was inferred that the positive charge and mass of every atom is confined to a particle smaller than 10^{-12} cm in diameter. Historically, this marks the beginning of the idea of a nuclear atom proposed formally by Niels Bohr several years later. A schematic diagram of the scattering experiments is given in Fig. C.

High-speed α particles (helium atoms with both electrons removed), from the radioactive element radon and confined to a narrow beam by a hole in a lead block, were made to strike a very thin gold foil, F. While most of the α particles go straight through the foil as if there were nothing there, some of them collide with atoms of the foil and bounce off at some angle. The latter phenomenon is known as *Rutherford scattering*.

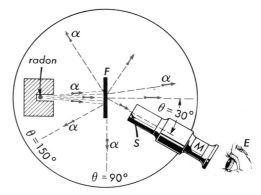

Fig. C. Diagram of the Rutherford scattering experiments.

The observations and measurements made in the experiment consisted of counting the number of particles scattered off at different angles θ. This was done by the scintillation method of observation. Each α particle striking the fluorescent screen, S, produces a tiny flash of light, called a *scintillation*, and is observed as such by the microscope, M. With the microscope fixed in one position, the number of scintillations observed in its field within a period of several minutes was counted, then the microscope was turned to another angle and the number again counted for an equal period of time.

In the schematic diagram of Fig. D, α

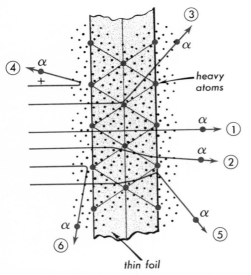

Fig. D. Schematic diagram of α particle being scattered by the atomic nuclei in a thin metallic film.

particles are shown passing through a foil three atomic layers thick. Although the nuclear atom was not known at the time the experiments were performed, each atom is drawn in the figure with the positively charged nucleus at the center and surrounded by a number of electrons. Be-

cause most of the film is *free space*, the majority of the α particles go through with little or no deflection, as indicated by ray (1). Other α's, like (2), passing relatively close to an atom nucleus are deflected at an angle of a few degrees. Occasionally, however, an almost *head-on collision* occurs as shown by (4) and the incoming α particle is turned back toward the source.

Repeated experiments with different films made of light and heavy elements, like copper, silver, and gold, showed that the relative number of the wide-angled deflections increases with atomic weight. From all of these results and numerous calculations, Rutherford came to the following conclusions: (1) *that all of the positive charge of an atom is confined to a particle smaller than 10^{-12} cm in diameter;* (2) *that practically all of the weight of an atom is confined to this same particle;* and (3) *that the amount of positive charge in atomic units is approximately equal to half the atomic weight.*

As an α particle approaches an atom, as represented by ray (6) in Fig. D, it is repelled by the heavy, positively charged nucleus and deflected in such a way as to make it follow a curved path. The magnitude of the repulsive force is at all times given by Coulomb's law:

$$F = k \frac{QQ'}{r^2} \qquad (1)$$

Whatever the force of repulsion may be at one distance r, it becomes four times as great at half the distance, nine times as great at one-third the distance, sixteen times as great at one-quarter the distance, etc. We see, therefore, that, at very close range, the mutual repulsion of the two particles increases very rapidly and finally becomes so great that the lighter α particle is turned away. The repelling force, still acting, gives the particle a push, causing it to recede with the same velocity it approached with. The actual trajectory is in every case a hyperbolic path with the nucleus at the focus. (See Fig. E.)

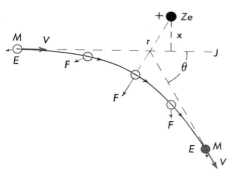

Fig. E. Diagram of the deflection of an α particle by a nucleus. Rutherford scattering.

Although an α particle (mass number, 4) is light compared with an atom of a metal like gold (mass number, 197), it is 7000 times heavier than a single electron. For this reason, the electrons surrounding the atomic nucleus are pushed to either side as the α particle goes speeding through, and they have little effect upon the shape of the trajectory.

A graph representing the force of repulsion between an α particle and a positively charged nucleus is shown in Fig. F. Diagram (a) shows the rapid increase in force as the distance decreases, while diagram (b) shows the rapid rise in potential energy.

The potential energy between electric charges is analogous to the potential energy of points in the gravitational field of a mass. (See Lesson 30.) In gravitational fields, magnetic fields, and electric fields, the force per unit mass, pole strength, and charge, respectively, is inversely proportional to the square of the distance, r, whereas the respective potential energies are inversely proportional to the distance.

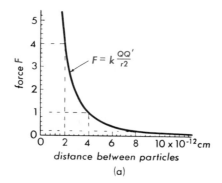

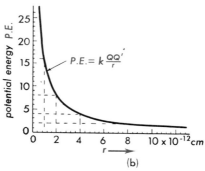

Fig. F. Graphs representing the repulsion between a positively charged nucleus and an α particle. (a) Coulomb's law giving the repelling force, F, and (b) the potential curve giving the energy.

For the potential energy of a charge, Q', in an electric field, we have—

$$PE = k \frac{QQ'}{r} \qquad (2)$$

The reason for giving this equation, and the potential energy curve in Fig. F, is that from it an interesting mechanical model for demonstrating Rutherford scattering can be derived. Such a model is illustrated in Fig. G(a), where the circular peak at the right represents the nucleus of an atom and has a form generated by rotating the curve of Fig. F, about its vertical axis at $r = 0$.

Marbles, representing α particles, roll down a chute and along a practically level plane where they approach the potential hill. Approaching the hill at various angles, the marbles roll up to a certain height and then off to one side or the other. The paths

Thus the potential energy of the α particle close to the nucleus is analogous to the potential energy of a marble on the hillside, and the electrostatic force of repulsion is

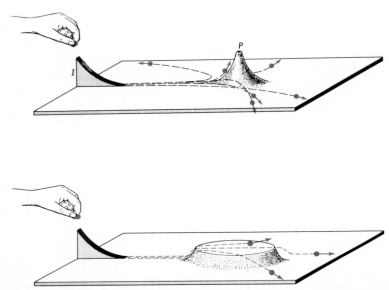

Fig. G. Mechanical model of an atomic nucleus for demonstrating Rutherford scattering. (a) Scattering from a concentrated center. (b) Scattering from a distributed center.

they follow, if watched from above, are hyperbolic in shape. Approaching the hill in a head-on collision, the ball rolls up to a certain point, stops, then rolls back again. By proper shaping of the hill, the potential energy of the marble of mass m is given by—

$$PE = k \frac{m}{r} \qquad (3)$$

analogous to the downhill component of the downward pull of gravity. In a later lesson, this same model is used to demonstrate the disintegration of atomic nuclei.

Figure $G(b)$ represents the Thomson model of the atom. The charge is smeared out rather than concentrated. This mechanical analogue shows that such a smeared-out charge would not deflect any incident particles to large angles.

QUESTIONS

1. Why must an atom be considered in terms of proposed models?
2. (a) What is a model? (b) How is it used?

3. (a) Propose a model for the surface of the planet Mars. (b) Describe how such a model might be useful.
4. (a) What was the form of the Thomson atom? (b) Where did he locate the positive charges? (c) Where did he locate the negative charges?
5. (a) What were the Rutherford scattering experiments? (b) What conclusions were drawn from these early experiments?
6. Can you describe a mechanical device or experiment that simulates the scattering of α particles by an atomic nucleus if the force on the α particle were attractive rather than repulsive?
7. What results should Rutherford's scattering experiments have yielded if the plum-pudding model of the atom were correct?
8. What evidence have you to indicate that there is an equal number of negative and positive charges in an atom?
9. Why did the electrons not interfere with the results of the scattering experiment?
10. Which α particle would approach closer to the nucleus of a gold atom, one with higher or lower initial velocity? When will it stop and go back?
11. In the Rutherford experiment, why do most of the α particles go right through the foil?
12. What force binds the electrons of an atom to the nucleus?

PROBLEMS

1. An α particle approaches to within 10^{-10} cm of a gold nucleus. (a) What is the force on the α particle? (b) What is its potential energy?
2. What would be the electrostatic force holding the electron to the nucleus in the hydrogen atom if they are 0.528×10^{-10} m apart?
3. How much energy would an α particle have to possess to get within 10^{-10} cm of a uranium-235 atom?
4. Develop the formula for potential energy in an electric field using the same basic argument as was used earlier for gravitational potential.

PROJECTS

1. Make a working model to demonstrate the plum-pudding atom as proposed by Thomson.
2. Make a working model based on the operation of a pin-ball machine to show how the Rutherford scattering experiment operates. This can also be used to show that indirect evidence can be used to deduce information about objects that cannot be seen.

ATOMIC PHYSICS

Lesson 101 *CONTINUOUS-EMISSION SPECTRA*

Most of the evidence bearing on the structure of the atom comes from the study of the light emitted and absorbed by matter. In this lesson, we shall study the continuous spectrum, which is characteristic of all solids and liquids.

Black-body Radiation. When a block of metal, such as iron or copper, is heated slowly to incandescence, the first noticeable change in its appearance occurs at a temperature of about 1000°K. At that temperature, the metal has a dull, red glow. As the temperature continues to rise, the color changes slowly to orange, then to yellow, and finally to white.

If the metal, as it is slowly being heated, is observed through a prism, the first appearance of visible light will be found at the extreme red end of the spectrum. As the temperature rises, the light spreads slowly out across the spectrum until, at white heat, the entire band of visible colors from red to violet is seen. At the orange stage, at which the temperature is about 1500°K, the pure spectrum colors contain red, orange, and yellow; when the yellow stage is reached (about 2000°K), the spectral green is included.

When the white stage is reached, at about 3000°K, and the spectrum is complete; a further rise in temperature continues to increase the intensity of each color with little change in colors. If the white hot metal is observed through a prism, one sees a band of pure spectrum colors: red, orange, yellow, green, blue, and violet.

What the prism has done in such an ex-periment is to separate all of the light waves according to their wave lengths, the longest waves of red light at the one side, the shortest waves of violet light at the other, and the intermediate waves at their proper places in between.

Continuous color from red through violet is characteristic of the spectrum of all solids and liquids. This means that there is a continuous set of different wave lengths present.

An experiment to demonstrate the existence of an ultraviolet and infrared spectrum is illustrated in Fig. A. The visible light from a carbon arc lamp is made to pass through a quartz lens and prism and is focused on a nearby screen.

If, at the violet end of the spectrum, the screen is painted with luminous paint, a bright fluorescence will be observed for some little distance beyond the visible violet. When the fluorescent screen is replaced by a photographic plate, the exposed and developed picture will again show the extension of the spectrum into the ultraviolet.

To detect the presence of the infrared radiations, a thermopile, connected to an ammeter, is conveniently used at the top of the screen to measure the amount of light energy falling upon the screen. The *thermopile*, made up of many thermocouples, detects slight variations in temperature, which produce current.

If the thermopile is first placed to receive ultraviolet light and slowly moved across the visible spectrum and out into the infrared region beyond, the ammeter will show a steady rise in current. The current

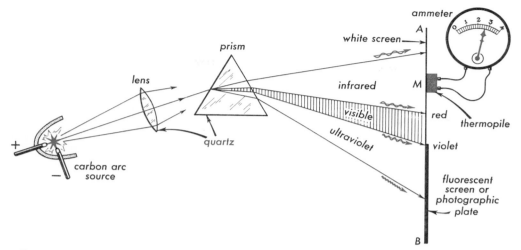

Fig. A. Experiment demonstrating the existence of the ultraviolet and infrared rays beyond the visible spectrum.

will continue to rise until a maximum is reached at a point in the region of *M*, and then it will drop off slowly as the thermopile approaches the end of the screen at *A*.

A graph of the energy from the carbon-arc source, for the different parts along the screen, is shown by the 3000°K curve in Fig. B. Each of the other curves represents

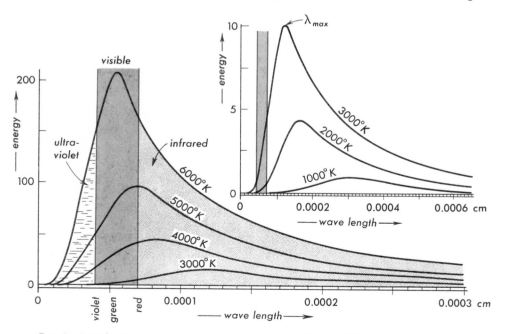

Fig. B. Distribution of energy emitted by a hot solid at different temperatures.

the amount of energy given out over the entire spectrum by some other solid at different temperatures. By studying these curves, one can observe that, at low temperatures, very little light is emitted in the visible spectrum. At 1000°K, only the visible red is seen and even that is very faint. At 2000°K, the brightness of the red not only increases, but the other colors, orange, yellow, and green, appear. At 3000°K, the temperature of a low-current carbon-arc or tungsten-filament light, all of the visible spectrum is emitted, but the maximum radiation is in the infrared. At 6000°K, the temperature of the surface of the sun, the maximum energy is radiated in the green of the visible spectrum, with an appreciable amount of ultraviolet light on the one side and the infrared on the other. Thus, the visible spectrum, as seen by the human eye, is but a small band out of all the waves emitted by a body as hot as the sun.

Wien's Displacement Law. It is an interesting fact that the wave length corresponding to maximum energy radiated by a hot body shifts to shorter and shorter waves as the temperature rises. To be more exact, if the temperature of a body is doubled, the radiated energy maximum, λ_{max}, shifts to half the wave length. If the temperature is tripled, the energy maximum shifts to one-third the wave length, etc. This is known as Wien's* displacement law and is written as an algebraic equation:

$$\lambda_{max} = C/T \qquad (1)$$

where C is a constant, found by experiment to have a value of 0.2897 cm degrees; T is the absolute temperature; and λ_{max} the

---

* Wilhelm Wien (1864-1928), German physicist, was known chiefly for important discoveries with cathode rays, canal rays, and the radiation of light. He was awarded the Nobel Prize in physics in 1911 for his discovery of the displacement law of heat radiation, named in his honor.

wave length in cm at which the maximum energy is radiated. By substituting the constant C in Eq. (1), the wave length maximum radiated by a hot body can be calculated for any temperature.

Total Radiated Energy. The total energy radiated by a hot, solid body is proportional to the fourth power of the absolute temperature. This law, known as the Stefan-Boltzmann law—

$$E = kT^4 \qquad (2)$$

has already been discussed in Lesson 45.

The Stefan-Boltzmann constant is $k = 5 \times 10^{-8}$ joule/m² − °C⁴.

The "Ultraviolet Catastrophe." Theoretical calculations were made in the early twentieth century concerning the type of spectrum that should be expected from heated matter. The expected spectrum is called the Rayleigh-Jeans law, for its proposers:

$$E = 8kT/\lambda^4 \qquad (3)$$

shows that the radiation emitted at each wave length increases rapidly as the wave length decreases. Comparison with the experimentally observed spectrum (see Fig. C(a)) shows good agreement at large wave

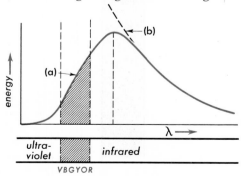

Fig. C. Graphs of the energy emitted by a hot solid. (a) The observed spectrum. (b) The Rayleigh-Jeans proposed law.

lengths, but poor agreement at short wave lengths.

In fact, the radiated energy approaches infinity at shorter wave lengths. This result, called the *ultraviolet catastrophe*, demonstrated a basic inadequacy of the current theories of matter. Max Planck, in search of an explanation, happened across the concept of *quantization*. He could explain the continuous spectrum only by assuming that light consisted of individual particles called *photons*. This theory seemed to contradict the wave theory, but, as we shall see later, both theories are compatible.

The Complete Spectrum. *Visible, ultraviolet,* and *infrared* light waves do not rep-

of a centimeter in length, all electromagnetic waves travel with the same velocity in vacuum; 186,300 mi/sec, or 3×10^{10} cm/sec.

Although their velocities in a vacuum are all the same, the properties of the various waves differ considerably. One striking illustration of these differences is found in the response of the human eye. Of the entire spectrum, only one very narrow band of waves can be seen, all the rest being invisible. Another illustration is the passage of light waves through the atmosphere. With the exception of the band of waves known as the extreme ultraviolet, the air is fairly transparent to all electromagnetic waves. To waves of the extreme ultraviolet,

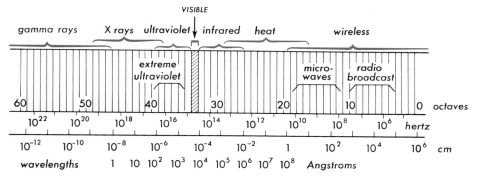

Fig. D. Complete wave length and frequency chart of the electromagnetic spectrum as it is now known.

resent all of the known kinds of electromagnetic radiation. A complete chart of the known spectrum is shown in Fig. D. Beyond the visible and infrared toward longer wave lengths, we find the *heat waves* and the *wireless waves,* while beyond the ultraviolet toward shorter wave lengths, we find the *X-rays* and the *gamma rays.*

In spite of the tremendous expanse of wave lengths, ranging all the way from the longest wireless waves several miles in length to γ-ray waves one-million-millionth

the air is quite opaque. *Fog is opaque to all but the longer radio waves.*

The Angstrom as a Unit of Length. Because the wave lengths of light are so very small, the physicist has adopted a smaller unit of length than the centimeter or millimeter. This unit is called the angstrom, A or Å, for the Swedish scientist by that name. In 1868, Ångstrom published a map of the visible spectrum of the sun. On this map, he labeled the wave lengths in ten-millionths of a millimeter. Since that time, light waves have been specified in these units.

In a centimeter, there are 100,000,000 A:

$$1 \text{ cm} = 10^8 \text{A}$$

The velocity of light c in a vacuum is given by—

$$c = \nu\lambda \tag{4}$$

where ν is the vibration frequency and λ is the wave length. From this, we see that the longer the wave length, the lower is the frequency; and the shorter the wave length, the higher is the frequency. It is common practice among physicists to designate the wave length of light waves by the Greek letter λ (lambda) and the frequency by the Greek letter ν (nu).

QUESTIONS

1. What is the main purpose of studying spectra?
2. The star *Betelguese*, in the constellation *Orion*, is clearly reddish. What can be said about its temperature?
3. The star *Rigel*, on the opposite corner of *Orion*, is clearly bluish. What can be said concerning its temperature?
4. Where does the term *ultraviolet catastrophe* get its name?
5. (a) How is infrared light detected? (b) How is ultraviolet light detected? (c) What is the color of infrared light?
6. (a) In the experiment illustrated in Fig. A, why must the lens and prism be made of quartz? (b) Why is not an ordinary electric light used?
7. Can you get sunburned if sunlight falls on your skin when there is ordinary window glass between the sun and your body? Explain.
8. (a) Why does color film come in two types, namely, one for indoor illumination and the other for outdoor? (b) Why do color pictures taken at high altitudes have a pronounced bluish tint?
9. (a) What theory of light did Rayleigh and Jeans use in developing their formula for black-body radiation? (b) What consequences did this have for this model of how light is produced and emitted by atoms when their results proved to be incorrect?
10. (a) How can astronomers measure the temperature of distant stellar objects? (b) Is there some way of checking their results?
11. What property is common to all electromagnetic waves?
12. Make a list of the electromagnetic waves in order of increasing wave lengths and give one use of each kind.
13. (a) What kind of a unit is an angstrom? (b) Why is it useful when studying spectra and atomic structure?

PROBLEMS

1. (a) What would be the wave length of maximum energy if the source of radiation had a temperature of 3000°K? (b) What, if the temperature were doubled?

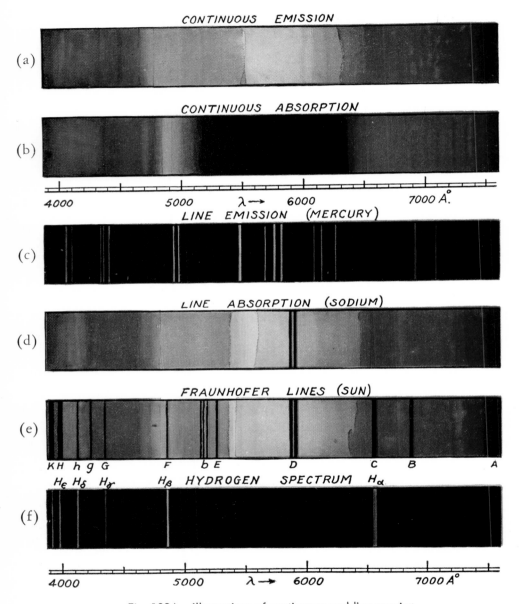

Fig. 102A. Illustrations of continuous and line spectra.

2. What is the temperature of a source of light whose wave length of maximum energy is 6.5×10^{-5} cm?

3. (a) What is the color of molten steel at 2500°K? (b) What is the wave length corresponding to maximum emission? (c) What is the frequency of the maximum emission?

4. How much more energy is emitted by a hot, solid body if its temperature is changed from 3000°K to 9000°K?

5. How much more energy would the earth receive from the sun if its temperature were to increase 1000°C?

6. What is the frequency of a radio transmitter that operates with a wave length of 250 m?

7. (a) What is the wave length of a station whose frequency is 680 KHz? (b) How does this compare with the wave length of visible light?

8. Derive a law relating the frequency of maximum light emission to the temperature. Give the value of the constant in your equation.

PROJECTS

1. Using infrared film and a suitable filter, take a variety of pictures by infrared light.

2. Make a small arc lamp and measure the energy output of its spectrum from ultraviolet to infrared.

ATOMIC PHYSICS

Lesson 102 DISCRETE ATOMIC SPECTRA

In Lesson 101, it was seen that heated matter emits a continuous spectrum; see Fig. A(a). Moreover, continuous absorption spectra may also be produced by passing a continuous emission spectrum through matter in the solid or liquid state. Good demonstrations of continuous absorption can be performed by allowing white light to pass through colored glass. When the light is later dispersed by a prism, the missing colors will, in general, cover a wide band of wave lengths. See spectrum (b) in Fig. A.

Heated or excited gases can be made to emit and absorb light of discrete, or specific, wave lengths. Whereas all heated objects emit the same continuous spectra, each type of atom or molecule emits its own characteristic discrete spectrum. A study of discrete spectra is important, not only in identifying atoms, but in investigating their structure as well.

Line-emission Spectra. When the slit of a prism spectrograph (see Fig. B) is illuminated by the light from a mercury arc, so-

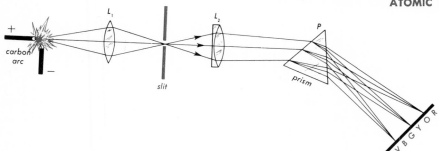

Fig. B. Experimental arrangement used in demonstrating spectrum lines in emission.

dium lamp, neon discharge tube, or the flame of a carbon arc, a number of bright lines appear on the screen or photographic plate in place of a continuous spectrum. See Fig. A(*c*).

It is important to realize that *line spectra* derive their name from the fact that, before entering the prism, the light passes through a narrow slit and that it is the differently colored images of this slit, formed by the lens, that constitute the lines. If a small circular opening were used in place of a slit, a disk image would appear in the place of each line in Fig. A.

The most intense sources of spectrum lines are obtained from metallic arcs and sparks. The flame of a carbon arc may be used for demonstration purposes by previously soaking the *positive carbon rod* in various chemicals. (The arrangement shown in Fig. B may also be used for projecting

the spectrum on a large screen.) Common salt water gives a brilliant yellow line characteristic of sodium. Solutions of strontium or calcium chloride will show other strong spectrum lines in the red, green, and blue.

While a continuous-emission spectrum always arises from hot solids and liquids, *a line spectrum always arises from a gas at high temperatures*. It is the free atoms of the element used in the gas flame of the carbon arc that give rise to the line-emission spectrum in the above experiment.

Line-absorption Spectra. Line spectra in absorption are produced by sending continuous white light through a gas. Experimentally, the gas is placed in the path of the light, as shown in Fig. C. Light from a carbon arc, after passing as a parallel beam through a glass tube containing sodium va-

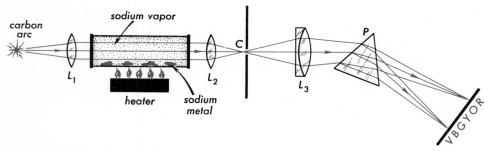

Fig. C. Experimental arrangement for demonstrating the line-absorption spectrum of sodium vapor.

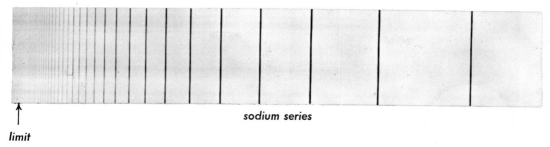

↑
limit

sodium series

Fig. D. Absorption spectrum of sodium vapor. The principal series of sodium (after Jenkins).

por, is brought to a focus at the slit, C. From there, the light passes through a lens, L_3, and a prism, P, to form a spectrum on the observing screen.

Sodium is chosen as an example for demonstration purposes because of its convenience. The vapor is produced by inserting a small amount of metallic sodium in a partially evacuated glass tube and heating it with a small gas burner. As the metal vaporizes, filling the tube with sodium vapor, a dark line will appear in the yellow region of the spectrum (see (d) in Fig. A).

If a photograph, extending into the ultraviolet, is taken of this absorption, many absorption lines as shown in Fig. D are detected. A systematic array of absorption lines like this occurs only with a few elements, principally with hydrogen and the *alkali metals* (lithium, sodium, potassium, rubidium, and cesium). All elements in the gaseous phase, however, give

rise to a number of absorption lines, usually in the ultraviolet region of the spectrum.

The Sun's Spectrum. The solar spectrum, consisting of a brightly colored, continuous spectrum interspersed by thousands of dark lines, was first observed by the English scientist, William Hyde Wollaston, in 1802, and independently discovered and studied by Joseph von Fraunhofer, a Bavarian optician, in 1817. Fraunhofer mapped out several hundred of these lines and labeled nine of the most prominent by the first letters of the alphabet. The strongest of these lines, now called *Fraunhofer lines*, are illustrated in Fig. E.

These lines are explained as due to the absorption of light by the solar atmosphere. The surface of the sun, at a temperature of 6000°K, emits light of all wave lengths, *i.e.*, a continuous-emission spectrum. As this light passes out through the

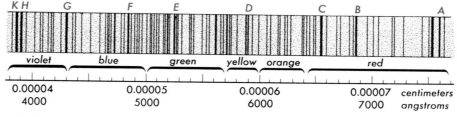

Fig. E. Diagram of the solar spectrum indicating the most prominent lines labeled as they first were by Fraunhofer with the first letters of the alphabet.

cooler gas layers of the solar atmosphere (see Fig. F), certain wave lengths are ab-

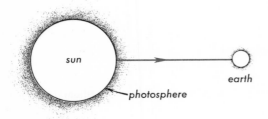

Fig. F. Light from the sun must pass through the solar atmosphere and the earth's atmosphere before reaching an observer on the earth's surface.

sorbed. Because the absorbing medium is in the gaseous state, the atoms and molecules there do not absorb all wave lengths equally, but principally only those wave lengths the atoms would emit if heated to a high temperature. Thus, the atoms of one chemical element, with their own characteristic frequencies, absorb certain wave lengths, whereas the atoms of other elements absorb certain other wave lengths.

Before the sunlight reaches the earth's surface, where it can be examined by an observer with a spectroscope, it must again pass through absorbing gases in the earth's atmosphere. Here, too, certain wave lengths are partially absorbed, producing other dark lines.

That the missing wave lengths correspond to certain definite chemical elements is illustrated in Fig. G (a). The center strip (b) represents a small section of the visible spectrum as obtained with sunlight entering the slit of a spectroscope. The upper and lower strips, (a) and (c), represent the bright-line spectrum observed when an iron arc and a calcium arc are successively placed in front of the same slit. Where each calcium line occurs in the laboratory source, an absorption line is found in the sun's spectrum. The same is true for each iron line. The remaining lines, not matched by an iron or calcium line, are due to other elements.

Dark lines in the sun's spectrum, which at first could not be matched with any element on earth, were later found to belong to the element helium. This element has the rare distinction of having been first discovered on an object 92,000,000 miles from earth.

The Balmer Series of Hydrogen. The hydrogen atom is the simplest of all atoms, consisting of a single electron and a singly charged nucleus. It is natural then to try to understand the structure of the hydrogen atom before considering more complex atoms.

A look at the visible portion of the hydrogen spectrum, as shown in Fig. A(f), shows a regular pattern to the spectrum. To

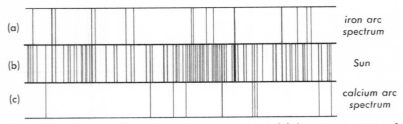

Fig. G. Schematic diagram illustrating the comparison of laboratory spectra from different elements with the many-line spectrum of the sun.

the left of the H_α line, the intervals between lines are progressively smaller. The first successful attempt to obtain a formula that represents the hydrogen series was made by Balmer, in 1885. Since that time, these lines have become known as the Balmer series of hydrogen. Balmer's formula is written—.

$$\frac{1}{\lambda} = C\left(\frac{1}{m^2} - \frac{1}{n^2}\right)$$

where λ is the wave length in meters.

$$C = 1.09737 \times 10^7 m^{-1}$$
$$m = 2$$
$$n = 3, 4, 5, 6, 7, \ldots.$$

If the number 3 is substituted for n in the above formula, the λ of the first line of the series is calculated. Likewise, if the number 4 is substituted in its place, the λ of the second line can be calculated, etc. When these calculations are carried out, the following wave lengths are obtained for the first four lines:

Calculated	Measured
$H_\alpha = 6561.1 \times 10^{-10}$m	6562.1×10^{-10}m
$H_\beta = 4860.1 \times 10^{-10}$m	4860.7×10^{-10}m
$H_\gamma = 4339.4 \times 10^{-10}$m	4340.1×10^{-10}m
$H_\delta = 4100.7 \times 10^{-10}$m	4101.3×10^{-10}m

These wave lengths, as well as those calculated for other lines of the series, agree exactly with the measured values. Balmer did not derive his formula from any theory, but simply formulated it from the measured wave length for each series line. The meaning of those whole numbers m and n is given in Lessons 104 and 105.

QUESTIONS

1. From what kind of light source does one obtain (a) a continuous-emission spectrum and (b) a line-emission spectrum?
2. (a) What are spectrum lines? (b) Why are they in the form of lines?
3. From what kind of source does one obtain the most intense line-emission spectrum?
4. How can one produce a line-absorption spectrum in the laboratory?
5. (a) What kind of spectrum does sunlight exhibit? (b) To what process are the dark lines attributed?
6. How can we prove that the same elements existing on the earth are to be found in the sun as well?
7. If white light is allowed to pass through a piece of crimson- or magenta-colored glass and then into a prism, what kind of spectrum is produced?
8. What would the appearance of the spectrum of hydrogen be if, instead of a slit, a triangular hole were used?
9. How did Balmer arrive at his formula for calculating the wave length of the hydrogen spectrum?
10. When sodium chloride is heated in the flame of a carbon arc, only the brilliant yellow lines of sodium are seen. Why does one not see lines for the chlorine element?
11. How would one show that all the elements in the universe are the same as those found on earth?
12. What is the easiest way to see the sodium spectrum?

PROBLEMS

1. Find the wave length of the tenth line of the Balmer series of hydrogen.
2. Determine the wave length of the series limit of the Balmer series of hydrogen. (Note: $n = \infty$.)
3. The wave length of one of the Balmer series of hydrogen is 3888.1A. Which line is it?
4. What is the frequency of the dominant sodium line?
5. In the Balmer formula, if $m = 1$ and $n = 2$, (a) what wave length would be obtained? (b) In what part of the electromagnetic spectrum would this be?
6. In the Balmer formula, if $m = 3$ and $n = 4$, (a) what wave length would be obtained? (b) In what part of the electromagnetic spectrum would this be?

PROJECT

Make a simple spectrograph, using a diffraction-grating replica. Measure the wave length of the Balmer series of hydrogen gas.

ATOMIC PHYSICS

Lesson 103 *THE PHOTOELECTRIC EFFECT*

Photoelectrons. The photoelectric effect in its simplest form is demonstrated in Fig. A. Light from a carbon arc is focused by means of a quartz lens onto a freshly polished plate of zinc. When the plate is charged negatively and the light is turned on, the gold leaf of the attached electroscope slowly falls. It falls because the electrons, under the action of the light, leave the zinc plate at the illuminated spot P. When the plate is positively charged, the gold leaf does not fall, showing that the plate retains its charge.

The same result of no discharge is observed if the zinc plate is negatively charged and a sheet of glass is inserted as shown in the figure. When the glass is re-moved, the gold leaf again falls. Since common glass transmits visible and infrared light, but not ultraviolet, we conclude that the electrons in this case are liberated only by ultraviolet light. This has been found generally true for nearly all of the known metals.

A few elements, namely the alkali metals —*lithium, sodium, potassium, rubidium,* and *cesium*—are exceptions to this, for they will eject electrons when visible light falls on them. For this reason, they are often used in the manufacture of photoelectric cells.

Although these electrons are the same negatively charged particles that constitute cathode rays, they are called *photoelectrons,*

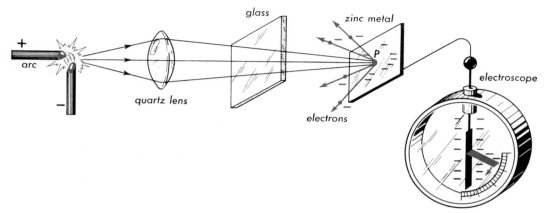

Fig. A. Experimental arrangement for demonstrating the photoelectric effect. When the glass plate is inserted, the effect stops.

because they are liberated by means of light.

The Photoelectric Cell. Photoelectric cells are usually made by depositing a thin layer of an alkali metal on the inner surface of a small vacuum tube (see Fig. B). If the cell is to operate in ultraviolet light, the tube is made of quartz, whereas if it is to be used in visible light, it is made of common glass. The cell must be thoroughly evacuated, for the oxygen content of the air

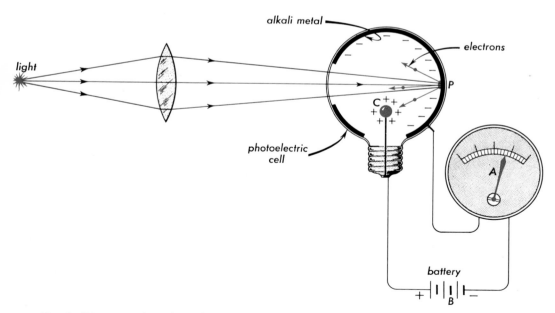

Fig. B. Diagram of a photoelectric cell showing the light beam and electrical connections necessary for its operation.

will combine chemically with the active metal layer, contaminating its surface and making it insensitive to visible light. A small section of the cell is always left clear to serve as a window for the incoming light.

mitter and a photoelectric cell as a receiver. A convenient laboratory demonstration can be made by using a small ¼-watt neon glow lamp as a source of light, as shown at N in Fig. C.

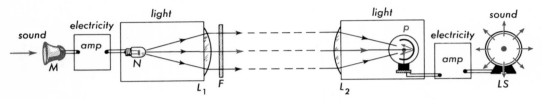

Fig. C. Voice and musical sounds can be sent long distances over a beam of light.

Photoelectrons, upon leaving the metal surface, are attracted and collected by the positively charged electrode, C. The negative charge on the metal film and the positive charge on the central collector-electrode are maintained at a constant potential by the battery, B.

A beam of light shining through the window of a photoelectric cell acts like a switch that completes an electric circuit. When the light strikes the metal, P, there is a flow of electrons to the collector, C, thus causing a current to flow around the circuit. This current can be measured by means of an ammeter at A. If the intensity of the light increases, the number of photoelectrons increases and the current, therefore, rises. When the light is shut off, the photoelectric action ceases and the current stops. If the metal film is positively charged, the cell becomes unreactive to light, since electrons, attempting to leave the plate, are held back by electrostatic attraction. All of these factors are readily demonstrated by a simple electrical circuit arranged as shown in Fig. B.

Sound Over a Light Beam. The sending of voice and musical sounds for several miles over a light beam is readily accomplished with a suitable light source as trans-

Sound waves entering the microphone, M, produce electric-current fluctuations that, after being strengthened by a two-stage amplifier, cause the intensity of the neon glow lamp, N, to fluctuate accordingly. Made into a parallel beam by a lens, L_1, the light travels across the room to a second lens, L_2 and into a photoelectric cell, where the light is changed back into a varying electric current. This faint signal is then amplified by a two-stage amplifier before it is delivered to the loudspeaker.

If the microphone is replaced by a phonograph "pick-up," records can be played at the transmitter end and excellent reproduction can be obtained from the loudspeaker. The light beam can be made completely invisible by placing an ultraviolet filter in it at F.

The Velocity of Photoelectrons. Suppose that the intensity of light producing photoelectrons is doubled. What would happen? According to the old Newtonian theory that light consists of corpuscles, the number of corpuscles would be doubled. Because each corpuscle would produce one photoelectron, the number of photoelectrons would be doubled, but their energies would be unchanged.

The wave theory of light, however,

which accounts for all the optical phenomena, predicts that the energy density striking each small area around the electron would be doubled. Therefore, one would expect little increase in the number of emitted electrons, but, instead, an increase in their energies.

The first measurements of the velocity of photoelectrons led to the startling discovery that the velocity does not increase at all as the intensity of the light increases. *Increasing the intensity of the light increases the number of photoelectrons but not their velocity.* This discovery clearly agrees with the corpuscular theory. As we shall see later, the far-reaching implications of this result have played an important role in the development of our modern concepts of light and atomic structure.

Philip Lenard's experiments, performed in Germany as far back as 1902, showed that, to increase the velocity of photoelectrons, one must increase the frequency of the light, *i.e.*, use shorter wave lengths. The shorter the wave length of the light used, the higher are the velocities of the electrons.

Einstein's Photoelectric Equation. Following an earlier idea of Max Planck, that light waves consist of tiny bundles of energy called *photons* or *quanta*, Albert Einstein proposed an explanation of the photoelectric effect in 1905. His ideas are expressed by one simple relation, an algebraic equation, destined to become famous in the annals of physics. Two Nobel Prizes, one to Einstein in 1921 and one to Robert A. Millikan in 1923, have been granted for this, the photoelectric equation:

$$h\nu = W + \tfrac{1}{2}mv^2 \qquad (1)$$

The first term, $h\nu$, represents the total energy content of a single quantum of light incident on a metal surface, as shown in Fig. D. The h is a constant called *Planck's con-*

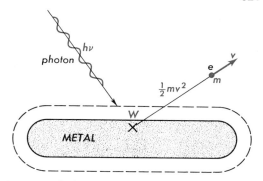

Fig. D. A light quantum (photon) of energy $h\nu$, incident on a metal surface, ejects an electron with a velocity v given by Einstein's equation.

stant of action, which has the same value for all light waves regardless of the frequency, v. At or beneath the surface of the metal, this *light quantum*, better known as a *photon*, is completely absorbed and, in disappearing, imparts its total energy to a single electron. Part of this energy, W, is consumed in getting the electron free from the atoms and away from the metal surface. The remainder is used in giving kinetic energy $\tfrac{1}{2}mv^2$ and, therefore, a velocity to the electron. For some metals, like platinum, the energy required to pull an electron away from the surface is large, whereas for other metals, like the alkalies, it is quite small. W is called the *work function* of the metal.

Actually, many electrons require more energy than that given by W to escape the surface. Therefore, the photoelectric equation refers to the maximum energy of the escaping electrons. It should be pointed out that the photon, in ejecting an electron from a metal surface, as in the photoelectric effect, disappears completely, *i.e.*, it is annihilated.

Millikan's Measurement of h. The first experimental confirmation of Einstein's photoelectric equation came in 1912 when

A. L. Hughes, and, independently, O. W. Richardson and K. T. Compton, observed that the energy of photoelectrons increases proportionately with the frequency. The constant of proportionality they found to be approximately equal to Planck's constant, h.

Subsequently, Millikan carried out extensive experiments that established the photoelectric equation accurately and determined h.

To do this, it was necessary for him to measure the three factors v, W, and $\frac{1}{2}mv^2$, and calculate h as the unknown quantity in Eq. (1). The most recent value obtained for this universal constant is—

$$h = 6.6256 \times 10^{-34} \text{ joule sec} \qquad (2)$$

Because the frequency of visible light is about 6×10^{14} Hz, the energy in a single photon or quantum of visible light is the product of these two numbers, or 3.936×10^{-19} joule.

Unit of Angular Momentum. The h in Einstein's photoelectric equation is important, because it is fundamental to the structure of all matter and, therefore, *a universal constant*. Having first been introduced by Planck in 1901, the name *Planck's constant* has become firmly attached to this symbol, h.

A check of the units in Eq. (1) shows that h is measured in joule-sec, which is the unit of angular momentum. It is meaningful to ask if it is possible that h is a basic unit of angular momentum, in the same sense the electron charge, e, is a basic unit of electric charge. If so, all angular momenta must be an integral number of the basic units, just as any electric charge is an integral number of electron charges. As will be seen in Lesson 104, the quantity $h/2\pi$, rather than h itself, is, in fact, a basic unit of angular momentum in nature.

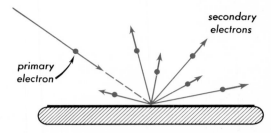

Fig. E. The impact of a single electron liberates additional electrons from a metal surface.

Secondary Electrons. When electrons strike the surface of a metal plate, they knock other electrons free from the surface. These are called *secondary electrons* and the process is called *secondary emission* (see Fig. E). As the speed of a primary, or incident, electron increases from zero to a few hundred volts, the number of secondaries increases toward a definite maximum. For most metal surfaces, this maximum is in the neighborhood of two, while for certain alkali-metal films, it may be as great as

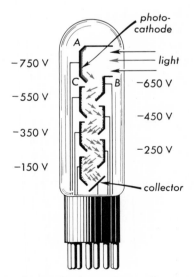

Fig. F. Photomultiplier tube with six stages. Cesium-antimony-coated photo cathode.

eight or ten. In general, it is greatest for surfaces having a low *work-function, i.e.,* surfaces that require the least energy for releasing electrons.

Photomultiplier Tubes. The process of secondary electron emission is widely used in a special type of photoelectric cell that is most effective in detecting faint light. A cross-section diagram of such a photomultiplier tube is given in Fig. F.

The number of photoelectrons from the photocathode, *A*, is proportional to the intensity of the incident light. These are attracted toward the next dynode, *B*, more positive by 100 volts, where upon impact additional electrons are liberated. Attracted to the next more positive dynode, *C*, still more electrons are liberated. By the time the collector plate has been reached, a small avalanche of electrons has developed and a correspondingly large charge and current are led off through that electrode to a suitable recording device.

If each electron on impact releases *n* secondaries, then in a tube with *k* stages, the number arriving at the collector would be n^k. For example, if $n = 6$ and if $k = 5$, then $n^k = 7776$ electrons. This is an enormous gain over the signal obtained from a standard phototube. Photomultiplier tubes have been used most successfully with faint light, not only with visible light but with infrared and ultraviolet as well.

QUESTIONS

1. (a) What is the photoelectric effect? (b) What are photoelectrons? (c) How do they differ from cathode rays?
2. (a) What is a photoelectric cell? (b) What can it be used for?
3. (a) What determines the velocity of photoelectrons? (b) What is the Einstein photoelectric equation?
4. (a) What is a photon? (b) What is a light quantum?
5. (a) What is Planck's constant? (b) What is its significance?
6. (a) What are secondary electrons? (b) How is the principle employed in a photomultiplier tube?
7. (a) How can sound be transmitted over a beam of light? (b) Where is the photoelectric cell used in this application? (c) Could this device be made to operate on invisible light?
8. (a) What is the work function of a metal? (b) Is the work function for alkali metals larger than for most other metals or smaller?
9. How would you go about the problem of sending sound waves, like those from your voice, over a beam of ultraviolet light?
10. Why is a neon lamp used in light-beam transmission, rather than an incandescent light?
11. Do the photoelectron-velocity measurements substantiate the wave theory of light? Explain.
12. What is meant by "quantized angular momentum"?
13. Why can't we tell that angular momentum, or charge, is quantized in an ordinary laboratory experiment where angular momentum, or charge, is measured?

14. (a) What kind of experiment would bear on the question of quantization of charge? (b) of angular momentum?

PROBLEMS

1. Find the energy equivalent to a light wave of wave length 5×10^{-7} m. Such light is in the green region of the visible spectrum.
2. Calculate the energy, in joules, of ultraviolet light of wave length 3×10^{-7} m.
3. If X-rays with a wave length of 5.0×10^{-10} m fall on a metal plate, what would be the maximum velocity of the photoelectrons emitted? (Assume the work function to be negligibly small.)
4. Taking the work function of sodium to be 10^{-18} joule, what will be the velocity of photoelectrons emitted as the result of incident light of wave length 3×10^{-8} m? This is ultraviolet light.
5. Find the over-all gain of a ten-stage photomultiplier tube if the average number of secondary electrons produced by each primary electron is five.
6. A six-stage photomultiplier tube has an over-all gain of 15,625. Find the average number of secondary electrons produced by each primary electron.
7. Make a diagram showing how a photoelectric cell could be used to count the number of cars passing a given point on a highway in a single day.
8. Suppose that light of wave length 4×10^{-8} m is incident on a metallic surface, but that no photoelectrons are emitted. What can be said about the work function?
9. A ball on the end of a string has an angular momentum of 4×10^{-6} joule sec. How many basic units of angular momentum does it have (basic unit = $h/2\pi$)?
10. Suppose that light of frequency v_1 liberated electrons of maximum energy E_1 from an unknown metal. In addition, you find that light of frequency v_2 liberated electrons of energy E_2. Derive an equation for evaluating Planck's constant from these data.

PROJECTS

1. Make an apparatus for sending sound over a light beam. For added interest use ultraviolet as the invisible beam.
2. Make a photocell to open and close a door when a light beam is interrupted.

ATOMIC PHYSICS

Lesson 104 *THE BOHR ATOM*

Bohr's Theory of the Hydrogen Atom. In 1913, Niels Bohr* proposed a theory of the hydrogen atom that marked the beginning of a new era in the history of physics. With his theory, Bohr gave not only a satisfactory explanation of the Balmer series of hydrogen, but a model for the structure of all other atoms as well.

Starting with what should be the simplest of all atoms, Bohr assumed that a hydrogen atom, Z = 1, consists of a nucleus with one positive charge, +e, and a single electron of charge −e, revolving around it in a circular orbit of radius r (see Fig. A). Because it is 1840 times heavier than the electron, the nucleus could be assumed at rest.

To keep the electron in its orbit and prevent it from spiraling in toward the nucleus, or away from it to escape, Bohr next assumed that the inward centripetal force is owing to and, therefore, is the inward electrostatic force F. From Eq. (7) in Lesson 29, the centripetal force is mv^2/r, and from Coulomb's law, Eq. (1) in Lesson 70, the electrostatic force is kee/r^2. Equating these two, we obtain—

* Niels Bohr (1885-1962), Danish physicist, was born at Copenhagen, the son of Christian Bohr, professor of physiology at the University of Copenhagen. After taking his Ph.D. degree at Copenhagen in 1911, he studied for one year under J. J. Thomson at Cambridge and one year under Ernest Rutherford at Manchester. Returning to Copenhagen in 1913, with the results of the Rutherford scattering experiments fresh in his mind, he worked out and published his now famous theory of the hydrogen atom. In 1920, Bohr was appointed head of the institute for theoretical physics at the University of Copenhagen. In 1921, he was awarded the Hughes Medal of the Royal Society and, in 1922, the Nobel Prize in physics.

$$m \frac{v^2}{r} = k \frac{ee}{r^2} \qquad (1)$$

At this point, Bohr introduced his second assumption, *the quantum hypothesis.* The electron, he assumed, cannot move in just any orbit that is stable under the condi-

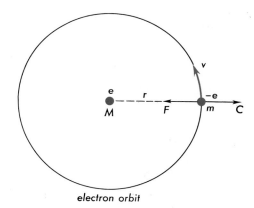

electron orbit

Fig. A. Orbital diagram of the hydrogen atom according to the Bohr theory.

tions of the equation above, but only in certain *definite and discrete orbits.* The sizes of these orbits are governed by Eq. (1) and the rule that *the angular momentum of the electron in its orbit is equal to an integer, n, times the constant $h/2\pi$:*

$$mvr = n \left(\frac{h}{2\pi} \right) \qquad (2)$$

In this equation, n is called the principal *quantum number* and, because it can take only whole-number values (1, 2, 3, 4, etc.), it fixes the sizes of the allowed orbits.

The idea of angular-momentum quantization was a natural consequence of

Planck's studies and of the photoelectric effect. At the time of Bohr's proposal, arguments were presented attempting to "derive" Eq. (2) from basic principles. Although these arguments were not convincing, the model was tentatively accepted, because it correctly describes the experimental observations, as we shall see. Thirteen years were to pass before the basic understanding would be found from the wave picture of the atom (see Lesson 108).

Orbit Radius and Velocity. To find the radii of these "Bohr circular orbits," Eq. (2) is solved for v, then squared and substituted in Eq. (1) to give—

$$r = \frac{n^2}{me^2k}\left(\frac{h}{2\pi}\right)^2 \qquad (3)$$

Putting into this equation the known values of the constants e, m, h, and k—

$e = 1.60 \times 10^{-19}$ **coulomb**
$m = 9.10 \times 10^{-31}$ **Kg**
$h = 6.62 \times 10^{-34}$ **joule sec**
$k = 9 \times 10^9$ **newtons m²/coulomb²**

the orbits shown in Fig. B are calculated. The innermost orbit, with $n = 1$, has a radius $r = 0.000,000,000,0528$ m, or 0.528 A. The radius of the second orbit is four

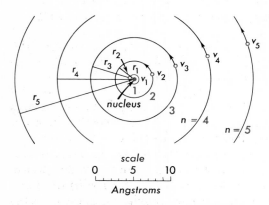

Fig. B. Scale diagram of the Bohr circular orbits of hydrogen.

times as large, and the third is nine times, etc. The constant h is *Planck's constant*.

The velocity of the electron, when it is in any one orbit, can be determined from Eq. (2). In the innermost orbit, $n = 1$, the velocity v is 1/137 the velocity of light. In the second orbit the speed is only half as great, and in the third, only one-third as great, etc. With such small orbits and such high velocities, the number of revolutions per second becomes very high. In the second orbit, the frequency is calculated to be 10^{15} r/sec. This, by comparison with the frequency of vibration of visible light waves, is of the same order of magnitude.

It should be noted that the one and only electron in each hydrogen atom can occupy only one orbit at any one time. If the electron changes its orbit, it must move to one of the allowed orbits and never stop in between.

Bohr-Stoner Scheme of the Building Up of Atoms. Bohr and Stoner proposed an extension of the orbital model of hydrogen to include all of the chemical elements. As shown by the examples in Fig. C, each atom is composed of a positively charged nucleus with a number of electrons around it.

Although the nucleus is a relatively small particle, less than 10^{-12} cm in diameter, it contains almost the entire mass of the atom, a mass equal in *atomic mass units* to the *atomic weight. The positive charge carried by the nucleus is equal numerically to the atomic number, and it determines the number of electrons located in orbits outside.* A helium atom, atomic number $Z = 2$, has two positive charges on the nucleus and two electrons outside. A lithium atom, atomic number $Z = 3$, contains three positive charges on the nucleus and three electrons outside. A mercury atom, atomic number 80, contains 80 positive charges on the nucleus and 80 electrons outside.

The orbits to which the electrons are confined are the Bohr orbits of hydrogen with $n = 1, 2, 3$, etc., and are called electron shells. Going from element to element in the periodic table, starting with hydrogen, electrons are added one after the other, filling one shell and then another. A shell is filled only when it contains a number of electrons given by $2n^2$. To illustrate this, the first shell, $n = 1$, is filled when it has 2

be distinguishable from each other. For the $n = 1$ shell, for example, the two electrons are distinguishable, because one is spinning clockwise, and the other counterclockwise.

Among the heavier elements, there are several departures from the order in which the shells are filled. Although these departures are not important to our present discussion, their nature is illustrated by the mercury atom, Fig. C. The four inner shells,

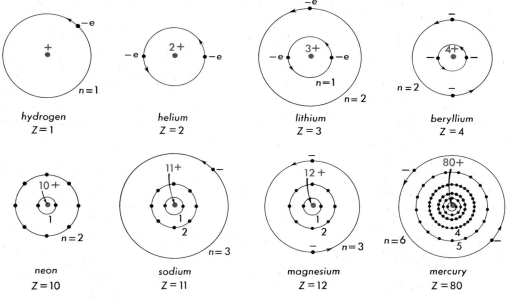

Fig. C. Bohr-Stoner orbital models for the light and heavy atoms of the periodic table.

electrons, the second shell, $n = 2$, when it has 8 electrons, the third shell, $n = 3$, when it has 18 electrons, etc. $2 \times 1^2 = 2, 2 \times 2^2 = 8, 2 \times 3^2 = 18$, etc.

quantum number	$n = 1$	$n = 2$	$n = 3$	$n = 4$
number of electrons	2	8	18	32

The fact that only a certain number of electrons can occupy a given shell is explained by the *Pauli exclusion principle*. This principle states that all electrons must

$n = 1, 2, 3$, and 4, are entirely filled with 2, 8, 18, and 32 electrons, respectively, while the fifth shell contains only 18 electrons and the sixth shell 2 electrons. The reasons for such departures are now well understood and are indicative of the chemical behavior of the heavy elements.

It is important to note that, as the nuclear charge increases and additional electrons are added in outer shells, the inner shells, under the stronger attraction by the nucleus, shrink in size. The net result of this shrinkage is that the heaviest elements in the periodic table are not much larger in diameter than the lighter elements. The schematic diagrams in Fig. C are drawn approximately to the same scale.

QUESTIONS

1. What was Bohr's first assumption regarding the structure of a hydrogen atom?
2. What was Bohr's assumption regarding the centripetal force of an electron in a circular orbit?
3. (a) What was Bohr's second assumption? (b) What is the principal quantum number?
4. What are the relative diameters of the Bohr circular orbits given by $n = 1, 2, 3$, and 4?
5. (a) What force keeps the electron from escaping the area around the nucleus? (b) What evidence is there that shows that this force can be overcome?
6. Why doesn't the size of the atoms increase as the number of electrons increases?
7. Which of Bohr's hypotheses is based upon the results of Rutherford's scattering experiments? See Lesson 100. Explain.
8. Which of Bohr's hypotheses is suggested by the studies of the photoelectric effect? Explain.
9. How should the Bohr model be tested to determine whether or not it is correct?
10. (a) Give some examples of substances that are evidently quantized. (b) Give a few others that, on a gross scale, appear to be continuous in nature.
11. Would you say a stream of water is continuous or quantized? Explain.
12. Why do most objects we normally handle appear not to be quantized?
13. (a) What is the Bohr-Stoner scheme of the building up of atoms? (b) How does it differ from the Thomson atom?
14. (a) How many electrons can each shell have? (b) What is the formula?
15. Make a diagram of a zinc atom ($Z = 30$) according to the Bohr-Stoner scheme.
16. Make a diagram of a krypton atom ($Z = 36$) according to the Bohr-Stoner scheme.

PROBLEMS

1. Find the diameter of the first four circular orbits of hydrogen according to the Bohr theory.
2. What would be the approximate quantum number n for a circular orbit of hydrogen 0.0001 mm in diameter? This would be just big enough to see under a microscope.
3. What would be the approximate quantum number n for a circular orbit of hydrogen 1 mm in diameter?
4. How many hydrogen atoms in the $n = 1$ state could be placed side by side on a 1-cm line?

5. (a) Solve Eq. (1) for r as the only unknown. (b) Solve Eq. (2) for r as the only unknown.

6. Set the right-hand sides of the equations obtained in Problem 5 equal to each other and solve for v as the unknown quantity.

7. Using this equation for v and the known values of e, m, h, and k, calculate the electron's velocity in the first Bohr circular orbit.

PROJECTS

1. Make plastic-foam models of the lighter atoms on the basis of the Bohr-Stoner theory, as suggested by Fig. C.

2. Make a plastic-foam model of the hydrogen atom to scale, showing the allowed orbits.

ATOMIC PHYSICS

Lesson 105 *ATOMIC RADIATION*

The success of Bohr's theory is not to be attributed so much to the mechanical picture, or model, of the atom just proposed, but rather to the development of an equation that agrees exactly with experimental observations.

Electron Jumps. Bohr's third and final assumption regarding the hydrogen atom concerns the emission of light. Bohr postulated that light is not emitted by an electron when it is moving in one of its fixed orbits, but only when the electron jumps from one orbit to another, as illustrated in Fig. A. The frequency of this light, he said, is not determined by the frequency of revolution, but by the difference in energy between the initial and final orbit:

$$E_2 - E_1 = h\nu \qquad (1)$$

where E_2 is the energy of the *initial orbit*, E_1 the energy of the *final orbit*, h is Planck's

constant, and ν is the frequency of the light.

To illustrate this, let E_1, E_2, E_3, E_4, etc., represent the total energy of the electron when it is in the orbits $n = 1, 2, 3, 4$, etc., respectively. When, for example, the electron is in the orbit $n = 3$ where its energy is E_3, and it jumps to the orbit $n = 2$ where the energy is E_2 (see Fig. A), the energy

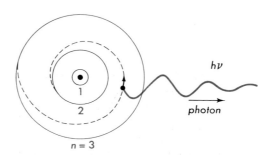

Fig. A. Schematic diagram of Bohr's quantum hypothesis of the radiation of light from a hydrogen atom.

difference, $E_3 - E_2$, is ejected from the atom in the form of a light wave of energy, $h\nu$, called a *photon*. Here, then, is the origin of light waves from within the atom.

Energy Levels. By combining Bohr's equations, Eqs. (1) and (2) in Lesson 104, the energy of an electron in a circular orbit of the hydrogen atom can be calculated. The total energy is just the sum of the kinetic energy, $\tfrac{1}{2}mv^2$, and the potential energy:

$$E_t = E_k + E_p \qquad (2)$$

To find the potential energy of the electron in its orbit, we use Eq. (2) in Lesson 100. By this equation, we see that the potential, V, at any point at a distance, r, from the nuclear charge, $+e$, is given by—

$$V = k\,\frac{e}{r}$$

Because V is the work done per unit charge in carrying any charge from a distance r out to infinity, one must multiply by the electron's charge, $-e$, to obtain as the stored potential energy, $-Ve$.

The two forms of stored energy are, therefore—

$$E_k = \tfrac{1}{2}mv^2$$

$$E_p = -k\,\frac{e^2}{r}$$

Substituting these values of E_k and E_p in Eq. (2) and the value of r from Eq. (5) in Lesson 104, we obtain, as Bohr did—

$$E_t = -\frac{me^4k^2}{2n^2(h/2\pi)^2} \qquad (3)$$

The minus sign signifies that one must do work on the electron to remove it from the atom.

With the exception of the principal quantum number n, all quantities in this equation are the same for all orbits. We can, therefore, write—

$$E_t = -\frac{1}{n^2}\,R \qquad (4)$$

where R is constant and equal to—

$$R = \frac{me^4k^2}{2(h/2\pi)^2}$$

which, upon substitution of the known values of all the constants, gives—

$$R = 2.1797 \times 10^{-18}\ \text{joule} \qquad (5)$$

Equation (3) is an important equation in atomic structure, for it gives the energy of the electron when it occupies any one of the different orbits of the hydrogen atom. Instead of drawing orbits to the scale of their radius, as in Fig. B, it is customary to

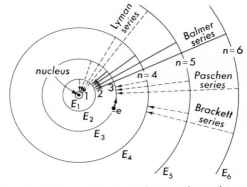

Fig. B. Diagram of the Bohr circular orbits of hydrogen showing the various electron jumps giving rise to the emission of light waves of different frequency.

draw horizontal lines to an energy scale, as shown in Fig. C. This is called an *energy-level* diagram. The various electron jumps between the allowed orbits of Fig. B now become vertical arrows between the energy levels.

The importance of this kind of diagram is to be attributed to Bohr's third relation,

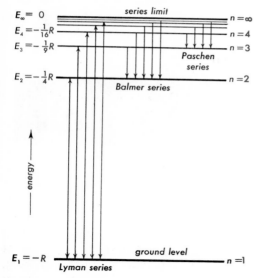

Fig. C. Energy-level diagram for the hydrogen atom. Vertical arrows represent electron jumps.

Eq. (1), where the energy, $h\nu$, of each radiated light wave is just equal to the difference between two energies. The energy of each radiated photon is, therefore, proportional to the length of its corresponding arrow.

The Hydrogen Spectrum. Eq. (1) can now be written—

$$h\nu = R \left(\frac{1}{n_1^2} - \frac{1}{n_2^2} \right) \qquad (6)$$

where n_1 and n_2 represent the *principal quantum numbers* of two orbits.

If we introduce the wave equation, valid for all waves—

$$c = \nu\lambda \qquad (7)$$

and replace ν by c/λ, where c is the speed of light, Eq. (1) can be written—

$$\frac{1}{\lambda} = \frac{R}{ch} \left(\frac{1}{n_1^2} - \frac{1}{n_2^2} \right) \qquad (8)$$

where λ is the wave length of the light in centimeters, n_2 is the quantum number of any orbit of the hydrogen atom in which an electron is confined, and n_1 is the quantum number of the orbit to which the electron jumps to emit light of wave length λ. The quantity R/hc has the numerical value 109,-722 cm^{-1}.

Bohr found that, if in Eq. (8) he placed $n_1 = 2$ and $n_2 = 3$, the calculated wave length, $\lambda = 0.000065647$ cm, is exactly equal to the measured wave length of the red spectrum line of hydrogen. See Fig. A(f) in Lesson 102. If he placed $n_1 = 2$ and $n_2 = 4$, the calculated wave length agreed exactly with the measured wave length of the blue-green spectrum line of hydrogen.

In fact, the entire series of lines in the hydrogen spectrum is exactly represented by Eq. (8), by setting $n_1 = 2$ and $n_2 = 3$, 4, 5, 6, etc. This series of lines, so prominently displayed by the sun and stars, as well as by any hydrogen-discharge tube in the laboratory, is known as the *Balmer series*.

These quantum-number changes correspond, as shown in Fig. B, to an electron jumping from any outer orbit n to the next to the smallest orbit $n = 2$. In any high-voltage electrical discharge in a glass tube containing hydrogen gas, many thousands of atoms may each have their one and only electron jumping from orbit 3 to 2, while in many other atoms, the electron may be jumping from other orbits to $n = 2$. Hence, upon observing the light through a spectroscope, one may observe the entire Balmer series of lines.

Bohr's Predicted Series. Bohr's orbital model of the hydrogen atom not only accounts for the Balmer series of hydrogen, but also for many other observed lines as well.

By substituting $n_1 = 1$ and $n_2 = 2$, 3, 4,

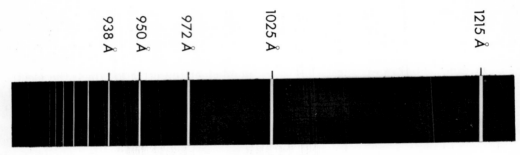

938 Å   950 Å   972 Å   1025 Å   1215 Å

Lyman series of hydrogen

Fig. D. Photograph of the extreme ultraviolet series of hydrogen predicted by Bohr's theory and first observed by Lyman.

etc., in Eq. (8), one obtains a series of spectrum lines in the ultraviolet region of the spectrum. These lines were first photographed by T. Lyman of Harvard University, and the wave lengths are found to check exactly with calculations. This series, now called the Lyman series, which can only be photographed in a vacuum spectrograph, is reproduced in Fig. D. On the orbital picture of Fig. A, the Lyman series of lines arises from electron jumps from any outer orbit directly to the innermost orbit, the *ground state*.

If in Eq. (8), n_1 is set equal to 3 and n_2 to 4, 5, 6, etc., the calculated frequencies predict spectrum lines in the infrared spectrum. These lines were first looked for and observed, exactly as predicted, by Friedrich Paschen, and the series is now known by his name. Another predicted series of lines arising from electron jumps, ending on orbit $n = 4$, was observed in the far infrared by Brackett.

Normal and Excited Atoms. When the single electron of a hydrogen atom is in the innermost orbit, $n = 1$, the atom is said to be in its ground state. As the name implies, this is the condition of most free hydrogen atoms in a gas under normal room temperature and pressure. If an electrical discharge

is sent through a vessel containing hydrogen gas, cathode rays (electrons) moving at high speed make frequent collisions with electrons, knocking some of them out of the atom completely and some of them into one of the outer allowed orbits, $n = 2, 3, 4$, etc.

When the electron is completely removed from the atom, the atom is said to be *ionized;* whereas when it is forced into an outer orbit, the atom is said to be excited. Once in an excited state, an atom will not remain that way long, for the electron under the attraction by the nucleus will jump to an inner orbit. By jumping to an inner orbit the electron loses all or part of the energy it had gained. It does not necessarily return to the innermost orbit by a single jump, but may return by several jumps, thereby emitting several different light waves, or quanta.

Resonance-absorption Spectra. If a whole continuous spectrum of light waves is sent through a tube containing hydrogen gas, the hydrogen atoms will be in the ground level, $n = 1$, and by *resonance* may absorb frequencies corresponding to any one of the Lyman series. In absorbing one of these frequencies, the electron of that atom will jump to an upper energy level. The arrowheads at the tops of these vertical lines in Fig. C correspond, therefore, to resonance absorption. Those same excited electrons can then return by downward jumps, emitting light, and stopping finally on the ground level.

Resonance absorption is the explanation of the dark lines of the sodium spectrum shown in Fig. A(d) and the solar spectrum in Fig. A(e) in Lesson 102.

Spectra of Other Atoms. The breakthrough in understanding atomic spectra involves the hydrogen atom, because it is the simplest of all atoms. The spectra of other more complicated atoms are considerably more difficult to interpret, owing to the fact that several electrons may be involved. There is some simplification, because usually only the outer valence electrons are involved in electron transitions, whereas the inner electrons remain tightly bound to the nucleus.

Lasers. The term laser derives its name from the description, *Light Amplification by Stimulated Emission and Radiation.* In principle, the laser is a device that produces an intense, concentrated, and highly parallel beam of light. So parallel would be the beam from a visible-light laser 1 ft in diameter that, at the distance of the moon from the earth, the beam would be no more than a mile wide.

Historically, the laser is the outgrowth of the maser, a device using microwaves instead of light waves. The first successful maser was built by C. H. Townes at Columbia University in 1953. During the next seven years, great strides were made in developing intense microwave beams, the principal contributions being made by the Bell Telephone Research Laboratories and the Lincoln Laboratories at the Massachusetts Institute of Technology.

The first successful laser, using a large synthetic-ruby crystal, was built by T. H. Maiman of Hughes Aircraft Company Laboratories in the summer of 1960. Hundreds of extensive researches on laser development have been carried on since that time and, because such devices appear to have great potential in so many different fields of research and development, a brief account of their basic principles will be presented here.

Lasers are of three general kinds, those using solids, those using liquids, and those using gases. Liquid or gas lasers have a hollow tube with silvered end plates that is filled with a fluid. In the solid laser, the ends of a crystal are polished and silvered, as in Fig. E. Since the first successful laser was made with a large single crystal of ruby, this device will be explained as representative of solid state lasers. Ruby is a

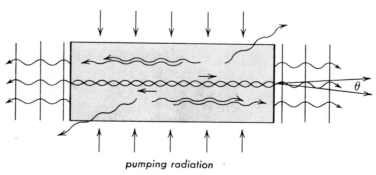

pumping radiation

Fig. E. Diagram illustrating the coherent stimulation of light waves in a solid-state laser, such as a ruby crystal.

crystal lattice of aluminum and oxygen atoms, Al_2O_3, with a small amount of chromium ions as an impurity, 0.04% of Cr^{3+}. The atomic lattice structure of a ruby crystal has the properties of absorbing light of certain frequencies, ν_0, and of holding this absorbed energy for a period of time. Then, by bouncing light of a different frequency, ν_1, back and forth between the silvered ends, the excited atoms may be stimulated to emit their stored energy as light of the same frequency, ν_1, and in exact phase with the original light waves. As these intensified waves bounce back and forth, they stimulate others, thus amplifying the original beam intensity.

Because the light waves emerging from the end of the laser are all in phase, the beam is said to be *coherent*.

Optical Pumping. A convenient method of describing laser action is to refer to an energy-level diagram of the electronic states involved in light absorption and emission.

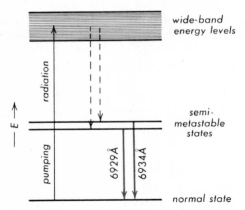

Fig. F. Energy-level diagram of the energy states of a ruby crystal.

An energy-level diagram for the electrons in the atomic lattice of a ruby crystal is given in Fig. F. Here, there are three sets of levels, the *ground state, the semimeta-*

stable states, near the middle, and the top *wide-band energy* levels. Semimetastable states are states in which there is a delay in the electrons' jumping down to a lower level.

When a beam of white light enters a ruby crystal, strong absorption occurs in the blue and green part of the spectrum, and the transmission of only the red region gives the ruby its red color.

When a strong beam of blue-green light shines into a ruby crystal, the absorption that takes place raises many electrons to the wide-band levels, as shown by the up arrow at the left in Fig. F. Because of internal atomic activity, the electrons quickly drop down to the intermediate levels, not by the emission of photons, but by the conversion of energy into vibrational kinetic energy of the atoms forming the crystal lattice.

Once in the intermediate levels, the electrons may remain there for some time before randomly jumping back to the normal state, emitting visible red light. This fluorescent light, as it is called, enhances the red color of the ruby.

Since an incident beam of blue-green light steadily increases the number of electrons that are in semimetastable states, the process is called optical pumping. To greatly increase the electron populations in the middle levels, very intense light sources, as well as efficient light-gathering systems, are frequently used.

One of many systems developed for doing this is shown in Fig. G. By placing the exciting light source at one focus of an elliptical reflector and the laser at the other focus, high efficiency can be obtained.

In the laser, the random emission of light from the metastable state will by chance find some of the waves emitted along the axis. See Fig. E. This light, because it may bounce back and forth many times between the highly reflective ends,

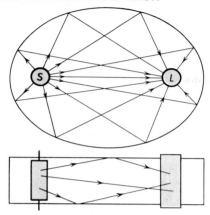

Fig. G. Elliptical reflector for concentrating light from a source, S, on a laser, L.

duce other emission, thereby giving rise to a rapid growth or chain reaction. Thus, by continuous pumping action from a separate light source, a large part of the stored energy is converted into a coherent beam of light of a different wave length. Under these conditions the device is said to "laze" spontaneously.

If the silvered ends are not highly reflecting, too much light escapes from the ends and spontaneous lazing cannot occur. Under these conditions, a beam of light of the stimulating frequency from another laser can be sent into the crystal where it is intensified. By modulating the input beam, the greatly intensified output beam will be modulated accordingly. This modulation capability is one of the important properties that gives lasers their promising future applications to the field of communications.

will stimulate other metastable states to emit coherent light parallel to itself and to the axis. These two waves traveling back and forth in step with each other now in-

QUESTIONS

1. (a) What is the Balmer series of hydrogen? (b) What particular electron jump gives rise to the red spectrum line?

2. (a) What is the Lyman series of hydrogen? (b) Are these wave lengths in the visible spectrum? (c) What electron jump is responsible for the longest wave length of the series?

3. (a) What is the Paschen series of hydrogen? (b) Are these wave lengths of light in the visible spectrum?

4. (a) What is an excited atom? (b) What is an ionized atom? (c) What is the normal state of hydrogen?

5. Why is the potential energy of an electron negative in an atom?

6. What is the source of the spectrum of the sun?

7. What is the source of the dark lines in the solar spectrum?

8. What will happen to energy of the "wrong" frequency that is sent through hydrogen gas?

9. (a) How are the atoms of a gas ionized in a glass tube? (b) Are they more easily ionized if the gas pressure is high or low? Explain. (c) What happens to energy used to ionize the gas?

10. (a) What is the meaning of the arrowheads on the upper ends of the Lyman series markers, Fig C? (b) Why are there no arrowheads on the upper ends of the other series?

11. (a) What is an electron jump? (b) How is such a process related to the emission of light?
12. If an electron jumps from orbit $n = 2$ to orbit $n = 1$ and the emitted light meets another hydrogen atom with its electron in orbit $n = 1$, what would happen in this second atom?
13. What is the significance of the series limit?
14. (a) What is a laser? (b) What possible uses does it have?
15. (a) Why are the ends of a laser silvered? (b) Why is the silvering not complete on one end?
16. What is meant by "coherent" light waves?
17. (a) What is "optical pumping"? (b) Explain how a ruby laser works.

PROBLEMS

1. Calculate the wave length of the third line of the Balmer series of hydrogen.
2. Find the wave lengths of the fourth and fifth lines of the Balmer series of hydrogen.
3. Compute the wave lengths of the first three lines of the Lyman series of hydrogen.
4. Find the wave lengths of the first three lines of the Paschen series of hydrogen.
5. What energy must be absorbed by the hydrogen atom in its normal state to ionize it?
6. A hydrogen atom is raised to an excited state with the electron in the $n = 5$ level. By electron jumps back to the normal state, the longest-wave length Paschen line is observed, but no Balmer line. Draw an energy-level diagram showing which jumps occurred; give the wave lengths emitted.

PROJECT

Make a large chart similar to Fig. C. Put in other data, such as wave length, frequency, and color of emission produced.

ATOMIC PHYSICS

Lesson 106 X-RAYS

One of the most interesting episodes in the history of modern science began with the accidental discovery of X-rays by Wilhelm Röntgen* in 1895. While studying

* Wilhelm Konrad von Röntgen (1845-1923) was born at Lennep on March 27, 1845. Röntgen

the green fluorescent stage of an electrical discharge in a Crookes tube, Röntgen observed the bright fluorescence of some nearby crystals of barium platino-cyanide. Even though the discharge tube was in a darkened room and entirely surrounded with black paper to prevent the escape of visible light, a distant screen covered with crystals would fluoresce brightly when the discharge was turned on. Röntgen reasoned, therefore, that some kind of invisible yet penetrating rays of an unknown kind were being given out by the discharge tube. These rays he called *X-rays,* the letter *X* meaning, as it so often does in algebra, an unknown.

In the short series of experiments that followed his discovery, Röntgen found that the unknown rays were coming from the glass walls of the tube itself and, in particular, from the region where the most intense part of the cathode-ray beam was striking the glass. So great was the importance of this discovery that, within but a few weeks of Röntgen's announcement, X-rays were being used as an aid to surgical operations in Vienna. This, along with other practical applications and uses to be made of a single scientific discovery, is a good example of the role played by modern science in the rapid advancement of civilization.

received his education in Holland and Switzerland. His scientific career began at the age of twenty-five when he became an assistant in the physics laboratory at Würzburg, Germany. After a teaching period extending over a period of twenty-five years, which carried him to the University of Strasbourg, then to Hohenheim, back to Strasbourg, then to Giessen, and finally to Würzburg again, he discovered X-rays in his laboratory at Würzburg in 1895. For this discovery, he received the Rumford Medal of the Royal Society in 1896 and the first Nobel Prize in physics in 1901. Röntgen also conducted researches in light, heat, and elasticity, but none of these works compare in importance with his discovery of X-rays.

X-ray Tubes. The Crookes tube with which Röntgen made his discovery bears very little resemblance to the modern X-ray tube. In form, it had somewhat the appearance of the tube shown in Fig. C in Lesson 90. Within a short time after Röntgen's discovery, quite a number of improvements upon tube design were made.

The biggest improvement in X-ray tube design was made by William David Coolidge, an American physicist, in 1913. In the Coolidge tube (see Fig. A), a tungsten-wire

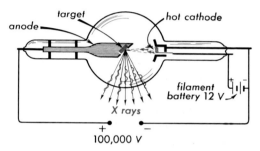

Fig. A. Diagram of a Coolidge X-ray tube employing a hot cathode.

filament is placed at the center of the cathode and heated to incandescence by a storage battery or low-voltage transformer. This filament, being a copious source of electrons, gives rise at the target to a far more intense source of X-rays than was previously possible with a cold cathode. Under the terrific bombardment of the target by so many electrons, most metals will melt. To overcome this difficulty a metal with a high melting point, such as tungsten or molybdenum, is imbedded in the face of a solid-copper anode to become the target. Copper, being a good heat conductor, helps to dissipate the heat.

The early sources of high voltage applied to the anode and cathode of an X-ray tube were induction coils of various descriptions. Although some of these sources are still in use, they have been almost entirely supplanted by a more efficient high-voltage transformer. The emf generated by these transformers varies between 50,000 and 2,000,000 volts. The normal emf used for surgical work is about 100,000 volts, whereas for the treatment of diseases, the higher emf's are employed. The high-voltage alternating emf supplied by a transformer is not applied directly to the X-ray tube but is first changed into direct current by means of rectifier tubes.

X-rays Are Waves. The discovery that X-rays are electromagnetic waves of extremely high frequency, and not high-speed particles, was made by Max von Laue in 1912. With the assistance of Friedrich and Knipping, X-rays were diffracted by a zinc sulfide crystal.

The equally spaced layers of atoms within such a crystal behave like the rulings of a diffraction grating and produce what is called an X-ray spectrum. X-ray wave lengths are, on the average, some ten thousand times shorter than visible light.

The X-ray spectrum, like the visible spectrum, is found to have two components, a discrete spectrum superimposed upon a

continuous spectrum. Fig. B shows the resultant spectrum. The fluted peaks are due to the silver bromide in the photographic emulsion and are not of interest here.

The discrete X-ray spectrum, like the discrete visible spectrum, originates from the jumping of an electron from one orbit to another. Owing to the large charge on the nucleus, the orbit energies are some ten thousand times greater than for the hydrogen atom. It is for this reason that the X-rays have much greater energies than visible light. However, visible light can be produced by electron transitions between the outer low-energy orbits.

When high-speed electrons from the cathode of an X-ray tube strike the target, they ionize many of the atoms composing the surface layers of the metal.

Owing to their very high speeds (about one-tenth the velocity of light), the electrons penetrate the atoms and remove an electron from the inner shells by collision. This is illustrated in Fig. C where an elec-

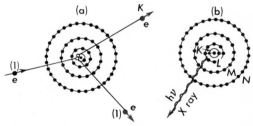

Fig. C. Schematic diagram illustrating (a) the ionization of an atom by a high-speed electron, and (b) the subsequent jumping of an inner electron with the simultaneous emission of an X-ray.

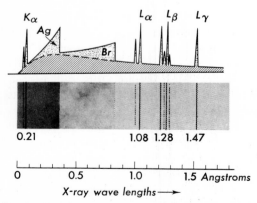

Fig. B. X-ray spectrogram taken with an X-ray tube containing a tungsten target. (After de Broglie.)

tron is knocked out of the K shell. The designations K, L, M, N, O, P, etc., for the various electron shells originated with the X-ray spectroscopist and are identical with the quantum numbers $n = 1, 2, 3, 4, 5, 6$, etc. When an electron is missing in the innermost K shell, a nearby electron from the next shell beyond jumps into the vacant space, simultaneously emitting a photon of energy $h\nu$. Such X-rays, arising from millions of atoms, produce the K lines shown in Fig. B.

Because the L shell now has one less electron, an M electron can jump into the L-shell vacancy, with the consequent emission of another but different X-ray frequency. These are the L lines in Fig. B. The jumping process continues until the outermost shell is reached, where an electron jumping in gives rise to visible light. Thus, we see how it is possible for a single atom to emit X-rays of different wave lengths.

The Continuous X-ray Spectrum. The continuous spectrum, illustrated by the shaded area under the curve in Fig. B, is owing to another phenomenon often referred to as *bremsstrahlung*. These radiations arise from the slowing down of high-speed electrons as they pass close to the nuclei of the atoms within the target of the X-ray tube. The process is illustrated in Fig. D. As the electron passes through

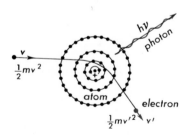

Fig. D. Diagram illustrating the production of a photon by a high-speed electron as it passes through an atom close to the nucleus ("bremsstrahlung").

the atom, it is attracted by the positive charge of the nucleus and deflected in its path.

During the deflection of the electron in

the strong electric field of the nucleus, a light wave of energy is $h\nu$ is emitted. The law of conservation of momentum holds for such a collision and the electron is deflected off to one side of the atom and the photon off to the other. Because of conservation of energy, some of the energy of the incoming electron $\frac{1}{2}mv^2$ is given up to the newly created photon $h\nu$, and the remainder $\frac{1}{2}mv'^2$ is retained by the electron. Thus, the electron is slowed down to a velocity v' by the encounter. The closer the electron comes to the nucleus, the greater is its loss in velocity and energy, and the greater is the frequency and energy of the radiated photon. By the conservation of energy—

$$\tfrac{1}{2}mv^2 - \tfrac{1}{2}mv'^2 = h\nu \qquad (1)$$

The highest frequency that is possible is one in which the electron is completely stopped by the atom. In this special case—

$$\tfrac{1}{2}mv^2 = h\nu_{\max} \qquad (2)$$

Because the kinetic energy of the electrons in the beam striking the target is given by the voltage, V, applied to the tube, we may use—

$$Ve = \tfrac{1}{2}mv^2 \qquad (3)$$

and obtain—

$$Ve = h\nu_{\max} \qquad (4)$$

An additional reason for using tungsten for the target is that the electron interacts more by bremsstrahlung for heavy-atom targets. This produces a higher ratio of continuous to discrete X-rays.

X-ray Diffraction by Crystals. As we have seen earlier, light waves are easily diffracted by a diffraction grating in the order of several thousand lines per centimeter. We would expect X-rays to similarly be diffracted. However, the wave length of X-rays is much shorter and, therefore, the grating would have to be made with

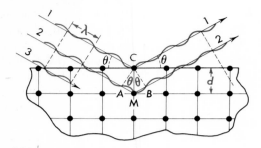

Fig. E. Illustration of the Bragg rule of reflection for X-rays from the surface layers of a crystal.

many more lines to the centimeter. The crystals of many atoms or molecules are arranged in the same regular fashion as a diffraction grating, but with the spacing in

reflected from adjacent atomic layers, move off together. This occurs when the additional distance traveled by ray (2), AMB in Fig. E, is exactly one whole wave length greater than that traveled by the ray (1) next above it. When the angle is adjusted so that this is true, other rays like (3), belonging to the same wave train as (1) and (2), will be reflected from the third crystal layer to be "in phase" with the others.

Suppose now that the X-ray tube in Fig. F emits X-rays of only one wave length. Then, as the crystal rocks back and forth, there will be no reflection except at one particular angle, θ, and this will occur where the conditions of Bragg's rule are satisfied. At this particular position on the

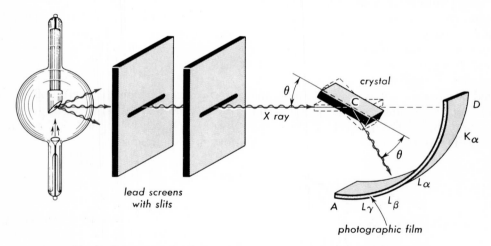

Fig. F. Schematic diagram of a Bragg X-ray crystal spectrograph.

the order of the wave length of an X-ray.

To reflect X-rays of one given wave length from a crystal, a certain relation must exist between the direction of the incident rays and the distance d between surface layers of the crystal. This relation, known as the *Bragg rule*, requires the waves to be incident on the crystal face at such an angle, θ, that the crests of the waves,

photographic plate, a single dark line will appear. If, now, the distance, d, between crystal layers is known and if the angle θ for the X-ray line is measured, the wave length of the X-rays can be calculated. One wave length, it will be noted in Fig. E, is equal to twice the length of the side AM of the right triangle AMC. Thus, with one side and two angles of a triangle known, either of the other sides can be calculated. Bragg's rule, therefore, becomes—

$$2d \sin \theta = \lambda \qquad (5)$$

In the case of a sodium chloride crystal, NaCl, the atomic spacing is 2.81 A, or 2.81×10^{-10} m.

QUESTIONS

1. (a) Who discovered X-rays? (b) How were they discovered?
2. What contribution did Coolidge make to the design and construction of X-ray tubes?
3. Is "X-ray" a good name for these rays at present? Explain.
4. (a) What determines how much energy an X-ray will have? (b) Why are large voltages needed on X-ray tubes?
5. Would an X-ray tube produce stronger X-rays if it were partially filled with an inert gas? Explain.
6. (a) Why is the target of an X-ray tube usually made of tungsten? (b) What charge is placed on the tungsten?
7. Why do X-rays have more energy than visible light waves?
8. What is meant by the "L shell"?
9. What is the origin of K and L X-rays?
10. Why do X-rays have much shorter wave lengths than visible light?
11. What is the source of the continuous X-ray spectrum?
12. The continuous spectrum of X-rays seems to violate the quantum nature of X-rays. Is this really so? Explain.
13. How could one measure the distance between the atoms of a diamond?

PROBLEMS

1. What is the energy of an X-ray whose wave length is 0.500 A?
2. What is the maximum-frequency X-ray that could be produced if an electron accelerated by 50,000 volts were stopped by an atom?
3. (a) What is the energy of an electron in an X-ray tube if 200,000 volts are applied? (b) What is the highest energy X-ray that can be produced? (c) What is its wave length?
4. If an electron strikes a target with a velocity of 10^7 m/sec and leaves with a velocity of 5×10^6 m/sec, what are the energy and wave length of the X-ray produced?
5. X-rays sent through a Bragg-crystal spectrograph using a rock salt crystal are reflected at an angle of 20.5°. What is the wave length of the X-rays?
6. X-rays sent through a Bragg-crystal spectrograph show three spectrum lines at 4.28°, 5.92°, and 7.56°, respectively. If the crystal used is rock salt, what are the wave lengths of the X-rays?

7. X-rays of wave length 1.45×10^{-8} cm are diffracted by a Bragg-crystal spectrograph at an angle of 12.4°. Find the effective spacing of the atomic layers in the crystal.

8. X-rays having a wave length of 0.36×10^{-8} cm are diffracted at an angle of 4.8° in a Bragg-crystal spectrograph. Find the effective spacing of the atomic layers in the crystal.

9. When a molybdenum target is used in an X-ray tube, the two shortest wave lengths emitted are found with a Bragg-crystal spectrograph to be diffracted at angles of 6°24′ and 7°15′, respectively. Find their wave lengths. Assume a crystal spacing of 2.81×10^{-8} cm.

10. When a tungsten target is used in an X-ray tube, the two shortest wave lengths emitted are found with a Bragg-crystal spectrograph to be diffracted at angles of 2°47′, and 3°16′, respectively. Find their wave lengths. Assume a crystal spacing of 2.81×10^{-8} cm.

PROJECT

Study the production of X-rays by a typical television tube. Use X-ray film and, with the help of a TV technician, attach it to the face of the tube that is unprotected by the shield of the receiver.

ATOMIC PHYSICS

Lesson 107 **X-RAY INTERACTIONS**

In the previous lesson, we have seen how X-rays were discovered and have examined the details of their production. In this lesson, we shall investigate the ways in which X-rays interact with matter and the useful applications of their interactions.

Ionizing Power. As X-rays pass through matter in the solid, liquid, or gaseous state, they are found to *ionize* atoms and molecules. This can be shown by charging a gold-leaf electroscope positively or negatively and placing it some 10 to 15 ft away from an X-ray tube. When the X-ray tube

is turned on (see Fig. A), the gold leaf falls, showing discharge.

The explanation of this experiment is as follows: X-rays pass through the electroscope and ionize the air by removing electrons from many of the oxygen and nitrogen molecules. Leaving these particular molecules with a net positive charge, the freed electrons move about until they are picked up by other neutral molecules, thus giving them a net negative charge. The result is that the passage of X-rays through matter produces both *positively charged* and *negatively charged ions.*

If the electroscope is negatively charged, it attracts the positively charged ions to the gold leaf, neutralizing the charge and repelling the negatively charged ions to the

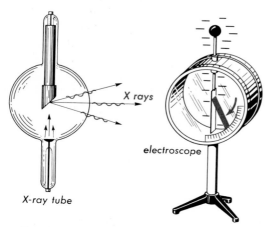

Fig. A. X-rays discharge an electroscope.

"grounded" walls where they, too, become neutralized. If the electroscope is positively charged, it attracts the negative ions to it, again neutralizing the charge. The positive ions in this case are repelled to the walls. In either case, whether the electroscope is positively or negatively charged, the gold leaf falls, showing discharge.

It is the ionization of atoms and molecules in a substance that limits the penetrating power of X-rays.

The Photoelectric Effect with X-rays. Ionization occurs mostly through two processes, the photoelectric effect and the Compton effect.

When a beam of X-rays is allowed to shine on the surface of a thin sheet of metal, such as gold, an interesting phenomenon may be observed to take place. Acting like particles, the X-rays may collide with atoms and eject electrons, as in the photoelectric effect.

Even though a beam of X-rays may contain waves with the same frequency, not all of the ejected photoelectrons acquire the same velocity, but are divided into several well-defined groups. These groups are illustrated schematically by the lengths of the arrows in Fig. B.

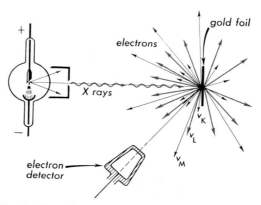

Fig. B. The photoelectric effect with X-rays experimentally establishes the existence of electron shells.

Careful measurements of the velocities of the photoelectrons, first made by the British chemist, Sir Robert Robinson, and his collaborators in 1914, have shown that each velocity group is to be associated with the various shells of electrons within the atoms. The slowest electrons, all with the same velocity v_K, are ejected from the innermost or K shell; the next faster group with a velocity v_L from the second shell out, the L shell; the next group with a velocity v_M from the M shell; etc. See Fig. C.

The closer an electron is to the nucleus, the greater is the attracting force and the greater is the force and energy necessary to liberate it from the atom. The velocity of the electrons in each group is given by Einstein's photoelectric equation:

$$hv = W + \tfrac{1}{2}mv^2 \qquad (1)$$

where W, the work function, is the energy

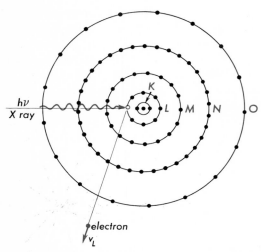

Fig. C. Detail of an X-ray ejecting an electron from the L shell in a heavy atom.

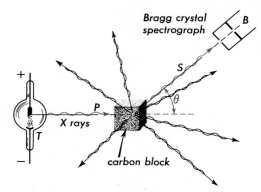

Fig. D. Diagram of Compton's experiment with X-rays.

necessary to free an electron from any one of the different electron shells. See Lesson 103.

The Compton Effect. While making a spectroscopic study of scattered X-rays in 1923, the American physicist, Arthur Holly Compton, discovered a new phenomenon now known as the Compton effect. After considerable controversy with other experimenters, Compton proved quite conclusively that an X-ray may collide with an electron and bounce off with reduced energy in another direction. This is analogous to the collision between two billiard balls.

Compton's historic experiment is illustrated in Fig. D. X-rays from a tube, T, were made to strike one face of a small carbon block and scatter out in various directions. With an X-ray spectrograph at one side of the block, he measured the wave lengths of the X-rays, S, scattered in a direction θ. These wave lengths he then compared with those of the incident beam, P, and found that some of the scattered X-rays had

changed their wave lengths whereas others had not. He also found that, as the angle increased, the change in wave lengths of the modified rays increased.

To explain the modified wave lengths, Compton invoked the quantum theory of light and proposed that a single X-ray photon, acting as a material particle, may collide with an electron and recoil as though it were a perfectly elastic sphere.

The fact that a beam of light has the equivalent of a momentum, mv, and can exert a pressure on a surface on which it falls, has long been known. According to the quantum theory, the momentum of a single photon is given by its energy, $h\nu$, divided by the velocity of light, c:

momentum of a photon $= h\nu/c$ (2)

Compton's experiment is considered a verification of this equation. The momentum of the X-ray before impact is $h\nu/c$, while its momentum after impact is $h\nu'/c$, and the momentum of the electron is mv. See Fig. E.

The discovery and early observations of the Compton effect were confined to the change in wave length of the scattered X-rays and not to the recoiling electrons predicted by theory. Compton's success is to be attributed to the exact agreement he

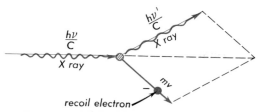

Fig. E. Momentum diagram for the collision between an X-ray photon and an electron. The Compton effect.

found between the wave-length shift, calculated from his application of the quantum theory, and the values measured by experiment.

The first discoveries of the recoil electrons from the Compton effect were made by the Scottish physicist, C. T. R. Wilson, and by Walter Bothe and George F. Becker, respectively German and American researchers. The existence of these collision products is readily shown by sending a beam of X-rays through a Wilson cloud chamber just prior to its expansion. The result is a photograph similar to the one reproduced in Fig. F.

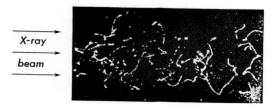

Fig. F. Recoil electrons from X-rays passing through the air in a Wilson cloud chamber. The Compton effect. (After C. T. R. Wilson)

Penetration of X-rays. Four useful and important properties of X-rays are their abilities (1) to penetrate solid matter, (2) to cause certain chemical compounds to fluoresce, (3) to ionize atoms, and (4) to affect a photographic plate. The penetration of X-rays depends upon two things:

first, the voltage applied between the anode and cathode of the X-ray tube; and second, the density of the substance through which the rays must travel. The higher the voltage applied to the tube, the higher is the X-ray energy and the greater is the penetration. *X-rays of great penetrating power are called hard X-rays, whereas those having little penetrating power are called soft X-rays.*

The relation between density and penetration may be illustrated in several ways. When X-rays are sent through a block of wood containing nails, or a closed leather purse containing coins, a clear and well-defined image of the nails or coins can be formed and observed on a fluorescent screen.

The experimental arrangement is the same as that shown in Fig. G. When X-rays

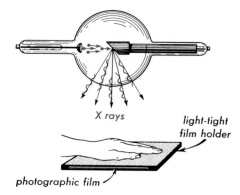

Fig. G. Arrangement for taking X-ray photographs of the bones of the hand.

are sent through the hand or any part of the body to obtain photographs of the bones, it is the difference in penetration between the flesh and the bones that permits a picture to be made. Such materials as paper, wood, and flesh composed principally of the light chemical elements at the beginning of the periodic table, are readily penetrated by X-rays. In other words, they are poor absorbers of X-rays.

For such materials as brass, steel, bone, and gold, composed partly of the heavy elements farther along and near the end of the periodic table, the penetration of X-rays is very poor. Hence, heavy elements are good absorbers.

The bones of the body, containing large amounts of calcium, are relatively good absorbers of X-rays, whereas the flesh, composed principally of much lighter elements —hydrogen, oxygen, carbon, and nitrogen —is a poor absorber. This explains the general appearance of X-ray photographs. X-ray pictures, like the ones in Fig. H, are similar to shadows cast by the objects being photographed. The focus point on the X-ray target, being bombarded by high-speed electrons, acts as a point source of rays. These spread out in straight lines, as shown in Fig. G. On passing through the hand to the photographic film, more X-rays are absorbed by the bones than by the flesh. The shadow cast by the bones is, therefore, very weak in X-rays and the photographic film develops out clear.

Where only flesh is traversed, the X-rays penetrate through to the photographic film, causing it to develop out black. The bones, therefore, appear white against a darker background. If this "negative film," as it is called, is printed on paper, as in Fig. H, it becomes a "positive," with the bones appearing black.

If the photographic film is placed farther away from the hand than shown in the diagram, the shadow picture will be larger and less distinct. The best pictures are obtained by placing the film in as close contact with the object to be photographed as is physically possible. Whenever a film is being exposed for an X-ray picture, it is mounted in a black paper envelope or thin aluminum box. This prevents visible light from reaching the film, but allows the X-rays to pass through.

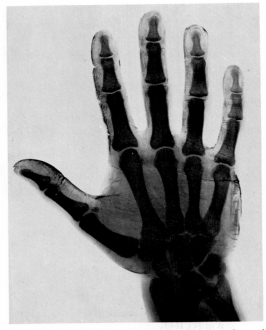

Fig. H. X-ray photograph of the hand and wrist bones. Lead oxide ointment was spread on the hand to show the flesh (Courtesy of the Stamford Research Laboratories, American Cyanamid Co.)

QUESTIONS

1. What happens to the X-ray wave that ejects a photoelectron from a solid?
2. Why is Compton's experiment, which proved that an X-ray may collide with an electron, so important?
3. How does the Compton effect help explain the dual nature of light?
4. What happens to the X-ray that ejects a Compton electron from a solid?

5. (a) Do light waves have momentum? (b) Could you write the formula for such momentum?

6. (a) What are hard X-rays? (b) What are soft X-rays? (c) How is hardness or softness related to X-ray wave lengths?

7. (a) How are X-ray photographs made? (b) Why do the bones of the body absorb more X-rays than the flesh?

8. How is X-ray absorption related to the periodic table of the elements?

9. Which of the following materials is the best absorber of X-rays: (a) beryllium, (b) magnesium, (c) calcium, (d) copper, (e) gold, (f) lead, or (g) uranium?

10. (a) What is the process of ionization by X-rays? (b) What happens to the liberated free electrons?

11. Why does the skin show so clearly in the X-ray photograph in Fig. H?

12. If a small child swallowed a safety pin, why would an X-ray photograph clearly show the location of the pin?

13. Can you name three important properties of X-rays?

14. Make a list of specific places in which X-rays would prove to be of considerable use.

15. How is the penetrating power of X-rays related to the voltage applied to the tube?

16. Suppose you had a sheet of iron and a sheet of tin of equal areas and weights. Which would absorb X-rays better? Why?

17. An electron strikes a target producing an X-ray, which in turn is absorbed in a sheet of metal. Into what form does all this energy ultimately go?

PROBLEMS

1. Calculate the momentum of an X-ray having a wave length of 1×10^{-10} m.

2. What are the (a) energy and (b) momentum of an X-ray with a wave length 2×10^{-10} m?

3. An X-ray of wave length 5×10^{-9} m is absorbed by the photoelectric effect, emitting a photoelectron with an energy of 2×10^{-17} joule. What was the total energy of the electron in the atom?

4. When an X-ray of wave length 6×10^{-9} m scatters from an aluminum foil, its resultant wave length is 8×10^{-9} m. What is the energy of the recoiling electron?

PROJECT

Make a collection of X-ray photographs showing various parts of the body. Doctors and dentists are good sources of supply.

ATOMIC PHYSICS

Lesson 108 ATOMIC WAVES

In preceding lessons, we have seen that light is a wave, as shown by its interference and diffraction properties. In the recent lessons, however, we have seen that light waves consist of small finite bundles of energy called quanta or photons and that they, too, like atomic particles, may be made to collide with atoms of one kind or another. This was the case both in the photoelectric effect and in the production and interaction of X-rays. There is, therefore, a corpuscular nature of light as well as a wave nature of light.

This last statement suggests a sort of "Dr. Jekyll and Mr. Hyde" existence for light waves. Under some conditions, light may act as though it were waves, whereas under other conditions, it may act like small particles.

In this lesson, the wave nature of electrons and atoms will be studied. The fact that atoms are described as corpuscles is obvious. The fact that they have a wave nature, too, is somewhat surprising.

de Broglie's Electron-Waves. In 1924, Louis V. de Broglie, a French theoretical physicist, derived an equation predicting that all atomic particles have associated with them waves of a definite wave length. In other words, a beam of electrons or atoms should, under the proper experimental conditions, act like a train of light waves or a beam of photons. The wave length of these waves, as predicted by de Broglie, depends upon the mass and velocity of the particles according to the following relations:

$$\lambda = \frac{h}{mv} \qquad (1)$$

This is known as *de Broglie's wave equation.* For an electron moving at high speed, the denominator, mv, is large and the wave length is small. In other words, the faster an electron moves, the shorter is the wave length associated with it. (See Fig. A.)

Fig. A. Schematic diagram of a de Broglie wave.

The Davisson-Germer Experiment. The first experimental proof of the wave nature of atomic particles was demonstrated in 1927 by two American physicists, C. J. Davisson and his collaborator, L. H. Germer. Their experiment is illustrated schematically in Fig. B. Electrons from a hot cathode are accelerated toward an anode, where, upon passing through a system of pinholes, they emerge as a narrow beam, as indicated. This source acts as an *electron gun* from which electrons of any desired velocity may be obtained by applying the proper potential, V.

Upon striking one of the polished faces of a nickel crystal, the equally spaced rows of atoms in the crystal act like the lines of a diffraction grating, and the electrons, acting like waves, are diffracted off in certain preferred directions. The electron wave length is given by Eq. (1) and the preferred directions by $\lambda = 2d \sin \theta$. These

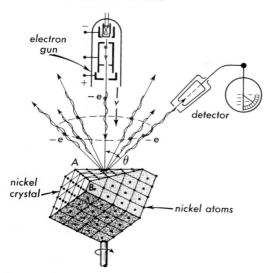

Fig. B. The Davisson-Germer experiment. Electrons striking the surface layers of a crystal are diffracted at different angles, just as if they were waves with a very short wave length.

preferred directions are located by means of a detector in which the electrons are collected and their accumulated charge measured. The detector is mounted so that it may be turned to any angle θ and the crystal is mounted so it may be turned about an axis parallel to the incident beam.

Electron Waves within the Atom. The most recent development in the theory of atomic structure, called *wave mechanics,* has shown that the Bohr picture of the atom with sharply defined electron orbits is not quite correct. The new wave theory does not discard the Bohr theory entirely, but only modifies it to the extent that the electron does not behave as though it were a particle. The electron behaves as if it were made up of waves of the type described in the previous sections.

The wave theory of the hydrogen atom was worked out by the German theoretical physicist Erwin Schrödinger, in 1925. Mak-

ing use of de Broglie's idea of electron waves, Schrödinger pictures the single electron in the hydrogen atom as moving around the nucleus as a kind of *wave packet.* This wave packet, as it is called, is formed in somewhat the same way that standing waves are set up and maintained in sound waves.

One method of representing the electron in the atom is to picture an electron wave as a cloud having a considerable length so that it extends around the atom far enough to overlap and form standing waves. These may be illustrated schematically as shown in Fig. C.

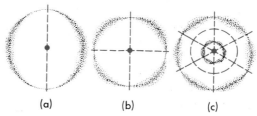

(a)   (b)   (c)

Fig. C. Schematic diagram of the waves of the orbital electron in a hydrogen atom.

To set up these standing waves, the length of the path of an electron around the hydrogen nucleus must be a whole number of wave lengths. The circumference of a circle is $2\pi r$.

Because this distance must be exactly equal to λ, 2λ, 3λ, etc., or $n\lambda$, we can write—

$$n\lambda = 2\pi r \qquad (2)$$

where $n = 1, 2, 3$, etc. Upon substituting the de Broglie wave length, Eq. (1), we obtain—

$$n\frac{h}{mv} = 2\pi r \qquad (3)$$

or—

$$2\pi r \times mv = nh \qquad (4)$$

This is exactly the condition proposed by

Bohr in his orbital theory, presented in Eq. (2) in Lesson 104. It is not surprising, therefore, that the new wave theory also gives exactly the Bohr equations for the wave lengths and the frequencies of the hydrogen spectrum. As we shall see, even this picture is oversimplified and is not valid for small values of n.

The Meaning of the Wave Packet. Even though the wave theory of the hydrogen atom is an improvement upon the older Bohr orbit theory and gives a more satisfactory explanation of all known phenomena, it is more difficult to form a mental picture of what an atom might look like. Indeed, the modern theoretical physicist goes so far as to say that the question, "What does an atom look like?" has no meaning, much less an answer. This is because one cannot measure something without interacting with it and, when one interacts with a wave, the wave is altered. Even "seeing" something is interacting with it, since light waves must be bounced from the object in order to see it.

There are many people, however, who still maintain that only those things that can be pictured are the things that are understood and that all thought processes are made in terms of things we detect by sight or touch. For this reason, an interpretation is often given to the theory and its resultant equations that *the amplitude of the electron waves within an atom represents the distribution of the electronic charge and mass.* At the nodes, where the motion is practically zero, there is assumed to be little or no charge, while at the antinodes, there is a maximum charge.

Suppose, now, one were to irradiate an atom with X-rays, or high-speed particles, and knock out electrons. One would find that the electron would very likely be knocked out of the denser portions of the wave packet and would seldom be knocked out of the rarer portions.

Such an experiment would demonstrate another aspect of the basic relationship between the wave and particle picture: *that the density of the wave at any point is related to the probability that the particle may be found at that point.*

The Classical Limit. One may ask why neither quantum effects nor wave aspects are seen in the natural events that we normally observe. For example, suppose you swing a rock in a circle at the end of a string. There appear to be no discrete quantized orbits since any radius or velocity is possible. Moreover, there is no obvious "wave" aspect or fuzzy cloud-like appearance to the rock. It is natural to ask why the quantum and wave features apply to an atomic electron, but not to the whirling rock.

The fact is that the rock does have quantum and wave properties, but they are not noticed, because the angular momentum is so large compared to the fundamental unit $h/2\pi$. For example, if the angular momentum of the rock is 10^{27} units, the next higher quantized states have angular momenta $10^{27} + 1$, $10^{27} + 2$, etc. These are so close together that one cannot tell that the states are quantized at all.

As atomic sizes are approached, say for a quantum number of 100, the quantum distinction between adjacent orbits starts to become apparent. The wave picture also starts to become apparent in that the electron cloud may look like a smoke ring about the nucleus. The Bohr-orbit picture, which looked valid at the classical limit, now is obviously no longer valid, although the radius of the electron cloud coincides with the Bohr radius.

At even smaller quantum numbers, the wave aspects and the quantum effects become even more prominent. The Bohr-orbit picture now disagrees drastically. The wave packet becomes a spherical cloud centered about the nucleus, and the angular momentum drops to zero, instead of one unit.

In spite of the disagreement with the Bohr model at low quantum numbers, the energies of the electron states are identical to those given by the Bohr model.

Photographs representing a few of the possible states of the single electron in hydrogen are shown in Fig. D. These three-

spherical node. In this representation, the electron is not thought of as a particle located at some point within the atom, but is considered as though its mass and charge were spread symmetrically throughout the space that immediately surrounds the nucleus of the atom.

The New Atomic Picture. Although the Bohr atom has been replaced by the more satisfactory model of a *nucleus surrounded*

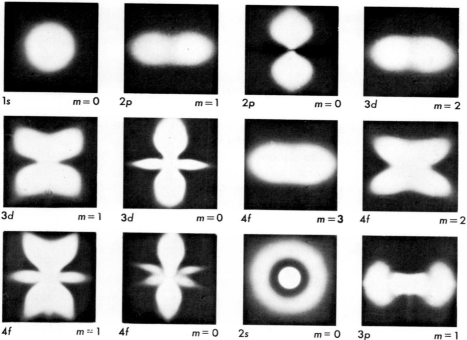

Fig. D. Electron wave density figures representing the single electron states of the hydrogen atom.

dimensional distributions can be visualized by imagining each figure to be rotating about a vertical axis. For example, the second figure in three dimensions would have a shape similar to a smoke ring.

In the first figure, there are two radial nodes; in the second, four radial nodes; and in the third, six radial nodes and one

by electron waves, it is still customary, for convenience only, to talk about electron *shells* and *orbits.* The reason for this is that there is a close connection between the old and the new models. When the Bohr-Stoner scheme of the building-up of the elements is extended to the new theory of electron waves, the electrons are found to distribute

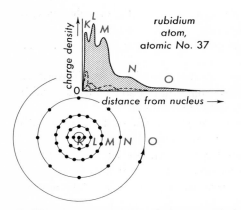

Fig. E. Diagrams comparing the new and the old theories of atomic structure, according to wave mechanics and the Bohr-Stoner model.

their charge in such a way that something analogous to shells is formed.

This is illustrated by the graph for a rubidium atom, atomic number 37, in Fig. E. The shaded area represents the distribution of the charge of 37 electrons on the new theory, and the lower orbital model represents the electron shells on the old theory. The new model is represented by a graph because it is spherically symmetrical in space, while the old model is represented by orbits because it is confined to one plane. Proceeding out from the nucleus, it is seen that the charge rises to several maxima at distances corresponding closely to the discrete shells of the orbital model.

QUESTIONS

1. What is the de Broglie wave equation? Write down the equation.
2. What was the Davisson-Germer experiment?
3. In what way do the wave properties of electrons modify the Bohr theory of circular orbits in hydrogen?
4. What was concluded from the Davisson-Germer experiment? In what way is the wave theory a more satisfactory description than the hypothesis of Bohr?
5. (a) Are wave aspects present in the case of a satellite moving about the earth? (b) Why aren't such aspects noticed?
6. Under what circumstances would wave aspects of a particle be noticed?
7. What is meant by the dual nature of light?
8. What experimental evidence do we have to indicate that light is corpuscular?
9. What relation exists between the wave length associated with an electron and its velocity?
10. An electron microscope can be focused in an analogous fashion to a light microscope. What does this suggest about the nature of an electron?
11. According to de Broglie's wave equation, why wouldn't the wave length of an automobile traveling at 60 mi/hr be detected?

PROBLEMS

1. Compute the wave length associated with an electron moving with one-tenth the speed of light.
2. Compute the wave length of a proton moving with one-tenth the speed of light.

3. If the electron beam in a TV picture tube is accelerated by 10,000 volts, what is the de Broglie wave length?

4. What would be the de Broglie wave length of a 2000-Kg car moving along the highway at 30 m/sec?

5. Draw standing wave diagrams to scale for the first three Bohr orbits of hydrogen.

6. (a) Find the de Broglie wave length for the electron in the first circular orbit of hydrogen. (b) How is this related to the orbit circumference?

7. Derive an equation for the de Broglie wave length of the electron in the different Bohr circular orbits of hydrogen. (See Lesson 104.)

8. A proton has a wave length of 2×10^{-14} m. How fast is it moving?

9. Find the speed of an electron whose wave length is equivalent to 1 A.

10. Find the wave length of an α particle accelerated by a potential difference of 10,000 volts.

11. A 100-gm rock is swung around the end of a string of radius 1.5 m with a velocity of 2 m/sec. (a) What is its angular momentum? (b) How many fundamental units of angular momentum does it have?

12. The Bohr model states that the angular momentum of an electron in the hydrogen atom is given by $n \times h/2\pi$, whereas the wave model gives $\sqrt{n(n-1)} \times h/2\pi$, where n is the principal quantum number. (a) Where do these models agree well? (b) Where do they agree poorly? Explain. (c) Compare for $n = 100$, 10,000, and 1.

ATOMIC PHYSICS

Lesson 109 *RELATIVITY*

The mention of the word "relativity" suggests the name of Albert Einstein,* the

* Albert Einstein (1879-1955), German-Swiss physicist, was born at Ulm, Württemberg, on March 14, 1879. His boyhood was spent in Munich, where his father, a dealer in chemicals, had settled in 1880. When the family moved to Italy in 1894, young Albert went to Switzerland to study. There he worked his way through school, finally taking his Ph.D. degree at the University of Zürich in 1902. He was appointed extraordinary professor of theoretical physics at the University of Zürich in 1909 and, in 1913, he was called to Berlin as director of the Kaiser-Wilhelm Institute for Physics. While at this post, he was elected a member of the Prussian Academy of Sciences and a member of the Royal Society of London. In 1921, he received the Nobel Prize in physics and, in

scientist to whom we are indebted for the now famous theory. To begin with, Einstein was a realist, and his theory rests upon physical facts that have been verified by repeated observations of well-planned experiments.

1925, the Copley Medal of the Royal Society. From 1933 to 1945, he was with the Institute for Advanced Studies in Princeton, where he died. He is best known for his theory of relativity, the theory and explanation of Brownian motion, the theory of the photoelectric effect, and the quantum theory of radiant heat energy. Twice married, Einstein had several children. He was a quiet, sincere, and modest man who loved his pipe and violin and disliked formality.

Two Theories of Relativity. Relativity is divided into two parts. One part is called the *special theory of relativity* and the other is called the *general theory*. The special theory, developed by Einstein in 1905, is limited to observers and their reference frames moving with constant velocities. The mathematics of the special theory is straightforward, and we will consider several of the relationships that are necessary for the satisfactory explanations of atomic phenomena.

The general theory, proposed by Einstein in 1915, deals with gravity and the motions of bodies in accelerated frames of reference. The mathematics of the general theory is quite difficult, and the experimental evidence for its validity is not as well founded as for the special theory.

The Velocity of Light. As we have seen in Lesson 9, a measurement of velocity depends upon the *frame of reference* in which it is observed. For example, if a man is walking across the deck of a moving ship (see Fig. A), his velocity is different if

frame of the air. In a heavy wind, a sound is heard more clearly if the wind is blowing from the source to the observer. If the vibration is created in a vacuum (see Lesson 52), no sound is heard at all. Sound waves move *relatively* to the frame of reference of the medium carrying the sound.

Light waves travel with a velocity 3×10^8 m/sec (see Lesson 59). It was assumed, prior to 1880, that, by analogy with sound waves, there must be some medium to carry the light waves. This medium, called the *ether*, must be transparent, weightless, and yet must fill all space. The velocity of light should then be a constant relative to the frame of reference of the ether.

The Michelson-Morley Experiment. This, the most famous experiment in optics, was first performed by the American scientists, Albert A. Michelson and Edward Morley, in 1881, in an effort to detect the motion of the earth through space. If the transmission of light through space requires an ether, that is, a medium for it to move in, then light should be dragged along by

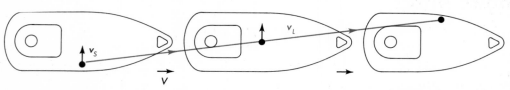

Fig. A. The motion of a man walking across the deck of a ship depends upon the frame of reference in which it is measured.

measured from aboard the ship, than if measured from a point on land.

When a velocity or position is given, the frame of reference must also be given, or implied. As we have seen, the velocity of various types of waves is measured with respect to the medium carrying the wave. The velocity of water waves is given with respect to the water. The velocity of sound through air is given with respect to the

this ether as the earth moves along through space. In order to detect such a drift, the Michelson interferometer appeared to be the most sensitive instrument to use.

In principle, the ether-drift test consists simply of observing whether there is any difference in the velocity of light parallel and perpendicular to the motion of the interferometer through the ether. The mirrors (Fig. B) allowed the light from S to be split, and sent along two equal paths, GM_1G and GM_2G. The difference in time taken by the light to travel along the two paths was measured at E by interference methods, which we shall not discuss here.

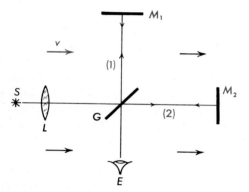

Fig. B. The Michelson interferometer arrangement for detecting an ether drift.

This would be similar to the difference in time of a boat crossing a moving stream and returning, compared with a boat going an equal distance up a moving stream and returning.

From the differences, they should then be able to determine from the measured speed of light in each frame whether they are moving through the ether at different rates.

Because neither the earth's motion, nor the ether, can be stopped, in an effort to observe this shift, a rotation of the interferometer through 90° should have a similar effect. By interchanging paths (1) and (2), the time difference $t_\parallel - t_\perp$ is reversed, and any change should be detected. Although very careful measurements were made, no difference was found, leading to the conclusion that either there is no such thing as an ether drift, or that the Michelson interferometer is incapable of detecting motion through an ether.

Einstein's Special Theory of Relativity. From the time Michelson and Morley announced the negative results of their ether-drift experiment, many scientists tried unsuccessfully to explain why the experiment failed. Einstein interpreted this failure to mean that the velocity of light is *invariant.* What is meant by this is that no matter how a source of light moves or how an observer moves, he will always find the velocity of light in free space to be the same. This velocity we designate c.

Because the Michelson-Morley experiment fails to provide a fixed frame of reference in space, Einstein's theory assumes that all such experiments will fail, and that at relatively high speeds the laws of Newton are not valid. Einstein's special theory of relativity shows that the laws of physics can be restated so that they will apply to any frame of reference and that, at low relative velocities, these laws reduce to Newton's laws of motion. The first postulate for setting up these equations is: *The laws of physics apply equally well for all observers as long as they are moving with constant velocities.*

The second postulate follows from the assumption that the velocity of light is *invariant. The velocity of light in free space has the same value regardless of the motion of the source and the motion of the observer.*

To see the meaning of this second statement, consider a reference frame and observer O at rest, as shown in Fig. C. A source of light, S, is set up and, by means of an experiment, the velocity of light is measured and found to be 3×10^8 m/sec. Another observer, O', moving with a velocity, v, with respect to O, allows the light from the same source, S, to pass through his apparatus. Upon measuring the velocity of this same light in his frame, he too finds 3×10^8 m/sec.

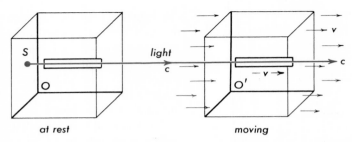

Fig. C. The velocity of light is the same to all observers, that is, it is invariant.

For these two identical results to be consistent, Einstein derived new transformation equations. To do this he assumed that *distance* and *time* are relative, *not invariant*. That is, measurements of distance and time depend upon the frame of reference in which the measurements are made.

spaceship of velocity v passing over a mirror on the ground at a height h. An observer on the ground measures its length to be l; see Fig. D(a). He notes that the spaceship emits a burst of light from the bow as it passes directly over the mirror. The light reflects from the mirror and reaches the aft

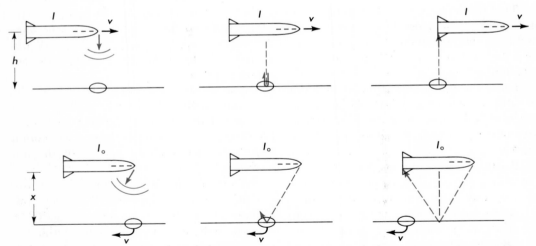

Fig. D. Illustration of a reflected light pulse as seen from (a) the stationary reflector and (b) the moving emitter.

Lorentz-Fitzgerald Contraction. We shall first show that *distance* is not invariant. To do this, we consider the following "thought experiment." Consider a very fast

of the ship just as it passes over the mirror. The time the light has traveled is just—

$$\Delta t = \frac{2h}{c} \tag{1}$$

But during this time, the spaceship has just traveled its own length:

$$l = v \Delta t$$

Using the value in Eq. (1) for Δt, we have—

$$l = v \times \frac{2h}{c} \qquad (2)$$

An observer in the spaceship measures its length to be l_0. As seen from the moving spaceship, the mirror appears to be moving backward at a velocity, v. The light, therefore, must follow the trajectory shown in Fig. D(b). This path is shown in Fig. E(a)

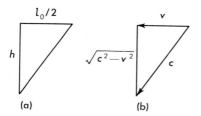

(a)   (b)

Fig. E. The light trajectory and velocity triangle as seen from the moving emitter.

to be the hypotenuse of a triangle with sides $l_0/2$ and h. In order for the light to strike the mirror properly, it must have a backward velocity component, v. A velocity triangle is thus defined as in Fig. E(b), with hypotenuse c and side v. By the Pythagorean theorem, the other side is $\sqrt{c^2 - v^2}$.

Because the two triangles are similar, we can write down the condition of proportionality:

$$\frac{h}{l_0/2} = \frac{\sqrt{c^2 - v^2}}{v}$$

or—

$$h = \frac{l_0}{2v} \sqrt{c^2 - v^2} \qquad (3)$$

Putting this value of h into Eq. (2), we have—

$$l = \frac{2v}{c} \times \frac{l_0}{2v} \sqrt{c^2 - v^2}$$

$$= l_0 \frac{\sqrt{c^2 - v^2}}{c}$$

or—

$$l = l_0 \sqrt{1 - \frac{v^2}{c^2}} \qquad (4)$$

This means that a rapidly moving object is found to be shorter than its length as measured in its own rest frame. The faster the object is moving, the shorter it becomes.

Suppose that an object is at rest, so that $v = 0$. Upon substitution of $v = 0$ in Eq. (4), we find $l = l_0$, which says the object's length, l, will be just equal to its rest length, l_0. If a rod were moving lengthwise with three-fourths the speed of light, however, the substitution of $v = \frac{3}{4}c$ into the equation gives $l = 0.66 \, l_0$. This indicates that the moving rod is only two-thirds as long as when it is at rest. (See Fig. F.)

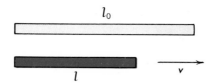

Fig. F. Diagram of the Lorentz-Fitzgerald contraction.

It is interesting to see what this equation reveals if a rod could move lengthwise with the speed of light, i.e., with $v = c$. The result is $l = 0$. This means that any object moving with the speed of light would be compressed to zero length. The velocity of light, therefore, becomes an upper limit for the velocity of any moving object.

Time Dilation. We shall secondly show that *time* is not invariant. The time for the light pulse to travel in the frame of reference of the spaceship is just—

$$\Delta t_0 = 2h/\sqrt{c^2 - v^2} \qquad (5)$$

Using the value of h from the stationary Eq. (1), we have—

$$\Delta t_0 = \frac{2}{\sqrt{c^2 - v^2}} \times \frac{c\Delta t}{2}$$

or—

$$\Delta t = \Delta t_0 \sqrt{1 - \frac{v^2}{c^2}} \qquad (6)$$

Time is not invariant, but depends upon the frame in which it is measured.

The factor—

$$\sqrt{1 - \frac{v^2}{c^2}} \quad \text{or} \quad 1 \Big/ \sqrt{1 - \frac{v^2}{c^2}}$$

is the important distinction between the relativistic equations and the nonrelativistic equations. The dependence on velocity is shown in Table 1, where it is seen to become very important at velocities approaching the speed of light.

This is why the relativistic effects are not noticeable.

Classical laws, such as Newton's laws of motion, can be used in most applications of kinematics and dynamics, but at speeds above 10% the speed of light, the relativistic equations should be used.

The Twin Paradox. A novel "thought experiment" has often been discussed to illustrate time dilation. Twin brothers plan to test the theory, one by traveling out into space on a fast spacecraft, the other remaining on the earth. Each has a clock, both running accurately and synchronized before the trip. See Fig. G. After the space trip, the clocks are found to read different times. Because of the time dilation effect, the clock on the spaceship shows less elapsed time. Less time has actually elapsed on the space voyage, and the twin taking the trip is now actually *younger* than his brother.

Table 1. Relativistic Factor for Different Velocities

Velocity ratio v/c in percent	1%	10%	50%	90%	99%	99.9%
$\sqrt{1 - \dfrac{v^2}{c^2}}$	1.000	.995	.87	.43	.14	.045
$\dfrac{1}{\sqrt{1 - \dfrac{v^2}{c^2}}}$	1.000	1.005	1.15	2.3	7.1	22.3

By setting $v = 0$ in Eqs. (4) and (6) we get—

$$l = l_0$$
$$t = t_0$$

All other relativistic equations reduce to the familiar laws such as Newton's laws.

Except for atomic and subatomic motion, the objects we encounter always have velocities that are small compared with c.

When a student first hears of such relativistic effects, he often says something like "I don't believe it; it just isn't reasonable." Whether or not something seems "reasonable" depends upon personal experience. People are normally unfamiliar with velocities near the speed of light. The notion of time passing at different rates or objects becoming shorter are unfamiliar and, therefore, seem unreasonable.

Fig. G. Time passes more slowly on a space flight than on earth.

The many scientists who have thoroughly studied relativity and who have carried out the experiments verifying the theory have come to understand and accept these interesting results.

Relativistic Mass. Einstein's special theory of relativity shows that, if the mass of an object is measured by two different observers, one moving with respect to the other, the results are different. Mass, therefore, is not invariant. Although the derivation will not be presented here, the special theory gives, for the transformation equation—

$$m = \frac{m_0}{\sqrt{1 - v^2/c^2}} \qquad (7)$$

where m_0 is the mass of an object at rest in the observer's reference frame and m is its

mass when it is moving with a velocity v. A schematic diagram of a practical situation is shown in Fig. H, in which the rest mass

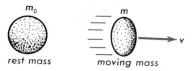

Fig. H. Schematic diagram illustrating the relativistic increase in mass, and the Lorentz-Fitzgerald contraction, due to motion.

m_0 is not moving with respect to you, the observer, while at the right, the same mass m is shown moving with a velocity v.

Table 1 gives the increase in the relativistic mass of objects for a large range of velocities.

At 10% the speed of light (18,630 mi/sec), the mass of a body is only half of

1% greater than its rest mass. At 50% the speed of light, the mass m has increased 15%, while at 99.9% the speed of light, it has jumped to over 22 times its rest mass. These values are in excellent agreement with experiments on high-speed atomic particles, a subject that will be considered in detail in later chapters.

It is important to note that, as the speed of any given mass increases, the mass rises slowly at first, and then much more rapidly as it approaches the speed of light. No object, however, can move with the speed of light, for by Eq. (7) its mass would become infinite.

For low velocities v, Eq. (7) is hard to evaluate, and the following approximation formula should be used:

$$\frac{1}{\sqrt{1 - v^2/c^2}} \cong 1 + \frac{1}{2}\frac{v^2}{c^2} \qquad (8)$$

Einstein's Mass-Energy Relation. Just as sound, heat, and light are forms of energy, Einstein's special theory of relativity shows that mass is a form of energy. The expression giving the relation between mass and energy is an equation familiar to everyone. It is—

$$E = mc^2 \qquad (9)$$

where m is the mass, c is the velocity of light, and E is the energy equivalence of the mass. The validity of this equation is now well established by hundreds of experiments involving atomic nuclei, as well as the general subject of *nuclear energy*.

If an object has a rest mass of m_0, it has stored within it a total energy m_0c^2. If the same mass is moving with a velocity v, its mass has increased to m and the total energy is mc^2. These two masses are related by Eq. (7).

When a force, F, is applied to accelerate a given mass, the amount of work done is given by—

$$W = F \times s$$

As a result of this *work done*, the object, whose rest mass is m_0, is moving with a velocity and has kinetic energy E_k:

$$F \times s = E_k \qquad (10)$$

Applying the law of conservation of energy, we can write—

$$m_0c^2 + E_k = mc^2$$

or solving for the kinetic energy of a moving mass, the relation becomes—

$$E_k = mc^2 - m_0c^2 \qquad (11)$$

The General Theory of Relativity. Realizing that the special theory of relativity did not consider acceleration, Einstein developed his *General Theory* in 1915. This theory modified Newton's law of gravity so as to describe the universe in terms of curved space, the curvature depending upon the gravitational field at each point. A central assumption of the theory is the *equivalence principle* (see Lesson 19):

$$m_I = m_g \qquad (12)$$

i.e., gravitational mass equals inertial mass.

Experiments to verify or disprove the general theory are very difficult and, as yet, have not been conclusive. One such experiment involves accurate measurement of the orbit of the planet Mercury.

It is hoped that satellite experiments will soon be carried out that will clearly verify or disprove the General Theory.

QUESTIONS

1. (a) How many theories of relativity are there? (b) How do they differ? (c) Which are well verified?

2. (a) What is a frame of reference? (b) Give an example of a system involving two frames of reference. (c) Three frames of reference.

3. (a) What is "ether"? (b) Why was its existence proposed? (c) Does it really exist? Explain.

4. (a) What was the Michelson-Morley experiment? (b) What did it show?

5. What is meant by the velocity of light being "invariant"?

6. Where did the word "relativity" come from?

7. When do relativistic effects become noticeably different from Newton's laws?

8. (a) What is the significance of the relativistic factor $\sqrt{1 - \frac{v^2}{c^2}}$? (b) When is it equal to 1? (c) Is it ever less than 1? (d) Is it ever greater than 1?

9. What is a "thought experiment"?

10. (a) What is Lorentz-Fitzgerald contraction? (b) Why don't we ever notice a moving object contracting?

11. (a) What is time dilation? (b) Why don't we ever notice time elapsing at different rates?

12. In the "twin paradox," would the twin who took the trip actually be younger when he returned, or does it just seem so?

13. Why do students newly exposed to these relativistic effects often find them unreasonable or unbelievable?

14. Why do scientists who have studied relativity in detail generally accept the theory?

15. (a) What is the equivalence principle? (b) What is meant by inertial mass? (c) What is meant by gravitational mass?

16. Why is the general theory still not universally accepted?

PROBLEMS

(Assume the speed of light to be 3×10^8 m/sec, or 186,300 mi/sec, in all of the following problems.)

1. Find the length of a meter stick moving lengthwise at a speed of 2.8×10^8 m/sec. Assume a Lorentz-Fitzgerald contraction.

2. If a space ship 50 m long were to pass the earth traveling at 2.4×10^8 m/sec, what would be its apparent length, assuming a Lorentz-Fitzgerald contraction?

3. Atomic particles in the form of a beam have a velocity of 92% speed of light. What is their relativistic mass as compared with their rest mass?

4. Atomic particles in the form of a beam have a velocity of 95% speed of light. What is their relativistic mass compared with their rest mass?

5. An atomic particle has a rest mass of 2.5×10^{-25} Kg. Find its total mass energy when it is (a) at rest, and (b) when it has a velocity of 0.90 speed of light.

6. If an atomic mass of 4.2^{-25} Kg were converted into energy, and all of it imparted as kinetic energy to another atomic particle with a rest mass of 2.0×10^{-25} Kg, what would be the atom's velocity?

7. An astronaut takes off in a spaceship going 10% speed of light and is gone for a year. How much time has elapsed in the spaceship?

Nuclear Physics

The main result of our investigations and of those of other scientists during these years, was to make known the nature of the rays emitted by radium, and to prove that they belonged to three different categories. Radium emits a stream of active corpuscles moving with great speed. Certain of them carry a positive charge and form the Alpha rays; others, much smaller, carry a negative charge and form Beta rays. The movements of these two groups are influenced by a magnet. A third group is constituted by the rays that are insensible to the action of a magnet, and that, we know today, are a radiation similar to light and to X-rays.

Marie Curie, *Pierre Curie*, Macmillan, New York, 1923, p. 103.

After long consideration of the experiments it seemed to me that there was no escape from the following conclusions:

(1) That atoms are not indivisible, for negatively electrified particles can be torn from them by the action of electrical forces, impact of rapidly moving atoms, ultra-violet light or heat.

(2) That these particles are all of the same mass, and carry the same charge of negative electricity from whatever kind of atom they may be derived, and are a constituent of all atoms.

(3) That the mass of these particles is less than one-thousandth part of the mass of an atom of hydrogen.

I at first called these particles corpuscles, but they are now called by the more appropriate name "electrons."

J. J. Thomson, *Recollections and Reflections,* Macmillan, New York, 1937, pp. 338-339.

◄ Henry Faul attaches an auxiliary source magnet to an argon mass spectrometer. The time at which a mineral crystallized can be determined by measuring its potassium content and the amount of argon evolved during the elapsed time by radioactive decay of isotope K^{40}.

U.S. Geological Survey

Lesson 110 RADIOACTIVITY

Radioactivity may be defined as a spontaneous disintegration of the nucleus of one or more atoms. The phenomenon was discovered originally by Becquerel * in 1896 and is confined almost entirely to the heaviest elements in the periodic table, from elements 83 on. What Becquerel discovered was that uranium, element 92, gave out some kind of rays that would penetrate through several thicknesses of thick black paper and affect a photographic plate on the other side. When the same phenomenon was confirmed several months later by Pierre and Marie Curie, these rays became known as Becquerel rays.

Discovery of Radium. Unlike the discovery of many new phenomena, the discovery of radium by Pierre and Madame Curie in 1898 was brought about intentionally by a set of carefully planned experiments. Having found that pitchblende was active in emitting Becquerel rays, the Curies treated chemically a ton of this ore in the hope of isolating from it the substance or element responsible for the activity. The first concentrated radioactive substance isolated was called *polonium* by Madame Curie, a name chosen in honor of her native country, Poland. Five months later came the isolation of a minute quantity of *ra-*

dium, a substance that was a powerful source of Becquerel rays. Continued experiments by the Curies, and others, soon led to the isolation of many other substances now also recognized as radioactive elements. Some of the more common of these are *uranium, radon,* and *thorium.*

The Properties of Becquerel Rays. It is to the experimental genius of Rutherford ** that we owe the complete unraveling of the mystery surrounding the nature of Becquerel rays. As the result of an extensive series of experiments, Rutherford and his co-workers discovered that these penetrating rays are of three quite different kinds. A simplified experiment demonstrating this is illustrated in Fig. A.

A small sample of radium is dropped to the bottom of a small hole drilled in a block of lead. This produces a narrow beam of rays emerging from the top of the block, because those rays entering the walls of the lead are absorbed before reaching the surface. When electrically charged plates are placed at the sides of this beam, the paths

* Antoine Henri Becquerel (1852-1908), French physicist, was born in Paris on December 15, 1852. Antoine succeeded to his father's chair at the Museum of Natural History in 1892. In 1896, he discovered radioactivity, the phenomenon for which he is most famous. The invisible but penetrating rays emitted by uranium and other radioactive elements are now called Becquerel rays. For these researches he was granted the Nobel Prize in physics in 1903.

** Lord Rutherford (1871-1937), British physicist, was born in New Zealand, where he attended the university. In 1898, he became Macdonald professor of physics at McGill University, Montreal, Canada, and, in 1907, professor of physics at Manchester University. In 1919, he became professor and director of experimental physics at the University of Cambridge and, in addition, held a professorship at the Royal Institution in London. He is most famous for his brilliant researches establishing the existence and nature of radioactive transformations and the electrical structure of the atom. For this work and until the time of his death in 1937, he was acclaimed by many as the greatest living experimental physicist. He was awarded the Nobel Prize in chemistry in 1908 and was knighted in 1914.

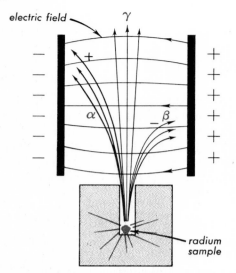

Fig. A. Becquerel rays are of three kinds: α, β, and γ.

ejected with a speed of from one tenth to one hundredth the velocity of light. β particles move faster than α particles, some of them traveling with 99 percent the velocity of light.

Transmutation by Spontaneous Disintegration. A careful study of radioactivity indicates that α, β, and γ rays originate from within the nucleus of the atom. When a radium atom disintegrates by ejecting an α particle, the nucleus loses a net positive charge of two. Since the number of positive charges on the nucleus determines the exact number of electrons outside of the atom and this, in turn, determines the chemical nature of an atom, the loss of an α particle, with two positive charges, leaves a new chemical element. Thus, a *radium atom*, for example, in disintegrating, changes into a new atom called *radon*. We say there has been a *transmutation*. Not only does a nucleus lose a double charge by emitting an α particle and thereby *drops down two places in atomic number*, but it also loses a weight of four units and thus *drops down four units in mass number*.

When a nucleus disintegrates by ejecting a β particle (an electron), the nuclear positive charge *increases by one unit*. Such a transmutation yields a new element one atomic number higher in the chemical table. Since an electron weighs only 1/1840 part of a hydrogen atom or proton, the change in mass owing to a β particle leaving a nucleus is too small to change the mass number. Although the loss in weight is measurable, it changes the atomic weight so slightly that, for most purposes of discussion, it can be and is neglected. A γ ray, like the β ray, changes the weight of a nucleus by a negligible amount and, since it has no charge, it does not alter either the atomic number or the mass number.

of some rays are bent to the left, some to the right, and some not at all. Those paths bending to the left indicate positively charged particles called α *rays*, or α *particles;* those bending to the right indicate negatively charged particles called β *rays*, or β *particles;* and those going straight ahead indicate no charge and are called γ *rays*.

Rutherford, by a series of experiments, was able to show that each α ray is in reality a *doubly ionized helium atom, i.e.,* a helium atom with both of its electrons gone. Such a particle is nothing more than a bare helium nucleus with double the positive charge of a hydrogen nucleus or proton, and with a mass number or atomic weight four times as great. The β rays he found to be ordinary electrons with a mass of 1/1840 the mass of a *proton*, or 1/7360 the mass of an α particle, while γ rays are electromagnetic waves of about the same or a little higher frequency than X-rays. Although γ rays all travel with exactly the velocity of X-rays and visible light, α rays are

It is common practice to designate all atomic nuclei in an abbreviated form. The nucleus of radium, for example, is written $_{88}Ra^{226}$. The subscript in the chemical symbol gives the *atomic number, i.e.,* the number of positive charges on the nucleus, and the superscript gives the *mass number,* or weight.

The disintegration of radioactive nuclei may be written in the form of simple equations called *nuclear reactions:*

$$_{88}Ra^{226} \longrightarrow _{86}Rn^{222} + _{2}He^{4} \qquad (1)$$

$$_{84}Po^{210} \longrightarrow _{82}Pb^{206} + _{2}He^{4} \qquad (2)$$

$$_{82}Pb^{214} \longrightarrow _{83}Bi^{214} + _{-1}e^{0} + \gamma \ \textbf{ray} \qquad (3)$$

In each reaction, the sum of the subscripts on the right side of the arrow is equal to the subscript on the left. The same is true for the superscripts. The designation $_{2}He^{4}$ represents the α particle and $_{-1}e^{0}$ represents the β particle. In most radioactive disintegrations when a β particle is emitted, one finds at least one γ ray also. In such cases, as shown by the example in Eq. (3), $_{82}Pb^{214}$ ejects a β particle and a γ ray to become $_{83}Bi^{214}$, a nucleus higher in atomic number by unity but with the same mass number.

Conservation Laws. Many physical laws may be stated in terms of quantities that are conserved during a reaction. The subscripts on the various isotopes refer to the charge on the nucleus. The statement that their sum is equal on both sides of the equation is equivalent to saying that no charge is lost or gained during the reaction. This is the law of *conservation of charge.* Similarly, the equality of superscripts may be called the law of *conservation of mass number.*

Ionizing Power. When Becquerel rays penetrate matter in the gaseous, liquid, or solid state, they do not continue to move indefinitely, but are brought to rest slowly by ionizing atoms all along their path. Being ejected from their radioactive source with tremendously high speeds, all three types of rays collide with electrons and knock them free from atoms. They are, therefore, *ionizing agents.* The relative number of ionized atoms created along the path of an α particle, however, is much greater than the number created by a β particle or γ ray. If, in traveling the same distance in a given material, a γ ray produces one ionized atom, a β particle will, on the average, produce approximately one hundred, and an α particle will produce about ten thousand. Thus α particles are powerful ionizing agents, while γ rays are not.

Penetrating Power. At each collision with an atom, Becquerel rays lose, on the average, only a small part of their initial energy. Usually an α particle or β particle will make several thousand collisions before being brought to rest. At each collision, some of the kinetic energy is expended in ionizing the atom encountered while giving that same atom a certain amount of kinetic energy. Since α particles produce the greatest number of ions in a given path, they penetrate the shortest distance and, therefore, have the poorest penetrating power. The penetrating powers of the three kinds of rays are roughly inversely proportional to their ionizing power.

	α	β	γ
relative ionizing power..........	10,000	100	1
relative penetrating power..........	1	100	10,000

We shall see later how ionizing power and penetrating power are used to identify particles and to determine their kinetic energy.

The Wilson Cloud Chamber. In 1912, C. T. R. Wilson devised a method by which one may actually observe the paths of α and β particles. As will be seen in the following lessons, this method is used extensively in modern atomic physics as a means of studying many different atomic processes. The device by which this is accomplished consists of an expansion chamber in which water vapor is made to condense upon ions produced by the high-speed particles that have previously passed through it.

A diagram of a laboratory type of Wilson cloud chamber is shown in Fig. B. The

Fig. C. Photograph of α particle tracks in a Wilson cloud chamber. (After C. T. R. Wilson)

rubber bulb is squeezed to compress the air in the top, and then released to cause an expansion, fogdrops will form on the ions created by the α particles. See Fig. C. The battery and the wires leading to the wire ring in the top of the chamber and the water below are for the purpose of quickly removing ions previously formed in the chamber. This clears the field of view for newly formed tracks.

Gamma rays are never observed in a cloud chamber, because they produce so few ions. In passing through several feet of air, a single γ ray will, on the average, produce only one or two ions. This is not enough to produce a recognizable cloud track. If a very strong source of γ rays is available, however, their presence can be observed in a cloud chamber by the chance collisions some of them make with electrons.

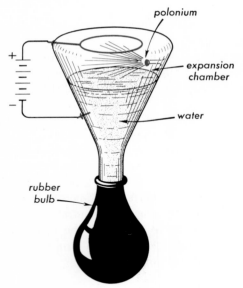

Fig. B. Diagram of a small laboratory type of Wilson cloud chamber.

arrangement is made from an ordinary flat-bottomed flask with a rubber bulb attached to the neck. A tiny deposit of radium or polonium is inserted in the end of a thin-walled glass tube as indicated. When the

The Diffusion Cloud Chamber. Another type of cloud chamber, one that is readily made in any laboratory workshop, is shown in Fig. D. This is the so-called *diffusion cloud chamber*, a device that is continuously sensitive to track formation. A glass cylinder separates and insulates a shallow metal pan below from a metal ring and glass disk above. The bottom pan contains

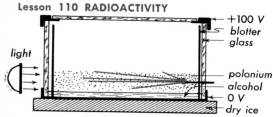

Fig. D. Cross-section diagram of a diffusion cloud chamber.

alcohol and rests on a slab of "dry ice" (solid CO_2).

A blotter, extending 80% of the way around the walls, rests with its lower edge in the alcohol. Evaporated alcohol around the warm upper edge of the blotter mixes with the air and slowly settles as it cools. In the dotted region, alcohol vapor is saturated and small droplets will form on any ions present. Alpha particles shooting out through this space create positive and negative ions and, hence, tracks are observed.

A potential of 100 volts or so between the bottom pan and the top ring will clear the field of ions, so that newly formed tracks are not masked by a dense fog of droplets. A strong source of light, shining through the 20% space of glass not covered by the blotter wall, illuminates the tracks, thus making them visible.

Range. *The range of any nuclear particle is defined as the distance such a particle will travel through dry air at normal atmospheric pressure.* In a partial vacuum, where there are few air molecules per centimeter to bump into, the distance traveled by the particle before coming to rest will be greater, whereas in air, under higher than normal atmospheric pressure, there are more molecules per centimeter and the traveled distance will be diminished. Experiments show that some radioactive elements eject α particles with a higher speed than others. The higher the initial speed, the greater is the range. The range of the α particles from $_{88}Ra^{226}$ is 3.39 cm, whereas the range of those from $_{84}Po^{212}$ is 8.62 cm.

In the Wilson cloud chamber in Fig. E,

Fig. E. Wilson cloud-chamber tracks from a mixture of $_{83}Bi^{212}$ and $_{84}Tl^{212}$. (After Rutherford, Chadwick, and Ellis; courtesy of Cambridge University Press)

α particles of two different ranges are observed. The radioactive sample used to obtain this picture was a mixture of $_{83}Bi^{212}$ and $_{84}Po^{212}$. The shorter tracks, with a 4.79-cm range, are made by the α particles from $_{83}Bi^{212}$ disintegrating to become $_{81}Tl^{208}$. The longer tracks of 8.62-cm range are made by the α particles from $_{84}Po^{212}$ disintegrating to become *lead*.

QUESTIONS

1. (a) Who discovered radioactivity? (b) What were the circumstances?
2. Who discovered radium, polonium, and thorium?

3. What names are given to the different radioactive rays? Who unraveled this mystery?
4. What are α rays, β rays, and γ rays?
5. How was it experimentally discovered that there are three different kinds of Becquerel rays?
6. What are the relative ionizing powers and penetrating powers of the different rays?
7. Why is lead a better shield for protection from gamma rays than aluminum?
8. (a) What is a Wilson cloud chamber? (b) How does it work?
9. (a) What kinds of particles do not leave tracks in a Wilson cloud chamber? (b) Why not?
10. Why is a diffusion cloud chamber better for some purposes than the Wilson cloud chamber?
11. What is spontaneous disintegration?
12. (a) What is transmutation? (b) What change takes place in the nucleus of an atom when an α particle is emitted? (c) What change takes place when a β particle is emitted?
13. (a) What is meant by the range of radioactive rays? (b) Which of the three kinds of rays should have the greatest range?
14. Would you be safe if you were in the same room with an alpha-emitting element, but were never closer to the source than 2 ft? Explain.
15. What is the abbreviated designation for atomic nuclei?
16. (a) What is meant by conservation of charge? (b) How is it involved in balancing nuclear reactions?
17. Why do rays with a high ionizing power have a low penetrating power, and vice versa?

PROBLEMS

1. Write the nuclear reaction, in the abbreviated form, for the emission of an α particle by the ionium nucleus thorium-230. See Appendix II.
2. Write the nuclear reaction for the emission of an α particle by polonium-218.
3. Write the nuclear reaction for the decay of uranium-238.
4. Write the nuclear reaction for the emission of a β particle by actinium-227.
5. Write the nuclear reaction for the decay of lead-214.

PROJECTS

1. Build a Wilson cloud chamber.
2. Build a diffusion cloud chamber.

NUCLEAR PHYSICS

Lesson 111 *RADIATION MEASUREMENTS*

Half Life. The decay of a single radioactive atom is governed purely by the laws of chance. *The half life of a radioactive atom is that interval of time during which its probability for decay is one-half.* If it has not decayed during that interval, its probability for decay during the next half life is again one-half; and so on until it decays.

For a large collection of radioactive atoms, one would expect about half the atoms to decay during one half life. Therefore, an alternative definition is: *The half life of a radioactive element is the time required for half of a given quantity of that element to disintegrate into a new element.* For example, it takes about 1600 years for half of a quantity of radium-226 to change into radon. In another 1600 years, half of the remainder will have disintegrated, leaving one quarter of the original amount. The half life of radium-226 is, therefore, said to be about 1600 years.

The rate at which a given quantity of a radioactive element disintegrates, that is, *decays*, is found by observing the activity of a given sample over a period of time and plotting a graph of the type shown in Fig. A. Here, for polonium, the activity drops to half of its original value in 140 days. In another 140 days, it again drops to half value, etc. The term *activity* may be defined as the number of rays given off per second of time, or as the number of ionized atoms produced each second by the rays.

The only difference between the decay curve of one element and that of another is the horizontal time scale to which they are plotted. To turn Fig. A into a decay curve

for radium, the *times*—140, 280, 420 days— need only to be changed to read 1600, 3200, 4800 years, etc., respectively. Since, therefore, all radioactive decay curves follow the

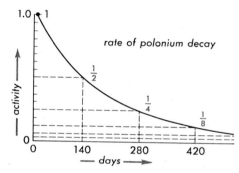

Fig. A. Typical graph of the decay of a radioactive element.

same law, one does not have to wait for half of a given sample to disintegrate to be able to calculate the half life. This would require too many years of waiting for some isotopes.

A decay curve for the radioactivity of any given substance is best shown on what is called a *semilog graph*. Such a graph involves the use of graph paper in which the spacings on the horizontal scale are uniform, while on the vertical scale they are proportional to the logarithms of numbers. Such graph paper can be purchased, or made by using the B or C scale on the slipstick of a slide rule.

In Fig. B, the fractions $\frac{1}{1}$, $\frac{1}{2}$, $\frac{1}{4}$, $\frac{1}{8}$, $\frac{1}{16}$, etc., are plotted on semilog graph paper with the polonium *time scale* plotted horizontally. Note that a straight line is the re-

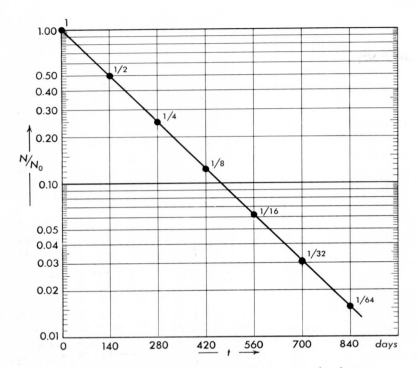

Fig. B. Semilog graph of α particle activity of polonium.

sult. If a semilog graph is plotted for the activity of any other radioactive element, it too will be a straight line, but with a different slope.

To find the half life of an element from the semilog graph, we find the point where $N = \frac{1}{2}N_0$ and call the corresponding time, t, the *half life, T*.

Daughter Products. When an element disintegrates by emitting α or β rays, it produces a new chemical element. Such "offspring" atoms are referred to as the *daughter element,* an element that, itself, may or may not be radioactive. Consider as an example the radioactive element radon, $Z = 86$. Of the several known isotopes of this element (see the Appendix), isotope 220 is a derivative of the thorium series beginning with $_{90}\text{Th}^{232}$.

Radon-220 is a gas and is α-active, that is, it disintegrates by giving off α particles. The daughter product, polonium-216, is α-active and has an extremely short half life of 0.158 sec. The daughter product of this isotope, however, has the relatively long half life of 10.6 hours. The reactions involved here are as follows:

$$_{86}\text{Rn}^{220} \rightarrow {}_{84}\text{Po}^{216} + {}_2\text{He}^4 \quad (T = 54.5 \text{ sec})$$
$$_{84}\text{Po}^{216} \rightarrow {}_{82}\text{Pb}^{212} + {}_2\text{He}^4 \quad (T = 0.158 \text{ sec})$$
$$_{82}\text{Pb}^{212} \rightarrow {}_{83}\text{Bi}^{212} + {}_{-1}\text{e}^0 \quad (T = 10.6 \text{ hr})$$

If a given quantity of Rn^{220} gas is confined to a closed vessel, the nuclei that disintegrate will tend to accumulate as Po^{216}. Not much of this daughter product can accumulate, however, because, with the short half life of 0.158 sec, most of the nuclei quickly disintegrate into Pb^{212}. In the period of 10 to 15 min, few of these Pb^{212}

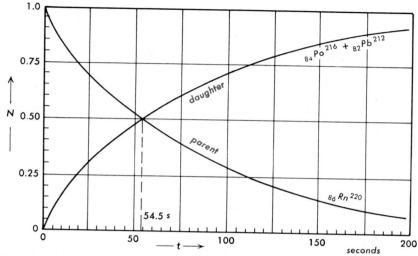

Fig. C. Decay curve for $_{86}Rn^{220}$ and the growth curve for the daughter products, $_{84}Po^{216} + _{82}Pb^{212}$.

disintegrate and they accumulate. A graph of this decrease of the parent element, Rn^{220}, and the accumulation of the daughter element, Po^{216}, with its daughter element, Pb^{212}, is shown in Fig. C.

Radioactive Series. It was Rutherford and his colleagues who discovered that, when one radioactive atom disintegrates by ejecting an α or β particle, the remaining atom is still radioactive and may sooner or later eject another particle to become a still different atom. This process they found to continue through a series of elements, ending up finally with a type of atom that is stable and not radioactive. It is now known that all natural disintegration processes, occurring among the heaviest elements of the periodic table, finally end up with *stable lead and bismuth atoms.*

There are four radioactive series or chains of elements. One of these series is given in Table 1. All four series are given in a graphical tabulation in the Appendix.

As we saw, all atoms with the same atomic number, but different mass num-

ber, are called isotopes of the same element. For example, Pu^{236}, Pu^{238}, Pu^{239}, and Pu^{241} are isotopes of the same chemical element (see Appendix). Chemically, they behave exactly alike and are separated only with difficulty.

Methods of Detecting Radiation. There are several well-known methods for detecting and measuring nuclear radiation. The most common of these are

> electroscopes
> cloud chambers
> bubble chambers
> spark chambers
> Geiger-Mueller counters
> scintillation counters
> semiconductor detectors
> ionization gauges
> photographic emulsions

We have already seen, in Lesson 107, how X-rays passing through an electroscope cause the charge to disappear and the gold leaf to fall. This same action may be demonstrated with α, β, and γ rays. The stronger

Table 1. Neptunium Series

Element	Symbol	Atomic Number	Mass Number	Particle Ejected	Range in Air	Half life
Plutonium........	Pu	94	241	β	..	...
Americium.......	Am	95	241	α	4.1 cm	500 yr
Neptunium.......	Np	93	237	α	3.3	2.25×10^6 yr
Protoactinium.....	Pa	91	233	β	..	27.4 days
Uranium.........	U	92	233	α	3.3	1.63×10^5 yr
Thorium.........	Th	90	229	α	3.3	7×10^3 yr
Radium..........	Ra	88	225	β	..	14.8 days
Actinium.........	Ac	89	225	α	4.4	10 days
Francium........	Fr	87	221	α	5.0	4.8 min
Astatine.........	At	85	217	α	5.8	0.018 sec
Bismuth..........	Bi	83	213	$\beta(94\%)$ $\alpha(4\%)$	4.6	47 min
Polonium........	Po	84	213	α	7.7	10^{-6} sec
Lead...........	Pb	82	209	β	..	3.3 hr
Bismuth..........	Bi	83	209	stable	..	infinite

the source of rays or the nearer the sample is brought to the electroscope, the more rapid is the discharge. Experiments show that, if the walls of the electroscope are too thick, only the γ rays get through to produce ionization on the inside. For this reason, specially designed electroscopes, made with thin windows of such light material as aluminum, are used for measuring α and β rays.

The Geiger Counter. A most effective detector of radioactivity, known as a *Geiger counter,* is used in the laboratory experiment described here. The principal element of this device, known as a *Geiger-Mueller,* or *G-M, tube,* is one of the simplest devices ever designed. It consists, as shown in Fig. D, of an open-ended cylindrical conductor, from 1 cm to 100 cm long, fitted inside a sealed, thin-walled glass tube. A fine tungsten wire is stretched along the axis.

After the tube has been evacuated and then partially filled with some gas, such as air, a potential of several hundred volts is applied, the positive to the center wire and the negative to the cylinder.

When a single high-speed particle from a radioactive source goes through the Geiger-Mueller tube, ions are created along its path by the freeing of electrons from the gas molecules.

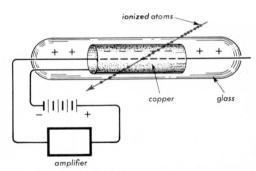

Fig. D. Diagram of a Geiger-Mueller tube.

These freed electrons are attracted to the positively charged wire and move toward it, acquiring, within a short distance of the wire, a high velocity of their own. Because of this velocity, they too can ionize molecules, thus freeing more electrons. This multiplication of electrons repeats itself in rapid succession, producing, within a very short interval of time, an avalanche of electrons surging toward the central wire.

The sudden arrival of charge at the wire gives rise to the flow of a small current impulse to an electrical circuit. When this current has been intensified by an amplifier, it may be made to activate an electric switch, a radio loudspeaker, or any kind of electrical device.

Quite frequently, the impulses of a Geiger-Mueller tube are made to operate a small counting device. Each cosmic ray particle passing through the tube is thereby counted automatically. The number of counts received per second depends upon the size of the counter tube. An average-sized tube, 1 in. in diameter and several inches long, gives from 50 to 100 counts per minute, at sea level.

A common form of Geiger counter is shown in Fig. E. It consists of a G-M

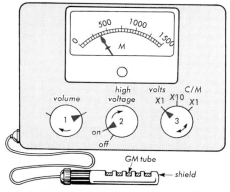

Fig. E. Geiger counter complete with G-M tube and counting-rate meter.

counter tube about 10 cm long connected to a box containing vacuum-tube circuits, a small loudspeaker, and a counting-rate meter, M.

Scintillation Counters. A scintillation counter is a sensitive device used in nuclear-physics studies for the detection and measurement of high-energy atomic radiation. In principle, it is based upon the earliest discoveries in radioactivity that α particles, upon striking such a fluorescent material as zinc sulfide, produce a tiny flash of light. These flashes, called *scintillations*, can be seen by the dark-adapted eye, or they can be detected by a photomultiplier tube and amplified.

It is now well known that when high-energy-charged atomic particles pass through certain transparent materials, fluorescent light is produced all along the path. (See Fig. F.) As the fast-moving particle

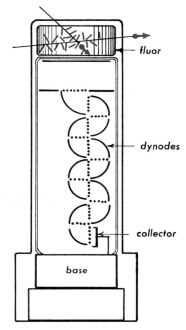

Fig. F. Scintillation-detector tube using a photomultiplier tube with a fluorescent block.

collides with atoms and molecules, electrons are raised to excited energy levels and, in returning to their ground states, emit light. For many crystals and plastics, this *fluorescent light* is blue or violet in color, while for others, it is ultraviolet or infrared.

A typical scintillation-counter tube is shown in Fig. G. A block of fluorescent ma-

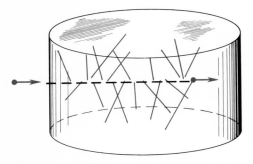

Fig. G. Diagram of the fluorescent light developed by an atomic particle traversing a transparent crystal or plastic fluor.

terial is mounted on the flat end of a special photomultiplier tube and then encased in a thin-walled, light-tight aluminum shield. When a particle traverses the fluor, the light ejects electrons from the photocathode by the photoelectric effect. The charge multiplication built up by the eight or more dynodes makes a sizable voltage pulse (see Fig. H). This voltage pulse is proportional

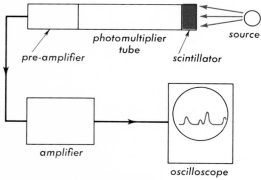

Fig. H. Schematic diagram of a scintillation-counter circuit.

to the amount of scintillation in the crystal, which, in turn, is proportional to the kinetic energy lost by the incident particle. The

Geiger counter, on the other hand, indicates only that a particle has passed.

When γ rays are to be detected, the fluorescent material most frequently used is a single crystal of sodium iodide, NaI. For high-energy β rays, such plastics as polystyrene, impregnated with anthracene, are used. These are inexpensive and very effective and can be quite large in size. For α particles, with their relatively low penetrating power, a thin layer of zinc sulfide deposited on the photomultiplier tube or a plastic surface is commonly used.

The principal advantages of scintillation counters over other detectors of nuclear radiation are: (1) they operate in air or in a vacuum, (2) they deliver an electrical impulse that is proportioned to the energy lost by the traversing particle, and (3) they can count at amazingly high speeds.

While the duration of a single pulse from a NaI-crystal counter will last about one microsecond, the pulse time from an anthracene counter can be as short as one thousandth of a microsecond (10^{-9} sec).

Cerenkov Radiation. In 1934, Cerenkov, in Russia, discovered that fast-moving electrons, such as β particles from radioactive materials, will produce light within a transparent medium if their velocity is greater than the speed of light in that medium. In such a medium as glass or plastic, the speed of light is about three-fourths the speed of light in a vacuum, yet many β particles are ejected at speeds greater than this and some of them close to c.

The phenomenon of Cerenkov radiation is analogous to (a) the production of the V-shaped wave from a ship when the ship travels through water at a speed greater than the wave velocity or (b) the shock waves from a missile traveling through the air at a speed greater than sound.

In Fig. I, a particle is shown generating a conical wave as it travels with a velocity, V, through a medium of refractive index μ. While the conical wave front make-

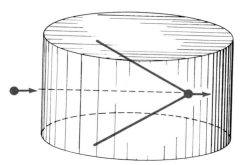

Fig. I. The conical wave from a high-speed atomic particle in a transparent medium— Cerenkov radiation.

an angle with the particle's direction, the light travels outward at right angles to the wave front.

The principle of Cerenkov radiation is frequently used to detect high-energy atomic particles. A Cerenkov counter has the same general construction as shown in Fig. G, except that the fluor is replaced by a transparent medium, liquid or solid, and

with a refractive index specified for the particular particle speeds to be detected.

Semiconductor Detectors. Recent experiments show that semiconducting materials, like those used in transistors, are useful detectors of charged particles. One type of semiconductor detector is shown in Fig. J. Thin layers of metal are deposited

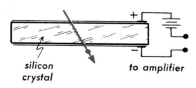

silicon crystal   to amplifier

Fig. J. Semiconductor detector using silicon.

on the two surfaces of a thin silicon PN diode (Lesson 95) and the two conducting surfaces are connected to a 100-volt battery and amplifier. When a charged particle enters the crystal, free electrons and holes develop. The sudden current pulse thereby created is amplified and then measured or counted.

QUESTIONS

1. Are the two definitions of half-life equivalent? Explain.
2. (a) Why is the second definition of half-life not exactly correct? (b) When would this definition be especially bad?
3. Is it possible to predict the exact time that an individual atom will disintegrate if you know the half-life of the element? Explain.
4. (a) What advantage is gained by plotting a decay curve on semilog paper? (b) What can you use for a substitute for semilog paper if it is not available?
5. What kind of meter is useful to measure the half-life of an element?
6. What special precautions must be observed in the construction of an electroscope that will respond to β-rays? Explain.
7. What is the basic principle of the Geiger counter?
8. Explain why it is likely that not all β particles given off by a radioactive substance would be counted by a Geiger counter.

9. What is the basic principle of the scintillation counter?
10. In what way is the scintillation counter better than the Geiger counter?
11. Compare the relative merits of the scintillation counter with the Wilson cloud chamber for charged-particle measurements.
12. What condition must be met for a Cerenkov counter to work?
13. Einstein postulated that no object can travel faster than light. Cerenkov discovered that when β particles travel faster than light, they give off light. How do you account for this paradox?
14. A beam of α and β rays, all having the same kinetic energy, are incident upon a Cerenkov counter. Only one of the two types generates counts. Which one? Explain.
15. What is meant by a daughter product?

PROBLEMS

1. If the activity of a radioactive sample drops to one-eighth its initial value in 2 hr and 15 min, what is its half life?
2. If the activity of a radioactive sample drops to $\frac{1}{32}$ of its initial value in 7.5 hr, find its half life.
3. How long will it take a sample of radon to decrease to 10% if its half life is 3.82 days? Find your answer by plotting a decay curve.
4. How long will it take a sample of lead-210 to decrease to 10% if its half life is 22 years?
5. All the radium-226 in a piece of pitchblende has decayed, except for one remaining atom. What is the probability that it will decay in the next 6400 years?
6. If Cf^{249} disintegrates by α emission, (a) what will be the daughter product? (b) What stable nucleus will it ultimately become?
7. If Md^{256} disintegrates by various stages, what stable nucleus will it finally become? Explain how you can be sure. (Hint: Examine the sequences of mass numbers of the four series.)

PROJECTS

1. Make a simple Geiger counter using either a vacuum tube or transistor-type amplifier.
2. Make a simple solid-state counter to show the principle of its operation.

NUCLEAR PHYSICS

Lesson 112 NUCLEAR DISINTEGRATION

The discovery, by controlled experiments, of the disintegration and transmutation of stable elements is attributed to the great experimental genius of Lord Rutherford. Some might say that the discovery was an accident, but to those who knew him well, it was the result of a long series of well-planned experiments. True, he did not predict the phenomenon and then discover it, but his long experience with radioactivity and his keen insight enabled him to recognize the meaning and importance of the phenomenon when it was first observed. Due credit must also be given to the work of his collaborators and to experimenters in other laboratories who have since carried the work much further.

Elastic Collisions between Atoms. Collisions between free atomic particles were first studied by Rutherford with such apparatus as that shown in Fig. A. A long glass

were then permitted to travel through the gas to the other end of the tube, where, upon passing through a thin aluminum foil, *F*, to a fluorescent screen, *S*, they could be observed as scintillations in the field of view of a microscope, *M*. The plunger, *N*, permits adjusting the distance of *R* from *S*. This is exactly the arrangement used by Rutherford in measuring the range of α particles from different radioactive elements (see Lesson 110).

With air in the tube and $_{84}Po^{214}$ as a source of α particles, scintillations could be observed with the screen as far back as 7 cm. With hydrogen in the tube, it was found that the distance, *d*, could be increased to 28 cm. The conclusion Rutherford drew from his result was that an α particle occasionally collides with a hydrogen atom, in much the same way as a large ball collides with a lighter one, imparting to the hydrogen nucleus (proton) a similar velocity.

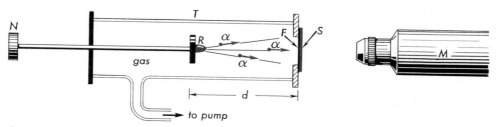

Fig. A. Rutherford's apparatus used in observing atomic collisions between α particles from radium and the atoms of a gas such as hydrogen, helium, nitrogen, oxygen, etc.

tube, *T*, containing a small sample of radioactive material, *R*, was first thoroughly evacuated by means of a vacuum pump and then filled with a gas of known composition. Alpha particles from the radioactive source

The proton, being less charged, has a greater penetrating power.

A more convincing study of such atomic collisions can be made with a Wilson cloud chamber. In thousands of cloud-chamber

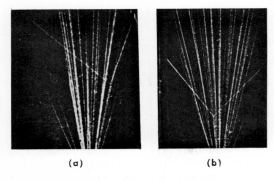

(a)   (b)

Fig. B. Wilson cloud-chamber photographs of collisions between α particles and (a) a hydrogen atom and (b) a helium atom. (After Rutherford, Chadwick, and Ellis.)

photographs of the ion tracks made by α particles from radioactive elements, one only occasionally observes forked tracks of the type shown in Fig. B. When each of these pictures was taken, the cloud chamber contained a different gas. For photograph (*a*), the cloud chamber contained hydrogen; for (*b*), it contained helium.

The Discovery of Nuclear Disintegration. Upon repeating the range experiments, illustrated in Fig. A, with a heavy gas in the tube, *T*, Rutherford in 1919 made a new and startling discovery. When nitrogen gas (atomic weight 14) was admitted to the tube, scintillations could be observed at a distance of 40 cm or more from the source.

Rutherford was not long in coming forward with the correct explanation of the

phenomenon. An α particle, near the beginning of its range where its velocity is high, may make a "head-on" collision with a nitrogen nucleus and be captured. This capture is then followed immediately by a disintegration in which a proton is ejected with high speed. The process is illustrated in Fig. C, and the transformation can be represented by the following simple reaction:

$$_2\text{He}^4 + {_7}\text{N}^{14} = ({_9}\text{F}^{18}) = {_8}\text{O}^{17} + {_1}\text{H}^1 \quad (1)$$

When the α particle, with a charge of $+2$ and mass 4, collides with the nitrogen nucleus, with a charge of $+7$ and mass 14, they form a single particle with a charge of $+9$ and mass 18. Since an atom with a nuclear charge of $+9$ would be expected to have all the chemical properties of *fluorine*, atomic number 9, the newly formed nucleus is labeled $_9\text{F}^{18}$.

An examination of the table of isotopes, however (see App. II), shows that no such isotope exists in nature. The reason becomes apparent when it is realized that such a combination of particles is not stable. A fluorine nucleus of mass 18 is unstable and disintegrates by discharging a proton (a hydrogen nucleus with a charge of $+1$ and a mass of 1). This leaves behind a residual nucleus with a charge of $+8$ and a mass of 17. Under atomic number 8 in the same Appendix, an oxygen isotope of mass 17 is seen to have been found in nature.

Thus, the above disintegration process started with two stable nuclei, *helium* and *nitrogen* and out of them were created two new stable nuclei, *oxygen* and *hydrogen*. This is called a transmutation of elements. Because the intermediate step indicates but a momentary existence of a fluorine nucleus, $_9\text{F}^{18}$, this step is often omitted from any discussion of the above process and the disintegration reaction simply written—

$$_2\text{He}^4 + {_7}\text{N}^{14} = {_8}\text{O}^{17} + {_1}\text{H}^1 \quad (2)$$

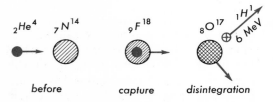

$_2He^4$ $_7N^{14}$ $_9F^{18}$ $_8O^{17}$ $_1H^1$ 6 MeV

before   capture   disintegration

Fig. C. Illustrating the disintegration of a nitrogen nucleus by a high-speed α particle.

Chadwick's Identification of the Neutron. In 1932, Sir James Chadwick, in England, performed an experiment for which he was later awarded the Nobel Prize in physics in 1935. As diagrammed in Fig. D, his

units is a stable carbon nucleus, such as found in nature.

The penetrating rays from the beryllium block in Fig. D are mostly neutrons, which, in bombarding the paraffin block, collide

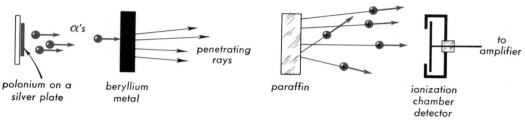

Fig. D. The experiment by which Chadwick discovered the neutron. The penetrating rays are neutrons and α rays.

experiment consisted of bombarding a beryllium target with α particles. Penetrating particles emerging from the beryllium were permitted to impinge upon a block of paraffin, from which protons were found to emerge with high speed. From energy calculations, he was able to show that the penetrating rays were uncharged particles with the mass of protons. These he called *neutrons*. The disintegration taking place in the metal target is the following (see Fig. E):

$$_2\text{He}^4 + {}_4\text{Be}^9 = {}_6\text{C}^{12} + {}_0\text{n}^1 \qquad (3)$$

The α particle, $_2\text{He}^4$, collides and unites with a beryllium nucleus, $_4\text{Be}^9$, causing a disintegration; whereupon a neutron, $_0\text{n}^1$, is expelled with high velocity. The residual particle with a charge of $+6$ and mass of 12

elastically with some of the many hydrogen atoms, knocking them out on the other side. During an elastic "head-on" collision between two particles of the same weight, such as a neutron and proton, the entire velocity of one is transferred to the other; the neutron is stopped and the proton goes on. The protons, having a positive charge, can be observed by their tracks in a Wilson cloud chamber, whereas neutrons cannot.

The reason fast neutrons have such a high penetrating power is that they are not slowed down by ionizing atoms as they pass close by them. A proton, electron, or α particle has a charge and can ionize atoms by attracting or repelling electrons from a distance, but a neutron without a charge cannot do this. It must make a direct collision with another particle to be slowed down or stopped.

The Nucleus Contains Neutrons and Protons. We now believe that the nucleus contains only two kinds of particles, neutrons and protons. Each neutron has a mass of one unit and no charge, whereas each proton has a mass of one unit and a positive charge of one unit.

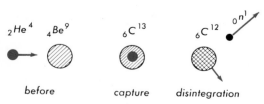

Fig. E. The neutron process discovered by Chadwick.

Because only the proton has a charge, any given nucleus of atomic number Z and mass number M has Z protons and $M - Z$ neutrons. In a neutral atom, the number of protons is equal to the number of orbital electrons. Schematic diagrams of the nuclei of five different atoms are given in Fig. F.

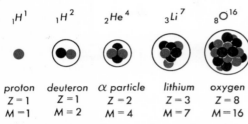

$_1H^1$	$_1H^2$	$_2He^4$	$_3Li^7$	$_8O^{16}$
proton	deuteron	α particle	lithium	oxygen
$Z = 1$	$Z = 1$	$Z = 2$	$Z = 3$	$Z = 8$
$M = 1$	$M = 2$	$M = 4$	$M = 7$	$M = 16$

Fig. F. Diagrams showing the number of protons and neutrons in the nuclei of hydrogen, deuterium, helium, lithium, and oxygen.

Atomic Mass. Improvements on the Aston mass spectrometer (see Lesson 99) permitted increasingly precise mass measurements to be made. It soon became clear that masses of various isotopes deviated slightly from the whole numbers assigned as the mass numbers. In fact, if unit atomic mass is taken to be exactly equal to the mass of the hydrogen atom, all other atoms would have atomic masses slightly smaller than their mass numbers.

Much closer agreement between atomic mass and mass number was achieved by taking unit atomic mass to be 1/16 the mass of the oxygen atom. Problems arose, however, when it was discovered that natural oxygen contained rare isotopes O^{17} and O^{18} in addition to the predominant O^{16}.

The newly accepted unit atomic mass is now taken to be 1/12 the mass of the carbon-12 isotope. On this basis, very accurate measurements give the mass of the hydrogen atom as 1.007276 atomic mass units, or amu, a value nearly 1% greater than unity. The neutron has an atomic mass of 1.008665

and is, therefore, slightly heavier than a proton. We can now examine the conservation of mass in a nuclear reaction.

Example 1. What is the total mass of the particles before and after the reaction—

$$_2He^4 + _4Be^9 \rightarrow _6C^{12} + _0n^1$$

Solution. (see App. III)

Initial State	Final State
$_2He^4 =$ 4.00260	$_6C^{12} =$ 12.00000
$_4Be^9 =$ 9.01219	$_0n^1 =$ 1.00866
13.01479	13.00866

It is noted that the final mass is 0.00613 amu less than the initial mass. One may, therefore, wonder where the missing mass went.

Mass Is a Form of Energy. Einstein, in working out the theory of relativity, arrived at a number of simple equations concerning the nature of the physical world. See Lesson 109. One of these equations, Eq. (9) in Lesson 109, has to do with mass as a form of energy. It is important at this point to consider this equation, since its proof can be demonstrated by, and is needed to explain, atomic-disintegration experiments. The relation referred to is known as *Einstein's mass-energy equation.* In its simplest form it is written,

$$E = mc^2 \qquad (3)$$

where m is the mass, c is the velocity of light, and E is the energy equivalence of the mass.

This relation would predict that mass can be turned into energy, or energy into mass. In other words, mass is a form of energy, for if a quantity of mass m could be annihilated, a definite amount of energy, E, would be available, in some other form. To illustrate this, suppose that a 1-Kg mass could be completely annihilated and the liberated energy given to another body in the form of kinetic energy.

$$E = 1 \times 3 \times 10^8 \times 3 \times 10^8$$
$$= 9 \times 10^{16} \text{ joules} \quad (4)$$

This is enough energy to propel the largest ship around the world.

The annihilation of mass, then, is a source of undreamed-of energy. Disintegration is one means, however, whereby mass can be annihilated or created more or less at the will of the experimenter.

If an atom, a part of an atom, or an electron is annihilated, the energy may either be transformed into kinetic energy and given to another atomic particle in the form of a velocity or it may appear as a γ ray of specified frequency ν and energy $h\nu$.

Example 2. If the alpha particle in example 1 had a kinetic energy of 4×10^{-13} joule, what is the total kinetic energy of the final $_6C^{12}$ and neutron?

Solution. The kinetic energy created by annihilated mass is—

$$E = mc^2$$
$$= .00613 \times 1.660 \times 10^{-27}(3 \times 10^8)^2$$
$$= 9.15 \times 10^{-13} \text{ joule}$$

where 1.660×10^{-27} (see Eq. (4) in Lesson 99) converts atomic-mass units to kilograms. The total kinetic energy after the reaction must be the initial kinetic energy, plus the created kinetic energy:

$$4 \times 10^{-13} + 9.15 \times 10^{-13}$$
$$= 13.15 \times 10^{-13} \text{ joule}$$

QUESTIONS

1. (a) What is meant by a perfectly elastic collision? (b) Do atomic nuclei ever collide perfectly elastically?
2. (a) Who discovered nuclear disintegration by α-particle collisions? (b) What was the experiment? (c) Can you write the nuclear reaction?
3. (a) Who discovered the neutron? (b) What was the experiment? (c) Why don't neutrons produce cloud-chamber tracks?
4. Will a Geiger counter detect neutrons? Explain.
5. Why did it take longer to discover neutrons than electrons?
6. (a) What is the difference between the nuclei of hydrogen and deuterium? (b) Would you expect this difference to have any effect on its chemical properties?
7. (a) How many protons are to be found in a given nucleus? (b) How many neutrons are there?
8. (a) What is the Einstein mass-energy equation? (b) What does it mean?
9. (a) Why is carbon-12 chosen for the atomic-mass standard? (b) Why not choose hydrogen?
10. (a) Why was it necessary to change the standard of mass from oxygen to carbon? (b) Will this make much difference in the usual chemical measurements made by chemists?
11. How must the law of conservation of mass be modified if it is to be valid?
12. What would you suggest as a most likely source of the enormous energy of the sun?
13. Suppose the kinetic energy of the particles following a nuclear transmutation is less than the initial kinetic energy. What can be said about the atomic masses?

PROBLEMS

1. Complete the following disintegration reactions:

$$_1H^2 + {_8}O^{16} \rightarrow {_7}N^{14} + \text{?} \qquad\qquad _1H^2 + {_5}B^{10} \rightarrow {_6}C^{11} + \text{?}$$
$$_2He^4 + {_{13}}Al^{27} \rightarrow {_{14}}Si^{30} + \text{?} \qquad\qquad _1H^1 + {_3}Li^6 \rightarrow {_2}He^4 + \text{?}$$

2. Complete the following disintegration reactions:

$$_1H^1 + {_4}Be^9 \rightarrow {_3}Li^6 + \text{?} \qquad\qquad _1H^2 + {_{15}}P^{31} \rightarrow {_{15}}P^{32} + \text{?}$$
$$_2He^4 + {_{13}}Al^{27} \rightarrow {_{15}}P^{30} + \text{?} \qquad\qquad _1H^2 + {_6}C^{12} \rightarrow {_7}N^{13} + \text{?}$$

3. The mass of 1 amu is equal to 1.66×10^{-27} Kg. If such a mass were annihilated, what would be the converted energy in joules?

4. If an oxygen atom, atomic-mass number 16, could be totally annihilated, how Hz?
   much energy, in joules, would be liberated?

5. What is the equivalent energy, in joules, of a γ ray whose frequency is 3×10^{18}

6. What is the equivalent energy, in joules, of a proton moving with one-tenth the speed of light?

7. If 1% of 1 Kg of uranium could be converted into energy, how many joules would be produced?

8. If 1% of 1 gm of uranium could be converted into heat, how many calories would be produced?

9. If the alpha particle in Eq. (2) had a kinetic energy of 5×10^{-13} joule, calculate the total energy of the final particles.

PROJECTS

1. Make a report on the importance of the peaceful uses of atomic energy in the light of rising population and diminishing oil and coal reserves.

2. Make a report on how Einstein developed his famous mass-energy equation.

NUCLEAR PHYSICS

Lesson 113 **HIGH-VOLTAGE ACCELERATORS**

Although much information was learned from α-particle irradiation, it was clear that more information could be gained using simpler charged particles, protons and deu- terons. These particles, however, are not emitted by any known radioactive source. In order to irradiate nuclei with protons, it is necessary to accelerate them artificially.

The simplest way to do this is to ionize hydrogen atoms and to accelerate the protons by means of electric forces.

To calculate the energy of a proton of charge e, accelerated through a potential difference, V, we simply equate the kinetic energy gained to the potential energy lost:

$$\tfrac{1}{2}mv^2 = Ve \qquad (1)$$

Example. What voltage is needed to obtain a kinetic energy of 2×10^{-13} joule, a value typical of the energies involved in nuclear reactions.

Solution.

$$V = \frac{2 \times 10^{-13}}{1.6 \times 10^{-19}}$$

$$= 1.25 \times 10^6 \text{ volts}$$

It is clear, then, that very high voltages are required to produce artificially accelerated particles of the necessary energy.

Electron-volt as an Energy Unit. By rewriting Eq. (1)—

$$V = \frac{1}{e} \times \frac{1}{2} mv^2 \qquad (2)$$

we see that the voltage, V, can be used as a unit of energy, if we consider $1/e$ as a constant of proportionality. A proton accelerated by a potential difference of 1 volt is said to have an energy of 1 electron-volt ($1\ eV = 1.60 \times 10^{-19}$ joule). More useful, however, is the unit of 1 million electron-volts ($1\ MeV = 1.60 \times 10^{-13}$ joule).

It is customary among physicists to express energies of all moving particles in terms of V in electron-volts. Thus, one speaks of a million-volt γ ray, a three-million-volt electron, or a 12.5 million-volt proton, etc. This terminology is used for convenience only and denotes the value of V in the above equation, which, with the electronic charge substituted for e, gives the

energy of the γ-ray photon, or of the moving atomic particle.

As an example, suppose that an electron were to be annihilated and we wished to express the liberated energy in volts. To calculate V, we make use of the equality between Eq. (1) in this Lesson and Eq. (1) in Lesson 112, that is—

$$mc^2 = Ve \qquad (3)$$

Substituting the known electronic mass $m = 9.1 \times 10^{-31}$ Kg, $e = 1.60 \times 10^{-19}$ coulomb, and $c = 3 \times 10^8$ m/sec, we obtain $V = 511,000$ volts, or—

annihilation energy of 1 electron
$$= 0.511 \text{ MeV} \qquad (4)$$

This means that, if the energy liberated by the annihilation of an electron could be given to another electron in the form of kinetic energy, the receiving electron would have a velocity equivalent to half a million volts. In other words, it would have the same velocity and energy as an electron that has been accelerated by a potential of 511,000 volts in a tube of the kind shown in Fig. H in Lesson 92.

The Cockcroft-Walton Experiment. Believing that the disintegration of atomic nuclei might be accomplished by using other than α particles as projectiles, Rutherford instigated, in 1930, the construction of a high-voltage, dc generator at the Cavendish laboratory. The purpose of this million-volt source of potential was to accelerate hydrogen nuclei, *protons*, to high speeds and then cause them to strike known substances. In this way, he hoped to produce new and various kinds of disintegrations.

Becoming impatient with the relatively slow progress of a difficult project, Rutherford suggested to Cockcroft and Walton that lower voltages be tried in the meantime to see if, by chance, disintegrations might

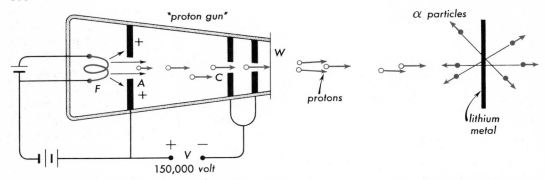

Fig. A. Schematic diagram of the Cockcroft-Walton experiment. Lithium is disintegrated by 150,000-volt protons.

occur. In 1932, Cockcroft and Walton announced that they had successfully disintegrated lithium atoms with protons accelerated by relatively low voltages. Their apparatus is schematically represented in Fig. A.

Electrons from a hot filament, F, passing through hydrogen gas in the region A, ionize many hydrogen atoms. These pro-

tons, with their positive charge, are then accelerated toward the other end of the tube by a potential, V, of 150,000 volts. Upon passing through the opening, C, and a window, W, they emerge from the acceleration chamber as a narrow beam of protons.

This tube, acting as a *proton gun*, is aimed at a target of lithium metal. Cock-

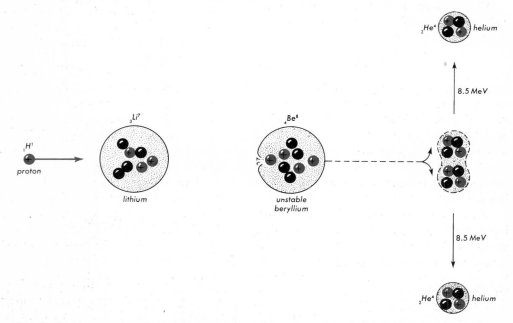

Fig. B. Disintegration of a lithium nucleus by a proton of 0.15 MeV energy. The Cockcroft-Walton experiment.

croft and Walton observed α particles emanating from the metal with a range of 8 cm, an energy equivalent to 8.5 MeV. Considering the relatively low energy of the bombarding protons, only 0.15 MeV, this is a tremendous release in nuclear energy. The transmutation taking place here is written—

$$_1H^1 + _3Li^7 + E_1 = _2He^4 + _2He^4 + E_2 \quad (5)$$

This reaction, illustrated in Fig. B, shows a proton, $_1H^1$, of energy $E_1 = 0.15$ MeV, entering a lithium nucleus, $_3Li^7$, to form a new but unstable beryllium nucleus, $_4Be^8$. Being unstable, this compact structure of eight particles splits up into two α particles, which are driven apart with great violence. Because the measured energy of each α particle is equivalent to 8.5 MeV, each disintegration involves the liberation of 17.0-MeV energy. The source of energy is to be found in the annihilation of a part of the total atomic mass.

If we make use of the Einstein mass-energy relation, as given by Eq. (3), and substitute unit atomic mass—

$$m = 1.66 \times 10^{-27} \text{ Kg} \quad (6)$$

as the mass to be annihilated, we find—

$$V = 931,000,000 \text{ volts}$$

or—

$$E = 931 \text{ MeV} \quad (7)$$

We will now see how this important number is used.

The loss in mass in Eq. (5) can be calculated from the table of atomic weights, given in the Appendix. List the involved masses in two columns and add:

$_1H^1 = 1.00814$		
$_3Li^7 = 7.01822$	$_2He^4 = 4.00387$	
$E_1 = 0.00016$	$_2He^4 = 4.00387$	(8)
8.02652	8.00774	

E_1 in amu is the mass equivalent to the energy of the incident proton and is obtained by dividing 0.15 MeV by 931. The difference between the two sums, 8.02652 − 8.00774 = 0.01878 mass unit, represents the loss in mass by the disintegration. When multiplied by 931, this gives 17.48 MeV as the liberated energy, a value in good agreement with the experimentally determined value of 17.0 MeV.

The Van de Graaff Generator. This machine, developed in 1931 by R. Van de Graaff at Princeton University, employs the

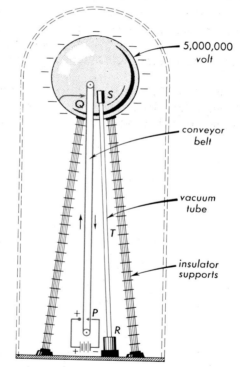

Fig. C. Diagram of a Van de Graaff generator of high voltage.

principle of the electrostatic generator discovered many years ago. A typical installation, as shown in Fig. C, consists of a large, hollow sphere supported on insulating columns and charged by a belt conveying electrical charges from a power supply at ground potential, depositing the charges inside the sphere. The fabric conveyor belt, a foot or more in width, and running over well-aligned rollers, travels about 60 mi/hr.

As the belt passes between the metallic surface and row of needle points at P, electrons from the points jump toward the positive electrode and are caught by the belt. Upon entering the sphere at the top, the electrons jump to the needle points Q, where they go quickly to the outside surface of the sphere. The "spraying" of electrons to and from the points is assured by keeping the spray potential high (about 50,000 volts) to maintain a "brush discharge." As more

and more electrons arrive at the sphere, its negative potential rises higher and higher until leakage into the surrounding air and through the insulators becomes equally fast.

Atomic particles to be accelerated are generated inside a vacuum-tube source, S, inside the sphere. Starting at the top of a long, straight vacuum tube, T, electrons are accelerated downward toward ground potential, where, acquiring the full energy of the available voltage, they are allowed to bombard whatever target is being studied. Where installations are designed for accelerating protons, deuterons, or α particles, the spray potential is reversed and the sphere acquires a high positive potential.

QUESTIONS

1. Why can an electron-volt be used as a unit of energy?
2. (a) Why cannot neutrons be accelerated by high-voltage accelerators? (b) Would it be useful if it could be done? Explain.
3. How did Cockcroft and Walton get ionized hydrogen atoms that could be accelerated by a potential?
4. Why are energies of the order of a million electron-volts required to do meaningful nuclear experiments?
5. Suppose a proton, an electron, a singly ionized helium nucleus, a doubly ionized helium nucleus (alpha particle), and a neutron were accelerated in a Van de Graaff accelerator. How would their energies be related?
6. (a) What was the Cockcroft-Walton experiment? (b) What was the interaction?
7. Where does the energy come from that causes lithium to split up with a hundredfold increase in kinetic energy?
8. Can you give a possible reason why the reaction discovered by Cockcroft and Walton was not used to produce useful energy for power production, since there is a tremendous gain in energy in the reaction?
9. (a) What is a Van de Graaff generator? (b) What is it frequently used for? (c) Can it be used to accelerate protons and electrons?
10. What limits the buildup of potential in the Van de Graaff generator?
11. Would it be possible to achieve voltages of several billion volts using high-voltage accelerators? Explain.
12. Two particles of different mass, but the same charge, are accelerated by a Cockcroft-Walton accelerator. (a) Will their resulting energies be the same? (b) Their velocities? (c) Their momenta?

PROBLEMS

1. (a) How much energy do the electrons possess when they strike the screen of a TV tube if they have been accelerated with 16,000 volts? (b) What happens to this energy?
2. Through what potential difference would an electron have to be accelerated to acquire a kinetic energy of 5×10^{-13} joule?
3. How many eV would be produced if a proton were completely annihilated?
4. If a carbon atom, atomic weight 12, could be totally annihilated, how much energy, in eV, would be liberated?
5. What is the equivalent energy, in eV, of a γ ray whose frequency is 5×10^{18} Hz?
6. What is the energy, in eV, of an alpha particle moving $\frac{1}{15}$ the speed of light.
7. (a) What would be the energy, in MeV, of a proton accelerated by a four-million-volt Van de Graaff accelerator? (b) What would be the energy of an alpha particle?

PROJECT

Make a small Van de Graaff generator using a small phonograph motor to drive the belt.

NUCLEAR PHYSICS

Lesson 114 RADIO-FREQUENCY ACCELERATORS

The Lawrence Cyclotron. At the time Cockcroft and Walton were performing their first disintegration experiments, E. O. Lawrence* and S. Livingston were develop-

ing a new type of atomic accelerator, which soon attracted the attention of physicists the world over. So successful was this "atomic machine gun" in producing high-

---

* Ernest O. Lawrence (1901-1958), American experimental physicist, received his early education in South Dakota. Obtaining his Ph.D. at Yale University in 1925, in 1928 he was appointed associate professor of physics at the University of California and, in 1930, was made full professor. Having built up the Radiation Laboratory (now named in his honor), he became its director in 1938. In 1937, he was awarded the Comstock Prize of the National Academy of Sciences, the Cresson Medal of the Franklin Institute, and the

Hughes Medal of the Royal Society of London. Lawrence was a member of the National Academy of Sciences and is noted principally for his development of the cyclotron and its application to the production of induced radioactivity. It is for these discoveries that he was awarded the Nobel Prize in physics for 1939. During World War II, he directed one of the main research projects leading to the isolation of uranium-235, used in atomic bombs.

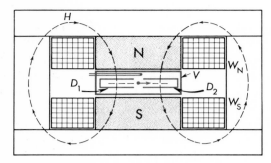

Fig. A. Cross-section diagram of a cyclotron.

speed atomic projectiles for disintegration experiments that a new and larger *cyclotron* was soon constructed and put into operation. Now, a cyclotron of considerable size occupies a most prominent position in many of the leading physics laboratories of the world.

The heart of the instrument, as shown in Figs. A and B, consists of two short, hollow, half cylinders, D_1 and D_2, mounted inside a vacuum chamber, V, between the poles of a powerful electromagnet and con-

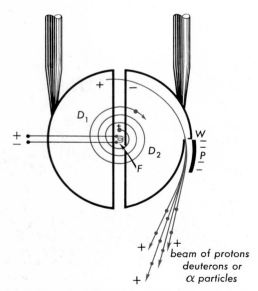

Fig. B. Detailed diagram of the D's of a cyclotron.

nected on the outside to the two terminals of a high-frequency ac generator. It is interesting to note that this generator is really a short-wave radio transmitter supplying energy to the *dees*, instead of to the antenna.

When a trace of hydrogen gas is admitted to the evacuated chamber, the hot-wire filament, F, ionizes some of the hydrogen atoms, thereby producing the protons to be used as atomic bullets. At the particular instant when D_1 is charged positively and D_2 is charged negatively, a proton in the neighborhood of F will be accelerated toward D_2. Moving through the strong magnetic field of the huge magnet, this positively charged particle traverses a circular path, as shown in the diagram.

If, after making a half turn, the potential is reversed, so that D_1 becomes negatively charged and D_2 positively charged, the proton will be attracted by one and repelled by the other, causing it to increase its speed. With added speed, it therefore moves in the arc of a larger circle as shown. After this second half turn, the potential again reverses, making D_1 positive and D_2 negative, and again the proton speeds up. Thus, as the potential reverses periodically, the proton travels faster and faster, moving in ever–expanding circles until, reaching the outer edge, it passes through a narrow open window, W.

Upon leaving W, all protons must pass close to a negatively charged plate, P, where, by attraction, their paths are straightened out and they become a separated beam of projectiles. Whatever substance is to be bombarded is then placed in this beam, and the disintegrated fragments are studied by means of various detecting devices.

The operation of the cyclotron involves simple classical laws describing the motion of a charged particle in a uniform magnetic field. By Eq. (1) in Lesson 80, the force on a particle in a magnetic field is given by Bev, and this is equal to the centripetal force mv^2/r:

$$Bev = \frac{mv^2}{r} \qquad (1)$$

Here, e is the charge on the particle in coulombs, m is its mass in kilograms, v is its velocity in meters per second, and r is the radius of its circular path in meters. To find the time required for any charged particle to make one complete circle, the formula $s = vt$ from mechanics is employed. The distance traveled in one turn is represented by s, and T represents the time:

$$T = \frac{s}{v} = \frac{2\pi r}{v} \qquad (2)$$

By solving Eq. (1) for v, and substituting Eq. (2), we obtain—

$$v = \frac{Ber}{m} \quad \text{and} \quad T = \frac{2\pi}{B} \cdot \frac{m}{e} \qquad (3)$$

The right-hand equation shows that the period, T, is independent of r and v and, for like particles (that is, the same e and m), that T varies with the magnetic induction, B. The alternating potential, E, applied to the cyclotron dees, must therefore match that of the particles' motion, which is determined by the field, B. It is customary, in practice, to apply a fixed frequency to the dees and adjust the current in the magnetic-field coils until resonance occurs.

The fundamental principle that makes the cyclotron work at all is the following fact: *The time required for a charged particle to make one complete turn within the cyclotron is the same for all speeds.*

The faster a particle travels, the larger is the circle it must traverse, thus keeping the time constant. Hence, with a constant frequency of the ac supply, some particles may be just starting their acceleration near the center, while others farther out have already acquired higher speeds. The result is a more or less continuous stream of protons emerging from the window, W.

If the ac voltage applied between the *dees* of the cyclotron is 200,000 volts, then in each half turn a particle gains an added velocity equivalent to 200,000 volts. If a proton makes twenty-five complete revolutions before leaving the chamber at W, it will have acquired a velocity equivalent to 200,000 times 25 times 2, or 10,000,000 volts. Here, then, is a beam of 10-MeV protons acquired by the application of a potential only one-fiftieth as great.

When hydrogen in the evacuated chamber of a cyclotron is replaced by heavy hydrogen of mass 2, called *deuterium*, and the magnetic field strength is doubled, a beam of high-energy *deuterons* is obtained. Having twice the mass of, but with the same charge as, protons, these particles acquire twice as much energy.

A photograph of an 11-MeV deuteron beam from the Harvard University cyclotron is shown in Fig. C. From the point where they emerge from the cyclotron window, at left center, to where they come to

Fig. C. Photograph of an 11 MeV deuteron beam from the Harvard University cyclotron. (Courtesy of the Harvard University Press and A. K. Solomon)

Fig. D. Photograph of the 184-in., 4000-ton, synchro-cyclotron at the University of California.

rest in midair at the lower right, the high-energy particles ionize the air molecules and atoms, causing them to emit visible light.

The high voltage of a Van de Graaff generator can accelerate the particle only once, whereas a cyclotron can accelerate the particles each time they make one turn. It would seem, at first thought, that there is no limit to the energy that could be produced by a cyclotron. But as we shall see next, there is a serious limiting factor.

The Relativistic-mass Effect. Einstein's special theory of relativity predicts that the mass of a moving particle increases as it approaches the speed of light according to the relation given by Eq. (7) in Lesson 109:

$$m = m_0/\sqrt{1 - (v/c)^2} \qquad (4)$$

where v is the particle velocity, c is the velocity of light, and m_0 is the particle's rest mass.

Example. What is the mass of an electron whose speed is half the speed of light?
Solution.

$$
\begin{aligned}
m &= 0.511/\sqrt{1 - (0.5)^2} \\
&= 0.511/.866 \\
&= 0.590 \text{ MeV}
\end{aligned}
$$

For velocities normally encountered, the value of $\dfrac{v}{c}$ is very small and the increase in mass is unnoticed.

Experiments with high-speed particles all verify Einstein's formula. For protons in a cyclotron, the increase in mass becomes noticeable at about 50 MeV. The increase in energy starts to go partly into increasing the mass, rather than increasing the speed.

Because of this variable mass, the period increases and the applied ac becomes out of phase; see Eq. (3). As a result, cyclotrons cannot accelerate protons above about 60 MeV.

The Synchro-cyclotron. The firm belief that new and fundamental discoveries in nuclear physics can be made with atomic projectiles having greater and greater energies has led scientists and engineers in various institutions to combine their efforts in groups to design and construct larger and larger atomic accelerators. One such instrument is the synchro-cyclotron.

This accelerator can accelerate protons well past the limit imposed on cyclotrons. This breakthrough was achieved by frequency modulating the alternating voltage. As seen in Eq. (3), if the frequency is properly decreased as the mass increases, the particles can be kept in phase with the applied voltage. The synchro-cyclotron at the University of California (see Fig. D) can accelerate protons to about 800 MeV.

The Linear Accelerator. Although linear accelerators were proposed as early as 1929 and several were constructed, they never proved satisfactory until recently. Applying the principles of tubular wave guides and resonant cavities, L. Alvarez and his collaborators, immediately after World War II, constructed the first successful linear accelerator. A giant 2-mile-long machine employing the same principles has recently been completed at Stanford University.

A cut-away diagram of part of the Alvarez *linac* is given in Fig. E. Protons are initially produced and accelerated to 4 MeV by a pressure Van de Graaff generator and then injected at that energy into one end of a 40-ft tank, as shown at the upper left. Once inside, they are further accelerated as they pass through a series of "drift tubes," and arrive at the other end with an energy of about 40 MeV.

The tank cavity within the copper lining, fed by 30 radar-transmitting oscillators, is set resonating at its *dominant mode* at a frequency of 200 MHz. The "standing-

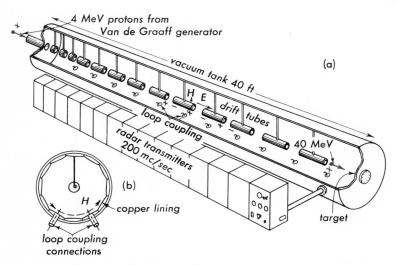

Fig. E. Diagrams showing the first section of a linear accelerator.

wave" conditions set up are such that the electric field, *E*, is parallel to the tube axis and is everywhere rising and falling together. The lengths of the drift tubes gradually increase so that the protons cross each gap when the field, *E*, is to the right, and are inside the tubes, in a field free space, when the field is to the left.

It now seems possible that additional tank sections can be added end to end to this system to obtain almost any desired energy. Calculations indicate that more than 1 MeV per lineal foot can be expected from such a system. The beam from a linear accelerator is much more compact than a cyclotron beam and can, therefore, be used for more exacting measurements in many applications.

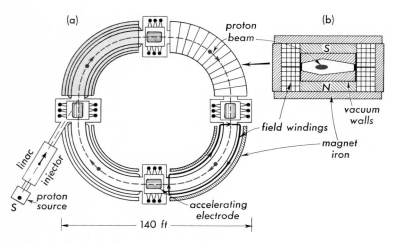

Fig. F. Berkeley Bevatron designed to produce 6.2 BeV protons.

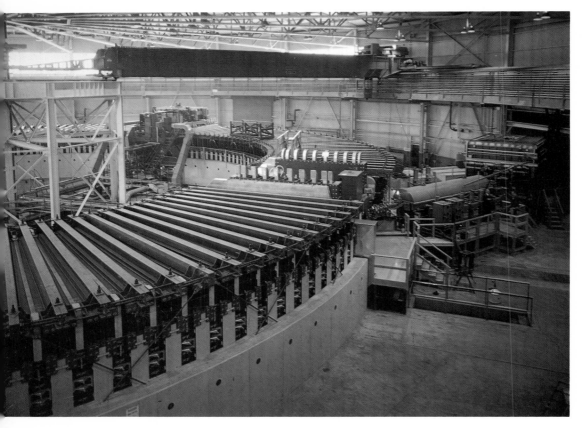

THE BEVATRON

Fig. 114G. A six-billion-volt accelerator of atomic particles, located at the University of California, Berkeley. Just behind the two men on the platform, at the far right and center, can be seen the rectangular housing of the atomic source and the Cockroft-Walton accelerator. The cylindrical tank section containing the linear accelerator is clearly seen leading into the inflector assembly between quadrants 1 and 4. The main accelerating electrode assembly with the yellow-colored ducts leading to it is seen farther back between quadrants 3 and 4. Note the overhead crane used for assembling, repairing, and the handling of massive apparatus and equipment. (Photographed by K. Hildebrand and G. Kagawa. Courtesy of E. L. Lofgren, D. Cooksey, the Radiation Laboratory at the University of California, and the Atomic Energy Commission.)

Billion Electron-Volt Accelerators. The design and construction of an instrument capable of accelerating particles to energies of billions of electron volts, BeV, involve many problems. Not the least of these is the economic factor concerned primarily with the initial cost of such an instrument as well as its subsequent maintenance.

A number of accelerators producing particles of 1 BeV or more are now in operation and others of greater and greater energy are being planned.

nected by 20-ft straight sections. The electrical power supplied to the 10,000-ton magnet is provided by a motor generator with a large flywheel. During buildup of the magnetic field, a peak power of 100,000 KW is drawn from the flywheel and stored in the magnet. As the field is reduced between beam pulses, the generator acts as a motor and returns energy to the flywheel.

The protons from a source, S, as shown in Fig. F, are first accelerated to 10 MeV by a linear accelerator, and then injected into

In Operation (1968)	
Pasadena, California	1.1 BeV (electrons)
Ithaca, New York	10 BeV (electrons)
Berkeley, California	6.2 BeV (protons)
Dubna, USSR	10 BeV (protons)
Geneva, Switzerland	28 BeV (protons)
Brookhaven, Long Island	32 BeV (protons)
Cambridge, Massachusetts	7.5 BeV (electrons)
Argonne, Illinois	12.5 BeV (protons)
Palo Alto, California	20 BeV (electrons)

Planned or Under Construction	
Weston, Illinois	200 BeV (protons)
Brookhaven, Long Island	1000 BeV (protons)

Most large accelerators are called *synchrotrons* and differ from the cyclotron and syncho-cyclotron in that the particles are kept in a fixed orbit. The operation requires that the frequencies of both the ac and the magnetic field change during acceleration. These synchrotrons all differ somewhat in design and are usually given a name of their own.

The basic design of one of these large instruments, the 6.3 BeV *bevatron*, is shown in Fig. F. The magnet arrangement consists of four quadrant segments spaced so that the particle orbits are quarter-circles con-

the 385-ft race track proper. As they pass through the accelerator electrode in one of the straight sections and are speeded up by the high-frequency potentials, the magnetic field increases at the proper rate to keep the beam in the same orbit. The output beam consists, as it does in all high-energy accelerators, of a series of pulses. From the time of injection, each pulse of protons takes about 2 sec to acquire its final speed and, in so doing, makes about four million revolutions of the orbit and travels about 300,000 miles. A color photograph of part of the bevatron is reproduced in Fig. G.

QUESTIONS

1. (a) What is a cyclotron? (b) What is its purpose? (c) What does it accelerate?
2. What is the principal advantage of the radio-frequency accelerators compared to high-voltage types?
3. What is the limiting factor in producing high-energy particles in an ordinary cyclotron?
4. Would a cyclotron work if the particles did not take the same time to go around no matter where they are located in the dees?
5. (a) What is deuterium? (b) Is deuterium the same as hydrogen?
6. What is gained in using deuterium instead of protons in a cyclotron?
7. (a) What does the abbreviation "MeV" stand for? (b) What does the abbreviation "BeV" stand for?
8. Approximately what is the highest energy to which atomic particles have been accelerated in the laboratory?
9. How does a synchro-cyclotron differ from a cyclotron?
10. How does a synchrotron differ from a synchro-cyclotron? The electrons in the Cornell Synchrotron (Ithaca, New York) travel at almost the speed of light as they are accelerated from the injected energy of 15 MeV to 10 BeV. How can they gain so much energy when their speed is changing only slightly?
11. Theoretically, does an airplane moving at 500 mi/hr have more mass than when it is on the ground? Explain.
12. Why is it desirable to build linear accelerators when circular accelerators do so well?
13. During acceleration in the Cornell Synchrotron (Question 10), (a) is the magnetic field changing drastically, or only slightly? (b) Is the alternating-voltage frequency changing drastically or only slightly? Explain.
14. Why can an alternating-voltage accelerator produce higher energy particles than a high-voltage accelerator, such as the Van de Graaff generator?

PROBLEMS

1. If the frequency of the potential applied to the dees of a cyclotron is 8 MHz, what must be the magnetic induction, B, to accelerate α particles?
2. Calculate the frequency of the oscillating potential that must be applied to a cyclotron in which deuterons are accelerated. Assume that the magnetic induction has a constant value of 2.5 newtons/amp-m.
3. The frequency applied to the dees of a cyclotron is 9.4 MHz. What must be the magnetic induction if protons are to be accelerated?
4. What total accelerator voltage will give protons a velocity of 99% the speed of light?
5. What is the mass of an electron whose speed is 99.9% the speed of light?
6. The frequency of a synchro-cyclotron is 50 MHz at the start of the acceleration

period. What should the frequency be when the particles are going (a) at 10% the speed of light? (b) At 40% the speed of light?

7. A circular synchrotron has particles moving in an orbit of diameter 2 m, with a magnetic field of 0.7 newton/amp-m and an applied frequency of 5.34 MHz. (a) What is the mass of the particle? (b) What is the particle?

PROJECTS

1. Make a model of a cyclotron.
2. Make a model of the bevatron.

NUCLEAR PHYSICS

Lesson 115 **TRANSMUTATION**

Proton and Deuteron Disintegrations. When high-energy protons or deuterons are used to bombard different elements, various disintegration products are formed. An experimental arrangement in which the cyclotron acts as the source of high-speed particles is shown in Fig. A. To determine the nature of the disintegration taking place within the substance under bombardment, it is common practice to identify the penetrating rays emerging from the other side by the use of suitable detectors.

Numerous experiments have shown that the disintegration products to be looked for may be protons, α particles, neutrons, γ rays, electrons, deuterons, and many other particles. For some of these penetrating rays, one kind of detector may be more suitable than another. The scintillation counters, for example, are particularly useful in detecting γ rays and electrons, whereas the Wilson cloud chamber and ionization chamber are useful in detecting protons, α particles, and deuterons.

The semiconductor detector is becoming increasingly popular for detecting almost all charged particles and gamma rays. Neutrons are detected by counting charged particles produced when the neutron collides with other nuclei. For example, when a neutron scatters from hydrogen nuclei in a plastic scintillator, the recoiling proton produces scintillations and is detected.

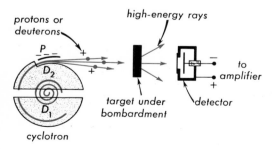

Fig. A. Experimental arrangement generally used for bombarding known substances with high-speed deuterons from the cyclotron and for detecting the disintegration products with an ionization chamber as a detector.

When a Wilson cloud chamber is used to identify disintegration products, charged particles can be identified with some degree of certainty by the density of their fog tracks, and their energy can be determined by the curvature of the tracks when a magnetic field is applied. Once the nature of the emerging rays from a bombarded target is known, the recoil product of the disintegration also becomes known by writing a reac-

values of the liberated energy over and above that supplied by the incident projectile.

As an example, consider Eq. (6) in which deuterons, bombarding beryllium metal, produce high-speed neutrons and recoiling boron nuclei. This particular disintegration is important experimentally, because it is used as a means of obtaining intense beams of neutrons for use as projec-

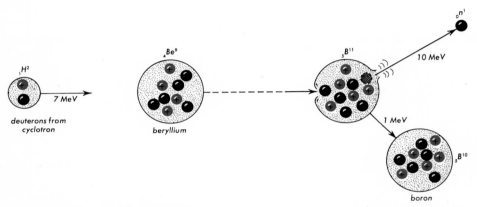

Fig. B. Deuteron disintegration of beryllium nucleus to produce high-speed neutrons.

tion equation. Six examples of such reaction equations are given by the following:

$$Q$$
$$_1H^1 + _9F^{19} = _8O^{16} + _2He^4 = \;\; 8.1 \,\text{MeV} \quad (1)$$
$$_1H^1 + _5B^{11} + _6C^{12} + \gamma \,\text{ray} = 15.8 \,\text{MeV} \quad (2)$$
$$_1H^2 + _7N^{14} = _6C^{12} + _2He^4 = 13.6 \,\text{MeV} \quad (3)$$
$$_1H^2 + _8O^{16} = _7N^{14} + _2He^4 = \;\; 3.1 \,\text{MeV} \quad (4)$$
$$_1H^2 + _3Li^6 = _3Li^7 + _1H^1 = \;\; 5.0 \,\text{MeV} \quad (5)$$
$$_1H^2 + _4Be^9 = _5B^{10} + _0n^1 = \;\; 4.4 \,\text{MeV} \quad (6)$$

It is customary to omit the kinetic energy of the bombarding particle from the left-hand side of all reaction equations and to designate the total energy liberated by the disintegration, as shown at the right above. The values of Q given, therefore, represent the experimentally determined

tiles in other disintegrations. The nuclear changes are illustrated schematically in Fig. B. The available energy from the loss in mass alone is equivalent to 4.4 MeV, so that, if deuterons with an energy of 7 MeV are used to bombard the beryllium target, the available energy becomes about 11.4 Mev, 1 MeV going to the recoil boron nucleus and approximately 10.4 MeV to the neutron.

Threshold Reactions. If protons were used to bombard lithium-7, the resulting reaction could be obtained by inverting Eq. (5):

$$_1H^1 + _3Li^7 = _3Li^6 + _1H^2$$
$$Q = -5.0 \,\text{MeV} \quad (7)$$

The Q of the reaction is just the negative

of the inverse reaction, as would be expected from conservation of energy. Such reactions are called *threshold reactions,* because the incident particle must have a kinetic energy equal to or greater than a threshold energy in order to supply the missing energy to make the reaction go.

Although one would expect the threshold energy to be 5 MeV for Eq. (7), it is actually slightly higher. This is because part of the incident kinetic energy must go to giving kinetic energy to the reaction products.

Multiple Disintegrations. A study of certain disintegration experiments shows that some of the unstable nuclei, which are created by the capture of a proton or deuteron by a stable nucleus, split up into more than two stable nuclei. Examples of this arise when boron is bombarded by protons and when nitrogen is bombarded by deuterons. In the case of boron (see Fig. C), the pro-

lion volts of energy, leaving behind a beryllium nucleus, $_4Be^8$:

$$_1H^1 + _5B^{11} = _4Be^8 + _2He^4$$
$$= _2He^4 + _2He^4 + _2He^4 \qquad (8)$$

This nuclear combination is still unstable and the $_4Be^8$ splits apart into two more α particles. When the phenomenon was first observed, it was thought that all three α particles came apart simultaneously, but further observations showed that first one and then two were ejected. The total energy liberated has been measured to be about 11 MeV and checks almost exactly with the value obtained from the loss in mass.

Discovery of Induced Radioactivity. The discovery of induced radioactivity was made in 1934 by Frédéric Joliot and Irène Joliot-Curie. For their work, this French couple were awarded the Nobel Prize in chemistry in 1935.

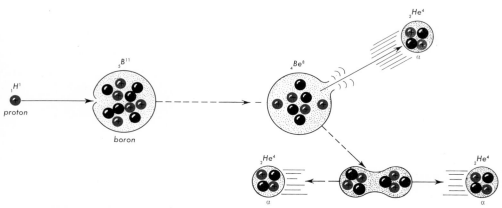

Fig. C. Diagram of the disintegration of a boron nucleus of mass 11 by a proton to produce three α particles.

ton is first captured by a $_5B^{11}$ nucleus to form an unstable carbon nucleus, $_6C^{12}$. This composite structure disintegrates by the expulsion of an α particle with several mil-

For years, these two researchers had been exposing various substances to the α rays from naturally radioactive elements and had been studying the various disintegrations that took place. In the specific instance referred to above, they bombarded aluminum with α *particles from polonium* and measured the energies of the ejected neutrons by the recoiling of protons from paraffin (see Fig. D). They observed that,

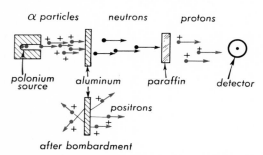

α particles   neutrons   protons

polonium source   aluminum   paraffin   detector

positrons

after bombardment

Fig. D. Experimental arrangement used by the Joliots when they discovered induced radioactivity.

even after the polonium source was taken away, the detector continued to respond to some kind of penetrating radiation. Upon investigating the nature of these rays, they found positrons (positively charged electrons) coming from the aluminum.

Repeating the experiments to make certain of the results, they came to the conclusion that, under the bombardment of α particles, the aluminum had become radioactive in its own right. What was happening has since been verified. Alpha particles striking aluminum nuclei are captured and the resulting nuclei disintegrate with the violent ejection of neutrons:

$$_2\mathbf{He}^4 + _{13}\mathbf{Al}^{27} = _{15}\mathbf{P}^{30} + _0\mathbf{n}^1 \qquad (9)$$

The newly created recoil particles, with a charge of +15 and mass 30, have been identified as phosphorus nuclei, which are not stable but radioactive. Spontaneously disintegrating, these radioactive phosphorus nuclei $_{15}\mathbf{P}^{30}$ shoot out positrons, decaying to stable silicon atoms of charge +14 and mass 30:

$$_{15}\mathbf{P}^{30} = _{14}\mathbf{Si}^{30} + _1e^0 \qquad (10)$$

The half life of this activity, which measures the rate of decay of the phosphorus into silicon, is only 2.5 min.

Although the mass of the electron is not zero, it is so small compared with unit mass (the mass of one electron, it will be remembered, is 1/1840 of one atomic mass unit) that e is written with a zero superscript. According to this notation, a positron is written $_1e^0$ and an electron $_{-1}e^0$.

More than two hundred different kinds of radioactive atoms have been produced in the laboratory. Three examples, in addition to the one already given, are illustrated by the following reactions:

$$_1\mathbf{H}^2 + _{15}\mathbf{P}^{31} = _{15}\mathbf{P}^{32} + _1\mathbf{H}^1,$$
$$_{15}\mathbf{P}^{32} = _{16}\mathbf{S}^{32} + _{-1}e^0 \qquad (11)$$

$$_1\mathbf{H}^2 + _6\mathbf{C}^{12} = _7\mathbf{N}^{13} + _0\mathbf{n}^1,$$
$$_7\mathbf{N}^{13} = _6\mathbf{C}^{13} + _1e^0 \qquad (12)$$

$$_1\mathbf{H}^2 + _{11}\mathbf{Na}^{23} = _{11}\mathbf{Na}^{24} + _1\mathbf{H}^1,$$
$$_{11}\mathbf{Na}^{24} = _{12}\mathbf{Mg}^{24} + _{-1}e^0 \qquad (13)$$

A photograph of the positrons from

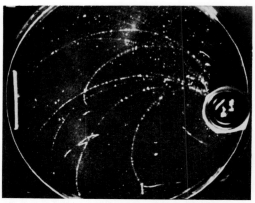

Fig. E. Photograph of the Wilson cloud-chamber tracks of positrons ejected by radioactive nitrogen, $_7\mathbf{N}^{13}$.

radioactive nitrogen, Eq. (12), is shown in Fig. E.

(a) $_1H^1$ $_1H^1$ (b)

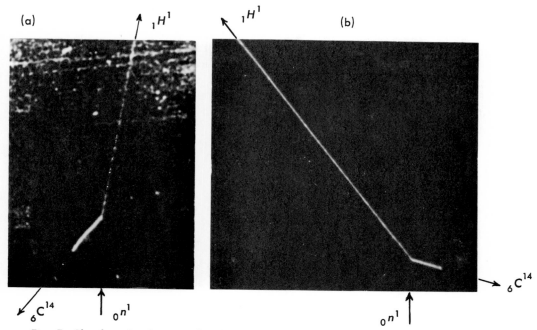

$_6C^{14}$ $_0n^1$ $_0n^1$ $_6C^{14}$

Fig. F. Cloud-track photographs of neutron disintegrations of nitrogen. (After Feather and Rasetti.)

Neutron Projectiles Produce Disintegrations. The first disintegrations produced by high-speed neutrons as atomic projectiles were announced in 1932 by the English physicist, Feather. Immediately following Chadwick's discovery of these neutral particles, Feather allowed neutrons from beryllium to enter a Wilson cloud chamber containing pure nitrogen gas. Numerous expansions of the chamber and the simultaneous clicks of a camera shutter gave many photographs of the ion tracks left by recoiling nitrogen atoms.

Although most of the photographs indicated elastic collisions between nitrogen atoms and neutrons, an occasional photograph showed a forked track, indicating a disintegration of a nitrogen nucleus:

$$_0n^1 + _7N^{14} = _6C^{14} + _1H^1 \qquad (14)$$

Two photographs of such disintegrations are reproduced in Fig. F. Although hundreds of neutrons enter the cloud chamber every second, they do not ionize atoms as charged particles do and, hence, leave no tracks. When a head-on nuclear collision occurs, however, the disintegrated nuclei, possessing as they do high speeds and posi-

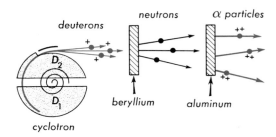

Fig. G. Experimental arrangement for producing intense beams of neutrons by bombarding beryllium with deuterons. The neutrons are then used as projectiles for further disintegrations as illustrated here for aluminum.

tive charges, leave a trail of ions behind them. The fork in each photo shows a proton track of considerable length originating at the same point as the more dense, short-ranged track of the recoiling carbon nucleus.

Strong sources of neutrons are produced by inserting a thin plate of beryllium metal in the intense beam of deuterons coming from the cyclotron, as shown in Fig. G. The disintegration process, giving rise to the neutrons, is the reaction Eq. (6) and the diagram of Fig. B.

Into such a beam of chargeless particles numerous substances of known chemical constitution have been inserted and the disintegration products studied with suitable detectors.

QUESTIONS

1. How can the cloud chamber be used to identify disintegration products of a bombardment reaction?
2. In a cloud-chamber picture, how does one know that a neutron is responsible for a reaction?
3. What is a positron?
4. (a) How are strong beams of neutrons produced? (b) Can neutrons be accelerated in a cyclotron?
5. (a) What is a multiple disintegration? (b) Give an example.
6. Chemists refer to exothermic and endothermic reactions as those which respectively give off and absorb heat. What would be meant by an exothermic and endothermic nuclear reaction? Give examples.
7. (a) What is the meaning of Q in a disintegration equation? (b) What is the significance of a negative value?
8. Suppose you had an energy equal to the negative Q of the threshold reaction in Eq. (7) that could be divided between the incident particles so as to produce a head-on collision. (a) What condition must be met for the reaction to go? (b) What would happen?
9. How are uncharged particles, such as neutrons, detected?

PROBLEMS

1. When nitrogen-14 is bombarded by deuterons, protons of considerable energy are observed being ejected. Write the disintegration equation.
2. When beryllium-9 is bombarded by protons, α particles are observed being ejected. Write the resultant reaction.
3. Nitrogen-14, bombarded by neutrons, liberates protons. Write the reaction.
4. When magnesium-24 is bombarded by neutrons, protons are found coming from the target. Write the resultant reaction.
5. When neutrons collide with oxygen-16 nuclei, α particles are observed to be given off. Write the reaction.

6. If radioactive sulfur-35 is produced by the neutron bombardment of chlorine-35, what is the reaction equation?

7. When α particles with 7-MeV energy bombard sodium-23, protons are observed being given off. (a) Write the reaction and (b) find the energy liberated.

8. Write the multiple disintegration for deuterons bombarding nitrogen-14 in which α particles are produced.

9. Suppose 3.9-MeV α particles were used to bombard $_7N^{14}$. (a) Write the resulting reaction (see Eq. 4). (b) What would be the total kinetic energy of the resulting particles?

10. Suppose 10.0-MeV α particles were used to bombard $_6C^{12}$. What would happen (see Eq. 3)? Explain.

PROJECT

If you have access to a supervised source of neutrons and a rate meter, irradiate a silver dime and measure the half life of the radioactive isotopes formed.

NUCLEAR PHYSICS

Lesson 116 *BETA AND GAMMA RAYS*

Beta rays emitted by the natural radioactive elements have been studied by many people. Becquerel first found them to be comparable to cathode rays. Today, we know them as electrons. One of the greatest mysteries of atomic physics has been the origin of these particles. The great mass of experimental evidence shows that most of them come from the nucleus, yet they do not exist in the same form inside any of the known nuclei. Furthermore, unlike α particles and γ rays, they do not emerge from the nuclei with the same energy and range, but with a wide band of velocities.

Beta Ray Spectrograph. This is an instrument by which one can experimentally determine the velocity of β particles from a radioactive source. Fig. A is a diagram of

one such instrument, developed in principle by Robinson in England. Beta particles from a small radioactive source, A, consisting of a fine wire with a deposit of material on its surface, are allowed to pass through

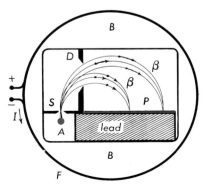

Fig. A. Diagram of a β-ray spectrograph.

a slit, S. With the entire vacuum tube located in a uniform magnetic field, the β particles follow circular paths and are brought to focus on a photographic plate, P, or at the open slit of an ionization chamber. Each of the three semicircular paths in any one group shown in the diagram has essentially the same radius and diameter. The focusing action indicated can best be demonstrated by using a compass and drawing several semicircles with the same radius, but slightly displaced centers. The velocity of any group of electrons is given by Eq. (1) in Lesson 114 as—

$$Bev = \frac{mv^2}{r} \qquad (1)$$

where r is the path radius, B the magnetic induction, and e, m, and v the electron charge, mass, and velocity, respectively.

If the field, B, is constant, and a photographic plate, P, is located as shown in the figure, its development after a time, t, will result in a photograph like the drawing in Fig. B. In addition to a darkened back-

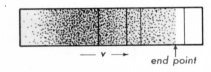

Fig. B. Diagram of a β-ray spectrogram.

ground all along the plate, one finds several lines parallel to the slit. The background indicates β particles present with all different velocities, while the lines signify groups with discrete and definite velocities. Not all spectrograms with such a continuous background contain these lines, however.

The Neutrino. In 1931, Wolfgang Pauli, of Austria, suggested that, in β-ray emission, all nuclei of the same isotope emit the same amount of energy and that this is the *end-*

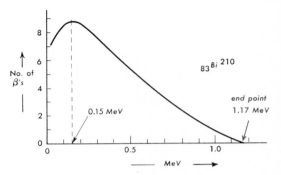

Fig. C. Graph of β-ray energies from $_{83}Bi^{210}$.

point energy shown in Fig. C (see also Table 1). To account for the observed fact that some β particles emerge with much less energy than others, he made the follow-

Table 1. End-Point Energies for β Rays

Isotope	End Point E	Half life
$_{82}Pb^{214}$	0.72 MeV	26.8 m
$_{83}Bi^{210}$	1.17 MeV	4.8 d
$_{87}Fr^{223}$	1.20 MeV	21.0 m
$_{88}Ra^{225}$	0.320 MeV	15 d
$_{89}Ac^{228}$	1.55 MeV	6.1 h
$_{90}Th^{231}$	0.21 MeV	25.6 y
$_{90}Th^{234}$	0.193 MeV	24 d

ing postulate. The emission of a β particle by any nucleus is accompanied by a companion particle having a variable energy, E. While the β particle is an ordinary negatively charged electron, the companion particle, now called a *neutrino*, has no charge. In some respects, a neutrino is like a photon; it has no rest mass, it has energy E, and it travels with the speed of light, c. Hence, the reaction for β emission by a nucleus like $_{83}Bi^{210}$, can be written—

$$_{83}\mathbf{Bi}^{210} \rightarrow {}_{84}\mathbf{Po}^{210} + \beta^- + \bar{\nu} \qquad (2)$$

See Fig. D.

Only recently have experiments been

performed that establish the existence of these phantom particles, neutrinos. Because nuclei are composed of neutrons and protons, the two ejected particles are created

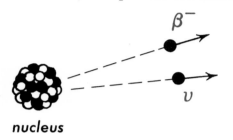

nucleus

Fig. D. Each β-particle from a nucleus is accompanied by a neutrino.

by the nucleus, a neutron transforming into a proton as it emits an electron of mass m_0 and charge $-e$, and a neutrino of energy, E, with no charge.

Neutrinos have been found to spin on their axes, like a top. Those that spin clockwise as they move (like a right-handed screw) are called *ordinary neutrinos* and are designated by v. Those spinning counterclockwise are called *antineutrinos* and are designated by $\bar{v}$. The type emitted with a β^-, as in Eq. (2), are now called antineutrinos. The type emitted with a β^+ (positron) are called neutrinos.

Conservation of Nuclear Energy. The simultaneous emission of a β particle and a neutrino from the nucleus of an atom requires energy. The disintegrating nucleus gives up not only the mass of the two particles, but some additional mass, which it converts into kinetic energy. By adding up all this energy in the form of mass, the total loss in the mass of an atom can be calculated.

Consider as an example the β emission of $_{83}Bi^{210}$ as represented by Eq. (2). The masses of the two atoms involved are known to be—

$$_{83}Bi^{210} \quad 209.984110 \text{ amu}$$
$$_{84}Po^{210} \quad 209.982866 \text{ amu}$$
$$\overline{\Delta m = 0.001244 \text{ amu}}$$

To convert this mass into MeV, we multiply Δm by the value 931 MeV, which gives—

$$E = 1.17 \text{ MeV}$$

This is just the end-point energy derived from experiment and shown in Fig. C. The mass of the ejected electron need not be included here, because the two masses above are for the neutral atoms. $_{83}Bi^{210}$ has 83 atomic electrons included in its mass of 209.984110 amu, while $_{84}Po^{210}$ includes 84 electrons. When $_{83}Bi^{210}$ ejects an electron from the nucleus, the daughter product, $_{84}Po^{210}$, picks up a stray electron to become a neutral atom, so that no electron masses are lost or gained during the disintegration.

Gamma Rays. For many radioactive elements, the emission of an α or β particle from a nucleus is immediately followed by the emission of a γ ray. It has been shown by crystal diffraction spectrographs that γ rays are electromagnetic waves and that they consist of sharp lines of discrete wave lengths. Just as visible light and ultraviolet and infrared radiation, as well as X-rays, are known to be emitted from the outer structure of the atom by an electron's jumping from one energy level to another, so γ rays are believed to arise from a transition of a nucleon from one energy state to another within the nucleus. (Neutrons and protons as constituents of nuclei are called *nucleons.*)

There is good evidence that γ rays are emitted by the daughter element, that is, that they are preceded by particle emission. A good example is to be found in the case of the lead isotope $_{82}Pb^{210}$, which has a half-life of 22 years, and emits a β particle. The reaction is—

$$_{82}\text{Pb}^{210} \rightarrow {}_{83}\text{Bi}^{210} + \beta^- + \bar{\nu} + \gamma \text{ ray} \quad (3)$$

These emissions are represented on a nuclear energy-level diagram in Fig. E.

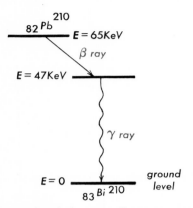

Fig. E. Energy-level diagram illustrating β-ray emission followed by γ-ray emission.

When a $_{82}\text{Pb}^{210}$ nucleus emits a β particle and a neutrino, the end-point energy is found to be 18,000 electron volts, or 18 KeV. This leaves a $_{83}\text{Bi}^{210}$ nucleus in an excited state. A transition down to the ground level is accompanied by the emission of a γ ray with an energy $h\nu$. This energy is equivalent to 47 KeV. Although it is not shown in this diagram, this nucleus, too, is radioactive and emits another β ray to become $_{84}\text{Po}^{210}$. See Eq. (2).

Artificially radioactive sodium-24 is an example of a nucleus emitting two gammas following beta emission. It is produced by irradiation from deuterons (see Fig. F) and decays with a 15-hour half-life. After emitting an electron, the nuclear charge increases by unity, and we have a magnesium nucleus in an excited state. With two successive transitions in which 2.75-MeV and 1.37-MeV γ rays are emitted, the nucleus becomes a stable system, a normal isotope of magnesium $_{12}\text{Mg}^{24}$.

The meaning of energy levels in a nucleus will be discussed more fully in the following lesson.

Electron Capture. Many radioactive nuclei, when created by some collision process, are unstable to the extent of one extra positive charge. Although many such nuclei disintegrate and become stable by the emission of a positron, others absorb an atomic electron from the K shell of the same atom. Because the probability cloud of the K-shell electron is densest at the nucleus (see first picture of Fig. D in Lesson 108), it is likely that the K-shell electron may be close enough to interact with the nucleus.

Inside the nucleus, this negative charge neutralizes a positive charge, whereas outside, an L or M electron jumps into the K-shell vacancy with the simultaneous emission of a characteristic X-ray (see Fig. G).

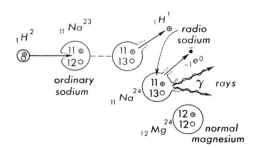

Fig. F. Diagrams illustrating the production and disintegration of radiosodium.

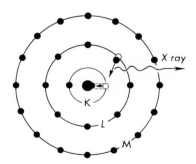

Fig. G. Unstable nucleus captures an electron from the K-shell of atomic electrons. As a consequence, an X-ray is emitted.

Beryllium-7 and gallium-65 are specific examples of unstable nuclei in which *K-capture* occurs. The reactions for these are—

$$_4\text{Be}^7 + _{-1}e^0 = _3\text{Li}^7 + \nu \qquad (4)$$

$$_{31}\text{Ga}^{65} + _{-1}e^0 = _{30}\text{Zn}^{65} + \nu \qquad (5)$$

Electron capture, or *E.C.*, changes one of the nuclear protons into a neutron and the atomic number drops by unity from 89 to 88. The emission of a β particle changes one of the neutrons into a proton and the atomic number increases by unity from 89 to 90.

Because the daughter nucleus has lost one unit of positive charge and the electron shell has lost one unit of negative charge, there will be no net loss or gain of electrons. The energy lost during the reaction will show up in the kinetic energy of the neutrino, ν, and the recoiling nucleus.

Example 1. What is the kinetic energy liberated during the reaction shown in Eq. (4)?

Solution. The masses are—

$$\begin{aligned}
_4\text{Be}^7 \quad & 7.016931 \\
_3\text{Li}^7 \quad & \underline{7.016005} \\
\Delta m = \quad & .000926
\end{aligned}$$

Multiplying by 931 MeV, we obtain—

$$E = .862 \text{ MeV}$$

Positron Emission. In some few isotopes, electron capture is the only means of radioactive decay. However, most isotopes that capture electrons also disintegrate by the alternative reaction of positron emission. A typical example is copper-64:

$$_{17}\text{Cl}^{36} \rightarrow _{16}\text{S}^{36} + _1e^0 + \nu \qquad (6)$$

The positron spectrum and all features of emission are similar to the electron emission.

Positron Annihilation. Positrons have never been found to exist in nature as stable particles. When they are produced, their lifetime is usually very short. Experiments indicate that all electrons and positrons spin around an axis through their center of mass. When a positron and an electron come close together, they frequently combine by revolving around each other as a double-star, with their spin axes parallel to one another. As such a pair, they are called *positronium*. Positronium is very short lived, for soon the two particles disintegrate completely. In their places, γ rays are created. Conservation of energy and momentum require each of these γ rays to have an energy of 0.511 MeV.

Nuclear Stability. We now know that, if we bombard targets with atomic particles of sufficiently high energy, every known stable element can be converted into radioactive isotopes of that element or of neighboring elements. Furthermore, a number of isotopes can be produced for any one element, some with masses smaller than any of its stable isotopes, and some with greater masses. In the case of copper, for example, the following isotopes have been produced.

Copper; $Z = 29$

Mass	Activity	Half life	
58	β^+	3s	
59	β^+ E.C.	81s	
60	β^+ E.C.	24m	
61	β^+ E.C.	3.3h	
62	β^+ E.C.	10m	
63	Stable	—	70%
64	β^-, β^+, E.C.	12.8h	42%
65	Stable	—	30%
66	β^-	5.1m	
67	β^-	58s	
68	β^-	32s	

The first five isotopes have too many protons to be stable nuclides and, by positron emission, convert a proton into a neu- a proton and become an isotope of zinc. Isotope $_{29}Cu^{64}$, lying between two stable isotopes, is unstable in several ways. This nu-

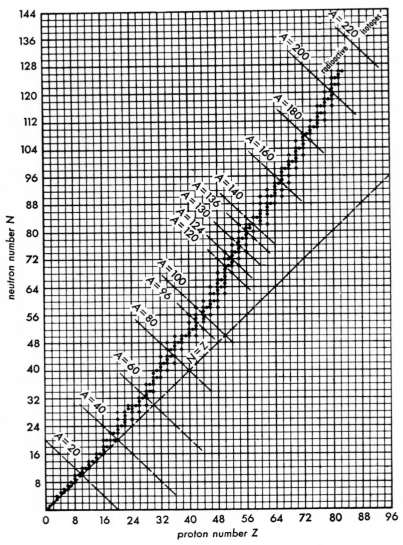

Fig. H. Neutron-proton diagram of stable nuclei.

tron and become an isotope of nickel. The last three isotopes have too few protons and, by electron emission, convert a neutron into cleus may emit a β^-, a β^+, or capture an electron (E.C.).

The stability of every nucleus is associated with the relative numbers of neutrons and protons bound together. If N represents the number of neutrons and Z the number of protons in any nucleus, and we plot a graph for all the known stable nuclides, we obtain a chart like the one in Fig. H.

If we plotted, vertically outward from the page in Fig. H, the accurately known atomic masses, M, for all known stable as well as radioactive nuclei, we would obtain a kind of valley running diagonally up the chart, with the lowest points near the center of the stable nuclei. This is illustrated by a cross-section diagram in Fig. I, for all nuclei with $A = 87$. Note that the only stable one of these nuclei, $_{38}Sr^{87}$, lies deepest in the valley curve.

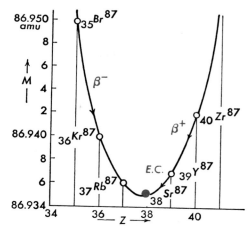

Fig. I. Atomic-mass graph for nuclei with $A = 87$.

QUESTIONS

1. Why do positrons exist only briefly?
2. Why are neutrinos and antineutrinos hard to find?
3. Why are the energies of the annihilation γ rays equal?
4. (a) In what way does positron emission differ from electron capture? (b) What features are similar?
5. (a) In what way does positron emission differ from electron emission? (b) What features are similar?
6. In view of the decay of copper-64, might there be "bumps" in the bottom of the valley of stability? Explain.
7. Do most nuclei have equal numbers of protons and neutrons? Explain.
8. Give an example in which mass is totally converted into kinetic energy.
9. Why do the annihilation γ rays each have an energy of 0.511 MeV?

PROBLEMS

1. Use a circular template to draw several circles and demonstrate the focusing action at 180°, as used in the beta spectrograph.
2. Write the equations for (a) the production and (b) the decay of sodium-24. (c) What is the beta end-point energy?
3. From the examples given, work out the rules that predict whether neutrinos or antineutrinos will be emitted in a particular type of reaction.

4. Describe an experiment that would show that an unseen particle is emitted during *K*-capture.
5. From the information in the Appendix, (a) work out the decay of oxygen-19 and (b) calculate the kinetic energy of the products.
6. Cesium-137 disintegrates with a 37-year half life, emitting a β^- and a 0.662 MeV γ. (a) Draw the energy-level diagram and (b) write the equation.

PROJECT

Make a report on recent experiments that have yielded experimental evidence of the actual existence of neutrinos.

NUCLEAR PHYSICS

Lesson 117 **INSIDE THE NUCLEUS**

Nuclear Binding Forces. Although the disintegrations of different nuclei give rise to some half dozen different kinds of particles, it now seems quite probable that we need assume only two kinds of particles existing within the nucleus: *neutrons* and *protons*. If this is correct, our task becomes the difficult one of explaining both the disintegration mechanism of an unstable nucleus and the binding forces that hold a stable nucleus together. An attempt to find an answer to the latter question will serve as a starting point for the following presentations.

According to the *neutron-proton theory* of the atomic nucleus (see Fig. A), the deuteron nucleus contains only one neutron and one proton. Let us compare, therefore, the masses of one free proton and one free neutron with their mass when combined as a deuteron (for masses, see Appendix).

neutron mass,	$_0\mathrm{n}^1$ =	**1.008665**
proton mass,	$_1\mathrm{H}^1$ =	**1.007825**
	sum =	**2.016490**
deuteron mass,	$_1\mathrm{H}^2$ =	**2.014103**

The difference in mass, 0.002387 amu, is not due to inaccurate measurements of mass but is a real difference to be accounted for as the annihilation energy that binds the two particles together. When a neutron and proton come together to form a deuteron, a small part of their mass—namely 0.002387 amu (equivalent to 2.22-MeV energy)—is

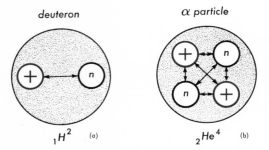

deuteron α *particle*

$_1H^2$ (a) $_2He^4$ (b)

Fig. A. Schematic diagram of the nucleus for (a) a deuterium atom and (b) a helium atom.

radiated from the newly formed nucleus. At close approach, in other words, the two particles attract each other so strongly that, once together, it takes the equivalent of a little more than two million volts of energy to pull them apart. This has been confirmed by a nuclear photoelectric effect, an experiment in which γ rays of 2.22-MeV energy or greater are found to break up deuterium nuclei into their constituent parts, while γ rays of lower energy have no effect. How neutrons and protons attract each other when very close together is a question of great importance, because the stability of all the universe depends upon these forces.

The term "binding energy" of a nucleon does not refer to the energy the nucleon *has,* but energy it does not have; that is, energy it *needs to acquire* in order to escape the nucleus.

To find the average energy binding a single proton or a single neutron to the nucleus of a heavier atom, we need only compare the masses of two heavy nuclei that differ from each other by only one proton or one neutron. Among the heavier atoms (see Appendix), it will be seen that consecutive nuclei differ from each other, on the average, by unity. Therefore, to remove a proton or neutron from the average nucleus, we must supply enough energy to increase the mass from 1.0000 to 1.0081 for a proton, or 1.0090 for a neutron. This means that, in either case, we must supply an energy equivalent to about 8 MeV.

The Nuclear Potential Barrier. Early in the development of ideas concerning nuclear disintegration, Gamow proposed a model by which one might represent the atomic nucleus. This model is based upon the forces acting between two positive charges.

Picture again a proton or α particle, with its positive charge, approaching a positively charged nucleus. As the two charges come closer and closer together, they repel each other with greater and greater forces, as given by Coulomb's law. Graphically, the increasing repulsion is represented by the potential curve shown in Fig. B. Such a

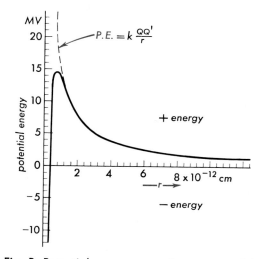

Fig. B. Potential energy curve for an α particle as it approaches a positively charged nucleus.

curve represents what is called the *potential barrier* of the nucleus. The highest point of the barrier is frequently called the edge of the nucleus, which is found to be given by—

$$r = 1.2 \times 10^{-13} \sqrt[3]{A} \text{ cm} \qquad (1)$$

where A is the atomic weight.

For want of a mechanical model of the nucleus, we can pattern a surface having a volcanic-crater form, similar to the surface obtained by rotating Fig. B around the vertical axis (see Fig. C). By such an analogy, the electrical potential energy, V, between the two positively charged particles is analogous to the potential energy of a ball at any point on the crater model.

If a small marble, representing a proton or α particle, approaches the nuclear barrier, it will roll up the hill, as shown in the diagram. Experiencing a rapidly increasing opposing force, the ball may be turned back, or off to one side. If the initial velocity

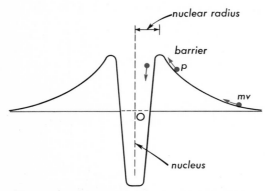

Fig. C. A graphic model of the atomic nucleus, as proposed by Gamow. The potential barrier of a nucleus to an approaching positive charge is analogous to the crater of a volcano.

is high enough, however, the ball may go over the top of the barrier and drop down inside, representing a capture. What happens inside the nucleus and the disintegration that follows is the subject of the following sections of this lesson.

Nuclear Models. As in the case of the atom, it is useful to discuss our knowledge of nuclei in terms of simplified models. It is not that any particular model is believed to be entirely correct. Rather, each model may explain particular properties of a nucleus. Although the true description of the nucleus is not yet completely known, it is hoped that a study of nuclear properties in terms of models will ultimately lead to a complete understanding of nuclear structure.

Bohr's Nuclear Model. In 1937, Niels Bohr, the famous Danish physicist, made another outstanding contribution to modern physics. He improved Gamow's model of

the nucleus by extending what is sometimes called the *waterdrop model* of the nucleus. Bohr and his collaborator, Kalkar, imagined the many particles in a heavy nucleus as moving about within a spherical enclosure with motions analogous to the molecules in a drop of water. The surface of the spherical enclosure, which corresponds to the top of the potential barrier in Fig. C, is analogous to the surface tension that holds a small waterdrop to its spherical form.

Just as the rapid motion of the molecules in water is a measure of the temperature, so Bohr speaks of the rapid motion of the neutrons and protons within the spherical boundary of the nucleus as a sort of "temperature." See Fig. D. To explain dis-

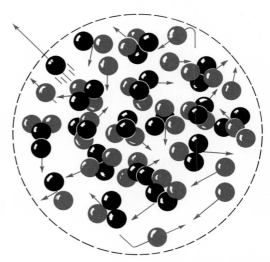

Fig. D. Nucleus in the act of ejecting a neutron, based upon the Bohr-Gamow waterdrop model.

integration, the analogy is drawn that *the ejection of a particle from the nucleus is like the evaporation of a water molecule from a drop of water*. Just as a rise in temperature brings about a more rapid evaporation of water, so an increase in the motions within the nucleus gives rise to a higher probability of disintegration.

In a stable nucleus, the particles within are moving about with very little kinetic energy and are in the analogous state of a relatively low temperature. When a high-speed particle from outside penetrates through the potential barrier, it is accelerated toward the center of the nucleus and acquires a very high kinetic energy before it collides with one or more of the particles inside. Soon the energy becomes divided among the many particles and the nucleus takes on a higher temperature state. Such a temperature corresponds to several million degrees.

Now as the particles move about inside, there is a certain probability or chance that, within a given interval of time, some one particle will be hit by several particles, giving it a sufficiently high velocity, in an outward direction, to permit an escape through the potential barrier. This is illustrated in Fig. D by one of the neutrons in the upper left part of the diagram. The more rapid the internal motions, *i.e.*, the higher the temperature, the greater is this chance of escape.

A direct disintegration may be described in this way: if, upon entering the nucleus, a high-speed particle, such as a proton, adds sufficient energy to give the nucleus a high temperature, another particle, such as a neutron, an α particle, a γ ray, or even another proton, may be ejected immediately. Since such an ejected particle has to be supplied with a certain minimum energy to get free, the remaining particles will be slowed down, and the nucleus will return to a lower temperature.

A potential-barrier model of an unstable nucleus is shown in Fig. E. For a stable atom, the particles are moving slowly about at the bottom of the volcano pit. When a proton or α particle from outside comes over the barrier and drops down inside, regaining its original speed, it collides with other particles and sets them into a more rapid

state of motion, as shown. If one of the particles near the outside is hit hard enough, it may acquire a sufficient energy

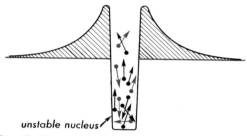

Fig. E. Diagram representing an unstable nucleus.

to escape over the barrier. This is the analogue of disintegration and radioactivity.

The Shell Model. The protons and neutrons within the nucleus are actually not moving about with quite the freedom pictured above, but are very likely confined in their motions to shells analogous to the electron structure in the outer part of the atom.

As we saw in the previous lesson, beta decay leads to specific energy levels of the daughter nucleus.

The first indication of a shell structure of the nucleus came from the existence of *magic numbers*. It had been noticed for some time that certain very stable and naturally abundant isotopes always had 2, 8, 20, 28, 50, 82, or 126 neutrons or protons. Thus these numbers are referred to as "magic." Nuclei in which both proton and neutron numbers are magic (such as $_{20}Ca^{40}$ and $_{82}Pb^{208}$) are called *doubly magic nuclei* and are especially stable and abundant.

It has been recently shown that the magic numbers correspond to closed shells, similar to the electron shells of the atom (see Lesson 105). Each shell represents a completed, tightly grouped, set of nucleons, which form a very stable structure.

Nuclear Model for Neutron Absorption. When a neutron approaches a nucleus prior to a disintegration, it does not encounter a potential barrier of the type already described for protons and α particles. A neutron has no charge, so that, at large distances, it is not repelled by the positively charged nucleus. It may, therefore, approach a nucleus with very little speed of its own and be captured when it comes too close. At very close range, a strong attractive force sets in, drawing the two together.

To an approaching neutron, the nucleus acts as though it were a pit into which the particle will fall. This is illustrated by the flat potential curve in Fig. F. The marble

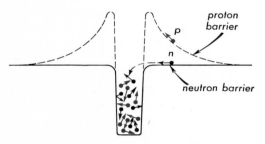

Fig. F. A graphic model of the nucleus as it is presented to an approaching neutron or proton.

rolling along the horizontal plane toward the pit represents the influence of the nucleus upon the neutron's motion, whereas the marble rolling up the hill (dotted line)

represents the influence of the same nucleus upon the motion of a proton.

When the neutron is absorbed, its binding energy is usually liberated by the emission of one or more gamma rays. Several light nuclei (such as lithium-6 and boron-10) will emit particles instead. Very heavy nuclei have been found to split apart completely when a neutron is absorbed, as we shall see in the next lesson.

The ease with which neutrons are absorbed accounts for the fact that there are no free neutrons in nature.

Nuclear Demonstration Models. A demonstration model illustrating the capture of a high-speed proton or α particle by a nucleus, prior to disintegration, is shown in Fig. G. Marbles rolled down the incline represent the speeding up of atomic projectiles by an accelerator like the cyclotron. Approaching the potential barrier, a marble may roll part way up and then be deflected off to one side, illustrating an elastic collision without capture; or it may roll up the side and drop into the crater opening at the top, representing a capture prior to disintegration.

A demonstration of what happens inside the nucleus is illustrated by another model, as shown in Fig. H. In this case, the vertical scale of the barrier has, of necessity, been reduced, i.e., flattened out. When a marble is rolled down the incline and into the

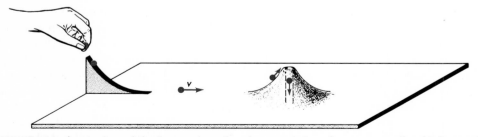

Fig. G. Mechanical model of a nucleus for demonstrating the capture of a high-speed proton, deuteron, or α particle, prior to disintegration.

group of marbles at the center of the barrier, there may be several collisions before another particle goes bouncing out on the other side. This corresponds to a direct dis-

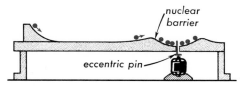

Fig. H. Mechanical model of a nucleus for demonstrating (a) the increased kinetic energy of nuclear particles after a capture and (b) the chance probability of radioactive decay or disintegration by the ejection of a particle.

integration in which one particle, such as a proton, goes in and a neutron comes out.

If a single particle does not emerge, most of the particles inside take on random motions, colliding with each other in much the same way as do the molecules or atoms in a gas or liquid. To prevent friction from stopping them (there is no friction in an atom), the marbles are continually agitated by a small pin protruding from underneath the barrier. This pin is mounted slightly off center at the end of the shaft of a small electric motor. If the motor is left running for some time, a single marble will eventually be hit by several particles moving in the same direction and will recoil with sufficient speed to carry it over the barrier and out. This corresponds to a disintegration or radioactive decay, which takes place according to the laws of chance, and to the resultant drop in temperature of the nucleus.

The faster the motor runs, the greater is the internal agitation and chance of ejection, and the shorter is the so-called half life of the element.

The Origin of Beta Rays. For years, the emission of electrons from radioactive ele-

ments has been a puzzle and a challenge to the best minds in physical science. Although many theories have been proposed, none appears to be entirely acceptable. From experimental evidence, one thing seems quite certain and that is that the appearance of a high-speed electron is the result of some violent disruption of the nucleus.

On numerous occasions it has been suggested that the neutron is a composite particle made up of one proton and one electron. The fact that the mass of a free neutron (1.00898) is slightly greater than the mass of a free proton (1.00814) and that the charge is zero would tend to confirm this. A β ray might, therefore, be explained as the result of a disintegration in which one of the neutrons in the nucleus splits apart with a violent ejection of an electron, the remaining particle, a proton, staying with the nucleus to increase its charge by unity.

A theory similar to this was proposed early to explain positron emission. According to this hypothesis, the proton is a composite particle, being made up of a positron and a neutron.

Because the difference in mass between the neutron and proton would seem to make one of these hypotheses wrong, it is assumed that both are incorrect. The difficulty is explained away by recalling that the average mass of neutrons and protons within the nucleus is unity and assuming that, so confined, both particles have the same mass and differ only in their charge. To explain electron or positron emission by a radioactive nucleus the electron has been assumed to be created at the expense of one-half million volts of energy.

Once a sufficient amount of energy is acquired by a certain nucleus, a neutron simply acts as an agent capable (1) of changing about ½-MeV energy into a particle having the mass of an electron and (2) of creating a negative charge for the electron and itself absorbing an equal positive charge to become a proton. Similarly, in the nucleus of another type of atom, a proton may act as an agent capable of changing energy into a positron and itself becoming, by the absorption of the complementary negative charge, a neutron.

Half Life of the Free Neutron. Recent experiments have shown that the free neutron has a half life of 13 min. The measurement of such a long half life is very difficult, since the probability of neutron capture by some nucleus, when in solid matter, reduces its life to about one thousandth of a second. In free space, a neutron will disintegrate into a proton, an electron, and an antineutrino.

The Origin of Nuclear Forces. Protons and neutrons, the fundamental "building blocks" of all atomic nuclei, are commonly called *nucleons*. Because the neutrons and protons of a stable nucleus are bound together by strong forces, it must be assumed that Coulomb's law for the attraction of unlike charges and the repulsion of like charges becomes secondary to much stronger but short-range attractive forces.

In 1937, the Japanese physicist, Hideki Yukawa, proposed that such a strong, short-range force could be explained in terms of the exchange of particles between the nucleons. Such a picture is similar to the way electrons hold a molecule together. From the range of the nuclear force, Yukawa predicted these elusive particles called *mesons* would have a mass of about 100 MeV.

Soon afterward, particles called *muons* having a mass of 106 MeV were found among cosmic rays. However, it was soon found that muons were simply very heavy electrons that quickly disintegrate with a half life of about 10^{-6} sec according to the reaction—

$$\mu \rightarrow e + \nu + \bar{\nu} \qquad (2)$$

Because experiments showed these positive and negative muons were not readily absorbed by nuclei, it was realized that these could not be the particles proposed by Yukawa.

With the advent of the high-energy accelerators in the late 1940's, it was found that particles called *mesons* could be knocked out of nuclei. Mesons have masses of around 139 MeV and are charged $+$, $-$, and 0.

Although the half-life was even shorter than for muons, the π mesons did satisfy Yukawa's prediction. The present concept of nucleons is that they consist of some sort of common core surrounded by a pulsating cloud of π mesons. Because π mesons are charged $+$, 0, or $-$, the rapid jumping back and forth between nucleons changes the nucleon identity equally fast, and at the same time binds the two nucleons together. (See Fig. I.) This diagram might well represent a deuteron.

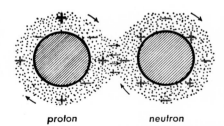

proton   neutron

Fig. I. Schematic diagram of the π-mesonic clouds around each of two nucleon cores, the charge exchange accounting for the strong attractive force.

QUESTIONS

1. Does Coulomb's law of repulsion between like charges hold within the nucleus of an atom?
2. About how much energy is required to remove a nucleon from a nucleus?
3. Why does a deuteron have less mass than the neutron and proton of which it is composed?
4. (a) What is a potential barrier? (b) What equivalent mechanical model is sometimes used to represent such a barrier?
5. (a) What is the waterdrop model of the nucleus? (b) How is it used to explain stable nuclei on the one hand and radioactive nuclei on the other?
6. How is the waterdrop model of a nucleus carried over to the potential-barrier model?
7. What mechanical model can be used to illustrate the conditions for the nuclear capture of a high-speed proton or α particle?
8. In what way does a radioactive nucleus of short half life compare with one of long half life?
9. Why are there no free neutrons in nature?
10. What is the latest theory for the source of electrons that come from the nucleus?
11. Because the nucleus consists primarily of positively charged protons and neutral neutrons, why doesn't the nucleus explode from the repulsion between the protons?
12. What is the relation between the "temperature" and motion of nuclear particles?
13. How does the Bohr nuclear model explain the disintegration of a nucleus when hit by a high-speed particle?
14. What are "magic numbers"?
15. How is the shell model of the nucleus related to the shell model of the atom?
16. Why were muons thought to be the particles predicted by Yukawa? Why were they rejected as being the source of nuclear forces?
17. What energy do you think must be added to a nucleus to knock out a π meson?
18. Explain how the presence of π mesons in the nucleus could explain the tremendously strong force in the nucleus.

PROBLEMS

1. Calculate the total energy in MeV required to separate a helium-4 nucleus into two deuterium nuclei.
2. How much energy in MeV is required to separate a helium-4 nucleus into two protons and two neutrons?
3. Calculate the total energy in MeV required to separate a lithium-7 nucleus into individual protons and neutrons.
4. How much energy in MeV would be liberated if the proper number of neutrons and protons could be brought together to make a sodium-23 nucleus?

5. By what other name are each of the following known: (a) electron, (b) proton, (c) deuteron, (d) α particle, (e) positron, (f) X-ray, (g) γ ray, and (h) photon?

6. Calculate the mass energy liberated when three neutrons and three protons combine to form lithium-6.

7. Draw a potential-energy curve for a proton approaching a nucleus.

8. Draw a potential-energy curve for a neutron approaching a nucleus.

9. What is the volume of a single nucleon?

10. Show how Eq. (1) results from the assumption that nucleons in a nucleus each have the same volume.

11. The "alpha-particle model" assumes that nucleons in a nucleus are clustered in α-particle groups, as indicated in Fig. D. What sort of experiments would demonstrate the value of this model?

12. (a) List the chemical elements that have a magic number representing their proton shell. (b) Are all these abundant in nature?

13. List four chemical isotopes that are doubly magic.

14. Calculate the β end-point energy for the disintegration of the free neutron.

15. If an α particle is bombarded by 500-MeV protons, how many π mesons can be knocked out?

PROJECT

Make a model to demonstrate how a nucleus might capture a high-speed particle as shown in Fig. G.

NUCLEAR PHYSICS

Lesson 118 *FISSION AND FUSION*

In Italy in 1937 Enrico Fermi, Emilio Segré, and their collaborators subjected uranium to the bombardment of neutrons, hoping that nuclear capture of the particles might produce elements heavier than uranium. At first, the experiments appeared to be successful, for after bombardment, the uranium target was found to give off electrons with a number of different half lives.

Although similar observations were later made by others, an important discovery was made in 1939. After bombarding uranium with neutrons, Otto Hahn and his collaborators in Germany performed a series of chemical separations of the uranium sample to determine the element to which the newly produced radioactivity belonged. To their amazement, they found the radioactive atoms to be identical chemically to a number of different elements, nearly all of which are near the center of the periodic table. In other words, a uranium nucleus, after the capture of a single neutron, seemed to be splitting apart into two nearly equal fragments, as illustrated in Fig. A. In the few weeks that followed this dis-

covery, many observers in different laboratories the world over not only confirmed the results but extended the observations by studying in detail the products of the disintegrations. To understand the phenomenon, consider the details of the process illustrated in Fig. A. An original uranium nucleus, $_{92}U^{235}$, with its 92 protons and 143 neutrons, is shown at the left as it captures a slow-moving neutron.

In diagram (b), the newly formed nucleus is unstable and starts to separate into two nearly equal parts. This separation

process is called *fission*. In coming apart, the uranium nucleus, behaving like the analo-

gous waterdrop, breaks apart into two smaller drops, and occasionally three. These fragments fly apart in opposite directions, with kinetic energies of up to 100 MeV apiece.

Fission Fragments. In general, fission fragments are not stable nuclei, but contain an excess number of neutrons. Typical ensuing events that occur to most fragments, as to those shown in Fig. A(c), are detailed in Fig. B. After quickly ejecting one or two neutrons, a series of β-emissions occurs in

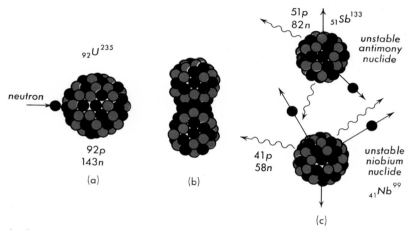

Fig. A. Diagrams of the fission of a uranium nucleus into two unstable nuclides.

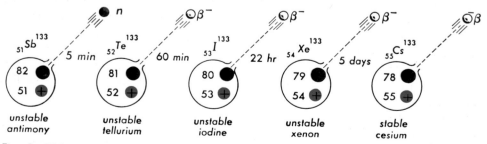

Fig. B. Disintegration series starting with unstable antimony, one of the fragments of the fission of a uranium-235 nucleus.

which neutrons are converted into protons in the nucleus. Finally, a stable nuclide (nucleus of a particular isotope) results.

Starting at the left in Fig. B, with the unstable antimony nuclide of charge +51 and mass 134 emitting a neutron, the successive emissions of four electrons raises the nuclear charge by four unit steps, ending with a stable cesium isotope, $_{55}Cs^{133}$. The other fragment, $_{41}Nb^{99}$, in Fig. A(c), carries out a similar series of β-ray emissions, ending up with $_{44}Ru^{99}$.

As proof that the above series is produced by fission, previously bombarded uranium has been chemically analyzed for elements near the center of the periodic table. After each chemical separation is performed, a test of the β-ray activity is made by a measurement of the half-life. A comparison of this measured half-life with the values already known for the same element from other disintegration experiments has made it possible to identify some of the radioactive nuclei produced. Such tests, for example, have been made for the series of four elements in Fig. B. Note the increasing half-lives identified for this series, indicating increased stability as the stable nucleus cesium is approached.

Approximately 99% of the neutrons ejected as the result of the fission of uranium occur within an extremely short time interval and are called *prompt neutrons*. About one out of a hundred neutrons are emitted one or more seconds later, and these are called *delayed neutrons*. Delayed neutrons originate from fragments that decay by neutron emission following a beta decay.

Transuranium Elements. Just prior to and during World War II, great strides were made in the study of nuclear structure and atomic energy. Not only were

methods developed for separating large quantities of U-235 from natural uranium mixtures, but a number of new elements, among them neptunium (Np) and plutonium (Pu), were produced and identified.

Neptunium (Np), element 93, was first detected and identified by Abelson and McMillan[*] in 1939. A slow neutron captured by $_{92}U^{238}$ forms $_{92}U^{239}$, which is followed by β emission to give $_{93}Np^{239}$. This is but one of several known radioactive isotopes of Np.

Plutonium (Pu), element 94, first identified by Kennedy, McMillan, Seaborg, Segré, and Wahl, arises from the spontaneous β emission of neptunium:

$$_{0}n^{1} + _{92}U^{238} \rightarrow _{92}U^{239} + \gamma \text{ ray} \xrightarrow{23 \text{ min}} _{93}Np^{239} + _{-1}e^{0}$$

$$_{93}Np^{239} \xrightarrow{2.3 \text{ days}} _{94}Pu^{239} + _{-1}e^{0} + \gamma \text{ ray}$$

Schematic diagrams of these processes are shown in Fig. C.

Following these elements, other artificially produced elements up to element 104 have been produced. It is now known that all transuranium nuclei starting with Th-232 and through Cf-244 are fissionable, *i.e.*, under proper excitation conditions they split apart with great violence into a pair of fragments. Some of them, like U-233, U-235, and Pu-239, fission by the capture of a slow neutron; whereas others, like U-238 and Pu-241, fission only by the capture of fast neutrons. Fission has also been induced by high-energy gamma-ray irradiation. In fact, some isotopes, such as Cf-252, are known to fission spontaneously.

The capture of a slow neutron by U-238 is followed by β decay to produce Np-239 and Pu-239, whereas fast neutron capture is followed by fission.

[*] For the discovery of neptunium and plutonium, Edwin M. McMillan and Glenn T. Seaborg were jointly awarded the 1951 Nobel Prize in chemistry.

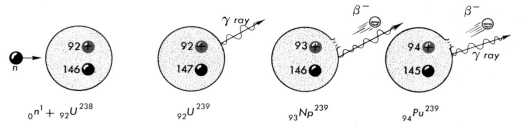

Fig. C. Neutron capture by uranium-238 produces, by radioactive β-decay, neptunium and plutonium.

Binding Energy. The helium nucleus consists of two neutrons and two protons:

neutron mass $_0n^1 = 1.00866$ **amu**
proton mass $_1H^1 = 1.00782$ **amu**

The sum of these components of the helium atom is—

$$2n + 2p = 4.03296 \text{ amu}$$

The helium nucleus has a mass of 4.00260 amu. It can be seen, then, that the helium nucleus has 0.03036 amu less than the mass of the free particles. From Ein-

stein's energy-mass equation it can be calculated that this is equivalent to 28 MeV or 7 MeV per particle. This is a measure of the energy that must be expended in breaking the attractive bonds between the particles in the nucleus. This is called the *binding energy*. If we make similar calculations for all the other nuclei, we obtain a graph of the binding energy per nucleon, as shown in Fig. D.

An examination of the graph shows an increase as one goes from hydrogen to higher mass numbers. There is a maximum

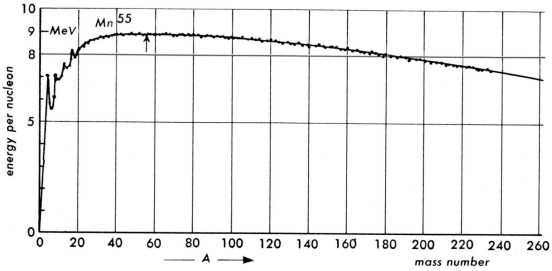

Fig. D. Binding energy per nucleon for the stable isotopes of the periodic table.

around iron, followed by a gradual decrease for higher mass numbers. This indicates that energy can be liberated by forming nuclei toward the middle from lighter or heavier ones. For example, fission of heavy elements liberates energy. However, it is also possible to liberate energy by the fusion of two light nuclei.

The Sun's Energy. Measurements of solar radiation reaching the earth each day make it possible both to calculate the surface temperature of the sun and to determine its total radiation. The fact that the sun, over a period of many years, shows no signs of cooling off, was long an unsolved mystery. With the discovery of nuclear disintegration and the development of methods of producing many new types of atoms, this mystery has, in a measure, been solved.

Although there is no direct way known of observing the interior of a star like our sun, mathematical calculations, based upon well-established physical laws, show that deep within such a mass the temperature is so extremely high that matter must be a high-density conglomeration of atoms, electrons, and light waves all moving about at tremendously high speeds.

Near the center of the sun, where the temperature is about 20 million degrees, the atoms are stripped of their electrons and the light waves produced there are of such high frequencies that they should be classified as γ rays and X-rays. There, where the average particle velocity is so high, nuclear reactions must be taking place on a large scale and the liberated energy must be filtering up through to cooler and cooler layers in the form of light waves of lower and lower frequency. At the surface, most of the escaping radiations are of sufficiently low frequency to be classified as *visible, ultraviolet,* and *infrared.*

In order for nuclei to free and release energy, they must overcome the coulomb repulsion. Calculations show that the thermal motions of atoms at several million degrees are sufficient to overcome the coulomb barrier.

Recent experiments and calculations indicate that the *proton-proton cycle,* Eqs. (1)-(3), is of major importance in the creation of solar and stellar energy:

$$_1H^1 + {}_1H^1 \rightarrow {}_1H^2 + {}_1e^0 + 0.93 \text{ MeV} \qquad (1)$$

$$_1H^1 + {}_1H^2 \rightarrow {}_2He^3 + \gamma \text{ ray} + 5.5 \text{ MeV} \qquad (2)$$

$$_2He^3 + {}_2He^3 \rightarrow {}_2He^4 + 2{}_1H^1 + 12.8 \text{ MeV} \qquad (3)$$

The net result is that four hydrogen atoms have been converted into one helium atom. Note that, since two $_2He^3$ nuclei are involved in the reaction in Eq. (3), two proton-proton reactions of the type in Eq. (1) are required to form one $_2He^4$ nucleus.

In summing up the equations, it is seen that four hydrogen atoms are consumed and that two positrons, two γ rays, and one helium nucleus are created. Hence, hydrogen is burned and helium is liberated. The loss in mass for each such cycle of reactions is, therefore, as follows:

$$4{}_1H^1 = 4.0326 \qquad {}_2He^4 = 4.0039$$
$$2{}_1e^0 = 0.0012$$

Subtracting gives—

$$4.0326 - 4.0039 - 0.0012 = 0.0275 \text{ amu}$$

This is equivalent to about 27 MeV energy.

The rates at which these reactions should take place are consistent with the temperature of 20 million degrees, calculated from other considerations. Moreover, hydrogen and helium are known to be the most abundant elements of which stars are made.

In order for the sun to radiate 3.8×10^{26} joules of energy per second, Einstein's equation, $E = mc^2$, indicates that mass must be annihilated at the rate of 4.2×10^9 Kg/sec (or 4,500,000 tons/sec). While this result tells us that the sun is losing mass at a tremendous rate, the amount is small compared with the sun's total mass of 1.98×10^{30} Kg. To illustrate, in one million years, the sun should lose one ten-millionth of its total mass.

Controlled Fusion. The conviction on the part of many physicists that controlled fusion is possible has led, these past few years, to the expenditure of a great deal of scientific manpower and money.

In principle, one would visualize a jet of fusible material, such as deuterium, being fed from a nozzle into a cavity where, upon fusion, great quantities of energy in the form of heat would be continuously generated and tapped off.

From the very start of all projects working on this problem, it has been realized that, owing to the temperature requirements of millions of degrees, no material walls can be close to the region in which fusion is to be consummated. This has led many to the use of a special discharge called a *plasma,*

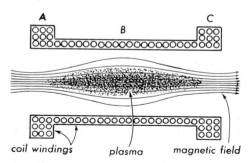

coil windings   plasma   magnetic field

Fig. E. Schematic diagram of a plasma held suspended in a magnetic field—a "magnetic bottle."

held suspended in space by the magnetic lines of force of an electromagnet.

A plasma is an electrically neutral stream or mass of ionized atoms, molecules, and electrons and may be produced in various ways. A high-current arc, such as that used in a searchlight, is a good plasma source. Plasma in many devices is confined by what has been termed a *magnetic bottle.* Visualize, as shown in Fig. E, a stream of ionized atoms injected into the central region of a hollow solenoid. Moving with the high speeds of ions in a hot gas, these particles spiral around in the field with the lines of force acting as guides.

Because a plasma is neither solid, liquid, nor gas, it is often considered to be a *fourth state of matter.*

As particles spiral into the stronger field at either end, the force components drive them back again toward the center. By increasing and decreasing the currents in the field coils A, B, and C, the field shape can be modified at will and the plasma widened or narrowed. By decreasing the field at the right and progressively increasing the field from left to right the plasma can be transported lengthwise from one tube to another.

If all fields are increased, the plasma volume is compressed and the temperature rises. A rising temperature means higher ion velocities and greater probability that impacts will produce fusion. If the field is decreased at one end and increased at the other, the plasma may be quickly moved along the cylinder axis, thus constituting a jet. Plasma jet studies by various aircraft and other research laboratories offer promising results for the near future. While much has been learned from the various controlled-fusion study projects, there is still much to be discovered before successful power sources are realized. There are many who now believe that greater research effort should be placed on studies of the basic principles of the plasma itself and that eventual rewards will be well worth the effort.

QUESTIONS

1. (a) What is fission? (b) Are the two masses always equal?
2. By what reactions is plutonium-239 produced from uranium-238?
3. (a) What is the difference between prompt and delayed neutrons? (b) What is the origin of each?
4. (a) What is spontaneous fission? (b) What isotope is known to be spontaneously fissionable?
5. Can fission of a nickel nucleus release energy? Explain.
6. What is the proton-proton cycle for solar energy?
7. Why is the controlled fusion of hydrogen into helium, as a continuous source of useful power, such a difficult problem?
8. Why are fission reactions so radioactive?
9. (a) Why is the production of Pu-239 important? (b) Is it radioactive?
10. How is it possible to overcome the tremendous coulombic forces necessary for nuclei to fuse?
11. What is the most likely source of the energy of the sun and other stars?

PROBLEMS

1. Make a diagram like Fig. A, showing a Pu-239 nucleus capturing a slow neutron and undergoing fission. Assume that four prompt neutrons are emitted, and that the fragments have initial charges of 139 and 97, one being Rb^{97}.
2. (a) If one of the fission fragments of U-235 is the radioactive isotope xenon-140, what stable isotope will it become if a series of β particles ensues? (b) Make a diagram like Fig. B.
3. (a) If one of the fission fragments of U-235 is the radioactive isotope krypton-97, what stable isotope will it become if a series of β-decays takes place? (b) Make a diagram like Fig. B.
4. If a small quantity of Am-244 is bombarded by deuterons and β particles are emitted, what is the reaction?
5. When Am-243 is bombarded by deuterons from a cyclotron, α particles are emitted. What is the reaction?
6. What are the reactions by which Np and Pu were discovered?
7. When a Pu-239 nucleus captures a thermal neutron, two fragments are produced that immediately emit a total of three neutrons. If one of the resulting nuclei is radioactive Kr-95, what is the other one?

PROJECTS

1. Make a report on how the man-made elements are made and detected.
2. Make models or charts on the several methods used to develop fusion reactions.

NUCLEAR PHYSICS

Lesson 119 *NUCLEAR REACTORS*

The Chain Reaction. Not long after the discovery of fission, it became evident to many scientific groups in America and in Europe that, if a sufficient quantity of pure uranium-235 (U-235) could be isolated from its more abundant isotope uranium-238 (U-238), it might have explosive powers many times greater than anything heretofore known. The reasons for believing this appeared, at the time, to be somewhat as follows. Suppose that a given mass of uranium metal, all composed of U-235 atoms, was brought together into one lump. The first cosmic ray that penetrated this mass and produced a neutron might well set off the chain reaction shown schematically in Fig. A. A U-235 nucleus would capture the neutron and, in splitting apart with great violence, liberate one or more additional neutrons. These in turn would be quickly absorbed by other nearby atoms, which in turn would split up and at the same time liberate other neutrons. Hence, a rapidly growing kind of avalanche might occur, a kind which, if fast enough, would have the characteristics of an explosion. A graph showing the rate of growth of such a chain process is given in Fig. B. Because even the slowest of neutrons in solid matter will have speeds of hundreds of thousands of centimeters per second, and since many neutron collisions will, on the average, oc-

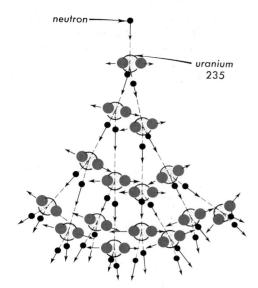

Fig. A. Schematic diagram of a chain reaction in pure uranium-235.

cur within several millimeters, the graph shows how quickly the growth reaches gigantic proportions. (The *time* scale is of the order of microseconds.)

The Critical Mass. The escape of neutrons from any quantity of uranium is a *surface effect* depending on the area of the surface, whereas fission capture occurs throughout the body and is, therefore, a *volume effect*. If the assembled mass of uranium is too small, the probability that most neutrons liberated by fission would escape through the surface before being captured might well be so large that a growing chain

paths of neutrons between two consecutive fission events is shown in Fig. C.

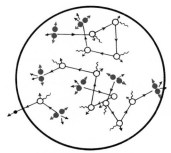

Fig. C. Schematic diagram of inelastic scattering between fission events in U-235 or Pu-239.

Starting out as fast neutrons, the neutrons lose considerable energy with each inelastic impact. As the neutron velocity decreases, the U-235 fission cross section increases and fission capture becomes more and more probable.

Owing to the random directions of the inelastic scattering (see Fig. C) the diffusion distance or *straight-line-distance* between fission events is from 5 to 8 cm.

The critical mass for a nuclear explosive device should lie somewhere between the size of a marble (2 cm diameter) and the size of a basketball (24 cm diameter). Visu-

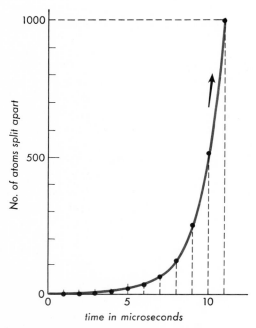

Fig. B. Growth curve of fission in pure uranium-235.

reaction cannot occur. Since the volume of a sphere increases with the cube of the radius, while the surface area increases with the square of the radius, the *probability of escape* would decrease with increasing size. In other words, if the uranium mass were too small, the growth process shown in Figs. A and B would be cut off before it became very large, and only if the mass were greater than some critical value would an explosion take place. A schematic diagram of possible

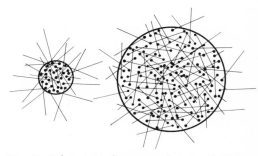

Fig. D. Schematic diagram of pure U-235, or Pu-239, showing escape of most of the neutrons for a subcritical size, and capture of most of the neutrons for a greater-than-critical size.

alized, therefore, this would appear as two spheres of pure U-235 or Pu-239, one large and one small, as shown in Fig. D. It is clear that, if the average straight-line distance between fission events is 6 cm (see Fig. C), few neutrons will be captured in the small sphere, while many will be captured in a mass the size of a basketball.

Whether or not any mass will sustain a chain reaction at all is determined by what is called the *reproduction factor*. The reproduction factor, k, is given by the ratio—

$$k = \frac{\text{rate of neutron production}}{\text{rate of neutron disappearance}} \quad (1)$$

If the rate of neutron production equals the rate at which neutrons disappear, the mass is said to be *critical*, and $k = 1$.

Curves showing the growth in an assembly where k is slightly greater, and slightly smaller, than unity are given in Fig. E. Because one generation of neutrons requires about 1 μsec the horizontal scale can represent time in microseconds.

In five generations, the curve $k = 1.1$ rises to 1.61, because—

$$1.1 \times 1.1 \times 1.1 \times 1.1 \times 1.1$$
$$= \textbf{1.61 neutrons}$$

In ten generations, this same curve rises to $(1.1)^{10}$ or 2.59 neutrons, and in 100 generations, to $(1.1)^{100}$ or 1×10^5 neutrons. In 1000 generations, or approximately $\frac{1}{1000}$ of a second, the number rises to approximately 1×10^{41} neutrons. Since this represents more atoms than would be available in any given assembly, 1000 generations would not materialize.

In pure U-235, or Pu-239 the size of a marble, the reproduction factor is approximately 0.1, while for a sphere the size of a basketball, $k = 2.4$.

Nuclear Reactors. A nuclear reactor, formerly called an atomic pile, is an apparatus in which nuclear fission can be maintained as a self-supporting, yet controlled, chain reaction. It is a kind of furnace in which uranium is the fuel burned, and many useful products, such as heat, neutrons, and radioactive isotopes, are produced.

Reactors are of many kinds, sizes, and shapes, the two principal ingredients of them being a quantity of fissionable material and a moderating substance for slowing down the neutrons to low velocities. A reactor is often designated according to the moderator, or coolant, used within it. Because of the immensity of the subject, only the simplest elements of these devices will be described here.

A self-sustaining chain reaction cannot be maintained in natural uranium alone, no matter how large the mass. By properly combining or surrounding the metal with a moderator, however, the 2-MeV neutrons produced in the fission of the U-235 can be slowed down by elastic scattering until, at a distance of several centimeters from the source, most of them have lost all of their original energy. What little energy they do

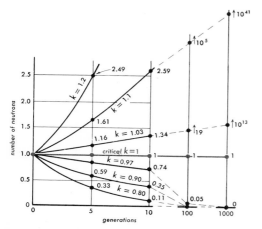

Fig. E. Growth curves for neutrons with reproduction factors barely above and below critical $k = 1$.

have is picked up by regular thermal collisions with other atoms.

Because their resultant motions become quite the same as the random motions of the atoms and molecules of the moderator, they are called thermal neutrons. Thermal neutrons are defined as neutrons in equilibrium with the substance in which they exist. At room temperature, neutrons have an average kinetic energy of 0.025 electron volt. Compared with fast neutrons moving with almost the speed of light, like those from a target of beryllium bombarded by the beam from a cyclotron, thermal neutrons have a velocity of only 2200 m/sec. This is essentially the velocity of hydrogen molecules in a gas at normal temperature and pressure. At these low energies, the probability of absorption to produce another fission is high.

The first self-sustaining chain reaction ever created by man was put into operation at the University of Chicago on December 2, 1942. This device consisted of a huge "pile" of small carbon blocks, carefully laid together to form one solid mass about the size of a normal school room. During construction, lumps of pure uranium metal were inserted at regular intervals throughout the mass.

A schematic diagram of a pile constructed of large carbon blocks is shown in Fig. F. Long cylindrical holes through the blocks provide for the insertion or removal of fuel elements, control rods, detecting devices, samples to be irradiated, etc. The fuel elements consist of pure uranium metal sealed in thin-walled aluminum cylinders.

The distance between uranium fuel elements in the moderator material is of importance in reactor design. The slowing-down distances for three commonly used moderators are as follows:

ordinary water	H_2O	**5.7 cm**
heavy water	D_2O	**11.0 cm**
carbon blocks	C	**19.0 cm**

When, within the uranium metal, a few U-235 nuclei undergo fission, fast neutrons are liberated. Most of these enter the surrounding carbon (the moderator), where they collide elastically with carbon nuclei and slow down. Eventually, many of them enter the uranium metal as thermal neutrons and are captured by U-235 nuclei to cause fission. A diagram showing this process is given in Fig. G.

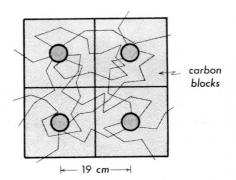

Fig. F. Uranium pile of carbon blocks used to produce Pu-239 and many other radioactive atomic nuclei. (Concrete protective walls are not shown.)

Fig. G. Diagram showing moderator action in a nuclear reactor. Elastic collisions of neutrons with carbon nuclei slow the neutrons to thermal energies.

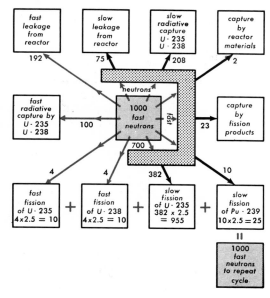

fast leakage from reactor	slow leakage from reactor	slow radiative capture U - 235 U - 238	capture by reactor materials
192	75	208	2

neutrons

fast radiative capture by U - 235 U - 238		1000 fast neutrons		capture by fission products
	100	700	23	

4	4	382	10

fast fission of U - 235 4 x 2.5 = 10	+	fast fission of U - 238 4 x 2.5 = 10	+	slow fission of U - 235 382 x 2.5 = 955	+	slow fission of Pu - 239 10 x 2.5 = 25

=

1000 fast neutrons to repeat cycle

Fig. H. A block diagram showing the balance of neutrons in a natural uranium reactor that is just critical. (Calculated numbers by courtesy of Westinghouse Electric Corp.)

Not all neutrons produced within a reactor are captured by U-235. Some escape through the surface, some are captured by U-238, as well as U-235, and some are lost to structural materials and fission products.

The neutron balance in a natural uranium reactor, operating at the critical rate $k = 1$, is shown in Fig. H. Of the millions of fast neutrons produced in the reactor in each microsecond, the diagram starts with 1000 fast neutrons at the center and shows what might reasonably happen to them in regenerating 1000 more fast neutrons. The average number of neutrons produced per fission is 2.5. This factor is directly involved in the bottom four unshaded squares, where it is used in accounting for reproduction. It should be noted that 60% of the neutrons disappear by other than fission processes.

If the reproduction factor, k, of the reactor assembly is greater than unity, see Eq. (1), the total number of neutrons will rise and, along with it, the temperature. To prevent the temperature from rising too high, control rods, which are made of such strong neutron absorbers as cadmium or boron, are lowered into the central core.

Power Reactors, or Nuclear Power Plants. The idea that the natural heat developed in a uranium or plutonium pile might be utilized as a source of great power has long been recognized as a feasible enterprise. The basic principles of one type of *power reactor* are shown in Fig. I. A quantity of enriched uranium or plutonium, in the form of a pure metal or of a solution of its soluble salt in water, forms the center of the heat-energy source.

The energy released by fission produces great quantities of heat, and the rising temperature is regulated to a predetermined value by control rods. To reduce the fission rate and thereby lower the temperature, the central rods are pushed in a little farther to absorb more neutrons until the power level has decreased to the desired level, after which the rods are returned to the equilibrium position. To raise the temperature, they are temporarily pulled out a little farther.

Because of the harmful effects of the intense neutron radiation to men and equipment, it is convenient to circulate a fluid through the shielded reactor and heat exchanger, as shown in the diagram.

The hot liquid, flowing through the heat exchanger, vaporizes a more volatile liquid, such as water, and the resulting pressure of hot gas or steam drives a turbine of special design. The turbine, in turn, drives an electric generator, developing power that can be used to light cities and factories, or to drive ships and submarines through the water and large planes through the air.

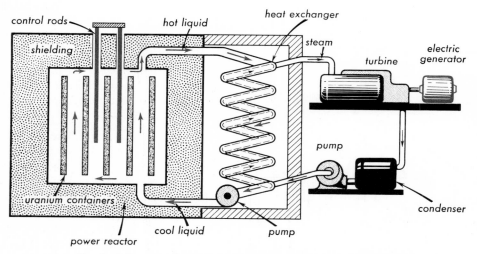

Fig. I. Schematic diagram of a proposed nuclear power plant.

One of the problems connected with such power reactors is the effect of the intense neutron radiation on the metal structures. The neutrons change some atoms and permanently displace others from their normal positions in the crystal lattice of the solids, and as a result weaken certain crucial mechanical parts. Intensive studies of the properties of various materials under conditions likely to be encountered in power reactors are continually carried on in research laboratories.

Another important problem concerns the nature of the coolant. It must be able to withstand high temperatures, not absorb neutrons and become radioactive to any appreciable extent, and yet it must be efficient in the transfer of heat in both the reactor and the heat exchanger.

"Swimming-Pool" Reactor. The swimming-pool type of reactor derives its name from the fact that a large tank of ordinary or, sometimes, heavy water serves as a protective shield for the operating personnel as well as a coolant and moderator. Fig. J is a

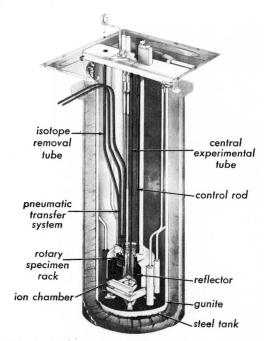

Fig. J. Cross-section diagram of a "swimming pool" type of reactor, showing fuel elements, carbon moderator, with access channels and equipment at the bottom. (Courtesy, General Atomics.)

cut-away diagram of a typical reactor of this kind, and one that is designed as a multipurpose instrument. The several fuel elements at the bottom of the tank are in in the region of the core and an observer can readily see the blue glow of the water around it, which is caused by the Cerenkov radiation from the beta rays.

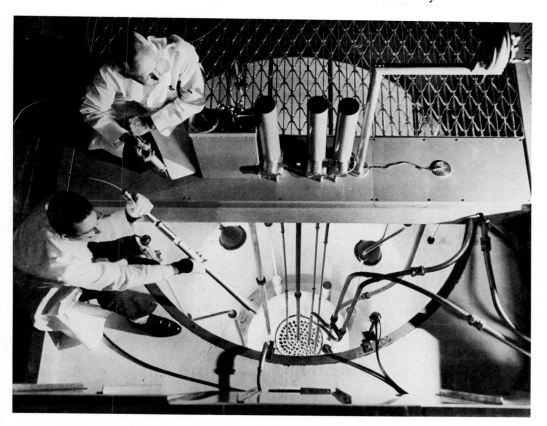

Fig. K. Photograph looking down through the water to the principal elements at the bottom of a "swimming pool" type of reactor. (Courtesy, General Atomics.)

the form of small cylindrical rods, each composed of a solid homogeneous alloy of uranium and zirconium hydride moderator, clad in aluminum cylinders. The uranium is enriched to 20% of U-235. The three control rods are of boron carbide.

Full physical and visual access to the core is possible at all times from the top, as shown in Fig. K. Samples to be irradiated by neutrons can be lowered into the water

A rotary specimen rack ("lazy susan"), located just above the large carbon or graphite moderator block, provides a water-tight facility for radioactive isotope production. A pneumatic tube running to the bottom of the tank permits a sample element, in a small container called a *rabbit*, to be subjected to neutrons and quickly removed for the measurement of very short half lives.

QUESTIONS

1. (a) What is a chain reaction? (b) What are the conditions required for a chain reaction to be explosive?
2. Why is it possible for a chain reaction to occur in a large enough lump of U-235?
3. What is meant by the term critical mass?
4. (a) What is a nuclear reactor? (b) What is the fuel? (c) What is a moderator?
5. (a) What controls can be applied to a reactor? (b) How are operators protected from the intense neutrons in a pile? (c) Give three uses for the material surrounding the fissionable fuel in a reactor.
6. Why is a heat exchanger used in a power reactor, rather than just applying the coolant directly to drive the turbine?
7. What is a thermal neutron?
8. What properties are required of a good moderator?
9. Why must the reproduction factor for a reactor be exactly 1?
10. Why is a moderator necessary to sustain a chain reaction in natural uranium?
11. How is a nuclear reactor prevented from getting too hot and possibly exploding?
12. What properties must the coolant have to be useful in a power reactor?

PROBLEMS

1. Because the critical size for a uranium-235 explosion lies between that of a basketball and a marble, find (a) the ratio of these sphere diameters, (b) the ratio of their surface areas, (c) the ratio of their volumes, and (d) the ratio of volume to surface area.
2. For $k = 1.1$, how many neutrons are produced (a) in 20 generations? (b) in 60 generations?
3. For $k = 1.05$ how many neutrons are produced (a) in 3 generations? (b) in 9 generations? (c) in 27 generations?

PROJECT

Make a report on recent progress in the use of power reactors for the generation of electricity in the United States.

NUCLEAR PHYSICS

Lesson 120 COSMIC RAYS

Early Experiments. It has long been known that a charged electroscope, if left standing for some little time, will discharge regardless of how well the gold leaf is insulated. Realizing that the rays from radioactive materials can be stopped by a sufficient thickness of heavy matter, Rutherford and Cooke (in Canada, 1903) surrounded an electroscope with a thick wall of brick and found very little decrease in the rate of discharge. McLennan and his coworkers (also in Canada) lowered an electroscope into a lake, hoping that the thick layer of water would screen off the rays. This experiment, like the other, failed.

In 1910 Glockel, with an electroscope, rose nearly 3 mi in a balloon in order to get away from the ground radiation, but to his astonishment he found that the rate of discharge did not decrease, but increased, the higher he went. The same effect was observed by Victor F. Hess (in Austria, 1911) and Kolhörster (in Germany, 1914). Rising to heights as great as $5\frac{1}{2}$ mi, both of these observers independently found that the intensity of these unknown radiations became greater the higher they went.

Because in one of his scientific publications concerning these results, Hess suggested the possibility that some kind of penetrating rays were entering the earth's atmosphere from outer space, he is usually credited with the discovery of cosmic rays. For this reason he was granted the Nobel Prize in physics for the year 1936.

Millikan and Bowen's Discovery. Soon after World War I (1922), R. A. Millikan,

with the help of I. S. Bowen, constructed several small, self-recording string electroscopes. Making use of their wartime experiences with sounding balloons, they sent these electroscopes high into the stratosphere by fastening each one to two sounding balloons.

On one of the best record flights, only one of the balloons burst at a height of 10 mi and the other brought the instruments safely to earth. Like the earlier results obtained by other experimenters, Millikan and Bowen found the ionization to increase with increasing altitude. After extending the observations of previous workers to higher altitudes, Millikan and Bowen became convinced and announced their belief that the rays were coming from interstellar space.

The Penetration of Cosmic Rays. In order to determine the nature of the new rays, Millikan and his co-workers, Otis, Cameron, and Bowen, in the fall of 1922, began an extensive study of the penetrating power of cosmic rays. Because cosmic rays penetrate our atmosphere of many miles of air, how far might they penetrate into the earth?

Self-recording electroscopes were lowered to various depths in snow-fed lakes, as illustrated schematically in Fig. A. Measurements taken at Lake Arrowhead in Southern California (at an elevation of 5100 ft) agreed approximately with those taken at Muir Lake near Mt. Whitney (at an elevation of 11,800 ft), provided one took into account the increased air path for the lower elevation. The extra mile and a quarter of air is equivalent in weight to 6 ft of water.

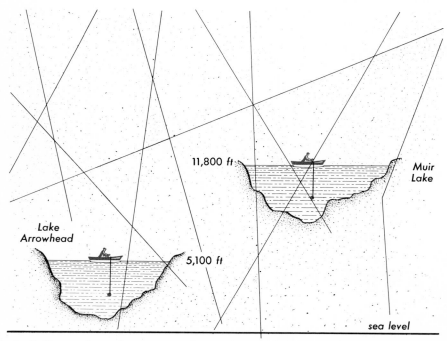

11,800 ft

Muir Lake

Lake Arrowhead

5,100 ft

sea level

Fig. A. Self-recording electroscopes lowered into deep, snow-fed lakes are used to measure the absorption of cosmic rays.

As cosmic rays penetrate deeper and deeper below the surface of water, their number decreases until, at a depth of 100 ft, the intensity is reduced to about one ten-thousandth of that at the surface. With very sensitive electroscopes, cosmic radiation capable of penetrating 2000 ft of water has more recently been detected. This is a far greater penetrating power than that possessed by any known X-rays or γ rays from radioactivity.

Directional Effects. To observe the direction of the greatest cosmic-ray intensity, a *cosmic-ray telescope* is used. Such a telescope is made by connecting two or more Geiger-Mueller tubes *in coincidence,* and mounting them on a common support some distance apart. Tubes in coincidence are so connected electrically that a current will

flow in the accompanying electric circuit only when both tubes discharge at the same time. When the tubes are set one above the other, as shown in Fig. B(*a*), a single cosmic ray on going through both cylinders

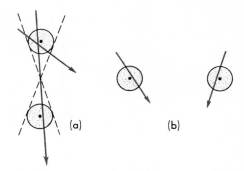

(a)   (b)

Fig. B. Diagram of two Geiger counters. Connected in coincidence, they form a cosmic-ray telescope.

will cause a current to flow and a count to be made. If, however, a particle goes through one and not the other, no count is recorded. Experiments at sea level show that when the telescope is mounted in the horizontal position (*b*), few counts are made; whereas when it is mounted in a vertical direction, many more counts are re-

corded. The interpretation to be made, therefore, is that cosmic rays come principally from overhead.

As a verification of the telescope method, a Wilson cloud chamber is frequently inserted between two Geiger-Mueller tubes, as shown in Fig. C, and a photograph of each cosmic ray passing through both counters is taken. Thousands of such photographs are made automatically by having a single cosmic ray take its own picture. This is accomplished by allowing the sudden electric current from the counter tubes, produced by a ray in transit, to open and close a camera shutter, to cause the cloud chamber to expand, and to flash a light, illuminating the fog track that forms.

In Fig. C, either one of the two cosmic rays would have tripped the electrical devices and taken the picture. It should be noted that both rays passed right through a 0.5-in. lead plate without being deviated. Cloud-chamber pictures are not photographs of cosmic rays but of the path traversed by the rays.

Effect of the Earth's Magnetic Field. In 1931, the Dutch physicist Clay, sailing from Amsterdam in the Northern Hemisphere to Batavia, Dutch Guiana, in the Southern Hemisphere, carried Geiger counters with him aboard ship. Measuring the cosmic-ray intensity daily en route, he observed that the counting rate decreased as he approached the equator, and increased again as he reached higher latitudes.

The decrease in cosmic-ray intensity at the earth's magnetic equator is now explained as owing to the earth's magnetic field. This is illustrated in Fig. D. The paths of all charged particles crossing the earth's magnetic field are bent by a force that is perpendicular to the direction of the field.

Because of these forces, many charged particles from the sun and outer space are

Fig. C. Wilson cloud-chamber photograph of two cosmic-ray tracks. Mounted between two Geiger-Mueller tubes connected in coincidence, the cosmic rays are made to take their own picture. (After Brode.)

trapped by the field in two belts. The recent discovery of these belts by James Van Allen and his colleagues at Iowa State University was made from instruments carried into space by American earth-circling satellites. These belts surround the earth, except at the regions of the magnetic poles, the outer one being caused largely by the slower par-

into space as *c* and *d*. At still lower energies they may follow paths like *e*, *f*, and *g*.

Particle *e* spirals around the field lines of the belts and follows them in toward the earth. As the field gets stronger, a point is reached where the particle turns back and, spiraling around the field lines, approaches the earth again on the other side. Such par-

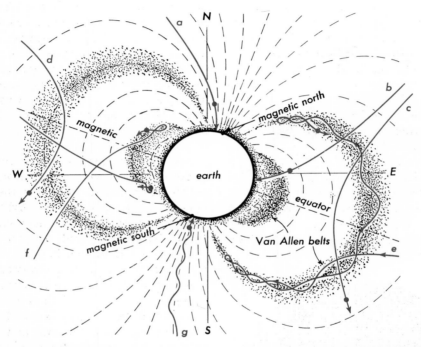

Fig. D. The behavior of primary cosmic rays in the earth's magnetic field. The shaded arches are the Van Allen belts.

ticles, protons and electrons, from the sun. The inner Van Allen belt is formed by more energetic particles from outer space and is centered about 2500 mi above the magnetic equator.

If the primary cosmic-ray energy is very large, little deflection will occur, and particles like *a* and *b* will reach the atmosphere and, perhaps, the ground. At somewhat lower energies, they will be deflected back

ticles running back and forth are trapped; they account for the large number of ionized particles that form the Van Allen belts.

Slow particles, such as *g*, entering the earth's field parallel to the lines of force from far away, will be guided by the field and reach the earth's surface. A day or two after an active display of solar flares, so many particles become trapped in the outer Van Allen belt that they spill out into the earth's atmosphere, creating auroras. Because particles with only the highest of energies can get down to the earth's atmosphere near the magnetic equator, the cosmic-ray latitude effect is well understood.

Discovery of the Positron. The positron, or positive electron, was discovered by Anderson in 1932 by photographing the tracks of cosmic rays in a Wilson cloud chamber. Under the influence of a strong magnetic field, applied perpendicularly to the face of the cloud chamber, positively charged particles should bend to the right and negatively charged particles should bend to the left.

In order to be certain that those bent one way were not all coming from above and those bent the other way were particles of the same kind and charge coming from below, Anderson inserted a block of lead in the chamber to slow down the particles. Under these conditions, photographs similar to the one shown in Fig. E were obtained. Here, Anderson could be quite certain, from the curvature of the track on each side of the lead, that the particle entered from the side shown above, for in passing through the lead plate, it could only have been slowed down and not speeded up.

Knowing the direction of motion, the direction of the field, and the direction of bending, Anderson concluded that such a particle had a positive charge. Comparing the track with well-known electron tracks and α particle tracks, he concluded that the new particle had about the same mass as the electron. Later experiments continued to give more positive proof of the existence of a positive electron. Now, very strong beams of positrons can be produced in the laboratory.

Creation of Electron Pairs. Soon after Anderson's discovery of the positron, several people attempted to calculate the conditions under which a positron might exist in nature. An extension of the quantum theory of the electron, proposed earlier by Paul A. M. Dirac in Britain, led him to the prediction that if a high-energy photon, *i.e.*, a high-frequency γ ray, were to come close enough to the nucleus of an atom, the electric field of the nucleus would be strong enough to annihilate the γ ray and create in its place a *pair of particles, an electron and a positron*. These two particles, the theory predicts, should have the same mass and equal but opposite charges. A schematic diagram of pair production is given in Fig. F, and a photograph of such pair production is given in Fig. G.

When an electron pair is created, *conservation of energy and momentum* requires the two particles to move almost straight forward. Without a magnetic field applied to the cloud chamber, the particles travel side by side in almost parallel paths. But

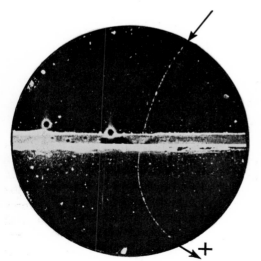

Fig. E. Wilson cloud-chamber photograph of a positron. (After Anderson.)

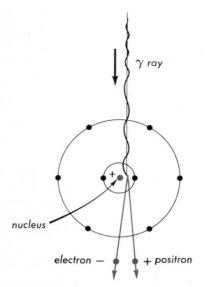

γ ray

nucleus

electron —   + positron

Fig. F. Schematic diagram of pair production.

they do not exist long in the free state. As soon as a positron meets with an electron, the two are annihilated. In their place two γ rays of half the original energy are created, each with an energy corresponding to the rest mass of an electron.

Cosmic-Ray Showers. Out of hundreds and hundreds of cloud-chamber photo-

with a magnetic field, the path of the positron bends to one side and that of the electron to the other.

The reason positrons were not discovered earlier in the history of physics is that

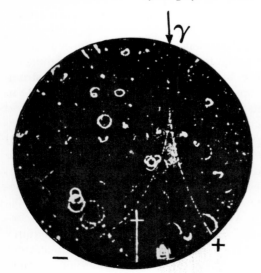

Fig. G. A γ-ray, entering the cloud chamber from above, creates a pair of particles, one +, the other —. (After Lauritson and Fowler.)

Fig. H. Cloud-chamber photographs of cosmic ray showers. (Courtesy of R. B. Brode, and C. D. Anderson and the Physical Review.)

graphs of cosmic rays, the experimenter is occasionally rewarded with a picture of a cosmic-ray shower. Instead of one or two tracks in the picture in this instance, one finds anywhere from half a dozen or more to several hundred. As shown by the photographs in Fig. H, most of the tracks of a shower seem to come from one localized region, usually within a solid piece of matter like a lead plate or the wall of the cloud chamber. In photograph (a), a small shower of very high-energy particles enters the chamber from above, having been produced far above the cloud chamber in a shower-producing process, probably by a single particle of extremely high energy. As some of these secondaries pass through the lead, each produces a shower of its own.

Fig. I. Cloud-chamber photograph showing cascade shower of cosmic rays developed in 13 lead plates, each 1.3 cm thick.

Direct evidence that some showers originate with a single high-energy particle is shown in Fig. I. Here, in a cloud chamber with equally spaced lead plates, a relatively large shower is seen to have grown from one or possibly two particles at the top. Not only does this avalanche grow in numbers with each traversal of a lead plate, but the relatively small spread of the tracks indicates how nearly each new particle recoils along with the others in the forward direction. Because of the lead plates, one observes in the small space of several inches the process that, in air, requires several miles.

Primaries and Secondaries. Experimental observations show that the cosmic rays entering our atmosphere are almost entirely composed of positively charged atomic nuclei. About two-thirds of these so-called *primary cosmic rays* are protons and the other third (by mass) are about 90% α particles and 10% heavier nuclei such as carbon, nitrogen, oxygen, and iron.

Upon entering the atmosphere, a high-energy primary particle soon collides with another atomic nucleus, splitting one or both particles into a number of smaller nuclear fragments, each one of which carries away some of the primary's energy. These high-speed particles, in turn, collide with other nuclei, further dividing their energy to produce other high-speed particles. All of these, with the exception of the primary particle, are called *secondary cosmic rays*. See Fig. J.

The presence in cosmic rays of charged particles having a mass several hundred times that of an electron, yet considerably lighter than a proton, was discovered by Anderson and Nedermeyer in 1938. These particles are of several kinds and experimental data, taken in balloons and airplanes, show that most of them are produced high in the atmosphere by the collisions of primary cosmic rays with air nuclei.

In these collisions, positively and negatively charged π mesons are produced,

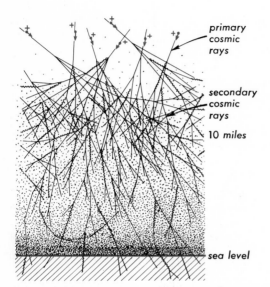

Fig. J. Schematic illustration of secondary cosmic rays produced from primaries entering the earth's atmosphere.

along with neutral π mesons, protons, and neutrons, as shown in Fig. K. The π mesons, each with a mass of about 139 MeV, along with other nucleons, recoil forward with speeds close to that of light. The term nucleons is here applied to only protons and neutrons.

All charged π mesons have a half-life of 2×10^{-8} sec and each one decays into a charged μ particle, called a *muon*, and a neutrino. The charged muon in turn decays, with a half-life of 2×10^{-6} sec, into an electron and two neutrinos, as shown in Figs. L and M.

The uncharged π^0 mesons are very unstable. With a half-life of less than 10^{-15}

sec, they decay into two γ rays. In the upper atmosphere, these γ rays create cascade

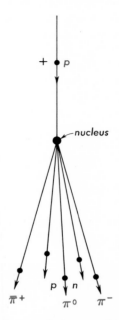

Fig. K. Primary cosmic ray produces π mesons by nuclear collision.

showers of electrons and gammas by electron pair-production and bremsstrahlung. See Fig. I. Many of the charged muons,

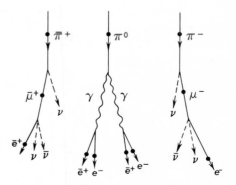

Fig. L. π mesons disintegrate into muons, γ-rays, electrons, and neutrinos.

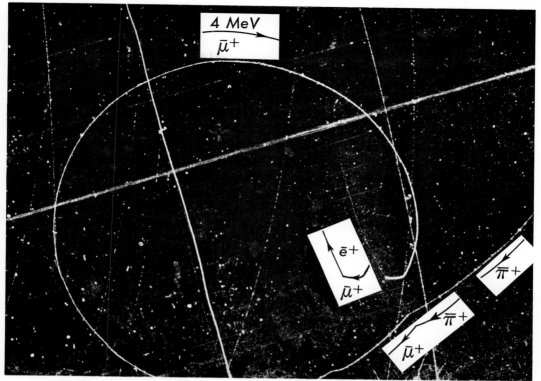

Fig. M. Wilson cloud chamber photographed in a magnetic field of 0.8 newton/amp-m showing decay of a π meson into a muon and of the muon into a positron.

with their mass of about 106 MeV, traverse the atmosphere before decaying and reach the surface of the earth. At sea level, the charged cosmic rays are about 70% muons and 29% electrons and positrons, with about 1% heavier particles, such as protons, deuterons, and α particles.

Recent cosmic-ray observations at high altitudes and at sea level show the following:

Table 1. Composition of Primary and Secondary Cosmic Rays

Primaries		Sea Level	
H	89%	Muons	70%
He	9%	e^+ and e^-	29%
Li, Be, B	0.5%	Heavier particles	1%
C, N, O	0.5%		
Ne, Mg, Si	0.1%		
Fe	0.03%		

QUESTIONS

1. (a) Who discovered cosmic rays? (b) How does the cosmic ray intensify as one goes up into the air above the earth's surface?

2. (a) What kinds of detectors were used in the early cosmic-ray experiments? (b) Name six other detection and measuring devices.
3. How are cosmic rays made to take their own photographs?
4. (a) What are primary cosmic rays? (b) Of what are they composed?
5. (a) What are secondary cosmic rays? (b) Where do they come from? (c) Of what are they composed?
6. (a) What are positrons? (b) Who discovered them? (c) In what ways are positrons and electrons alike?
7. How are positrons produced?
8. What is a cosmic-ray shower?
9. What are mesons?
10. (a) What is a cosmic-ray telescope? (b) How is it made? (c) How does it operate? (d) What is its purpose?
11. How are auroras produced?
12. The small amount of cosmic radiation detected in deep mines consists of muons. Describe how these are produced.
13. A cosmic-ray shower consists mostly of electrons that produce gammas, which produce more electrons, etc. (a) What processes are involved in this shower? (b) When does it all stop?

PROBLEMS

1. Assuming that all the energy of a γ ray could be used in creating a pair of electrons (a positron and an electron), what must be its frequency?
2. What is the minimum energy, in electron volts, that a γ ray must have to produce an electron pair?
3. When a positron combines with an electron and the two are annihilated, what is the frequency of the two γ rays produced?
4. A *K meson* has a rest mass of about 495 MeV and usually decays into π mesons. What is the maximum number of π mesons it could produce?
5. (a) If a π^+ meson decays at rest, what is the total kinetic energy of the products? (b) If a π^0 decays at rest, what is the total kinetic energy of the products?
6. If a π^- meson has a kinetic energy of 850 MeV and decays, what is the kinetic energy of the products?

PROJECTS

1. Make a cosmic-ray telescope. As described in the text, you will need two Geiger tubes and a coincidence circuit.
2. Make a cloud chamber and take pictures of a cosmic-ray event.

NUCLEAR PHYSICS

Lesson 121 *ELEMENTARY PARTICLES*

For many decades, physicists have searched for the ultimate particles of which all matter is composed. From the atom and its electron structure, the search has extended into the nucleus, and from the nucleus to the structure of nucleons themselves.

The purpose behind the planning and building of atomic accelerators that will produce higher and higher energies, reaching into the BeV and hundreds of BeV ranges, has been, and continues to be, the hitting of nuclei harder and harder. When a nucleon is hit by a very high-energy particle, a variety of particles is frequently produced.

The questions concerning the origin and nature of these particles present challenging problems to experimentalist and theorist alike. Do these particles exist in some strange form within the nucleus, or are they created from the release of mass and impact energy? If they are created, what is the mechanism involved? How long do they last, and what becomes of their energy?

In this last chapter we will take a brief look at some recent discoveries and observations in *"high-energy physics,"* in the hopes that such glimpses may instill some interest and give you, the reader, some clue as to what new experiments might be performed that would shed new light on these *"elementary particles."*

Elementary Particles. With the discovery of the neutron by Sir James Chadwick in 1932, the number of elementary particles became four in number: the *electron*, the *proton*, the *neutron,* and the *photon*. The first three are the atomic particles of which atoms are built, while the photon is the quantum unit of radiation emitted or absorbed by the electrons in the outer structure of atoms or by the particles within the nucleus.

The photon can only exist when traveling with the speed of light and, because of its motion, possesses energy $h\nu$. By the mass-energy relation, $E = mc^2$, a photon also has mass $h\nu/c^2$. It possesses mass by virtue of its motion, for at rest it would have no energy and no mass.

The electron, proton, and neutron, on the other hand, have a definite rest mass m_0 and a rest energy m_0c^2. When they are set into motion, their mass increases and their total energy is given by mc^2.

Antiparticles. The positron, discovered by Anderson in 1932, is a positively charged electron. We have seen in the previous lesson how electron pairs can be created and how a free positron, in coming together with an electron, is annihilated and becomes two γ rays. It is this very property that gives the positron the name antiparticle—it destroys itself along with an electron and becomes another form of energy.

We have also seen, in Fig. G in Lesson 120, that, when a high-energy photon comes close to the nucleus, mesons may be produced. If a pair of mesons is produced, one positive and one negative, one is the antiparticle of the other. These π mesons may react with other nuclei or they may decay into muons, as shown in Fig. M in Lesson

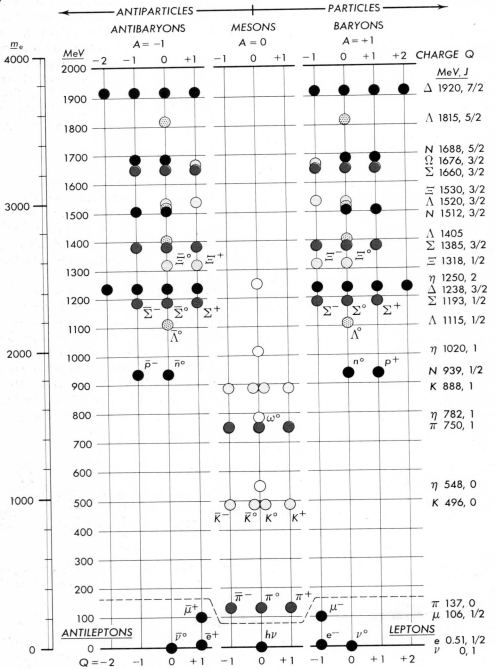

Fig. A. Energy-level diagram of strongly interacting and elementary particles as compiled by Geoffrey F. Chew, Murray Gell-Mann, and Arthur H. Rosenfeld. (Scientific American, February 1964.)

120. The muons in turn may decay into electrons and positrons, or they may be captured by some other nucleus.

The discovery of the positron; the three pi mesons π^+, π^0, and π^-; the two muons and μ^-; along with the two neutrinos ν^0 and $\bar{\nu}^0$, raised the number of elementary particles to twelve. by 1950

Particle Classification. The energy-level diagram in Fig. A represents an orderly array of eighty-nine *elementary particles.* Some of these particles were predicted before they were identified in laboratory experiments.

The vertical column of symbols and numbers on the right gives the *particle designations* suggested for general adoption by Geoffrey F. Chew, Murray Gell-Mann, and Arthur H. Rosenfeld, along with the *restmass energy* in millions of electron volts, MeV. The numbers in the third row across the top give the *atomic mass*, A, and the numbers in the fourth row give the *particle charge*, Q, in units of the electronic charge, e. All mesons (center) and leptons (bottom) have mass number $A = 0$.

The scale on the left gives the rest mass in MeV. The specifically labeled dots, with the exception of ω^0, represent the thirty so-called elementary particles identified prior to 1957. Note that the left half of the table is a mirror image of the right half, except that the signs are reversed. The term *baryon* applies to all elementary particles having a mass equal to or greater than a nucleon. Most of the unlabeled particles are equivalent to corresponding labeled particles, but with heavier masses owing to additional internal energy.

The photon $h\nu$, the π^0 mesons, and the η^0 mesons are placed on the center line because they differ from all the rest in one respect: each of these particles acts as its own antiparticle.

The very interesting idea put forward that some distant galaxies in the heavens might be made up of antimatter might well be true. In such a galaxy, all hydrogen atoms would be made of antiprotons and positrons, and the protons and electrons would be their antiparticles. Thus Fig. A *carries a double meaning*, and *either half represents the antiparticles for the other half.*

Photographic Emulsions. When a photon or ionizing particle traverses the sensitive emulsion of a photographic film, the clear silver bromide crystal grains that are penetrated are turned into black silver upon development by regular film-developing processes.

Because the sensitive emulsion on most film is extremely thin, satisfactory emulsions up to 1 mm in thickness, containing about 80% silver bromide, were first developed by C. F. Powell in England. These can be stacked in layers to build up larger volumes, exposed to high-energy nuclear beams, or cosmic rays, and then developed. See Fig. B. By studying consecutively num-

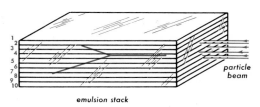

emulsion stack

Fig. B. Numbered stack of extra-thick photographic emulsions used in photographing high-energy nuclear events.

bered films separately, under a suitable measuring microscope, one can observe nuclear collision events and make measurements of the different particles, their direc-

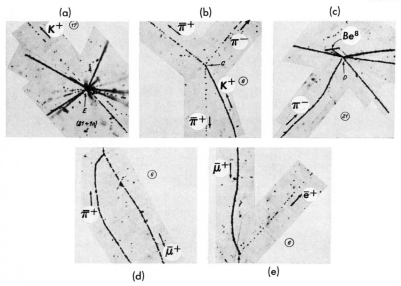

Fig. C. Five directly related events traced through a photographic emulsion stack.

tions, ranges, track densities, and other characteristics.

Track densities vary widely with particle *charge* and *velocity*, as seen in Fig. C and D. The energies required of various particles to travel 1 mm in an average nuclear emulsion are

e	0.7 MeV	p	14.0 MeV
μ	5.5 MeV	d	20.0 MeV
π	6.1 MeV	α	55.0 MeV

Because emulsion densities are far greater than that of the gas in a cloud chamber, the track ranges are extremely small. This high-density and short-range feature is particularly useful, therefore, to the study

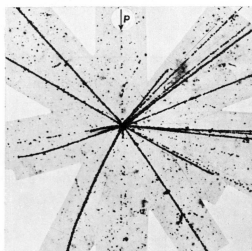

Fig. D. Photographic emulsion star produced by a cosmic-ray proton.

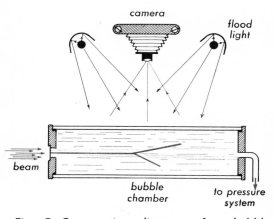

Fig. E. Cross-section diagram of a bubble chamber showing track illumination, camera, and incident particle beam.

of nuclear events involving very high-speed particles.

The procedure used for displaying emulsion tracks is to make enlargements of microscope photographs of neighboring sections and to piece the photographic prints together, as shown in Fig. C. These print assemblies were made from a stack of 46 emulsions. 15 cm × 15 cm, exposed at high altitude over England in 1952.

The first assembly (*a*) shows a "star" of tracks in emulsion 17, one track being that of a K^+ meson as indicated. Six cm along this track in the emulsion (this corresponds to 60 ft on the enlarged scale shown here), we come to assembly (*b*) from emulsion 6. There the K^+ meson disintegrated into π mesons. Two cm along the π^- track, in assembly (*c*), the meson was captured by a

heavy nucleus, resulting in a nuclear explosion. Among the secondary products were four singly charged particles and a $_3\text{Li}^8$ nucleus. The latter, on reaching the end of its range, emitted a β particle forming $_4\text{Be}^8$, which spontaneously splits up into two α particles to produce the "hammer track" shown.

About 3 cm along the π^+ track, in assembly (*d*), the meson decays into a μ^+ and a neutrino. A short distance along this track, in assembly (*e*), the μ^+ decays into a positron, e^+, a neutrino, ν, and an antineutrino, $\bar{\nu}$.

The nuclear-emulsion photograph in Fig. D shows a "star" of 22 tracks. A primary cosmic ray, a proton, enters from the top, and collides with a silver or bromine nucleus in the emulsion, causing an explo-

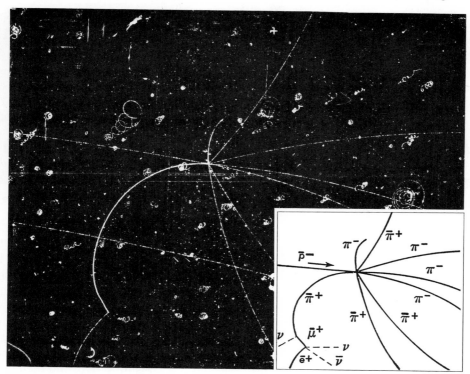

Fig. F. π-meson star produced by the proton capture of an antiproton in a liquid-hydrogen bubble chamber.

sion. Most of the tracks were made by π mesons, and the others, probably by K mesons and protons.

While the number of stars of this general nature is small relative to other kinds of nuclear events observed in emulsions, a great many have been observed and studied.

liquid, form local heat centers in which tiny gas bubbles develop and grow.

The basic principles of the bubble chamber involve the superheating of a liquid and the bubbles that form in the process of boiling. Water, for example, boils at 100°C at standard atmospheric pressure. If the pressure is increased, as in a pressure cooker,

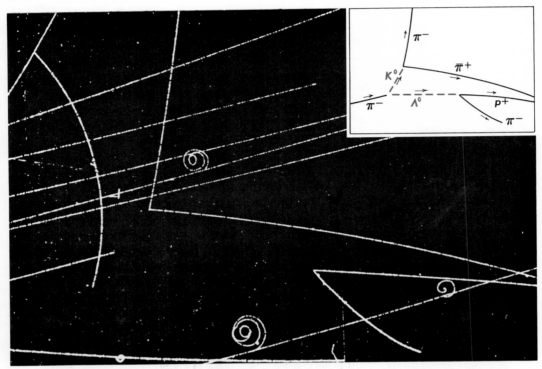

Fig. G. Bubble-chamber photograph with π^-, p, K°, Λ°, π^+, and π^- tracks, all in one related event. Legend diagram at upper right.

The Bubble Chamber. The bubble chamber, invented in 1952 by D. H. Glaser, has become one of the most valuable instruments for studying the minute details of high-energy nuclear events. In a cloud chamber, fog drops form on the ions produced by charged atomic particles that have just previously traversed the gas-filled chamber. In the bubble chamber, the ions, formed by charged particles traversing the

boiling will not begin until a higher temperature is reached. If the pressure is then suddenly reduced, boiling begins with the sudden formation of tiny bubbles that grow quickly in size.

A simplified diagram of a bubble chamber is shown in Fig. E. A box with thick glass walls, filled with a liquid, is connected to a pressure system and then heated to some predetermined temperature. High-energy particles enter the liquid through a thin window. A sudden release of a valve in the pressure system is quickly followed by the flash of floodlights and the snap of a camera shutter. If the chamber is operating strange particle events. The difficulties of handling liquid hydrogen at $-253°C$ in large bubble chambers have been overcome by L. Alvarez and his colleagues at the University of California over a period of several

Fig. H. Cutaway model of the 72-in. liquid-hydrogen bubble chamber at the Lawrence Radiation Laboratory.

properly and events are correctly timed, sharply defined trails of bubbles that have formed on the paths of ions made by the traversing particles will be photographed. See Figs. F and G.

The extensive use of liquid hydrogen in bubble chambers has been particularly effective in the study of elementary and years. Liquid hydrogen is particularly useful in that it provides a high concentration of "target protons," the simplest of atomic nuclei and, at the same time, greatly shortens the distance between events that would be required in the gas-filled space of a cloud chamber. See Figs. H and I. It is customary to locate a bubble chamber in the strong field of a large electromagnet so that particle charge and momentum relations can be obtained from track curvature. (See Figs. F and G.)

Antiprotons. The existence of antiprotons was discovered in 1955 by Chamberlain, Segrè, Wiegand, and Ypsilantis at the University of California. This discovery came as the result of long-range plans laid for the purpose of answering the question, "Is there in nature, or can there be created by a strong interaction, a negatively charged particle with the mass of a proton?" One of the principal objectives in building the 6.2-BeV proton accelerator in 1953 was to find an answer to this question. Protons accelerated to a high enough energy should, in colliding with heavier nuclei, impart sufficient energy to create, if such were possible,

a pair of protons, one plus, the other minus.

The first antiprotons were discovered as high-energy, negatively charged particles emerging from a copper target in the proton beam of the bevatron. They had all of the anticipated properties. By means of a strong magnet, the antiprotons were bent away from the protons and into a scintillation counter. Today, antiproton events are commonly observed and studied by means of a bubble chamber.

Fig. F is a photograph in which an antiproton entered the liquid hydrogen bubble chamber from the left. Near the center of the picture it interacted with a proton and both particles were annihilated in the production of four pairs of π mesons. Since the bubble chamber operated in the uniform field of a strong electromagnet, the π^- tracks curve clockwise, and the π^+ tracks

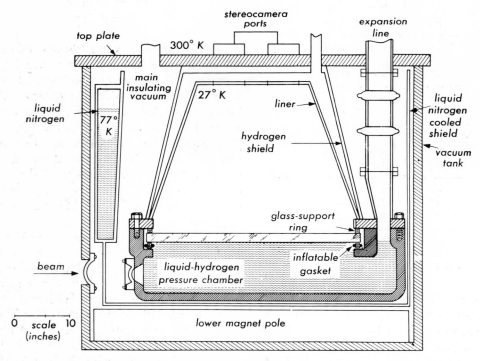

Fig. I. Cross-section diagram of the 72-in. liquid-hydrogen bubble chamber.

curve counterclockwise. The π^+ that curved back to the left and down decayed into a μ^+ and an e^+, as shown in the accompanying legend diagram.

The reactions for this event are written as follows:

$$p^- + p \rightarrow 4\pi^- + 4\pi^+$$
$$\pi^+ \rightarrow \mu^+ + \nu$$
$$\mu^+ \rightarrow e^+ + \nu + \bar{\nu}$$

Mean Lives of Elementary Particles. One interesting aspect of the nature of the particles themselves concerns their *mean life*. See Table 1.

Table 1. Mean Lives of the Unstable Elementary Particles

Particle	Mean Life (sec)
Ξ^+	1.3×10^{-10}
Ξ^0	1.5×10^{-10}
Ξ^-	1.3×10^{-10}
Σ^+	0.8×10^{-10}
Σ^0	1.0×10^{-9}
Σ^-	1.6×10^{-10}
Λ^0	2.5×10^{-10}
n	1.0×10^{3}
K^+	1.2×10^{-8}
K^0	1.0×10^{-10}
K^-	1.2×10^{-8}
π^+	2.5×10^{-8}
π^0	2.2×10^{-16}
π^-	2.5×10^{-8}
μ^+	2.2×10^{-6}
μ^-	2.2×10^{-6}

The best and most direct means of determining the lifetime of any identified particle is to measure the length of the track it produces in a cloud chamber, bubble chamber, or photographic emulsion, and determine its velocity from conservation laws or the curvature of its path in a magnetic field. The lifetime, τ, is then given by the distance traveled divided by the velocity. It is evident from these extremely short life-times why the unstable particles travel such a short distance before disintegrating.

Fig. G is a photograph in which a π^- meson enters a liquid-hydrogen bubble chamber from the left. As shown in the legend diagram, interaction with a proton cancels the charges and ends the track by creating two neutral particles.

These two recoiling particles, K^0 and Λ^0, do not produce tracks in the chamber but, having short lifetimes, quickly disintegrate. The neutral K particle decays into a pair of mesons, π^+ and π^-, while the Λ particle decays into a proton and a π^-. As reactions—

$$\pi^- + p \rightarrow K^0 + \Lambda^0$$
$$K^0 \rightarrow \pi^+ + \pi^-$$
$$\Lambda^0 \rightarrow p + \pi^-$$

The Future of Nuclear Physics. The discovery of so many elementary particles in recent years has greatly complicated all previous theories of the atomic nucleus. The fundamental questions arising in the minds of the physicists include both the different properties of the individual particles and how they fit into the structure of the atomic nucleus. At the present stage of development, in trying to unravel the many mysteries concerning elementary particles, some important questions stand out.

Are all of the particles listed in Fig. A really elementary, or are some of them just composites of others? Could it be that some of the stars in the universe, or entire galaxies, are made of antimatter, with hydrogen atoms composed of antiprotons and positrons, etc.? Why are elementary charges limited to values of $+1$, 0, and -1?

Every physicist believes that some day

we will know the answers to these and many other questions about the nature of elementary particles, the building blocks of the universe.

QUESTIONS

1. (a) What is an elementary particle? (b) Why have most of them only been seen since 1950?
2. In 1950, only the π mesons were discovered. (a) How many mesons are now known? (b) What are they called? (c) How are they related to nuclear forces?
3. (a) What happens when two antiparticles meet? (b) What would happen if an antineutron met a neutron?
4. How does an antineutron differ from a neutron?
5. (a) What is a bubble chamber? (b) How does it work?
6. Why is a magnetic field applied to a bubble chamber?
7. (a) How is a photographic emulsion used to record particle tracks? (b) Is a camera necessary?

PROBLEMS

1. Calculate the threshold energy for the production of a proton pair.
2. Calculate the kinetic energy released in the production of four pairs of π mesons, starting with an antiproton (see Fig. F).
3. Write down all equations involved in Fig. G, including all disintegrations, so that only stable particles are left.

PROJECT

Obtain some films which have been exposed to radiation. Study them under a high-power microscope to see how many different atomic events you can discover. Most radiation laboratories have old exposed film they will give to the serious student.

INDEX OF TABLES—*in both Text and Appendix*

Appendix

APPENDIX I. *Values of Trigonometric Functions*

Sines and tangents, read down.
Cosines and cotangents, read up.

∠	sin		tan		∠	∠	sin		tan		∠
0°	.0000	.0175	.0000	.0175	89°	45°	.7071	.7193	1.000	1.036	44°
1°	.0175	.0349	.0175	.0349	88°	46°	.7193	.7314	1.036	1.072	43°
2°	.0349	.0523	.0349	.0524	87°	47°	.7314	.7431	1.072	1.111	42°
3°	.0523	.0698	.0524	.0699	86°	48°	.7431	.7547	1.111	1.150	41°
4°	.0698	.0872	.0699	.0875	85°	49°	.7547	.7660	1.150	1.192	40°
5°	.0872	.1045	.0875	.1051	84°	50°	.7660	.7771	1.192	1.235	39°
6°	.1045	.1219	.1051	.1228	83°	51°	.7771	.7880	1.235	1.280	38°
7°	.1219	.1392	.1228	.1405	82°	52°	.7880	.7986	1.280	1.327	37°
8°	.1392	.1564	.1405	.1584	81°	53°	.7986	.8090	1.327	1.376	36°
9°	.1564	.1736	.1584	.1763	80°	54°	.8090	.8192	1.376	1.428	35°
10°	.1736	.1908	.1763	.1944	79°	55°	.8192	.8290	1.428	1.483	34°
11°	.1908	.2079	.1944	.2126	78°	56°	.8290	.8387	1.483	1.540	33°
12°	.2079	.2250	.2126	.2309	77°	57°	.8387	.8480	1.540	1.600	32°
13°	.2250	.2419	.2309	.2493	76°	58°	.8480	.8572	1.600	1.664	31°
14°	.2419	.2588	.2493	.2679	75°	59°	.8572	.8660	1.664	1.732	30°
15°	.2588	.2756	.2679	.2867	74°	60°	.8660	.8746	1.732	1.804	29°
16°	.2756	.2924	.2867	.3057	73°	61°	.8746	.8829	1.804	1.881	28°
17°	.2924	.3090	.3057	.3249	72°	62°	.8829	.8910	1.881	1.963	27°
18°	.3090	.3256	.3249	.3443	71°	63°	.8910	.8988	1.963	2.050	26°
19°	.3256	.3420	.3443	.3640	70°	64°	.8988	.9063	2.050	2.145	25°
20°	.3420	.3584	.3640	.3839	69°	65°	.9063	.9135	2.145	2.246	24°
21°	.3584	.3746	.3839	.4040	68°	66°	.9135	.9205	2.246	2.356	23°
22°	.3746	.3907	.4040	.4245	67°	67°	.9205	.9272	2.356	2.475	22°
23°	.3907	.4067	.4245	.4452	66°	68°	.9272	.9336	2.475	2.605	21°
24°	.4067	.4226	.4452	.4663	65°	69°	.9336	.9397	2.605	2.747	20°
25°	.4226	.4384	.4663	.4877	64°	70°	.9397	.9455	2.747	2.904	19°
26°	.4384	.4540	.4877	.5095	63°	71°	.9455	.9511	2.904	3.078	18°
27°	.4540	.4695	.5095	.5317	62°	72°	.9511	.9563	3.078	3.271	17°
28°	.4695	.4848	.5317	.5543	61°	73°	.9563	.9613	3.271	3.487	16°
29°	.4848	.5000	.5543	.5774	60°	74°	.9613	.9659	3.487	3.732	15°
30°	.5000	.5150	.5774	.6009	59°	75°	.9659	.9703	3.732	4.011	14°
31°	.5150	.5299	.6009	.6249	58°	76°	.9703	.9744	4.011	4.331	13°
32°	.5299	.5446	.6249	.6494	57°	77°	.9744	.9781	4.331	4.705	12°
33°	.5446	.5592	.6494	.6745	56°	78°	.9781	.9816	4.705	5.145	11°
34°	.5592	.5736	.6745	.7002	55°	79°	.9816	.9848	5.145	5.671	10°
35°	.5736	.5878	.7002	.7265	54°	80°	.9848	.9877	5.671	6.314	9°
36°	.5878	.6018	.7265	.7536	53°	81°	.9877	.9903	6.314	7.115	8°
37°	.6018	.6157	.7536	.7813	52°	82°	.9903	.9925	7.115	8.144	7°
38°	.6157	.6293	.7813	.8098	51°	83°	.9925	.9945	8.144	9.514	6°
39°	.6293	.6428	.8098	.8391	50°	84°	.9945	.9962	9.514	11.43	5°
40°	.6428	.6561	.8391	.8693	49°	85°	.9962	.9976	11.43	14.30	4°
41°	.6561	.6691	.8693	.9004	48°	86°	.9976	.9986	14.30	19.08	3°
42°	.6691	.6820	.9004	.9325	47°	87°	.9986	.9994	19.08	28.64	2°
43°	.6820	.6947	.9325	.9657	46°	88°	.9994	.9998	28.64	57.29	1°
44°	.6947	.7071	.9657	1.000	45°	89°	.9998	1.000	57.29	∞	0°
	cos		cot	∠			cos		cot	∠	

APPENDIX II. *Stable Isotopes of the Chemical Elements*

Carbon 12 = 12.000

At. No.	Element	Sym.	Isotopes, Mass. No.	At. Wt.
1	hydrogen	H	1, (2)	1.00797[a]
2	helium	He	4, (3)	4.0026
3	lithium	Li	6, 7	6.939
4	beryllium	Be	9	9.0122
5	boron	B	10, 11	10.811[a]
6	carbon	C	12, (13)	12.01115[a]
7	nitrogen	N	14, (15)	14.0067
8	oxygen	O	16, (18), (17)	15.9994[a]
9	fluorine	F	19	18.9984
10	neon	Ne	20, (21), 22	20.183
11	sodium	Na	23	22.9898
12	magnesium	Mg	24, 25, 26	24.312
13	aluminum	Al	27	26.9815
14	silicon	Si	28, 29, 30	28.086[a]
15	phosphorus	P	31	30.9738
16	sulfur	S	32, 33, 34	32.064[a]
17	chlorine	Cl	35, 37	35.453[b]
18	argon	Ar	(36), (38), 40	39.948
19	potassium	K	39, (40), 41	39.102
20	calcium	Ca	40, (42), (43), 44	40.08
21	scandium	Sc	45	44.956
22	titanium	Ti	46, 47, 48, 49, 50	47.90
23	vanadium	V	51	50.942
24	chromium	Cr	50, 52, 53, 54	51.996[b]
25	manganese	Mn	55	54.9380
26	iron	Fe	54, 56, 57, (58)	55.847[b]
27	cobalt	Co	59	58.9332
28	nickel	Ni	58, 60, 61, 62(64)	58.71
29	copper	Cu	63, 65	63.54
30	zinc	Zn	64, 66, 67, 68, (70)	65.37
31	gallium	Ga	69, 71	69.72
32	germanium	Ge	70, 72, 73, 74, 76	72.59
33	arsenic	As	75	74.9216
34	selenium	Se	(74), 76, 77, 78, 80, 82	78.96
35	bromine	Br	79, 81	79.909[b]
36	krypton	Kr	(78), 80, 82, 83, 84, 86	83.80
37	rubidium	Rb	85, 87	85.47
38	strontium	Sr	(84), 86, 87, 88	87.62
39	yttrium	Yt	89	88.905
40	zirconium	Zr	90, 91, 92, 94, 96	91.22
41	niobium	Nb	93	92.906
42	molybdenum	Mo	92, 94, 95, 96, 97, 98, 100, 102	95.94
43	technetium	Tc	99	97.2
44	ruthenium	Ru	96, 98, 99, 100, 101, 102, 104	101.07
45	rhodium	Rh	103	102.905
46	palladium	Pd	(102), 104, 105, 106, 108, 110	106.4
47	silver	Ag	107, 109	107.870[b]

[a] These atomic weights are known to be variable because of natural variations in isotopic composition. The observed ranges are: hydrogen ±0.00001; boron ±0.003; carbon ±0.00005; oxygen ±0.0001; silicon ±0.001; sulfur ±0.003.

[b] These atomic weights are believed to have the following experimental uncertainties: chlorine ±0.001; chromium ±0.001; iron ±0.003; bromine ±0.002; silver ±0.003.

At. No.	Element	Sym.	Isotopes, Mass. No.	At. Wt.
48	cadmium	Cd	106, (108), 110, 111, **112**, 113, 114, 116	112.40
49	indium	In	113, **115**	114.82
50	tin	Sn	112, (114), (115), 116, 117, 118, 119, **120**, 122, 124	118.69
51	antimony	Sb	**121, 123**	121.75
52	tellurium	Te	(120), 122, 123, 124, 125, 126, **128**, 130	127.60
53	iodine	I	**127**	126.9044
54	xenon	Xe	(124), (126), 128, **129**, 130, 131, 132, 134, 136	131.30
55	cesium	Cs	**133**	132.905
56	barium	Ba	(130), (132), 134, 135, 136, 137, **138**	137.34
57	lanthanum	La	**139**	138.91
58	cerium	Ce	(136), (138), **140**, 142	140.12
59	praseodymium	Pr	**141**	140.906
60	neodymium	Nd	**142**, 143, **144**, 145, 146, (148), (150)	144.24
61	promethium	Pm		146.0
62	samarium	Sa	144, 147, 148, 149, 150, **152**, 154	150.35
63	europium	Eu	**151, 153**	151.96
64	gadolinium	Gd	155, **156**, 157, **158**, 160	157.25
65	terbium	Tn	**159**	158.924
66	dysprosium	Dy	161, 162, 163, **164**	162.50
67	holmium	Ho	**165**	164.930
68	erbium	Er	**166**, 167, 168, 170	167.26
69	thulium	Tm	**169**	168.934
70	ytterbium	Yb	171, 172, 173, **174**, 176	173.04
71	lutecium	Lu	**175**	174.97
72	hafnium	Hf	176, 177, 178, 179, **180**	178.49
73	tantalum	Ta	**181**	180.948
74	tungsten	W	182, 183, **184, 186**	183.85
75	rhenium	Re	185, **187**	186.2
76	osmium	Os	186, (187), 188, 189, 190, 192	190.2
77	iridium	Ir	191, **193**	192.2
78	platinum	Pt	(192), 194, **195**, 196, 198	195.09
79	gold	Au	**197**	196.967
80	mercury	Hg	(196), 198, 199, 200, 201, **202**, 204	200.59

APPENDIX II. *Stable Isotopes of the Chemical Elements* (*continued*)

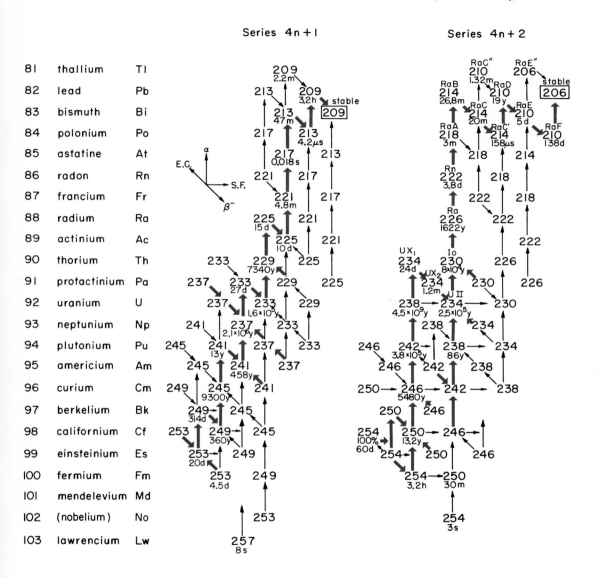

Series 4n + 1

Series 4n + 2

81	thallium	Tl			
82	lead	Pb			
83	bismuth	Bi			
84	polonium	Po			
85	astatine	At			
86	radon	Rn			
87	francium	Fr			
88	radium	Ra			
89	actinium	Ac			
90	thorium	Th			
91	protactinium	Pa			
92	uranium	U			
93	neptunium	Np			
94	plutonium	Pu			
95	americium	Am			
96	curium	Cm			
97	berkelium	Bk			
98	californium	Cf			
99	einsteinium	Es			
100	fermium	Fm			
101	mendelevium	Md			
102	(nobelium)	No			
103	lawrencium	Lw			

			Series 4n + 3	Series 4n
81	thallium	Tl		
82	lead	Pb		
83	bismuth	Bi		
84	polonium	Po		
85	astatine	At		
86	radon	Rn		
87	francium	Fr		
88	radium	Ra		
89	actinium	Ac		
90	thorium	Th		
91	protactinium	Pa		
92	uranium	U		
93	neptunium	Np		
94	plutonium	Pu		
95	americium	Am		
96	curium	Cm		
97	berkelium	Bk		
98	californium	Cf		
99	einsteinium	Es		
100	fermium	Fm		
101	mendelevium	Md		
102	(nobelium)	No		
103	lawrencium	Lw		

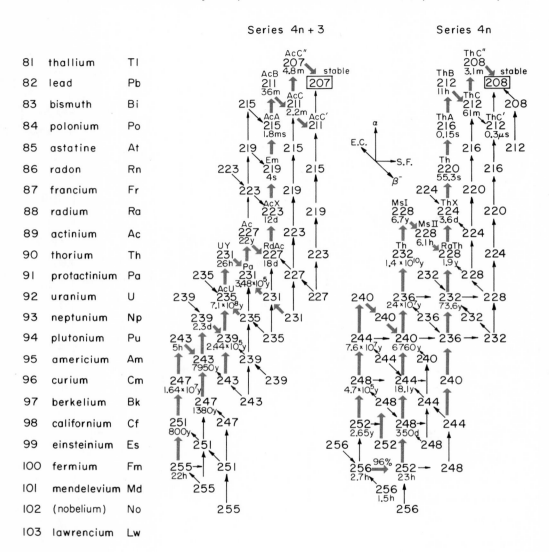

APPENDIX III. *Properties of Some Isotopes*

Carbon 12 = 12.000

Symbol	Atomic Mass (amu)	Abundance, Activity	Half-life	Symbol	Atomic mass (amu)	Abundance, Activity	Half-life
$_{-1}e^0$	0.000 549	—	stable	$_8O^{14}$	14.008 597	β^+	74 s
				O^{15}	15.003 072	β^+	2.0 m
$_1p^1$	1.007 276	—	stable	O^{16}	15.994 915	**99.76**	stable
				O^{17}	16.999 133	**0.04**	stable
$_0n^1$	1.008 665	β^-	13 m	O^{18}	17.999 160	**0.20**	stable
				O^{19}	19.003 577	β^-	29.4 s
				O^{20}	20.004 071	n	13.6 s
$_1H^1$	1.007 825	**99.985**	stable				
H^2	2.014 103	**0.015**	stable	$_9F^{17}$	17.002 098	β^+	66 s
H^3	3.016 049	β^-	12.2 y	F^{18}	18.000 950	β^+	1.87 h
				F^{19}	18.998 405	**100**	stable
$_2He^3$	3.016 030	**0.00013**	stable	F^{20}	19.999 986	β^-	11.2 s
He^4	4.002 604	**99.9999**	stable	F^{21}	20.999 972	β^-	5 s
He^5	5.012 296	$\alpha + n$	inst.				
He_6	6.018 900	β^-	0.82 s	$_{10}Ne^{18}$	18.005 715	β^+	1.6 s
				Ne^{19}	19.001 892	β^+	19 s
$_3Li^5$	5.012 541	$\alpha + p$	inst.	Ne^{20}	19.992 440	**90.92**	stable
Li^6	6.015 126	**7.52**	stable	Ne^{21}	20.993 849	**0.26**	stable
Li^7	7.016 005	**92.48**	stable	Ne^{22}	21.991 385	**8.82**	stable
Li^8	8.022 488	β^-	0.86 s	Ne^{23}	22.994 475	β^-	40.2 s
Li^9	9.027 300	β^-	0.17 s	Ne^{24}	23.993 597	β^-	3.4 m
$_4Be^6$	6.019 780	β^+	0.4 s	$_{11}Na^{20}$	20.008 890	β^+	0.3 s
Be^7	7.016 931	E.C.	53.6 d	Na^{21}	20.997 638	β^+	23 s
Be^8	8.005 308	2α	inst.	Na^{22}	21.994 435	β^+, E.C.	2.6 y
Be^9	9.012 186	**100**	stable	Na^{23}	22.989 773	**100**	stable
Be^{10}	10.013 535	β^-	2.5×10^6 y	Na^{24}	23.990 967	β^-	15.0 h
				Na^{25}	24.989 920	β^-	60 s
$_5B^8$	8.024 612	β^+	0.6 s				
B^9	9.013 335	$2\alpha + p$	inst.	$_{12}Mg^{23}$	22.994 135	β^+, E.C.	11 s
B^{10}	10.012 939	**18.6**	stable	Mg^{24}	23.985 045	**78.60**	stable
B^{11}	11.009 305	**81.4**	stable	Mg^{25}	24.985 840	**10.11**	stable
B^{12}	12.014 353	β^-	0.022 s	Mg^{26}	25.982 591	**11.29**	stable
				Mg^{27}	26.998 346	β^-	9.45 m
$_6C^{10}$	10.016 830	β^+	19.1 s	Mg^{28}	27.983 880	β^-	21.4 h
C^{11}	11.011 433	β^+	20.5 m				
C^{12}	12.000 000	**98.892**	stable	$_{13}Al^{24}$	24.000 090	β^+	2.1 s
C^{13}	13.003 354	**1.108**	stable	Al^{25}	24.990 414	β^+	7.6 s
C^{14}	14.003 242	β^-	5.6×10^3 y	Al^{26}	25.986 900	β^+, E.C.	10^5 y
C^{15}	15.010 600	β^-	2.3 s	Al^{27}	26.981 535	**100**	stable
				Al^{28}	27.981 908	β^-	2.3 m
$_7N^{12}$	12.018 709	β^+	0.012 s	Al^{29}	28.980 442	β^-	6.6 m
N^{13}	13.005 739	β^+	10.1 m				
N^{14}	14.003 074	**99.635**	stable	$_{14}Si^{27}$	26.986 701	β^+, E.C.	4.9 s
N^{15}	15.000 108	**0.365**	stable	Si^{28}	27.976 927	**92.27**	stable
N^{16}	16.006 089	β^-	7.36 s	Si^{29}	28.976 491	**4.68**	stable
N^{17}	17.008 449	β^-	4.14 s	Si^{30}	29.973 761	**3.05**	stable
				Si^{31}	30.975 349	β^-	2.6 h
				Si^{32}	31.974 020	β^-	7×10^2 y

APPENDIX IV. *General Physical Constants* (*after Du Mond*)

Planck's constant of action	$h = 6.6238 \times 10^{-34}$ joule sec
electronic charge	$e = 1.6019 \times 10^{-19}$ coulomb
electronic charge	$e = 4.8022 \times 10^{-10}$ e.s.u.
specific electronic charge	$e/m = 1.7598 \times 10^{11}$ coulombs/Kg
specific proton charge	$e/M_p = 9.5795 \times 10^7$ coulombs/Kg
electronic mass	$m = 9.1072 \times 10^{-31}$ Kg
mass of atom of unit atomic weight	$M = 1.6600 \times 10^{-27}$ Kg
mass of proton	$M_p = 1.6722 \times 10^{-27}$ Kg
ratio mass proton to mass electron	$M_p/m = 1836.1$
Wien's displacement-law constant	$C = 0.28976$ cm deg
velocity of light	$c = 299,790$ Km/sec
square of velocity of light	$c^2 = 8.9874 \times 10^{10}$ Km²/sec²
unit atomic angular momentum	$\hbar = 1.0544 \times 10^{-34}$ joule sec

APPENDIX V. The Periodic Table of the Elements

	I-A	II-A	III-B	IV-B	V-B	VI-B	VII-B	VIII-B			I-B	II-B	III-A	IV-A	V-A	VI-A	VII-A	VIII-A
First Period	1 H 1.0080																	2 He 4.003
Second Period	3 Li 6.940	4 Be 9.013											5 B 10.82	6 C 12.011	7 N 14.008	8 O 16.0000	9 F 19.00	10 Ne 20.183
Third Period	11 Na 22.991	12 Mg 24.32											13 Al 26.98	14 Si 28.09	15 P 30.975	16 S 32.066	17 Cl 35.457	18 Ar 39.944
Fourth Period	19 K 39.100	20 Ca 40.08	21 Sc 44.96	22 Ti 47.90	23 V 50.95	24 Cr 52.01	25 Mn 54.94	26 Fe 55.85	27 Co 58.94	28 Ni 58.71	29 Cu 63.54	30 Zn 65.38	31 Ga 69.72	32 Ge 72.60	33 As 74.92	34 Se 78.96	35 Br 79.916	36 Kr 83.80
Fifth Period	37 Rb 85.48	38 Sr 87.63	39 Y 88.91	40 Zr 91.22	41 Nb 92.91	42 Mo 95.95	43 Tc [99]	44 Ru 101.1	45 Rh 102.91	46 Pd 106.4	47 Ag 107.880	48 Cd 112.41	49 In 114.82	50 Sn 118.70	51 Sb 121.76	52 Te 127.61	53 I 126.92	54 Xe 131.30
Sixth Period	55 Cs 132.91	56 Ba 137.36	57-71 Lanthanide Elements	72 Hf 178.50	73 Ta 180.95	74 W 183.86	75 Re 186.22	76 Os 190.2	77 Ir 192.2	78 Pt 195.09	79 Au 197.0	80 Hg 200.61	81 Tl 204.39	82 Pb 207.21	83 Bi 208.99	84 Po [210]	85 At [210]	86 Rn 222
Seventh Period	87 Fr [223]	88 Ra 226	89-103 Actinide Elements	104 [260]														

Metals — **Transition Elements** — **Nonmetals**

Lanthanide Elements (Rare Earth)	57 La 138.92	58 Ce 140.13	59 Pr 140.91	60 Nd 144.27	61 Pm [147]	62 Sm 150.35	63 Eu 152.0	64 Gd 157.26	65 Tb 158.93	66 Dy 162.51	67 Ho 164.94	68 Er 167.27	69 Tm 168.94	70 Yb 173.04	71 Lu 174.99
Actinide Elements	89 Ac [227]	90 Th 232	91 Pa 231	92 U 238.07	93 Np [237]	94 Pu [242]	95 Am [243]	96 Cm [247]	97 Bk [249]	98 Cf [251]	99 Es [254]	100 Fm [253]	101 Md [256]	102 No [254]	103 Lw [257]

An atomic weight value in brackets indicates the mass of the most stable known isotope.

APPENDIX VI-1. *Conversion Factors for Units of Length*

		Km	m	cm	in.	ft	mi
1 kilometer	=	1	1000	100,000	39370	3280.83	0.62137
1 meter	=	0.00100	1	100	39.370	3.28083	6.21×10^{-4}
1 centimeter	=	1.0×10^{-5}	0.0100	1	0.39370	0.032808	6.21×10^{-6}
1 inch	=	2.54×10^{-5}	0.02540	2.5400	1	0.08333	1.58×10^{-5}
1 foot	=	3.05×10^{-4}	0.30480	30.480	12	1	1.89×10^{-4}
1 mile	=	1.60935	1609.35	160935	63360	5280	1

APPENDIX VI-2. *International System Prefixes* and Abbreviations*

(*Adopted by the 11th General Conference on Weights & Measures, 1960*)

Prefix	Symbol	Power of Ten	Abbreviations** for Length	Volume†	Mass
tera	T	10^{12}	Tm	Tl	Tg
giga	G	10^{9}	Gm	Gl	Gg
mega	M	10^{6}	Mn	Ml	Mg
kilo	k##	10^{3}	**km**	kl	**kg**
hecto	h	10^{2}	hm	hl	hg
deca	da	10^{1}	dam	dal	dag
(elemental units)		10^{0}	**m**	**l**	**gm**
deci	d	10^{-1}	dm	dl	dg
centi	c	10^{-2}	**cm**	cl	cg
milli	m	10^{-3}	**mm**	**ml**	**mg**
micro	μ	10^{-6}	μm‡	μl	μg
nano	n	10^{-9}	nm#	nl	ng
pico	p	10^{-12}	pm	pl	pg
femto	f	10^{-15}	fm	fl	fg
atto	a	10^{-18}	am	al	ag

* Unit prefixes are Greek, subdivision prefixes are Latin.

** 1. Periods and double prefixes are no longer used (*e.g.*, use nm [for nanometer] instead of mμ [for millimicron]).

2. Bold-face type indicates the most-often-used units. *E.g.*, while 1,000 kilograms = 1 megagram, 1,000 kg is usually referred to as a metric ton.

† The liter is the elemental unit of volume, but it is most often used in reference to fluids. Volume can be and is usually expressed as the cube of a linear measure (m^3, cm^3, etc.).

‡ micrometer or μm, formerly micron or μ.

nanometer or nm, formerly millimicron or mμ.

Some researchers, including the authors of this text, prefer that the symbol for kilo be capitalized, K.

APPENDIX VI-3. *Greek Alphabet and English Equivalents*

Greek Letter	Name	English Equiv.	Greek Letter	Name	English Equiv.	Greek Letter	Name	English Equiv.
A α	alpha	a	I ι	iota	$\bar{\imath}$	P ρ	rho	r
B β	beta	b	K κ	kappa	k	Σ σ s	sigma	s
Γ γ	gamma	g	Λ λ	lambda	l	T τ	tau	t
Δ δ	delta	d	M μ	mu	m	Υ υ	upsilon	u
E ϵ	epsilon	$\breve{e}$	N ν	nu	n	Φ ϕ	phi	ph
Z ζ	zeta	z	Ξ ξ	xi	x	X χ	chi	ch
H η	eta	$\bar{e}$	O o	omicron	$\breve{o}$	Ψ ψ	psi	ps
Θ θ ϑ	theta	th	Π π	pi	p	Ω ω	omega	$\bar{o}$

APPENDIX VI-4. *Densities and Weight-densities of Common Substances*

Material	gm/cm^3	lb/ft^3	Material	gm/cm^3	lb/ft^3
Liquids			**Wood**		
alcohol (20°C)	0.79	49.3	balsa	0.11-0.13	7-8
benzine (0°C)	0.90	56.2	cedar	0.49-0.57	30-35
blood (37°C)	1.04	65.0	cork	0.22-0.26	14-16
gasoline (0°C)	0.69	41.2	maple	0.62-0.75	39-47
mercury (20°C)	13.6	849	oak	0.60-0.90	37-56
olive oil (15°C)	0.918	57.3			
water (0°C)	1.000	62.4	**Gas**		
			air	0.00129	0.080
Metals			CO_2	0.00198	0.124
aluminum	2.7	168.7	helium	0.000178	0.011
brass	8.5	530	hydrogen	0.00009	0.005
copper	8.9	556	nitrogen	0.00125	0.078
gold	19.3	1205	oxygen	0.00143	0.089
iron	7.9	493			
lead	11.4	712			
platinum	21.5	1342	**Miscellaneous**		
silver	10.5	655	glass	2.4-2.8	150-175
tin	7.3	456	ice	0.91	57.2
zinc	7.1	446	quartz	2.65	165

APPENDIX VI-5. *Electrical Conductivity and Other Properties of Some Metals*

Metal	Resistivity microhm-cm, 20°C	Specific gravity	Tensile strength, lb/in.	Melting point °C
aluminum	2.824	2.70	30,000	659
antimony	41.7	6.6	....	630
arsenic	33.3	5.73	....	....
bismuth	120	9.8	....	271
brass	7	8.6	70,000	900
cadmium	7.6	8.6	....	321
climax	87	8.1	150,000	1250
cobalt	9.8	8.71	....	1480
constantan	49	8.9	120,000	1190
copper: annealed	1.7241	8.89	30,000	1083
hard-drawn	1.771	8.89	60,000	....
German silver, 18% Ni	33	8.4	150,000	1100
gold	2.44	19.3	20,000	1063
iron, 99.98% pure	10	7.8	....	1530
lead	22	11.4	3,000	327
magnesium	4.6	1.74	33,000	651
Manganin	44	8.4	150,000	910
mercury	95.783	13.546	0	−38.9
molybdenum, drawn	5.7	9.0	....	2500
Monel metal	42	8.9	160,000	1300
Nichrome	100	8.2	150,000	1500
nickel	7.8	8.9	120,000	1452
palladium	11	12.2	39,000	1550
phosphor bronze	7.8	8.9	25,000	750
platinum	10	21.4	50,000	1755
silver	1.59	10.5	42,000	960
steel	10.4	7.7	53,000	1510
steel, Siemens-Martin	18	7.7	100,000	1510
steel, manganese	70	7.5	230,000	1260
tantalum	15.5	16.6	....	2850
tin	11.5	7.3	4,000	232
tungsten, drawn	5.6	19	500,000	3400
zinc	5.8	7.1	10,000	419

APPENDIX VII. *The Nobel Prize Awards in Physics*

A Name-Year Index follows this listing.

1901 Wilhelm Konrad Röntgen, German.
Discovery of X-rays.

1902 Hendrik Antoon Lorentz and
Pieter Zeeman, Dutch.
Zeeman effect of magnetism on light.

1903 Antoine Henri Becquerel, French,
Pierre Curie, French, and
Marie Sklodowska Curie, Polish.
Discovery and studies of radioactivity.

1904 John William Strutt (Baron Rayleigh),
British.
*Studies of gas densities, discovery of
argon.*

1905 Philipp Lenard, German.
Studies of cathode rays.

1906 Sir Joseph J. Thomson, British.
Discharges through gases.

1907 Albert A. Michelson, American.
*Precision optical instruments, measuring
speed of light.*

1908 Gabriel Lippmann, French.
Interference color photography.

1909 Guglielmo Marconi, Italian, and
Karl Ferdinand Braun, German.
Wireless telegraphy.

1910 Johannes D. van der Waals, Dutch.
Gas laws.

1911 Wilhelm Wien, German.
Heat-radiation laws.

1912 Nils Dalén, Swedish.
Automatic gas lighting of lighthouses.

1913 Heike Kamerlingh Onnes, Dutch.
Low-temperature studies.

1914 Max Theodor Felix von Laue, German.
Diffraction of X-rays.

1915 Sir William Henry Bragg and his son,
Sir William L. Bragg, British.
Crystal structure.

1916 *No award.*

1917 Charles G. Barkla, British.
Characteristic X-rays of the elements.

1918 Max Planck, German.
Quantum theory of radiation.

1919 Johannes Stark, German.
Stark effect of spectral lines.

1910 Charles E. Guillaume, Spanish.
Nickel-steel alloys.

1921 Albert Einstein, German.
Relativity theory, photoelectric effect.

1922 Niels Bohr, Danish.
Theory of atomic structure and radiation.

1923 Robert A. Millikan, American.
Charge on electron, photoelectric effect.

1924 Karl M. Siegbahn, Swedish.
X-ray spectroscopy.

1925 James Franck and
Gustav Hertz, German.
Electron impact on atoms.

1926 Jean B. Perrin, French.
*Measurement of atoms, discontinuous
structure of matter.*

1927 Arthur H. Compton, American.
Compton effect.
Charles T. R. Wilson, British.
Cloud chamber.

1928 Owen Willans Richardson, British.
Thermal-ions studies.

1929 Louis V. de Broglie, French.
Wave character of electrons.

1930 Sir Chandrasekhara V. Raman, Indian.
Raman effect.

1931 *No award.*

1932 Werner Heisenberg, German.
Creation of quantum mechanics.

1933 P. A. M. Dirac, British, and
Edwin Schrödinger, Austrian.
Atomic theory.

1934 *No award.*

1935 Sir James Chadwick, British.
Discovery of the neutron.

1936 Victor F. Hess, Austrian.
Discovery of cosmic rays.
Carl D. Anderson, American.
Discovery of positron.

1937 Clinton J. Davisson, American, and
George P. Thompson, British.
Electron diffraction by crystals.

1938 Enrico Fermi, Italian.
Discovery of transuranium elements.

1939 Ernest Orlando Lawrence, American.
Development of cyclotron.

1940 *No award.*

1941 *No award.*

1942 *No award.*

1943   Otto Stern, American.
       Magnetic moment of proton.

1944   I. I. Rabi, American.
       Magnetic moments of nuclei.

1945   Wolfgang Pauli, Austrian.
       Pauli exclusion principle.

1946   P. W. Bridgman, American.
       Physical effects of high pressures.

1947   Sir Edward Appleton, British.
       Ionosphere exploration.

1948   P. M. S. Blackett, British.
       Cosmic-radiation discoveries.

1949   Hideki Yukawa, Japanese.
       Theoretical prediction of meson.

1950   Cecil F. Powell, British.
       Photographic nuclei studies.

1951   Sir John D. Cockcroft, British, and
       Ernest T. S. Walton, Irish.
       First nuclear transmutation.

1952   Felix Bloch, American.
       Nuclear magnetic moments.
       Edward M. Purcell, American.
       Radio astronomy.

1953   Frits Zernike, Dutch.
       Phase-contrast microscope.

1954   Max Born and
       Walther Bothe, Germans.
       Quantum mechanics, wave functions.

1955   Polykarp Kusch, American.
       Magnetic moment of electron.
       Willis E. Lamb, American.
       Microwave spectroscopy and atomic structure.

1956   William Shockley,
       Walter H. Brattain, and

John Bardeen, Americans.
       Semiconductors, transistors.

1957   Chen Ning Yang and
       Tsung Dao Lee, Americans.
       Altered concepts of conservation of parity.

1958   Pavel A. Cerenkov,
       Igor Y. Tamm, and
       Illya M. Frank, Russians.
       Discovery of Cerenkov radiation.

1959   Emilio Segrè and
       Owen Chamberlin, Americans.
       Discovery of antiproton.

1960   Donald A. Glaser, American.
       Bubble chamber.

1961   Robert Hofstadter, American.
       Structure of the nucleon.
       Rudolph L. Mossbauer, German.
       Nuclear radiation and absorption.

1962   Lev D. Landau, Russian.
       Mathematical explanation of very-low temperature phenomena.

1963   Maria Goeppert-Mayer, American, and
       J. Hans Jensen, German.
       Nuclear shell model.
       Eugene Wigner, American.
       Theory of symmetry and parity.

1964   Charles H. Townes, American,
       Nicolai G. Basov, Russian, and
       Aleksander M. Prokhorov, Russian.
       Maser-laser principle.

1965   Richard P. Feynman, American,
       Julian S. Schwinger, American, and
       Shinichiro Tomonaga, Japanese.
       Quantum electrodynamics.

1966   Alfred Kastler, French.
       Optical study of Herzian resonances in atoms.

Name-Year Index to Nobel Physics Prizes

Jensen, J. H., 1963

Kastler, A., 1966
Kusch, P., 1955

Lamb, W. E., 1955
Landau, L. D., 1962
Lawrence, E. O., 1939
Lee, Tsung Dao, 1957
Lenard, P., 1905
Lippmann, G., 1908
Lorentz, H. A., 1902

Marconi, G., 1909
Michelson, S. A., 1907
Millikan, R. A., 1923
Mossbauer, R. L., 1961
no award—1916, 1931, 1934, 1940, 1941, 1942

Onnes, H. K., 1913

Pauli, W., 1945
Perrin, J. B., 1926
Planck, M., 1918
Powell, C. F., 1950
Prokhorov, A. M., 1964
Purcell, E. M., 1952

Rabi, I. I., 1944
Raman, C. V., 1930
Rayleigh (Baron), 1904
Richardson, O. W., 1928
Röntgen, W. H., 1901

Schrödinger, E., 1933
Schwinger, J. S., 1965
Segrè, E., 1959
Shockley, W., 1956
Siegbahn, K. M., 1924
Stark, J., 1919

Stern, O., 1943
Strutt, J. H., 1904

Tamm, I. Y., 1958
Thompson, G. P., 1937
Tomonaga, S., 1965
Tompson, J. J., 1906
Townes, C. H., 1964

van der Waals, J. D., 1910
von Laue, M. T. F., 1914

Walton, E. T. S., 1951
Wien, W., 1911
Wigner, E., 1963
Wilson, C. T. R., 1927

Yang, Chen Ning, 1957
Yukawa, H., 1949

Zeeman, P., 1902
Zernicke, F., 1953

INDEX

aberration, 367

absolute pressure, 226; temperature, 242-243, 263; zero, 263, 281

absorption, resonance, 632-633; selective, 419

acceleration, 48-54; average velocity, 49; centripetal, 162; concept, 4; defined, 48; derived equations, 52; uniform, 48-50

accelerator, high-voltage, 684-688; linear, 693; proton, 750; radio-frequency, 689-695

actinium, 674

action force, 87

adhesion, 216

agonic line, 481

air, column, vibrating, 331, 583; friction, falling bodies, 66; liquefaction, 281; saturated, 269

airflow, mechanics, 127-128

airfoil, 236-237

airplane, fluid friction, 128-129; wing lift, 236; velocity vectors, 56-57

algebra, 29-34

alkali metals, 615

alpha (α) factor, in transistor, 571

alpha (α) particle, artificial acceleration, 684-685; bombardment, 700; deflection in collisions, 604; mass number, 605; scattering experiments, 603; spontaneous disintegration, 666; see also Becquerel rays

alternating current (ac), 503-504; current-frequency relationships, 527; damped oscillations, 529; generator, 503; heat losses, 525; magnetism, 517-522; oscillating circuit, 529; power, 526; Q-value, 527; series circuit, 522; transformer, 513; vacuum-tube rectification, 556; vector diagrams, 521-522; voltage-current relationships, 520-521

alternating voltage, 519-520; vacuum-tube amplification, 561-562; see also alternating current

aluminum, bombardment of nucleus by alpha particles, 700; as conductor, 432; density, 213; impurity in semiconductors, 566-567; coefficient of expansion, 245; melting and boiling points, 251; heat conductivity, 255, 257; resistivity, 455; specific heat, 249; Young's modulus, 197

Alvarez, L., 693, 749

amber, attractive properties of, 425

americium, 674

ammeter, 496-498; shunt, 497

Ampère, André Marie, 452 n., 495; Jean J., 452 n.

ampere, defined, 452, 492

amplifier, vacuum-tube, 561-562; see also transistor; triode

amplitude, simple harmonic motion, 303; wave, 306; modulation, 588

Anderson, Carl D., 737, 743

aneroid barometer, 222-223

angle, attack, 129; declination, 481; functions, 37; uniform slip, 122-123

angstrom, defined, 611-612

angular momentum, conservation of, 179-185; unit, 622; speed, 159; velocity, 160

annihilation energy, 685, 737

anode, 447, 483

antenna, radar, 582; radio, 587

antiferromagnetic material, 478

antineutrino, 705

antinode, 325, 330

antiparticle, 743

antiproton, 750

aperture mask, in color television, 579

aphelion, 167

aragonite, 418

Archimedes, 3, 116; principle, 211-215

argon lamp, 352

Aristotle, 3, 65

arsenic, in semiconductors, 566

astatine, 674

Aston, F. W., 599

astronomical clock, 15

atmosphere, 221-227

atmospheric pressure, 27, 221, 224-225

atom, affinity or attraction, 427; Bohr model, 625-630, 650, 712; Bohr-Stoner model, 626-627, 652; elastic collisions, 679; excited, 632; ionized, 632, 638; kinds, 189; light and heavy, 627; models, 602; normal vs. excited, 632; positive charge, 604; structure, 602-606; wave-density model, 651

atomic, mass, 600, 682, 745, graph, 709; mass unit, 682, 687; nucleus, 5, model, 606; number, 189, 600, mass number, 626, nuclear reactions, 667, transmutation, 666; physics, 595-660, radiation, 629-635, structure, 602-606, "waves," 648-652, continuous-emission spectra, 609-612, discrete atomic spectra, 613-617, photoelectric effect, 618-623, relativity theory, 653-660, X-rays, 636-646; theory, 189-193; weight, 189, 626

atomizer, perfume, 235

audiogram, 320

audion tube, 559

Bacon, Roger, 3

balance wheel, bimetallic, 246

ballast coil, 353

ballistics, 156-157

Balmer, Johann J., 616; series, hydrogen lines, 616-617, 631

barometric pressure, 222

Bartholinus, Erasmus, 418

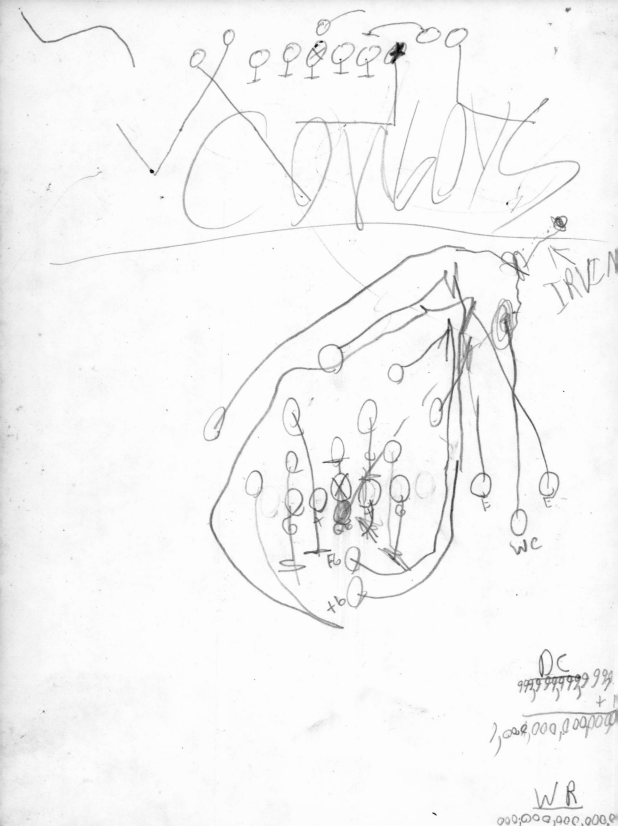